COLLEGE ALGEBRA

Supplemented with:

- Multimedia Electronic Lecture Notes for Teachers
- Multimedia Tutorial for Students
- On-line Testing and Practice Testing
- Several Technology Tools to support Instruction including:
  - ✔ On-line grade book for faculty and progress reports for students
  - ✔ On-line student survey and reports
  - ✔ Student activity reports
  - ✔ Solution manuals

Fourth Edition

What is new in this Edition?

- Four Color printing with enhanced images of graphs.
- More examples on problem solving and mathematical models.
- Chapters and topics rearranged to follow the sequence recommended by the users.
- Enhanced technology features.
- On-line Home work assignments can be completed in multiple sessions.
- On-line home work assignment is now embedded with tutorials.

AUTHOR:

MAN M. SHARMA

Other Contributors:

Jagmohan Kapoor ○ **Ray Treadway** ○ **Ravinder Kumar**

Published by: EDUCO International Inc.(1-800-963-3826)

ACKNOWLEDGEMENTS

Managing Editor   **Madan G. Chopra**, Educo International Inc.

Production Services   Educo International, Inc.

Desktop Publishing   Ramesh Thomas, Sunita Verma, Anita Rajput,
and Graphics   Mohit Arora, and Prachi Gupta
                             Educo International, Inc.

Electronic Version   Arindam Chowdhury, Pushpish Chandra, Sanjeev Rathi, and their team
of this textbook and   of 25 programmers
Assessment System

Reviewers/Editors   The following persons have made significant contributions to this edition of the
                             book. The authors express their sincerest thanks for the suggestions, evaluation,
                             and preparation of support materials to:

• **Ray Treadway**	Bennett College, NC
• **Kamal Hajallie**	La Guardia Community College, NY
• **Eldon Baldwin**	Prince George's Community College, MD
• **Richard Andrews**	Florida A & M University, FL
• **Angel Rivera**	University of Turabo, PR
• **Luis Bermudez**	University of PR, Ponce

Question Banks   Ray Treadway for Part I
                          Ruben Pereira for Part II

Solution Manual   P. P. Hallan   Visiting Scientist, Clark Atlanta University, GA
                          Kathy Hess   Anne Arundel Community College, Arnold, MD
                          Alicia Mores   Anne Arundel Community College, Arnold, MD

ISBN# 1-888 469-60-9

Printed at Replika Press Pvt. Ltd.

Preface

During the past few years there has been an upward shift in the learning objectives of calculus courses. Unlike the traditional calculus, the calculus reforms have introduced the study of calculus graphically, numerically and algebraically. Consequently, the learning objectives of pre-calculus underwent a similar change. As a result, two approaches to the study of pre-calculus evolved. In one, the objectives are met through an applied approach, that is, the student is taught the basics of the course through modeling problems. The other approach contains the improved form of the traditional topics. In this text, the authors have adopted the latter approach with the following goals and approaches to achieve these goals.

Goals:

- To present pre-calculus topics in an analytical manner.
- To prepare students for calculus courses.
- To develop students' logical and visual thinking.

Special Features

1. **Intuitive Concept of Function**

   Since one of the main recommendations in the reforms is that a function should not only be presented in a formula form but also in a numerical and graphical form, therefore the concept of function should play a central role in the study of pre-calculus. For an intuitive look at a function, the authors have attempted to give the anatomy of the functional notation:

   $$f(x) = \text{Expression}$$

   by calling $f(x)$ the 'dependency statement' which implies that the quantity f depends on quantity x. The new look at the functional notation provides not only the missing consistency in developing transcendental functions but also gives the functional approach to various topics like variation and half parabolas.

2. **Higher Order Thinking Skills**

   The NCTM recommendations of developing higher order thinking skills in students were the primary guidelines while developing chapters, examples, exercises and an intuitive functional approach. The authors feel that analytical presentations are good teaching tools in developing logical thinking in the reader. These presentations are conspicuously different in the graphing methods for rational functions, circular functions, and conic sections.

3. **4 R's Treatment**

   Each concept is explained with a function in its algeb**R**aic, g**R**aphical and nume**R**ical form. Each section has w**R**iting exercises for students to express his/her understanding of the basic concepts and thus develop good writing skills.

4. **Graphing Calculator**

   Graphing Calculator is used as a means to enhance clarity and is not recommended as an alternative to algebraic approach. All graphical demonstrations in the book refer to a graphing calculator but a student can experience the same benefits by using any other graphing tool. Other than developing visual thinking (NCTM guidelines), the graphs are also used in making conjectures.

5.   Step-by-Step Strategies

All examples and procedures are explained using a step-by-step approach.

6.   Applications

The book contains many applied examples and exercises. The solutions of examples and exercises is aimed at giving a smooth linkage to calculus.

7.   Analytical Approach

Most of the changes in traditional methods are made for the sole purpose of staying consistent and analytical. Our focus is to develop students' higher order thinking skills. For example, in graphing functions, the authors have avoided the machine methods (plotting points and joining them) and instead have given analytical approaches.

8.   Margin Notes

The margin notes are used to recall important facts and definitions.

9.   End of Chapter

At the end of each chapter there is a chapter summary, chapter review and self test.

Highlights of Contents:

Chapter 1:	Review of Basic Algebra.
Chapter 2:	Functions.
Chapter 3:	Equations and Inequalities.
Chapter 4:	Graphing Techniques.
Chapter 5:	Exponential and Logarithmic Functions.
Chapter 6:	Variation and Conic Sections.
Chapter 7:	Systems of Equations, Matrices and Determinants.
Chapter 8:	Sequences, Series and Binomial Expansion.

TECHNOLOGY SUPPORT:

A.   Multimedia Electronic Lecture Notes (ELN) for Teachers and Tutorials for Students

- Tutorials with animated color-coded examples embedded with dynamic graphics and step by step solutions. Each example is randomized with several versions, prepares students for homework and assessments.

- Vivid Screens, and animations make the presentation of topics very clear as documented by students and teachers in several pilot studies.

- ELN are designed to enhance interactivity with students, which affords instructors minimal writing and drawing on the board and more emphasis on class discussion.

- The ELN used in class to supplement conventional teaching, are available to students as tutorials from the Web for self study, anywhere - anytime. Each example in the tutorials has several versions generated by randomized parameters. The student can see the solution to the first version, and then click the 'Next Version' to see similar exercises for a self - attempt.

B. **Homework on Internet with embedded tutorial**

- Different types of free response questions, with several versions for each type of question, are used to create online homework. For example, six questions types with five versions of each type make a homework assignment of 30 questions.

- Each student gets a different set of questions, instant feedback to each response, provision to change answers during the session, and can complete the assignment in multiple sessions.

- Homework can have due dates, are graded by the system, and scores transferred automatically to the grade book.

- The first version of each question will have step by step solution, and no solutions for other versions, just the instant feedback with option to change the answers.

C. **Quizzes/Tests on Internet (Free-Response or Multiple-Choice)**

- A large question bank, both Objective and Free-response, is available **for each chapter**. Questions with hints and solutions are used for computerized testing and practice testing through local network, and from internet using Educo web site.

- Test-Editors to print multiple versions of class test with answer keys, or to generate and administer on-line tests.

- You can choose free-response quizzes where students have to solve problems on their notebooks and enter answers on screens. Each item in the question bank has several versions, and each student gets a different quiz from versions.

- You may allow students to take quizzes, more than once, from anywhere at any time, and every time the quiz is different, covering similar type of items.

- After every quiz, students get instant feedback on score, can see step-by-step solutions, and have the option to go to practice mode with embedded tutorial, and take the quiz over again if allowed by the instructor.

- For every graded test created by the teacher, system generates online practice test for students. Items for these practice tests are selected by the system covering the objectives selected by the instructor for the actual test. The system provides different set of items for every practice test session.

- Enhanced electronic grade book (online or offline) with several unique features including : direct transfer of scores from computerized testing to the grade book, and **individualized progress reports for students.**

- You may print multiple versions of quizzes or tests (multiple-choice or free-response) along with answer keys with just a click of a button.

- There will be no loss of work done by the students if during the Test/homework sessions the power goes off, or web connection is lost, or student closes Test/Assignment windows improperly.

- The work completed at the time of disconnect will be considered work submitted and the rest of the work can be completed in a new login session.

- No use of **keyboard** keys for any kind of response entry to avoid entry of invisible characters that may happen sometimes.

- Response entry will become easier for students that are not used to keyboard. Students enter responses through a **small keypad** and not the whole keyboard.

- The keypad contains mathematical symbols needed only for the response to the item being attempted, and a few more.

- Conduct proctored major tests, password protected, in local computer labs, or use hand graded tests and transfer the scores to the online graded book.

D.   Activity Reports

- Teachers can view/print student activity reports at any time. The reports provide detailed information about which student is spending how much time on what activity, and how they are progressing.

E.   Internal E-mail

- Instructors can compile e-mails using system's full function e-mail editor: bolding, underlining, bulleting, spell check, and attachment. You can select multiple target audience

    Students to instructor or classmates

    Instructor to his students (of a section, or course, or all courses).

    Campus coordinator to instructors, students, Educo.

- Message waiting prompt on login.

F.   Drop Box for students to send papers to instructors.

G.   Announcements by:

- Faculty to his/her students.
- Campus coordinator to Instructors, students of a section/course or to all.
- Educo to different groups of users.

All the above activities are fully automeated. Teachers may modify any of the assessment components (practice sessions, assignments, quizzes) using the system editor.

Acknowledgements:

The production of this book and other support material would not have been possible without the support and encouragement from family members of authors and several faculty members from institutions across the United States who contributed to the refinement of this book and support materials.

Partial funding for developing some of the technology supplements was provided in part by a grant from the **U.S. Department of Education (Grant #P120A20048).**

To the teachers and students using the book:	The authors will appreciate suggestions for improvement. Suggestions can be forwarded through Educo website using Enhancements hyperlink.

We sincerely hope that the approaches followed in this book with several options of technology support will help the students better prepare for Calculus.

Man M Sharma

TABLE OF CONTENTS

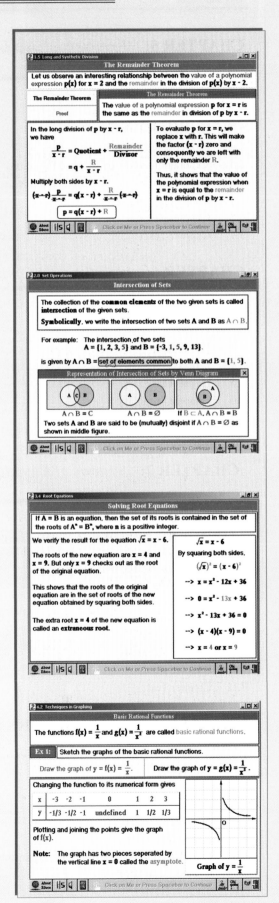

TABLE OF CONTENTS

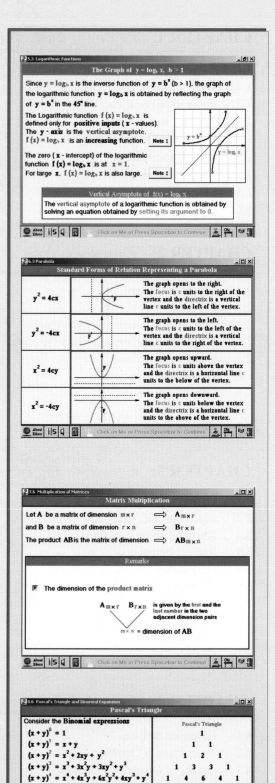

Review of Basic Algebra

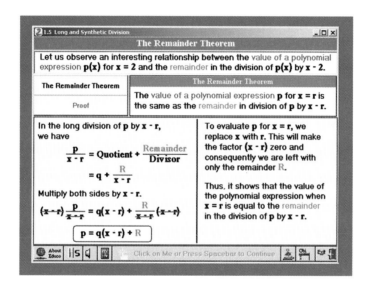

Review of Basic Algebra

1

REVIEW OF BASIC ALGEBRA

In this chapter we will review several basic topics from elementary algebra such as factoring polynomials, simplifying rational expressions and radicals. In our discussions we may include additional topics like synthetic division of polynomials and we may go deeper into some of the other topics. Therefore, when you look at the titles of topics, do not feel that materials will be redundant. While the names of the topics may be the same as in other algebra courses you have taken, the information here will be more advanced. Furthermore, an understanding of the concepts presented here will lay a solid foundation for the study of other chapters.

The discussion in this chapter is divided into six sections:

> **1.1**   *Real Number System;*
>
> **1.2**   *Absolute Value;*
>
> **1.3**   *Polynomials and Factoring;*
>
> **1.4**   *Rational Expressions;*
>
> **1.5**   *Division of Polynomials; and*
>
> **1.6**   *Radical Expressions.*

1.1   REAL NUMBER SYSTEM

The numbers used everyday to describe quantities in business, in industry, and in the scientific world are real numbers. This section introduces both a common terminology and a graphical representation of the number system.

A. REAL NUMBER SYSTEM

Objectives ▶ ▶

In this section you will learn about:

A . Real Number System;

B . Real Number Line;

C . Ordering of the Real Numbers;

D . Intervals on the Number Line; and

E . Union and Intersection of intervals.

We use real numbers to describe quantities like weight, age, volume and distance. Some examples of real numbers are

$$3, \quad 2.52, -12, \frac{1}{3}, \frac{5}{3}, \pi, \sqrt{3}, \text{ and } 1.0353535\ldots$$

Writing these numbers in decimal form, we get

$$3.0, \ 2.52, \ -12.0, \ 0.\overline{3}, \ 1.\overline{6}, \ 3.1415\ldots, 1.732\ldots, \text{ and } 1.0\overline{35} \cdot$$

(The bar above a block of digits indicates that the block repeats indefinitely.) These examples show that, in fact, any real number can be written using decimal notation.

Real Numbers

A **real number** is any number that can be expressed as a decimal.

Sometimes the decimal form of a real number requires only a finite number of decimal places. Such a real number is called a **terminating decimal**, for example,

$$3.0, \quad 2.52, \quad \text{and} \quad -120.$$

Any real number that requires an infinite number of decimal places to express its value is called a **non-terminating decimal**, for example,

$$0.\overline{3}, \quad 1.\overline{6}, \quad 3.1415\ldots, 1.732\ldots, \text{and} \quad 1.0\overline{35}$$

A non-terminating decimal is called a **repeating decimal** if it has a repeating pattern after some point, for example,

$$0.\overline{3}, \quad 1.\overline{6}, \quad 7.3\overline{6}, \quad \text{and} \quad 1.0\overline{35}$$

A non-terminating decimal without a repeating pattern is called a **non-repeating decimal**, for example,

$$2.123456789101112\ldots, \quad 1.101001000100001\ldots$$

An integer can be written as a decimal with only zeros to the right of the decimal point.

$$3, -5, 0, 200$$

$$\text{Integers} : \ldots, -3, -2, -1, 0, 1, 2, 3, \ldots$$

A quotient $\dfrac{p}{q}$ of two integers p and q, $q \neq 0$, is called a **rational number**. When a quotient $\dfrac{p}{q}$ is written as a decimal, it will either be a terminating decimal or a repeating non-terminating decimal.

---

* We show that a **terminating** or a repeating non-terminating decimal can be written as $\dfrac{p}{q}$, where p, q, are integers and $q \neq 0$.

1. A terminating decimal like 2.357 is $\dfrac{2357}{1000}$, and therefore is a quotient of two integers.

Rational Numbers

Numbers of the form $\dfrac{p}{q}$ where p and q are integers and $q \neq 0$ are

* **terminating** or repeating **non-terminating** decimals.

A real number that is not a rational number is called an **irrational number.**

Irrational Numbers

Numbers that are not rational are non-terminating and non-repeating decimals.

EXAMPLE 1   Consider the following numbers:

$$8, \quad -\frac{2}{3}, \quad 0, \quad -5, \quad 1.232323...$$

$$\sqrt{3}, \quad \sqrt{25}, \quad 5.9021..., \quad \sqrt[3]{8}, \quad \pi$$

    a.   List the numbers that are integers.

    b.   List the numbers that are rational.

    c.   List the numbers that are irrational.

Solutions: **a.**   Integers : $8, \ 0, \ -5, \ \sqrt{25} = 5, \ \sqrt[3]{8} = 2$

    b.   Rational Numbers : $8, -\frac{2}{3}, 0, -5, 1.\overline{23},$

$$\sqrt{25} = 5, \quad \sqrt[3]{8} = 2$$

    c.   Irrational Numbers: $5.9021..., \sqrt{3}$, and π

---

2. To write a **repeating non-terminating decimal** $2.\overline{357}$ as a quotient of integers, we set

$$x = 2.\overline{357} \qquad (1)$$

Multiply both sides by 1000, to get:

$$1000x = 2357.\overline{357} \qquad (2)$$

Subtract equation **(1)** from equation **(2)** to get:

$$999x = 2355$$

Dividing by 999 gives

$$x = \frac{2355}{999} = \frac{785}{333}$$

Thus, the repeating non-terminating decimal $2.\overline{357}$ is equal to the quotient $\frac{785}{333}$ of integers.

Note   The ratio of the circumference of a circle to its diameter is a constant. This constant is known to be an irrational number and is denoted by (lower-case Greek letter) π. An approximate value of π is 3.14142.

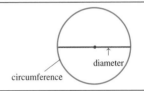

circumference   diameter

B. REAL NUMBER LINE

Real numbers can be represented as points on a line. Each point on the line corresponds to exactly one real number. This line is called the **real number line.** The real number corresponding to a point is called the **coordinate** of that point. The point with number zero as its coordinate is called the **origin**.

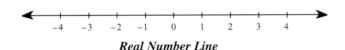

Real Number Line

Remark: *There is a **one-to-one correspondence** between the real numbers and points on the number line. That is, for every real number there is a point on the line and for every point on the line there is a unique real number.*

EXAMPLE 2   Plot the point on the number line whose coordinate is

    a. -2.5 **b.** $\sqrt{2}$ **c.** π

Solutions: **a.**   The point with coordinate -2.5 is half-way between -3 and -2.

b. If we construct a right triangle whose two sides are each equal to 1, then by the Pythagorean Theorem, the length of its hypotenuse is $\sqrt{1^2 + 1^2} = \sqrt{2}$. The graph of the point with coordinate $\sqrt{2}$ is shown in the following diagram:

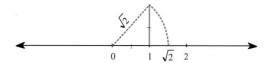

The plot of $\sqrt{2}$ lies approximately half-way between the plots of the numbers 1 and 2. Use your calculator to verify that $\sqrt{2} \approx 1.4$.

c. $\pi \approx 3.14$ is represented by a point somewhat to the right of 3.

⬤ Note   "≈" stands for "approximately equal to."

C. ORDERING OF THE REAL NUMBERS

If on the number line the plot of a real number '*m*' is to the left of the plot of a real number '*n*', we say that the real number *m* is **less than** the real number *n*. In short we write this as

$$m < n$$

Similarly, "***m > n***" is read as "***m is greater than n***" and it means that on the number line the point *m* is to the right of the point that corresponds to *n*.

Remarks: **1.** *The symbols > and < are called **inequality** symbols.*

2. *Other inequality symbols are ≤ and ≥ where "≤" is read as "less than or equal to" and "≥" is read as "greater than or equal to."*

3. *In mathematics we use expressions like "positive", "negative" and "non-negative". These expressions can be written with the inequality symbols as follows:*

' n is positive' ⟶ *n > 0,*   *'n is negative'* ⟶ *n < 0*

' n is non-negative' ⟶ *n ≥ 0, and 'n is non-positive'* ⟶ *n ≤ 0*

EXAMPLE 3   Write the following true statements with an inequality symbol.

a. $\sqrt{k}$ is always a non-negative number, where $k \geq 0$.

b. $-k^2$ is always a non-positive number.

Solutions: **a.** $\sqrt{k} \geq 0$ **b.** $-k^2 \leq 0$

D. INTERVALS ON THE NUMBER LINE

An uninterrupted portion of the number line is called an **interval.** The portion of the number line between real numbers a and b, where $a < b$, is called the **open interval** if it consists of all real numbers x such that

$$a < x < b$$

If the end points of the interval between a and b are also included, then the interval is called a **closed interval.** Any number x in that interval satisfies

$$a \leq x \leq b$$

Notation

An **open interval** between real numbers a and b is written as (a, b).

A **closed interval** between real number a and b is written as $[a, b]$.

 Note On a graph of these intervals, brackets or solid dots are used to indicate that the numbers are included, whereas parentheses or open circles indicate the exclusion.

Open interval

The **open interval** (a, b) consisting of all real numbers x such that $a < x < b$ is represented graphically as :

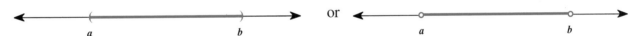

Closed Interval

The **closed interval** $[a, b]$ consisting of all real number x such that $a \leq x \leq b$ is represented graphically as :

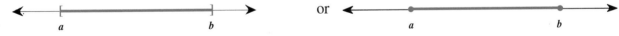

The set of points on the shaded portion on the number line represents the **graph** of the interval.

EXAMPLE 4 Graph the interval on the number line and write in interval notation.

a. $-2 < x < 5$ b. $1 \leq x < 3$ c. $0 \leq x \leq 4$ d. $-1 < x \leq 2$

Solutions: a. $-2 < x < 5$ defines an open interval $(-2, 5)$ or

     b. $1 \leq x < 3$ defines the **half open** or **half closed** interval $[1, 3)$ or

c. $0 \le x \le 4$ defines the **closed** interval [0, 4] or

d. $-1 < x \le 2$ defines the **half open** or **half closed** interval $(-1, 2]$ or

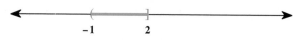

EXAMPLE 5   Graph the interval on the number line.

   a.   [-3, 0)   **b.**   (1, 5]   **c.**   (1, 4)   **d.**   [5, 8]

Solutions: **a.**   The interval [-3, 0) is closed on the left and open on the right.

   b.   The interval (1, 5] is open on the left and closed on the right.

   c.   The interval (1, 4) is an open interval.

   d.   The interval [5, 8] is a closed interval.

Unbounded Intervals

The portion of the number line that extends indefinitely, to either direction, is called an **unbounded interval.** For example, the portion of the number line that lies to the right of 5 is an unbounded interval.

Notation

The symbol ∞ is read as **infinity.** It is not a real number, and its use as $x \to \infty$ indicates that x is increasing without bounds and its use in the interval $(5, \infty)$ indicates that the interval has no right hand end point.

Similarly, $x \to -\infty$ indicates that x is **decreasing** without bounds.

Using this notation, the entire number line can be written as the interval $(-\infty, \infty)$.

Unbounded Intervals on The Number Line

The set of all real numbers such that $x \ge a$ or $[a, \infty)$ is the portion of the number line that is to the right of **a**, including **a**.

The set of all real numbers such that $x > a$ or (a, ∞) is the portion of the number line that is to the right of **a**, excluding **a**.

The set of all real numbers such that $x < b$ or $(-\infty, b)$ is the portion of the number line that is to the left to **b**, excluding **b**.

The set of all real numbers such that $x \leq b$ or $(-\infty, b]$ is the portion of the number line that is to the left of **b**, including **b**.

EXAMPLE 6   Write the interval with inequality symbols and show it on the number line.

      a. $(-\infty, -2]$ **b.** $(-1, \infty)$

Solutions: **a.** $(-\infty, -2]$ represents all real numbers x such that $x \leq -2$. It represents the portion of the number line that is to left of -2 and includes the real number -2.

        b. $(-1, \infty)$ represents all real numbers x such that $x > -1$. It represents the portion of the number line that is to the right of -1, excluding the real number -1.

E. UNION AND INTERSECTION OF INTERVALS

Recall that the **union** of two sets A and B, written as $A \cup B$, is the set of elements that belong to A or B (or both). The **intersection** of two sets A and B, written as $A \cap B$, is the set of elements that are common to both A and B.

Let $I = (-1, 3)$ and $J = (0, 4)$. On the number line the graph of $I \cup J$ is found by shading in the portions that represent **I** or **J** or both.

The graph of $I \cap J$ is found by shading in the portion common to the portions of the number line representing I and J.

EXAMPLES :   *I* **:** $(-1, 3)$

                 J **:** $(0, 4)$

                 I $\cup$ *J* **:** $(-1, 4)$

                 I $\cap$ *J* **:** $(0, 3)$

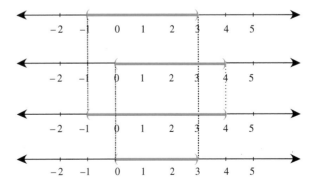

EXAMPLE 7   Write the union or intersection as an interval and show it on the number line.

   a. $x > 2$ and $x < 5$ **b.** $x < -1$ or $x \geq 1$ **c.** $x \leq 3$ and $x > 0$

Solutions: **a.**   Since $x > 2$ is $(2, \infty)$ **and** $x < 5$ is $(-\infty, 5)$.

   so

   $x > 2$ and $x < 5$ is represented by the intersection of two intervals ; $(2, \infty) \cap (-\infty, 5)$.
   On the number line, the intersection $(2, \infty) \cap (-\infty, 5)$ is the portion common to $(2, \infty)$ and
   $(-\infty, 5)$ which is the interval $(2, 5)$ as shown below.

   b.   Since $x < -1$ is $(-\infty, -1)$ and $x \geq 1$ is $[1, \infty)$.

   so

   $x < -1$ **or** $x \geq 1$ is represented by the union of two intervals: $(-\infty, -1) \cup [1, \infty)$.
   The graph of $(-\infty, -1) \cup [1, \infty)$ is obtained by shading in the set of points representing
   $(-\infty, -1)$ or $[1, \infty)$, or both.

   c.   Similarly, $x \leq 3$ **and** $x > 0$ is equivalent to $(-\infty, 3] \cap (0, \infty)$ or the set of values common
   to both $(-\infty, 3]$ and $(0, \infty)$ which is the interval $(0, 3]$ as shown below.

⬤Notes   **1.**   The intersection of two intervals is either an interval, or a singleton
(set consisting of a single element) or empty set.

   2.   The union of two intervals may or may not be an interval.

EXERCISE 1.1

In exercises (1-40), determine whether the number is an integer, a rational number, or an irrational number. (A number may fit in more than one category).

1. 13   **2.** -7 **3.** -1.7 **4.** 3.2   **5.** $\dfrac{13}{2}$

6. $-\dfrac{5}{3}$ **7.** 3π **8.** -2π **9.** $-\sqrt{4}$ **10.** $\sqrt{9}$

11. $\sqrt[3]{27}$ **12.** $\sqrt[3]{64}$ **13.** $-5.323232...$ **14.** $6.121212...$ **15.** $2.3333...$

16. $.6666...$ **17.** $\sqrt{\dfrac{4}{9}}$ **18.** $-\sqrt{\dfrac{9}{4}}$ **19.** $\sqrt{7}$ **20.** $-\sqrt{3}$

21. $\sqrt{3}$ **22.** $\sqrt[3]{2}$ **23.** $0.0175812...$ **24.** $3.14014001400014...$ **25.** $12.\overline{73}$

26. $-3.\overline{2}$ **27.** $9.\overline{72}$ **28.** $-25.\overline{6}$ **29.** $\sqrt{44} + 6$ **30.** $\sqrt{22} - 1$

31. $\dfrac{\sqrt{2}+5}{2}$ **32.** $3+\sqrt{5}$ **33.** $\dfrac{1.325}{2.158}$ **34.** $\dfrac{275}{25}$ **35.** 5%

36. 27% **37.** $\sqrt{\dfrac{8}{25}}$ **38.** $-\sqrt{\dfrac{16}{81}}$ **39.** π^2 **40.** $-\pi+4$

In exercises (41-60), indicate the approximate location on the number line. (You may use a calculator.)

41. $\dfrac{7}{4}$ **42.** $-\dfrac{3}{4}$ **43.** $-\dfrac{15}{6}$ **44.** $\dfrac{31}{7}$ **45.** $\sqrt{5}$

46. $-\sqrt{3}$ **47.** $\sqrt{5}+\sqrt{2}$ **48.** $3-\sqrt{8}$ **49.** $\sqrt{2}+3$ **50.** $\sqrt{14}-\sqrt{20}$

51. $\dfrac{\pi}{2}$ **52.** $\dfrac{15}{8}-\dfrac{14}{3}$ **53.** $\dfrac{3\pi}{2}$ **54.** $\dfrac{3}{5}+2\sqrt{7}$ **55.** $2\pi+1$

56. $\dfrac{13}{4}-3\sqrt{2}$ **57.** $\dfrac{\pi}{3}$ **58.** $-\dfrac{3\pi}{2}$ **59.** $\dfrac{2\pi}{3}$ **60.** $-5\pi+2$

In exercises (61-80), write the statement with inequality symbols.

61. Five is positive.   **62.** 20 is positive   **63.** -2 is negative   **64.** -17 is negative

65. x^2 is always non-negative.   **66.** $-x^4$ is always non-positive

67. $\sqrt{x}$ is non-negative, x being a whole number.   **68.** $-\sqrt{x}$ is non-positive, x being a whole number.

69. x is between 2 and 5, both inclusive.   **70.** x is between 3 and 8, both inclusive.

71. x is greater than -2.   **72.** x is less than 14

73. x is less than or equal to 9.   **74.** x is greater than or equal to -5

75. x is either greater than 10 or less than -10.   **76.** x is either less than 2 or greater than 20.

77. x is between -5 and -1, including -5.   **78.** t is between -3 and 0.

79. t is either less than 5 or greater than or equal to 10.

80. u is either less than or equal to 0 or greater than or equal to 7.

In exercises (81-106), graph the interval on the number line and write the interval without inequalities.

81. $1<x\leq4$ **82.** $-2<x\leq3$ **83.** $-4\leq x<2$ **84.** $-5\leq x<-2$ **85.** $-3\leq x\leq3$

86. $0\leq x\leq4$ **87.** $0<x<5$ **88.** $-3<x<0$ **89.** $x\geq1$ **90.** $x>3$

91. $x>-2$ **92.** $x\geq-4$ **93.** $x<3$ **94.** $x<-2$ **95.** $x\leq0$

96. $x\leq1$ **97.** $x>1$ and $x\leq3$ **98.** $x>-1$ and $x\leq2$ **99.** $x<2$ or $x>5$

100. $x\leq0$ or $x\geq2$ **101.** $x\leq10$ and $x\geq2$ **102.** $x\leq4$ and $x>0$ **103.** $x<-2$ or $x>2$

104. $x<5$ or $x>2$ **105.** $x<-2$ and $x\geq2$ **106.** $x\geq5$ or $x<-1$

In exercises (107-120), write the interval with inequality symbols and graph it on the number line.

107. $[1,5)$ **108.** $(-4,2]$ **109.** $(-1,3)$ **110.** $[-2,8]$ **111.** $[-7,2)$

112. $(-5,-1)$ **113.** $(3,7.5)$ **114.** $[-1,2]\cup(5,\infty)$ **115.** $(-\infty,-2)\cup(3,\infty)$ **116.** $(-2,1]\cap(1,8)$

117. $(-4,-1)\cup(-3,\infty)$ **118.** $(-\infty,1)\cup(0,10)$ **119.** $(-\infty,3)\cap(2,\infty)$ **120.** $(-\infty,4)\cap(0,5)$

1.2 ABSOLUTE VALUE

Objectives ▶ ▶

In this section you will learn about:

A. The Absolute Value of a Real Number;

B. The Absolute Value of an Algebraic Quantity; and

C. The Properties of Absolute Value.

To symbolize quantities, such as distance and speed, which are always non-negative, we use the concept of absolute value. We begin this section with the absolute value of real numbers. Then we will generalize it to the absolute value of any algebraic quantity.

A. THE ABSOLUTE VALUE OF A REAL NUMBER

The absolute value of a real number x, written as $\left| x \right|$, is the distance on the number line from x to the origin.

For example, the absolute value of -3 is

$$\left| -3 \right| = \text{the distance of } -3 \text{ from } 0$$
$$= 3$$

Also, the absolute value of 3 is

$$\left| 3 \right| = \text{the distance of } 3 \text{ from } 0$$
$$= 3$$

We notice that the **above rule** gives the absolute value of a single number x. The following example shows how to find the absolute value of a numerical expression. To find the absolute value of a numerical expression, first we simplify the numerical expression inside vertical bars (the absolute value sign).

EXAMPLE 1   Write each of the following without absolute value notation.

      a. $\left| 9 - 11 \right|$ **b.** $\left| 2 - \dfrac{11}{2} \right|$ **c.** $5 - \left| 2(3) - 10 \right|$

Solution: **a.** First, we combine $9 - 11$ into a single number -2. Then we use the above rule. It gives

$$\left| 9 - 11 \right| = \left| -2 \right| = 2.$$

      b. Writing $2 - \dfrac{11}{2}$ as a single number gives $2 - \dfrac{11}{2} = \dfrac{4}{2} - \dfrac{11}{2} = \dfrac{-7}{2}$.

         Now, using the above rule gives

$$\left| 2 - \frac{11}{2} \right| = \left| \frac{-7}{2} \right| = \frac{7}{2}$$

      c. Similarly, $5 - \left| 2(3) - 10 \right| = 5 - \left| 6 - 10 \right|$

$$= 5 - \left| -4 \right| = 5 - 4 = 1$$

B. THE ABSOLUTE VALUE OF AN ALGEBRAIC QUANTITY

To find the absolute value of an algebraic quantity K, we use the following rule.

$$|K| = \begin{cases} K & \text{if } K \geq 0 \\ -K & \text{if } K < 0 \end{cases}$$

Remarks: 1.   *This rule generalizes the rule that gives the absolute value of a number. For example, if $K = -3$, then according to this rule*

$$|-3| = -(-3) = 3$$

2.   *The absolute value of a quantity is always **non-negative.***

3.   *Since the square root $\sqrt{x^2}$ is a non-negative number, so $\sqrt{x^2} = |x|$.*

4.   *Before we use the rule, we first determine the sign of quantity that is inside the absolute value symbols (vertical bars).*

5.   *The rule says that if the inside quantity is non-negative, then simply write the quantity as it is. Otherwise, write the additive inverse of the quantity.*

EXAMPLE 2   Write each of the following expressions without absolute value notation (bars):

a. $\left|(x-2)^2\right|$ **b.** $\left|\pi - 12\right|$ **c.** $\left|x - 8\right|$, if $x < 8$

Solutions: **a.**   First, we determine the sign of the quantity that is inside the bars. In this case, the quantity $(x-2)^2$ is a perfect square, so the quantity is always non-negative. Using the above rule gives

$$\left|(x-2)^2\right| = (x-2)^2 \qquad {\scriptstyle |K| = K \;\text{if}\; K \geq 0}$$

b.   Since $\pi - 12$ is a negative quantity (why?), then by the above rule

$$\left|\pi - 12\right| = -(\pi - 12) \qquad {\scriptstyle |K| = -K \;\text{if}\; K < 0}$$
$$= 12 - \pi$$

c. $x < 8 \longrightarrow x - 8 < 0$. Therefore, using the definition of absolute value we get

$$\left|x - 8\right| = -(x - 8)$$
$$= 8 - x$$

EXAMPLE 3   Write $\left|x - 2\right|$ without absolute value bars, given that x is in the open interval $(1, 3)$.

Solution: The quantity $x - 2$ has different signs for different values of x in the interval $(1, 3)$. Since the quantity $x - 2$ becomes zero at $x = 2$, we examine the sign of the quantity on the left of $x = 2$ and on the right of $x = 2$. In other words, we determine the signs of $x - 2$ on the intervals $(1,2)$ and $[2, 3)$.

If x is in the interval (1,2), then $x < 2$. Consequently, the quantity $x - 2$ is negative, so

if $1 < x < 2$ then $\left|x - 2\right| = -(x - 2)$

$$= 2 - x$$

Similarly, if x is in the interval $[2, 3)$, then $x > 2$. Consequently, the quantity $x - 2$ is non-negative, so if $2 \leq x < 3$ then $\left|x - 2\right| = (x - 2)$

Writing the above results together, we have

$$\left|x - 2\right| = \begin{cases} 2 - x & \text{if } 1 < x < 2 \\ x - 2 & \text{if } 2 \leq x < 3 \end{cases}$$

EXAMPLE 4

Write $\left|x\right| - \left|x - 3\right|$ without absolute value bars, given that x is in the open interval $(-1, 4)$.

Solution:

Since the quantities x and $x - 3$ become zero at $x = 0$ and $x = 3$ respectively, we should examine the signs of these quantities on both sides of 0 and 3. This means that we should determine the signs of quantities in three intervals, namely, $(-1, 0)$, $[0, 3)$ and $[3, 4)$.

For x in the interval $(-1, 0)$ the quantity x is negative and the quantity $x - 3$ is also negative. Therefore,

if $-1 < x < 0$ then $\left|x\right| - \left|x - 3\right| = -(x) - \left(-(x - 3)\right)$

$$= -x + x - 3$$

$$= -3.$$

For x in the interval $[0, 3)$, the quantity x is non-negative, whereas, the quantity $x - 3$ is negative. Therefore,

if $0 \leq x < 3$ then $\left|x\right| - \left|x - 3\right| = x - \left(-(x - 3)\right)$

$$= x + x - 3$$

$$= 2x - 3.$$

Finally, for x in the interval $[3, 4)$, both quantities x and $x - 3$ are non-negative. Therefore, if $3 \leq x < 4$ then $\left|x\right| - \left|x - 3\right| = x - (x - 3)$

$$= x - x + 3$$

$$= 3.$$

Combining the three cases together, we write

$$\left|x\right| - \left|x - 3\right| = \begin{cases} -3 & \text{if } -1 < x < 0 \\ 2x - 3 & \text{if } 0 \leq x < 3 \\ 3 & \text{if } 3 \leq x < 4 \end{cases}$$

EXAMPLE 5   Write $2x + |x - 2|$ without absolute value bars.

Solution: Since the quantity inside the absolute value becomes zero at $x = 2$, we examine the signs of $x - 2$ on both sides of $x = 2$.

For $x < 2$, the quantity $x - 2$ is negative,

$$
\begin{aligned}
2x + |x - 2| &= 2x + [-(x - 2)] \\
&= 2x - x + 2 \\
&= x + 2.
\end{aligned}
$$

For $x \geq 2$, the quantity $x - 2$ is non-negative, so

$$
\begin{aligned}
2x + |x - 2| &= 2x + (x - 2) \\
&= 3x - 2.
\end{aligned}
$$

Writing the two cases together, we have

$$
2x + |x - 2| = \begin{cases} x + 2 & \text{if } x < 2 \\ 3x - 2 & \text{if } x \geq 2. \end{cases}
$$

EXAMPLE 6   Write $|(x + 2)(x - 6)|$ without absolute value bars.

Solution: The quantity $(x + 2)(x - 6)$ becomes **zero** when $x = -2$ or $x = 6$. Therefore, we examine the sign of $(x + 2)(x - 6)$ on both sides of -2, and 6.

*   This means that we should determine the sign of $(x + 2)(x - 6)$ on three intervals, namely $(-\infty, -2)$, $[-2, 6)$, and $[6, \infty)$.

> *   The points $x = -2$ and $x = 6$ divide the number line into three parts.

For $x < -2$, $(x + 2) < 0$ and $(x - 6) < 0$, so
$(x + 2)(x - 6) > 0$, and $|(x + 2)(x - 6)| = (x + 2)(x - 6)$

For $-2 \leq x < 6$ $(x + 2) \geq 0$ and $(x - 6) < 0$, so
$(x + 2)(x - 6) < 0$, and $|(x + 2)(x - 6)| = -(x + 2)(x - 6)$

For $x \geq 6$ $x + 2 > 0$, and $(x - 6) \geq 0$, so
$(x + 2)(x - 6) \geq 0$, and $|(x + 2)(x - 6)| = (x + 2)(x - 6)$

Writing the three results together, we have

$$
|(x + 2)(x - 6)| = \begin{cases} (x + 2)(x - 6) & \text{if } x < -2 \text{ or } x \geq 6 \\ -(x + 2)(x - 6) & \text{if } -2 \leq x < 6 \end{cases}
$$

C. THE PROPERTIES OF ABSOLUTE VALUE

For any real number a and b

1. the distance between a and b is $\left|a-b\right| = \left|b-a\right|$

2. $\left|ab\right| = \left|a\right|\left|b\right|$ **3.** $\left|\dfrac{a}{b}\right| = \dfrac{\left|a\right|}{\left|b\right|}$ $(b \neq 0)$

4. $\left|a+b\right| \leq \left|a\right| + \left|b\right|$ (the triangle inequality)

5. $\left|a\right| = p$ if and only if $a = p$ or $a = -p$.

6. For $p > 0$, $\left|a\right| < p$ if and only if $-p < a < p$.

7. For $p \geq 0$, $\left|a\right| > p$ if and only if $a < -p$ or $a > p$.

EXAMPLE 7   Write using absolute value symbols:
      a. the distance between -15 and -8.   **b.** the distance between x and -5.
      c. the distance between t and 3 is at least 4.   **d.** the distance between x and 2 is at most 1.

Solutions: **a.**   The distance between -15 and $-8 = \left|-15 - (-8)\right| = \left|-15 + 8\right|$ or $\left|15 - 8\right|$

       b.   The distance between x and -5 is $\left|x - (-5)\right| = \left|x + 5\right|$.

       c.   The distance between t and 3 **is at least 4:** $\left|t - 3\right| \geq 4$

       d.   The distance between x and 2 **is at most 1:** $\left|x - 2\right| \leq 1$.

EXAMPLE 8   Graph the interval representing the distance statements:

      a. $\left|x - 1\right| < 2$ **b.** $\left|x - 2\right| \geq 1$

Solutions: **a.**   For $\left|x - 1\right| < 2$ we look for those numbers x whose distance from the real number 1 is less than 2. So, from the real number 1 we move 2 units on each side of the number line.

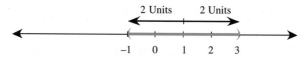

       Thus $\left|x - 1\right| < 2$ is equivalent to the interval $(-1, 3)$.

       b.   For $\left|x - 2\right| \geq 1$ we look for numbers x such that their distance from 2 is 1 or more than 1. Therefore, from the real number 2 we move 1 or more than 1 unit away on each side.

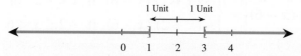

       Thus $\left|x - 2\right| \geq 1$ is equivalent to the interval $(-\infty, 1] \cup [3, \infty)$.

EXAMPLE 9   Given $\left| x - 3 \right| = \delta$, write each of the following expressions in terms of δ.

a. $\left| 2x - 6 \right|$ **b.** $\left| 15 - 5x \right|$ **c.** $\left| \dfrac{3x - 9}{7} \right|$ **d.** $\left| x + 3 \right|$

Solutions: **a.** $\left| 2x - 6 \right| = \left| 2(x - 3) \right| = \left| 2 \right|\left| x - 3 \right| = 2\delta$ $|ab| = |a|\,|b|$

b. $\left| 15 - 5x \right| = \left| 5(3 - x) \right| = \left| 5 \right|\left| 3 - x \right|$ $|b - a| = |a - b|$

$= \left| 5 \right|\left| x - 3 \right| = 5\delta$

c. $\left| \dfrac{3x - 9}{7} \right| = \left| \dfrac{3(x - 3)}{7} \right| = \dfrac{\left| 3(x - 3) \right|}{\left| 7 \right|}$ $\left| \dfrac{a}{b} \right| = \dfrac{|a|}{|b|}$

$= \dfrac{\left| 3 \right|\left| x - 3 \right|}{\left| 7 \right|} = \dfrac{3\delta}{7}$ $|ab| = |a|\,|b|$

d. $\left| x + 3 \right| = \left| x - 3 + 6 \right|$ $= \left| (x - 3) + 6 \right|$

$\leq \left| x - 3 \right| + \left| 6 \right|$ $|a + b| \leq |a| + |b|$

$\leq \delta + 6$

EXERCISE 1.2

In exercises (1-32), write without absolute value symbols and simplify.

1. $\left| 20 \right|$ **2.** $\left| \dfrac{2}{3} \right|$ **3.** $\left| -10 \right|$ **4.** $\left| -\dfrac{3}{5} \right|$ **5.** $5 + \left| -2 \right|$

6. $4 + \left| -3 \right|$ **7.** $-3 + \left| -5 \right|$ **8.** $-5 + \left| -9 \right|$ **9.** $-1 - \left| -2 \right|$ **10.** $-5 - \left| -3 \right|$

11. $-8 - \left| -4 \right|$ **12.** $-4 - \left| -1 \right|$ **13.** $\left| 5 - 9 \right|$ **14.** $\left| 6 - 7 \right|$ **15.** $\left| 4 - 10 \right|$

16. $\left| 3 - 4 \right|$ **17.** $\left| 1 - \dfrac{5}{4} \right|$ **18.** $\left| 2 - \dfrac{9}{4} \right|$ **19.** $\left| \dfrac{2}{3} - 1 \right|$ **20.** $\left| \dfrac{1}{4} - 1 \right|$

21. $9 - \left| 7 - 2 \right|$ **22.** $6 - \left| 5 - 3 \right|$ **23.** $8 + \left| 2 - 6 \right|$ **24.** $5 + \left| 3 - 4 \right|$

25. $\left| -2 \right| - \left| 5 - 9 \right|$ **26.** $\left| -4 \right| - \left| 7 - 12 \right|$ **27.** $\left| 10 - 12 \right| - \left| -3 \right|$ **28.** $\left| 5 - 10 \right| + \left| -7 \right|$

29. $\left| \dfrac{9 - 3}{2 - 4} \right|$ **30.** $\left| \dfrac{6 - 4}{5 - 9} \right|$ **31.** $\left| \dfrac{2 - 102}{-9 - 16} \right|$ **32.** $\left| \dfrac{-10 - 4}{15 - 7} \right|$

In exercises (33-87), write without absolute value symbols.

33. $\left| 1 - \sqrt{3} \right|$ **34.** $\left| 2 - \sqrt{5} \right|$ **35.** $\left| \sqrt{3} - 3 \right|$ **36.** $\left| \sqrt{3} - 2 \right| + 5$ **37.** $7 + \left| 5 - \sqrt{7} \right|$

38. $5 - \left| \sqrt{3} - 2 \right|$ **39.** $4 - \left| 3 - \sqrt{10} \right|$ **40.** $\left| \pi - 2 \right| + 1$ **41.** $\left| \pi - 3 \right| - 2$ **42.** $\left| 2 - \pi \right| + 1$

43. $\left|\pi - 6\right| + \sqrt{5}$ **44.** $\left|\sqrt{10} - \pi\right| + 2$ **45.** $\left|7 - 2\pi\right| + \sqrt{3}$ **46.** $\left|\pi - \sqrt{10}\right| + 2$ **47.** $\left|-5 - \pi\right| + 4$

48. $\left|2 - \sqrt{6}\right| + 1$ **49.** $\sqrt{5} - \left|1 - \sqrt{2}\right|$ **50.** $\left|\sqrt{6} - 2\right| + 1$ **51.** $\left|4 - \sqrt{3}\right| - 5$ **52.** $\left|y^2\right|$

53. $\left|-y^2\right|$ **54.** $\left|\sqrt{x}\right|$ **55.** $\left|-\sqrt{x}\right|$ **56.** $\left|x^2 + 2\right|$ **57.** $\left|y^2 + 6\right|$

58. $\left|-x^2 - 3\right|$ **59.** $\left|-\left(x^2 + 4\right)\right|$ **60.** $\left|x - 9\right|$ if $x < 9$ **61.** $\left|9 - x\right|$ if $x < 9$ **62.** $\left|x - 5\right|$ if $x \geq 5$

63. $\left|5 - x\right|$ if $x \geq 5$ **64.** $\left|x - 2\right|$ **65.** $\left|y - 3\right|$ **66.** $\left|x - 1\right|$ **67.** $\left|1 - x\right|$

68. $\left|x + 2\right|$ **69.** $\left|y + 7\right|$ **70.** $\left|x + 3\right|$ **71.** $\left|5 + x\right|$

72. $\left|x - 1\right| + \left|x - 3\right|$ if $1 < x < 3$ **73.** $\left|x + 2\right| - \left|x + 1\right|$ if $-2 < x < -1$ **74.** $\left|x - 1\right| + \left|x - 3\right|$ if $x \geq 3$

75. $\left|x + 2\right| - \left|x + 1\right|$ if $x \geq -1$ **76.** $x - \left|x - 1\right|$ if $x \geq 1$ **77.** $x + \left|x - 2\right|$ if $x \geq 2$

78. $x - \left|x - 1\right|$ if $x < 1$ **79.** $x + \left|x - 2\right|$ if $x < 2$ **80.** $\left|x + 1\right| + \left|x - 2\right|$ **81.** $\left|x - 1\right| - \left|x - 5\right|$

82. $\left|(x - 1)(x + 2)\right|$ **83.** $\left|(x + 1)(x - 2)\right|$ **84.** $\left|2p - 1\right| - \left|p + 3\right|$ **85.** $\left|5 - 2x\right| + \left|x - 4\right|$

86. $Z\left|2t + 3\right| - \left|3t - 5\right|$ **87.** $\left|(2x - 1)(x - 3)\right|$

In exercises (88-113), write with absolute value symbols.

88. $\sqrt{t^2}$ **89.** $\sqrt{(-x)^2}$ **90.** $\sqrt{(x - 1)^2}$ **91.** $\sqrt{(x + 1)^2}$ **92.** $\sqrt{(y + 2)^2}$ **93.** $\sqrt{(y + 3)^2}$

94. The distance between 10 and 4.   **95.** The distance between 7 and −4.

96. The distance between −2 and 5.   **97.** The distance between −8 and −3.

98. The distance between x and 12.   **99.** The distance between y and 7.

100. The distance between x and −7.   **101.** The distance between y and −4.

102. The distance between x and 2 is 5.   **103.** The distance between y and 5 is 7.

104. The distance between x and −1 is 4.   **105.** The distance between y and −2 is 5.

106. The distance between x and 5 is at least 1.   **107.** The distance between y and 7 is at least 3.

108. The distance between t and −2 is at least 1.   **109.** The distance between y and −3 is at least 2.

110. The distance between y and 1 is at most 2.   **111.** The distance between x and 2 is at most 4.

112. The distance between y and −3 is at most 1.   **113.** The distance between x and −5 is at most 6.

In exercises (114-125), use $\left|x - 2\right| = \delta$ to write the expression in terms of δ.

114. $\left|5x - 10\right|$ **115.** $\left|2x - 4\right|$ **116.** $\left|-3x + 6\right|$ **117.** $\left|-6x + 12\right|$

118. $\left|\dfrac{2x - 4}{5}\right|$ **119.** $\left|\dfrac{8x - 16}{7}\right|$ **120.** $\left|\dfrac{-7x + 14}{14}\right|$ **121.** $\left|\dfrac{-9x + 18}{3}\right|$

122. $\left|x + 2\right|$ **123.** $\left|x + 5\right|$ **124.** $\left|-x + 1\right|$ **125.** $\left|-x + 7\right|$

1.3 POLYNOMIALS AND FACTORING

In this section we will review special algebraic expressions called **polynomials.**

An expression of the type $a_n x^n + a_{n-1} x^{n-1} + \ldots + a_1 x + a_0$ is called a polynomial in x where a_i's are constants and n is a positive integer.

A polynomial may also be given as a product of non-constant polynomials. The second form of a polynomial is called the **factored** form. The process of changing the first form of a polynomial to the second form is called **factoring** a polynomial. We will also review a step-by-step procedure for **factoring.**

Objectives ▶ ▶

In this section you will learn about:

A. Algebraic Expressions;

B. Power Expressions;

C. Polynomial Expressions;

D. Algebra of Polynomials;

E. Factoring;

F. Evaluating a Polynomial; and

G. The value of a Polynomial expression when $|x|$ is large.

A. ALGEBRAIC EXPRESSIONS

Suppose John pledges \$5 more than what Dan pledges. Dan's pledge is unknown and can vary. If x is the amount that Dan pledges, then an **expression** for the amount for John's pledge is $x + 5$. This expression $x + 5$ is a simple example of an algebraic expression.

In the expression $x + 5$, x is the variable and 5 is a constant.

An algebraic expression can be in different forms. These expressions can be classified as follows:

      1. Power Expressions   **2. Polynomial Expressions**

      3. Rational Expressions   **4. Root Expressions**

In this section we will discuss power expressions and polynomial expressions. Rational expression are discussed in section 1.4, and root expressions are discussed in section 1.6.

B. POWER EXPRESSIONS

A power expression is an algebraic expression that consists of a variable raised to a constant power n, such as x^n.

In a power expression x^n, x is called the **base** and n is called the **exponent** or the **power.**

$$x^n \text{ means } \underbrace{x \cdot x \ldots x}_{n \ times}.$$

Laws of Exponents

1. $x^m \cdot x^n = x^{m+n}$ **2.** $\dfrac{x^m}{x^n} = x^{m-n}$ **3.** $\left(x^m\right)^n = x^{m \cdot n}$ **4.** $x^1 = x$

5. $(xy)^n = x^n y^n$ **6.** $\left(\dfrac{x}{y}\right)^n = \dfrac{x^n}{y^n}$ **7.** $x^{-m} = \dfrac{1}{x^m}$ **8.** $\dfrac{1}{x^{-m}} = x^m$

9. $\left(\dfrac{x}{y}\right)^{-n} = \left(\dfrac{y}{x}\right)^n$ **10.** $x^0 = 1$

EXAMPLE 1   Simplify the following expressions.

         a. $x^4(2x)^5$ **b.** $\dfrac{(3x)^3 (2x)}{36x^3}$

Solutions:

     a. $x^4(2x)^5 = x^4 \cdot 2^5 \cdot x^5 = 2^5 \cdot x^4 \cdot x^5 = 32x^9$

     b. $\dfrac{(3x)^3 (2x)}{36x^3} = \dfrac{3^3 x^3 \cdot 2x}{36x^3} = \dfrac{54x^4}{36x^3} = \dfrac{3}{2}x$

EXAMPLE 2   Simplify the following expressions.

         a. $\left(-2y\right)^3\left(\dfrac{x}{-2}\right)^2$ **b.** $\dfrac{a^3(-b)^2}{(ab)^3}\left(\dfrac{a}{2b}\right)^4$

Solutions:

     a. $\left(-2y\right)^3\left(\dfrac{x}{-2}\right)^2 = (-2)^3\, y^3\, \dfrac{x^2}{4} = \dfrac{-8}{4}\, y^3\, x^2 = -2x^2 y^3$

     b. $\dfrac{a^3(-b)^2}{(ab)^3}\left(\dfrac{a}{2b}\right)^4 = \dfrac{a^3 b^2}{a^3 b^3} \cdot \dfrac{a^4}{16b^4} = \dfrac{a^7 b^2}{16a^3 b^7} = \dfrac{a^4}{16b^5}$

EXAMPLE 3   Simplify the following expressions.

         a. $\dfrac{x^{-2} y^3}{x^4 y^{-2}}$ **b.** $\left(\dfrac{2y}{5x^2}\right)^{-3}$

Solutions: **a.** $\dfrac{x^{-2} y^3}{x^4 y^{-2}} = \dfrac{y^3 y^2}{x^4 \cdot x^2} = \dfrac{y^5}{x^6}$

     b. $\left(\dfrac{2y}{5x^2}\right)^{-3} = \left(\dfrac{5x^2}{2y}\right)^3 = \dfrac{5^3 \cdot x^6}{2^3 \cdot y^3} = \dfrac{125x^6}{8y^3}$

EXAMPLE 4   Simplify and write the result with positive exponents only: $\left(\dfrac{2x^{-3}y^2}{x\,y^3z^0}\right)^{-2}$.

Solution: Since $z^0 = 1$,

$$\left(\frac{2x^{-3}y^2}{xy^3z^0}\right)^{-2} = \left(\frac{2x^{-3}y^2}{xy^3}\right)^{-2} = \left(\frac{xy^3}{2x^{-3}y^2}\right)^{2} \qquad \text{(Property 9)}$$

$$= \left(\frac{x^4y^3}{2y^2}\right)^{2} = \left(\frac{x^4y}{2}\right)^{2} = \frac{x^8y^2}{4}\ .$$

C. POLYNOMIAL EXPRESSIONS

A polynomial expression is obtained by applying any combination of the operations of addition, subtraction, or a constant multiple to power expressions with non-negative powers. A polynomial is an algebraic expression of the form

$$a_nx^n + a_{n-1}x^{n-1} + \ldots + a_1x + a_0,$$

where a_n, a_{n-1}, ..., a_0 are real numbers $\left(a_n \neq 0\right)$ and n is a positive integer.

For example: •   The expression $3x^2 + 4x - 5$ is a polynomial.

        •   The expression $\dfrac{2x+3}{4x+1}$ is not a polynomial

        •   The expression $\sqrt{x^2 + x - 2}$ is not a polynomial.

Terminology

1.   **Terms** of a polynomial:

   The power expressions a_nx^n, $a_{n-1}x^{n-1}$, ... a_1x, and a_0 are called **terms** of the polynomial
   $$a_nx^n + a_{n-1}x^{n-1} + \ldots a_1x + a_0.$$

   •   A polynomial with only one term such as $2x^5$, is called a **monomial.**

   •   A polynomial with only two terms, such as $5x^2 - 7$, is called a **binomial.**

   •   A polynomial with only three terms such as $x^2 - 5x + 6$, is called a **trinomial.**

2.   **Leading term** of a polynomial:

   If the terms in a polynomial are arranged in descending order of the exponents of the variables then the **first** term is called the leading term of the polynomial.

Examples:

a. The **leading** term in the polynomial expression

$$5x^4 - 3x^2 + 10x + 9 \text{ is } \mathbf{5x^4}.$$

b. To find the **leading** term in the polynomial expression $3x - 5 + 2x^2 - 5x^3$, first we arrange the terms in descending order as $-5x^3 + 2x^2 + 3x - 5$. The first term $-5x^3$ is the **leading** term of the polynomial.

3. **Coefficients** of a polynomial:

The constant multiples a_n, a_{n-1}, ..., a_0 of the terms of the polynomials are called the **coefficients** of the polynomial expression $a_n x^n + a_{n-1} x^{n-1} + \ldots a_1 x + a_0$.

For example, the **coefficients** of the polynomial expression

$$-3x^4 + 6x^3 - x^2 + 7 \text{ are } \mathbf{-3, 6, -1,} \text{ and } \mathbf{7}.$$

Remark: *If all the coefficients are zero, the polynomial is called **zero polynomial**.*

---

4. **Degree** of a polynomial:

The **degree** of a polynomial is the exponent of the variable in the leading term, if the terms of the polynomial are arranged in descending order of the exponents.

Examples:

a. The polynomial $5x - 7$ is of degree one. Such polynomials are called **linear.**

b. The polynomial $2x^2 - 5x + 8$ is of degree two. Such polynomials are called **quadratic**.

c. The polynomial $x^3 + 2x$ is of degree three. Such a polynomial is called **cubic.**

d. The polynomial $3x + 5x^7 + 2x^2 + 1$ is of degree 7.

⬤Note   Sometimes we may use a polynomial in more than one variable, for example
$$3x^2 y^3 + 4xy^4 - x^2 y + y^3 + 2.$$

The degree of each term is the sum of its exponents. For example, the degree of $3x^2 y^3$ is $2 + 3$ i.e. 5, and the degree of y^3 is 3.

Degree of the polynomial is the maximum of the degrees of the various terms that constitute the polynomial. Thus, the degree of the above polynomial is 5.

Remark: *The degree of a polynomial in more than one variable is a generalization of the degree of a polynomial in one variable.*

D. ALGEBRA OF POLYNOMIALS

In elementary algebra courses we learned how to add, subtract, and multiply polynomials. In the multiplication of polynomials, we learned some special products which we review briefly in the following discussion.

Special Products (Formulas)

    a. $(A - B)(A + B) = A^2 - B^2$

    b. $(A + B)^2 = (A + B)(A + B) = A^2 + 2AB + B^2$

    c. $(A - B)^2 = (A - B)(A - B) = A^2 - 2AB + B^2$

    d. $(A + B)^3 = A^3 + 3A^2B + 3AB^2 + B^3$

    e. $(A - B)^3 = A^3 - 3A^2B + 3AB^2 - B^3$

EXAMPLE 5   Use the appropriate formulas to multiply each of the following:

    a. $(3x - 2y)(3x + 2y)$ **b.** $\left(5x^2 - 2\right)^2$ **c.** $(5x + 2)^3$

Solutions:

    a.   For $(3x - 2y)(3x + 2y)$ we substitute $A = 3x$ and $B = 2y$ in the formula.

$$(A - B)(A + B) = A^2 - B^2$$

We get $(3x - 2y)(3x + 2y) = (3x)^2 - (2y)^2 = 9x^2 - 4y^2$

* To see a more general method of expanding a binomial raised to a power like $(a + b)^n$, refer to Appendix C on the Binomial Theorem.

    b.   For $\left(5x^2 - 2\right)^2$, we substitute $A = 5x^2$ and $B = 2$ in the formula

$$(A - B)^2 = A^2 - 2AB + B^2$$

We get $\left(5x^2 - 2\right)^2 = (5x^2)^2 - 2(5x^2)(2) + (2)^2$

$$= 25x^4 - 20x^2 + 4$$

    c.   For $(5x + 2)^3$, replace A with $5x$ and B with 2 in the formula.

$$(A + B)^3 = A^3 + 3A^2B + 3AB^2 + B^3$$

We get $(5x + 2)^3 = (5x)^3 + 3(5x)^2(2) + 3(5x)(2)^2 + (2)^3$

$$= 125x^3 + 150x^2 + 60x + 8$$

E. FACTORING

We know how to multiply polynomials to get a new polynomial. In this objective we discuss the reverse process, that is, given a polynomial, we write it as a product of polynomials. This process is called **factoring.** It is useful in simplifying algebraic expressions and in solving equations. We briefly review the factoring methods that we learned in elementary algebra.

Factoring

The process of writing a given polynomial as a product of polynomials of lower degrees is called **factoring.** Each polynomial in the product is called a **factor.** A polynomial is said to be **prime** if it cannot be factored further.

Strategy for Factoring

Step 1 (*Common Factor*)

Among the numerical coefficients of the terms, factor out the largest number that divides into all the coefficients. Also factor out each variable common to **all** the terms.

For example, 8, x, and y^2 are common factors in $16x^2y^3 - 24xy^2$, so we write

$$16x^2y^3 - 24xy^2 = \mathbf{8xy^2}\,(2y) - \mathbf{8xy^2}\,(3) = \mathbf{8xy^2}\,(2y - 3).$$

Examine the expression that is inside the parentheses. If the expression is linear, then STOP. If the expression is non-linear with two terms (binomial) use Step 2, if there are three terms (trinomial) use Step 3, and for four terms use Step 4.

Step 2 (*Binomials*)

To factor a binomial, first try to write it as a difference of two squares and use the formula:

    a. $A^2 - B^2 = (A - B)(A + B)$

If it cannot be written as a difference of two squares, then try to write it as a difference of two cubes and use the formula:

    b. $A^3 - B^3 = (A - B)(A^2 + AB + B^2)$

The last attempt to factor a binomial is to write it as a sum of two cubes and use the formula:

    c. $A^3 + B^3 = (A + B)(A^2 - AB + B^2)$

If the binomial is a sum of two squares then it cannot be factored further.

Examples:

a. To factor $4x^2 - 9$, write it as a difference of two squares $4x^2 - 9 = (2x)^2 - (3)^2$. Replacing A with $2x$ and B with 3 in the formula,

$$(A)^2 - (B)^2 = (A - B)(A + B), \text{ we get}$$
$$(2x)^2 - (3)^2 = (2x - 3)(2x + 3)$$

b. To factor $27x^3 - 8y^3$, write it as a difference of two cubes $27x^3 - 8y^3 = (3x)^3 - (2y)^3$. Replacing A with $3x$ and B with $2y$ in the formula:

$$(A)^3 - (B)^3 = (A - B)(A^2 + AB + B^2), \text{ we get}$$
$$(3x)^3 - (2y)^3 = (3x - 2y)\left(9x^2 + 6xy + 4y^2\right)$$

c. To factor $8x^3 + y^3$, write it as a sum of two cubes, $8x^3 + y^3 = (2x)^3 + (y)^3$. Replace A with $2x$ and B with y in the formula,

$$(A)^3 + (B)^3 = (A + B)(A^2 - AB + B^2),$$

we get $(2x)^3 + \left(y^3\right) = (2x + y)\left(4x^2 - 2xy + y^2\right)$.

Step **3** $\left(\text{Trinomials } ax^2 + bx + c\right)$

a. Start each factor with ax and divide the product of two factors by a.

$$\frac{(ax\quad)(ax\quad)}{a}$$

b. Find two numbers α and β whose product is ac and whose sum is b.

Use one number (say α) in the first factor and the other (β) in the second factor as follows:

$$\frac{(ax + \alpha)(ax + \beta)}{a}$$

c. Factor out the common factors and cancel these factors with the number in the denominator.

Example $6x^2 - 11x + 3$

$$\frac{(6x\quad)(6x\quad)}{6}$$

Find two numbers whose product $= 6(3) = 18$ and sum $= -11$
These numbers are -2 and -9.

$$\frac{(6x - 9)(6x - 2)}{6}$$

$$\frac{\mathbf{3}(2x - 3)\,\mathbf{2}(3x - 1)}{\mathbf{6}}$$
$$= (2x - 3)(3x - 1)$$

Step **4** *(By grouping)*

Group the terms in such a way that there is something common to the terms in each group. Factor out the common factor(s).

Example: To factor $xa - 2bx + 3a - 6b$, we group the first two terms and the last two terms, as follows :

$$xa - 2bx \quad + \quad 3a - 6b$$

In the first group x is a common factor and in the second group 3 is a common factor. Pulling out the common factors gives :

$$x(a - 2b) \quad + \quad 3(a - 2b)$$

Since $(a - 2b)$ is common to both groups, so by factoring out $(a - 2b)$, we get :

$$(x + 3)(a - 2b)$$

EXAMPLE 6 Factor completely $2x^4 - 32$.

Solution:

Step **1** Factoring out the common factor 2 gives $2(x^4 - 16)$. The expression that is inside the parentheses is **not** linear, so we need to continue. The **two** terms inside the parentheses suggest using Step 2.

Step **2** We make the first attempt to write $x^4 - 16$ as a difference of two squares.

$$x^4 - 16 = (x^2)^2 - (4)^2$$

The difference of two squares gives two factors :

$$x^4 - 16 = (x^2)^2 - (4)^2 = (x^2 - 4)(x^2 + 4).$$

The two factors, expressions that are inside the parentheses, are not linear, so we need to continue. We examine both factors one by one.

- First, we try to factor $(x^2 - 4)$. We use step 2 (why ?)

$$x^2 - 4 = (x)^2 - (2)^2 = (x - 2)(x + 2)$$

Since both factors are linear, no further factoring is needed.

- Now, we try to factor $x^2 + 4$, if possible. This is a sum of two squares and cannot be factored.

Summarizing the above process, we get

$$\begin{aligned} 2x^4 - 32 &= 2(x^4 - 16) \\ &= 2(x^2 - 4)(x^2 + 4) \\ &= 2(x - 2)(x + 2)(x^2 + 4) \end{aligned}$$

EXAMPLE 7　Factor the following expressions:

　　a.　$x^2 - 3x - 18$　　　　**b.**　$4x^2 - 4x - 24$

Solutions:

a.　$x^2 - 3x - 18 = (x\quad)(x\quad)$. We can use the procedure of Step 3 with $a = 1$.

Two numbers whose sum is -3 and product is -18 are -6 and 3.

Therefore, $x^2 - 3x - 18 = (x - 6)(x + 3)$

b.　$4x^2 - 4x - 24 = 4(x^2 - x - 6)$

We factor the expression inside the parentheses

$$\begin{aligned} x^2 - x - 6 &= (x\quad)(x\quad) \\ &= (x - 3)(x + 2) \end{aligned}$$ 　The two numbers whose sum is -1 and product is -6 are -3 and 2.

Thus $\begin{aligned} 4x^2 - 4x - 24 &= 4(x^2 - x - 6) \\ &= 4(x - 3)(x + 2) \end{aligned}$

EXAMPLE 8　Factor the expression $18x^2 + 57x + 24$

Solution:　By pulling out the common factor 3, we get

$$18x^2 + 57x + 24 = 3\left(6x^2 + 19x + 8\right)$$

Since there are three terms inside the parentheses, we use Step 3 to factor $6x^2 + 19x + 8$.

a.　$\dfrac{(6x\quad)(6x\quad)}{6}$

b.　We look for two numbers whose product is $6(8) = 48$ and sum is 19.
The two numbers are 16 and 3.

c. By using one number in the first factor and the other number in the second factor, we get

$$\frac{(6x+16)(6x+3)}{6}$$

d. By pulling out the common factors and cancelling these factors with the number in the denominator, we get

$$\frac{\mathbf{2}(3x+8)\,\mathbf{3}(2x+1)}{\mathbf{6}} = (3x+8)(2x+1).$$

Thus, $18x^2 + 57x + 24 = 3(6x^2 + 19x + 8) = 3\,(3x+8)(2x+1)$

EXAMPLE 9   Factor the expression $(x+h)^3 + 8$

Solution :

Step 1   There are no common factors. The **two** terms direct us to Step 2.

Step 2   Since it is a cubic polynomial, we try to write it as a **sum** of two cubes.

$$(x+h)^3 + (2)^3$$

By replacing A with $x+h$ and B with 2 in the formula

$$(A)^3 + (B)^3 = (A+B)\,(A^2 - AB + B^2), \text{ we get}$$

$$(x+h)^3 + 2^3 = (x+h+2)\left((x+h)^2 - (x+h)2 + 2^2\right)$$

$$= (x+h+2)\,(x^2 + 2xh + h^2 - 2x - 2h + 4)$$

EXAMPLE 10   Simplify by factoring $3(3x+5)^5\,(x+2)^3 + 6(3x+5)^6\,(x+2)^2$

Solution:

Step 1   By factoring out the common factor 3, $(3x+5)^5$, and $(x+2)^2$, we get :

$$\mathbf{3(3x+5)^5\,(x+2)^2}\left[(x+2) + 2\,(3x+5)\right]$$

$$= \mathbf{3(3x+5)^5\,(x+2)^2}\,[x+2+6x+10]$$

$$= \mathbf{3(3x+5)^5\,(x+2)^2}\,(7x+12)$$

EXAMPLE 11   Simplify by factoring $x(2x+1)^{-1/2} + (2x+1)^{1/2}$

Solution: $x(2x+1)^{-1/2} + (2x+1)^{1/2}$

$$= (2x+1)^{-1/2}\,x + (2x+1)^{-1/2}\,(2x+1) \qquad a^{1/2} = a^{-1/2}\,a^1$$

Step 1   By factoring out the common factor $(2x+1)^{-1/2}$, we get:

$$(2x+1)^{-1/2}\left[x + (2x+1)^1\right]$$

$$= (2x+1)^{-1/2}\,(x + 2x + 1)$$

$$= (2x+1)^{-1/2}\,(3x+1) \text{ or } \frac{3x+1}{(2x+1)^{1/2}}$$

Alternative method:

Write the negative exponent as a fraction, get a common denominator, and add.

$$\frac{x}{(2x+1)^{1/2}} + (2x+1)^{1/2}$$

$$= \frac{x + (2x+1)}{(2x+1)^{1/2}} = \frac{3x+1}{(2x+1)^{1/2}}$$

F. EVALUATING A POLYNOMIAL

Given any polynomial, we can find its value for any specific value of the variable. For $x = a$ the value of the expression is obtained by substituting $x = a$ in the polynomial expression.

EXAMPLE 12   Evaluate $4x^3 - 3x^2 - 2x + 9$ for $x = -2$.

Solution: The value of the expression is

$$= 4(-2)^3 - 3(-2)^2 - 2(-2) + 9$$
$$= 4(-8) - 3(4) + 4 + 9$$
$$= -32 - 12 + 4 + 9 = -31$$

Remark: *The above method of evaluating an expression can be used for any number of unknowns. For an alternative method of evaluating polynomials refer to the section on Calculator Notes.*

G. VALUE OF A POLYNOMIAL EXPRESSION WHEN $|x|$ IS LARGE

Now consider what happens when we substitute larger and larger values of x into an algebraic expression.

As x gets larger ($x \to \infty$), its inverse $\dfrac{1}{x}$ gets smaller.

For example, $\dfrac{1}{10^3} = .001$, $\dfrac{1}{10^4} = .0001$, $\dfrac{1}{10^5} = .00001$, and so on.

This implies that $\dfrac{1}{x}$ is nearly zero as $|x|$ becomes very large.

In short $\dfrac{1}{x} \to 0$ as $|x| \to \infty$

We use the above observation to approximate the value of a polynomial expression for large values of x.

EXAMPLE 13   Approximate the value of $4x^3 - 3x^2 - 2x + 9$ when x is very large or $x \to \infty$.

Solutions: To get reciprocals like $\dfrac{1}{x}, \dfrac{1}{x^2}, \dfrac{1}{x^3}$ etc, we factor out x^n, where n is the degree of the polynomial expression.

$$4x^3 - 3x^2 - 2x + 9 = x^3\left(4 - \frac{3}{x} - \frac{2}{x^2} + \frac{9}{x^3}\right)$$

By using the fact that x is large, the terms $\dfrac{1}{x}, \dfrac{1}{x^2}$, and $\dfrac{1}{x^3}$ are very small (almost equal to zero),

$$4x^3 - 3x^2 - 2x + 9 = x^3\left(4 - \frac{3}{x} - \frac{2}{x^2} + \frac{9}{x^3}\right)$$
$$\approx x^3(4 - 0 - 0 + 0) = 4x^3$$

Thus, the leading term of a polynomial expression can approximate the value of the expression when x is large or $x \to \infty$.

An approximate value of a polynomial expression for large values of x is dominated by the leading term of the polynomial expression.

EXAMPLE 14   Approximate the value of
$$10x^5 - 8x^4 + 12x^3 + 7x^2 - 9x + 2 \quad \text{for} \quad x = 12734.$$

Solution: Since x is large, we use the fact that the value of the polynomial expression is dominated by the value of its leading term. Hence,
$$10x^5 - 8x^4 + 12x^3 + 7x^2 - 9x + 2 \approx 10x^5 = 10(12734)^5$$
$$= 3.34829895753(10^{21}).$$

The **exact** value is $3.34808862899(10^{21})$ Check with a Calculator.

EXERCISE 1.3

In exercises (1–20), simplify and write each answer with positive exponents.

1. $(7x^3)(9x^5)$
2. $(3x^8)(2x^{-7})$
3. $4x^2\left(3x^3\right)^2$
4. $5x^4\,(2x^2)^3$

5. $(9x^5)(-3x^{-2})$
6. $(3x^2)(-4x^{-9})$
7. $\dfrac{\left(4x^3\right)^2}{\left(2x^2\right)^3}$
8. $\dfrac{\left(9x^5\right)^2}{\left(3x^2\right)^5}$

9. $\dfrac{8x^{-2}y^3}{2^{-1}x^3y^{-2}}$
10. $\dfrac{7x^4y^{-3}}{3^{-1}x^{-2}y^4}$
11. $\dfrac{\left(x^{-3}y^4\right)^{-2}}{2}$
12. $\dfrac{\left(x^2y^{-3}\right)^4}{12\left(x^{-1}y^2\right)^2}$

13. $5(x+2)^3(2x+4)^2$
14. $7(3x+9)^4(4x+12)^3$
15. $2(x+1)^0 + 3(5)^0$
16. $-7(2x+3)^0 + 4(6)^0$

17. $\dfrac{10(2x+3)^5}{5(2x+3)^3}$
18. $\dfrac{7(3x+5)^3}{14(3x+5)^8}$
19. $\left(\left((3x+5)^{1/2}\right)^3\right)^6$
20. $\left(\left((4x+7)^4\right)^{\frac{1}{3}}\right)^{12}$

In exercises (21–44), multiply the polynomials.

21. $(5x-3)(5x+3)$
22. $(-7x-5)(-7x+5)$
23. $(2xy-7)(2xy+7)$
24. $(7xz-5)(7xz+5)$

25. $(3x^2-5)(3x^2+5)$
26. $(4x^3-3)(4x^3+3)$
27. $\{(x+2)^{1/2}-3\}\{(x+2)^{1/2}+3\}$

28. $\{(2-x)^{1/2}-5\}\{(2-x)^{1/2}+5\}$
29. $(9x^2-2yz)(9x^2+2yz)$
30. $(7yz-6x^3)(7yz+6x^3)$

31. $(7x+3z)^2$
32. $(5x+6y)^2$
33. $(4x-3y)^2$
34. $(3x-5y)^2$
35. $\left(2x^2+5\right)^2$

36. $(4x^2 - 7)^2$ **37.** $\left(3x^3 - 5y^2\right)^2$ **38.** $\left(6y^3 - 7x^2\right)^2$ **39.** $(x+1)^3$ **40.** $(x-1)^3$

41. $(2x+1)^3$ **42.** $(3x+4)^3$ **43.** $(3x-2)^3$ **44.** $(2x-3)^3$

In exercises (45–84), factor each expression completely.

45. $16 - x^2$ **46.** $4x^2 - 1$ **47.** $b^2 - a^2$ **48.** $4r^2 - 9s^2$ **49.** $9 - (x-2)^2$

50. $(x-4)^2 - 25$ **51.** $16 - (x+1)^2$ **52.** $(3x+2)^2 - 16$ **53.** $(x+h)^2 - x^2$ **54.** $(2t+7)^2 - t^2$

55. $3(x+h)^4 - 12(x+h)^2$ **56.** $4(x+2)^4 - 16(x+2)^2$ **57.** $2x^2 - 8x^4$ **58.** $2(x+h)^2 - 18x^2$

59. $3x^2 + 27x^4$ **60.** $45x^4 + 9x^2$ **61.** $x^3 + 8$ **62.** $x^3 + 216$ **63.** $x^3 - 8$

64. $x^3 - 64$ **65.** $x^4 - 16$ **66.** $x^4 - 81$ **67.** $x^4 + 16$ **68.** $x^4 + 81$

69. $y^4 - \dfrac{16}{81}$ **70.** $t^4 - \dfrac{1}{16}$ **71.** $x^3 - \dfrac{27}{8}$ **72.** $y^3 - \dfrac{27}{64}$

73. $x^2 - 5x - 24$ **74.** $x^2 + 3x - 18$ **75.** $x^2 - 13x - 30$ **76.** $x^2 + 8x + 15$

77. $2x^2 - 7x + 3$ **78.** $2x^2 + 9x + 4$ **79.** $6x^2 + 13x - 5$ **80.** $3x^2 - 14x - 5$

81. $x^3 - 3x^2 - 4x + 12$ **82.** $2x^3 - 5x^2 - 4x + 10$ **83.** $2x^3 + x^2 - 8x - 4$ **84.** $3x^3 + x^2 - 3x - 1$

In exercises (85–97), simplify by factoring.

85. $2(x+1)(3x-1) + 3(x+1)^2$ **86.** $(2x-3)(x+2) + 3(x+2)^2$ **87.** $6(2x+1)^2(x-2)^3 - 3(2x+1)^3(x-2)^2$

88. $4(3x-1)(4x+5)^2 - 8(3x-1)^2(4x+5)$ **89.** $12(x+5)^3(3x-2)^2 - 4(x+5)^2(3x-2)^3$

90. $(3x+5)^{-1/2} + (3x+1)^{1/2}$ **91.** $(2x-7)^{-2/3} + (2x+7)^{2/3}$

92. $\left(x^2+3\right)^{1/2} + \left(x^2+3\right)^{5/2}$ **93.** $\left(x^2+5\right)^{1/2} + \left(x^2+5\right)^{3/2}$

94. $(2x+1)^{-1/2} \cdot (5x+7)^{1/2} - (2x+1)^{1/2}(5x+7)^{-1/2}$ **95.** $(4x+5)^{-1/2}(6x-7)^{1/2} + (4x+5)^{1/2}(6x-7)^{-1/2}$

96. $3(2x-1)^{1/2}(x+1)^2 - 2(2x-1)^{3/2}(x+1)$ **97.** $(3x-4)^{1/2}(4x-3)^2 + (3x-4)^{3/2}(4x-3)$

In exercises (98–103), evaluate each polynomial expression for the given value of the variable.

98. $5x^3 + 9x^2 - 7x + 10$, for $x = -1$ **99.** $2x^3 - x^2 + 7x - 9$, for $x = 1$

100. $x^4 - 2x^3 + x + 1$, for $x = 2$ **101.** $-x^4 + x^3 - 7$, for $x = -3$

102. $-x^3 + 2x^2 - 8x + 1$, for $x = -2$ **103.** $-2x^3 - 7x^2 - 8x + 1$, for $x = -4$

In exercises (104–106), approximate the value of each polynomial expression for the given value of x.

104. $x^3 - 7x^2 + 8x + 11$, for $x = 1050$ **105.** $2x^3 - 4x^2 + 9x - 10$, for $x = 2010$

106. $-5x^4 + 3x^3 + 10x^2 - 15x - 10$, for $x = 1175$ **107.** $x^4 - 8x^3 + 7x - 4$, for $x = 1580$

Writing Exercises

108. Explain what is meant by the dominant part of a polynomial expression when $|x|$ is large.

1.4 RATIONAL EXPRESSIONS

We have seen that the sum, difference, or product of polynomials is again a polynomial. However, the quotient of two polynomials, called a rational expression, may not be a polynomial. In this section, we will review the algebra of rational expressions.

Objectives ▶ ▶

In this section you will learn about:

A. Reduction of a Rational Expression;

B. Addition and Subtraction of Rational Expressions;

C. Complex Fractions; and

D. Evaluating a Rational Expression.

Rational Expression

An algebraic expression $\frac{p(x)}{q(x)}$, where $p(x)$ and $q(x)$ are polynomial expressions and $q(x)$ is a non-zero polynomial, is called a **rational expression.**

For example,

$\frac{x^2-4}{x^2-5x+6}$ is a rational expression and $\frac{\sqrt{x^2-4}}{x^2-5x+6}$ is not a rational expression (why?).

A. REDUCTION OF A RATIONAL EXPRESSION

As in the case of a rational number, a rational expression is also reduced to its simplest form by canceling factors(s) common to the numerator and the denominator.

A rational expressions $\frac{a\cdot c}{b\cdot c}=\frac{a}{b}$ for $c\neq 0$.

Remark: *The process of removing common factors from the numerator and denominator is called reduction of a rational expression.*

For example,

$$\frac{x^2-x-2}{x^2-2x}=\frac{(x+1)(x-2)}{x(x-2)} \quad *$$

$$=\frac{x+1}{x} \text{ for } x\neq 2$$

* Cancellation is the same as division and since we can not divide by 0, we state that $x\neq 2$ before we cancel the factor $x-2$.

EXAMPLE 1 Reduce $\frac{x^2-5x+6}{x^4-4x^2}$ to its simplified form.

Solution: In order to find the common factor(s), we factor the numerator and denominator.

$$\frac{x^2-5x+6}{x^4-4x^2}=\frac{(x-2)(x-3)}{x^2(x^2-4)}=\frac{(x-2)(x-3)}{x^2(x-2)(x+2)}$$

$$=\frac{(x-3)}{x^2(x+2)} \text{ for } x\neq 2.$$

Remark: *In the reduced rational expression* $\dfrac{x-3}{x^2(x+2)}$ *we can not replace x with* 0, 2, *or* -2 *(why ?).*

EXAMPLE 2   Reduce $\dfrac{15(5x+3)^2(2x+5)^2 - 4(5x+3)^3(2x+5)}{(2x+5)^4}$ to its simplest form.

Solution: Factoring the numerator gives

$$\frac{(5x+3)^2(2x+5)\left[15(2x+5) - 4(5x+3)\right]}{(2x+5)^4}$$

$$\frac{(5x+3)^2\left[30x+75-20x-12\right]}{(2x+5)^3} = \frac{(5x+3)^2(10x+63)}{(2x+5)^3} \text{ for } x \neq -\frac{5}{2}$$

B. ADDITION AND SUBTRACTION OF RATIONAL EXPRESSIONS

Recall that when we add two or more fractions, we first change each fraction to an equivalent fraction with the same denominator (LCD). We proceed in a similar way when we add rational expressions.

EXAMPLE 3   (Adding with same denominator)

Add $\dfrac{5x}{x^2+7} + \dfrac{3}{x^2+7}$

Solutions: Since the denominators are the same, we need only to add the numerators.

$$\frac{5x}{x^2+7} + \frac{3}{x^2+7} = \frac{5x+3}{x^2+7}$$

EXAMPLE 4   (Adding with different denominators)

Combine $\dfrac{2}{x^2+x-6} - \dfrac{1}{x^2-x-2}$ into a single rational expression.

Solution:

	Procedure	**Solution**
Step 1	Factor each denominator	$\dfrac{2}{(x+3)(x-2)} - \dfrac{1}{(x-2)(x+1)}$
Step 2	Find the least common denominator (lcd). The lcd = product of all different factors; each factor is raised to its highest exponent.	$\dfrac{2}{(x+3)(x-2)} - \dfrac{1}{(x-2)(x+1)}$ lcd $= (x+3)(x-2)(x+1)$

	Procedure	*Solution*

Step 3   Compare each denominator with the lcd and multiply the numerator and denominator by the missing factors(s).

$$\frac{2(x+1)}{(x+3)(x-2)(x+1)} - \frac{1(x+3)}{(x-2)(x+1)(x+3)}$$

$$= \frac{2x+2-x-3}{(x+3)(x-2)(x+1)}$$

Step 4   Write the common denominator and add or subtract the numerators.

$$= \frac{x-1}{(x+3)(x-2)(x+1)}$$

Step 5   Reduce the rational expression, if possible.

EXAMPLE 5   Add and simplify $\dfrac{x-2}{x^2+4x+4} + \dfrac{x-1}{x^2+5x+6}$.

Solution:

Step 1   Factoring each denominator gives $\dfrac{x-2}{(x+2)^2} + \dfrac{x-1}{(x+2)(x+3)}$.

Step 2   The lcd is $(x+2)^2(x+3)$.

Step 3   Comparing each denominator with lcd and multiplying the numerator and the denominator by the missing factor(s) gives

$$\frac{(x-2)(x+3)}{(x+2)^2(x+3)} + \frac{(x-1)(x+2)}{(x+2)^2(x+3)}.$$

Step 4   Adding the rational expressions with like denominators gives

$$\frac{(x-2)(x+3)+(x-1)(x+2)}{(x+2)^2(x+3)} = \frac{x^2+x-6+x^2+x-2}{(x+2)^2(x+3)} = \frac{2x^2+2x-8}{(x+2)^2(x+3)}$$

Step 5   Factoring the numerator we get: $\dfrac{2\left(x^2+x-4\right)}{(x+2)^2(x+3)}$.

C. COMPLEX FRACTIONS

Sometimes the numerator or the denominator are not polynomials but rational expressions. Such expressions can be simplified as discussed in the following examples.

EXAMPLE 6   Simplify $\dfrac{\dfrac{2}{x+h+1} - \dfrac{2}{x+1}}{h}$.

Solution:

Step 1   Find the lcd of the denominators of the fractions in the numerator. In this case, the lcd of $x + h + 1$, and $x + 1$, is $(x + h + 1)(x + 1)$.

Step 2   Multiply each term in the numerator and the denominator by the lcd and cancel the common factors.

$$\frac{\dfrac{2(x+h+1)(x+1)}{x+h+1} - \dfrac{2(x+h+1)(x+1)}{x+1}}{h(x+h+1)(x+1)} = \frac{2(x+1) - 2(x+h+1)}{h(x+h+1)(x+1)}$$

Step 3   Simplify the numerator and the denominator.

$$\frac{2(x+1) - 2(x+h+1)}{h(x+h+1)(x+1)} = \frac{2x+2-2x-2h-2}{h(x+h+1)(x+1)} = \frac{-2h}{h(x+h+1)(x+1)}$$

Step 4   Reduce the rational expression to the simplest form.

$$\frac{-2h}{h(x+h+1)(x+1)} = \frac{-2}{(x+h+1)(x+1)}$$

EXAMPLE 7   Simplify $\dfrac{\dfrac{1}{(x+a)^2} - \dfrac{1}{x^2}}{2x+a}$.

Solution:

Step 1   The least common multiple of the denominators

$(x+a)^2$, and x^2 is $x^2(x+a)^2$

Step 2   We multiply each term in the numerator and the denominator by $x^2(x+a)^2$ and cancel the common factors.

$$\frac{\dfrac{1x^2(x+a)^2}{(x+a)^2} - \dfrac{1x^2(x+a)^2}{x^2}}{(2x+a)x^2(x+a)^2} = \frac{x^2 - (x+a)^2}{x^2(2x+a)(x+a)^2} \cdot$$

Step 3   We simplify the numerator.

$$\frac{x^2 - (x+a)^2}{x^2(2x+a)(x+a)^2} = \frac{x^2 - (x^2 + 2ax + a^2)}{x^2(2x+a)(x+a)^2} \qquad (x+a)^2 = x^2 + 2ax + a^2$$

$$= \frac{-2ax - a^2}{x^2(2x+a)(x+a)^2}$$

$$= \frac{-a(2x+a)}{x^2(2x+a)(x+a)^2}$$

Step 4   Reduce the rational expression to the simplest form.

$$\frac{-a(2x+a)}{x^2(2x+a)(x+a)^2} = \frac{-a}{x^2(x+a)^2}$$

D. EVALUATING A RATIONAL EXPRESSION

To evaluate a rational expression $\dfrac{p(x)}{q(x)}$ for $x = a$, we substitute a for x in the expression and simplify.

EXAMPLE 8   Evaluate $\dfrac{x^2 - 5x + 6}{x + 4}$ for ;

         a) $x = 1$ **b)** $x = 3$

Solutions:

a)   For $x = 1$: $\dfrac{x^2 - 5x + 6}{x + 4} = \dfrac{(1)^2 - 5(1) + 6}{1 + 4} = \dfrac{1 - 5 + 6}{5} = \dfrac{2}{5}$.

b)   For $x = 3$: $\dfrac{x^2 - 5x + 6}{x + 4} = \dfrac{(3)^2 - 5(3) + 6}{3 + 4} = \dfrac{9 - 15 + 6}{7} = \dfrac{0}{7} = 0.$

EXAMPLE 9   Evaluate $\dfrac{3x + 2}{80 - x}$ for ;   **a)** $x = 10$ **b)** $x = 80$

Solutions:

a)   For $x = 10$: $\dfrac{3x + 2}{80 - x} = \dfrac{3(10) + 2}{80 - 10} = \dfrac{32}{70} = \dfrac{16}{35}$

b)   For $x = 80$: $\dfrac{3x + 2}{80 - x} = \dfrac{3(80) + 2}{80 - 80} = \dfrac{242}{0}$

         * This is undefined because we cannot divide by zero.

Terminology

- When on substituting a for x in a rational expression $\dfrac{p(x)}{q(x)}$, the result is of the form $\dfrac{k}{0}$, where $k \neq 0$, we say that the expression $\dfrac{p(x)}{q(x)}$ is not defined (or is undefined) for $x = a$.

  This happens when $p(a) \neq 0$ but $q(a) = 0$.

- If $p(a)$ and $q(a)$ are both zero, then $\dfrac{p(x)}{q(x)}$ is said to be indeterminate at $x = a$. *

* $\dfrac{242}{0}$ is undefined, because we cannot divide by zero. To see how large $\dfrac{242}{a}$ gets as 'a' gets closer to zero, examine the value of $\dfrac{242}{.000001}$.

$\dfrac{242}{.000001} = 242 \times 10^6$, a large number.

Or $\dfrac{242}{.000000001} = 242 \times 10^9$ which is even a larger number. This suggests that as a gets closer to 0 ($a > 0$), then $\dfrac{242}{a}$ gets larger and larger without any limit.

* For $a \neq 0$, $\dfrac{a}{0}$ is **undefined** and $\dfrac{0}{0}$ is **indeterminate**.

EXAMPLE 10   Evaluate $\dfrac{x^2-2x-3}{2x-6}$ for $x=3$.

Solutions: For $x=3$,

$$\frac{x^2-2x-3}{2x-6}=\frac{(3)^2-2(3)-3}{2(3)-6}=\frac{9-6-3}{6-6}=\frac{0}{0}$$

We say that $\dfrac{x^2-2x-3}{2x-6}$ is **indeterminate** for $x=3$.

EXAMPLE 11   Approximate the value of $\dfrac{6x^3-7x+9}{2x^3+8x^2+1}$ when x is large or $x\to\infty$.

Solutions: By factoring out the variable part of the leading terms from the numerator and from the denominator, we get

$$\frac{x^3\left(6-\dfrac{7}{x^2}+\dfrac{9}{x^3}\right)}{x^3\left(2+\dfrac{8}{x}+\dfrac{1}{x^3}\right)}$$

By cancelling the common factors, we get

$$\frac{x^3\left(6-\dfrac{7}{x^2}+\dfrac{9}{x^3}\right)}{x^3\left(2+\dfrac{8}{x}+\dfrac{1}{x^3}\right)}=\frac{6-\dfrac{7}{x^2}+\dfrac{9}{x^3}}{2+\dfrac{8}{x}+\dfrac{1}{x^3}}$$

Since x is very large $(x\to\infty)$, so $\dfrac{1}{x},\dfrac{1}{x^2}$ and $\dfrac{1}{x^3}$ become very small, approximately zero.

This gives

$$\frac{6-\dfrac{7}{x^2}+\dfrac{9}{x^3}}{2+\dfrac{8}{x}+\dfrac{1}{x^3}}\approx\frac{6-0+0}{2+0+0}$$

$$\approx\frac{6}{2}=\frac{\text{leading coefficient of numerator}}{\text{leading coefficient of denominator}}$$

$$\approx 3$$

Thus for large x-values the value of a rational expression $\dfrac{p(x)}{q(x)}$, where the degree of

$p(x)=$ degree of $q(x)$, is approximately equal to the quotient of the leading coefficients of the numerator and the denominator.

Remark: *Using the observation in the above example, the expression*

$$\frac{6x^3 - 7x + 9}{2x^3 + 8x^2 + 1} \approx 3 \quad for \ \ x = 1250.$$

Verify, using a calculator, that the actual value is 2.99042839069.

EXAMPLE 12   Approximate the value of $\dfrac{6x^2 - 7x + 9}{2x^3 + 8x^2 + 1}$ when x is very large or $x \to \infty$.

Solution: By factoring out the variable part of the leading terms from the numerator and the denominator gives

$$\frac{x^2\left(6 - \dfrac{7}{x} + \dfrac{9}{x^2}\right)}{x^3\left(2 + \dfrac{8}{x} + \dfrac{1}{x^3}\right)} = \frac{6 - \dfrac{7}{x} + \dfrac{9}{x^2}}{x\left(2 + \dfrac{8}{x} + \dfrac{1}{x^3}\right)} = \left(\frac{1}{x}\right)\frac{6 - \dfrac{7}{x} + \dfrac{9}{x^2}}{2 + \dfrac{8}{x} + \dfrac{1}{x^3}}$$

Since x is large ($x \to \infty$), so $\dfrac{1}{x}$, $\dfrac{1}{x^2}$, and $\dfrac{1}{x^3}$ are approximately zero. This gives

$$\left(\frac{1}{x}\right)\frac{6 - \dfrac{7}{x} + \dfrac{9}{x^2}}{2 + \dfrac{8}{x} + \dfrac{1}{x^3}} \approx (0)\,\frac{6 - 0 + 0}{2 + 0 + 0} = (0)\left(\frac{6}{2}\right) = 0$$

Thus for large x-values the value of a rational expression $\dfrac{p(x)}{q(x)}$, where

the degree of $p(x) <$ degree of $q(x)$, is approximately equal to zero.

Remark: *The approximate value of* $\dfrac{6x^2 - 7x + 9}{2x^3 + 8x^2 + 1} \approx 0$ *for $x = 1314$. Verify, using*

a calculator, that the actual value is .0022274157043.

EXAMPLE 13   Approximate the value of $\dfrac{6x^2 - 7x + 9}{2x + 8}$ when x is large or $x \to \infty$.

Solution: As in the previous two examples, factoring out the variable part of the leading terms from the numerator and the denominator gives

$$\frac{x^2\left(6 - \dfrac{7}{x} + \dfrac{9}{x^2}\right)}{x\left(2 + \dfrac{8}{x}\right)} = \frac{x\left(6 - \dfrac{7}{x} + \dfrac{7}{x^2}\right)}{2 + \dfrac{8}{x}}$$

For large x, $\dfrac{1}{x}$ and $\dfrac{1}{x^2}$ are almost zero. This gives

$$\frac{x\left(6 - \dfrac{7}{x} + \dfrac{7}{x^2}\right)}{2 + \dfrac{8}{x}} = \frac{x(6 - 0 + 0)}{2 + 0} = \frac{6x}{2}$$

$$= 3x \text{ (quotient of the leading terms)}$$

Remark: *In the next section we will use long division in order to improve upon the above approximate value. We summarize the observations we made in Examples 11, 12, and 13 as follows:*

Approximate the Value of a Rational Expression $\dfrac{p(x)}{q(x)}$ when $|x|$ is Very Large

$\dfrac{p(x)}{q(x)}$ = quotient of leading **coefficients,** if deg $p(x)$ = deg $q(x)$

≈ 0, if deg $p(x) <$ deg $q(x)$

$\approx$ quotient of leading **terms,** if deg $p(x) \geq$ deg $q(x)$

EXAMPLE 14 Give an approximate value of each rational expression for $x = 1500$.

a) $\dfrac{8x^2 - 10x - 7}{4x^3 + 10x - 9}$ b) $\dfrac{10x^3 - 7x + 2}{6x^3 + 9x^2}$ c) $\dfrac{6x^3 - 7x^2 + 12x}{2x^2 + 8x - 13}$

Solutions: **a)** Since the degree of the denominator of the rational expression is greater than the degree of the numerator and $|x|$ is large,

$$\frac{8x^2 - 10x - 7}{4x^3 + 10x - 9} \approx 0, \text{ when } x = 1500$$

Check with a calculator that the value of this rational expression for $x = 1500$ is .001332220224.

b) In this case, the degree of the numerator is the same as the degree of the denominator. Therefore,

$$\frac{10x^3 - 7x + 2}{6x^3 + 9x^2} \approx \frac{10}{6}, \text{ or } \frac{5}{3} \text{ or } 1.66666666667$$

With a calculator we find that the value is 1.665001147.

c) Since the degree of the numerator is greater than the degree of the denominator, the value of the rational expression is dominated by the value of the quotient of leading terms. This gives

$$\frac{6x^3 - 7x^2 + 12x}{2x^2 + 8x - 13} \approx \frac{6x^3}{2x^2} = 3x$$

Therefore, an approximate value of $\dfrac{6x^3 - 7x^2 + 12x}{2x^2 + 8x - 13} = 3(1500) = 4500.$

⬤ Note   We will have a better approximation by using a method discussed in the next section.

EXERCISE 1.4

In exercises (1–20), reduce each rational expression to its simplest form.

1. $\dfrac{x^2 - 4}{x^2 + 4x + 4}$ 2. $\dfrac{x^2 - 4x + 4}{x^2 - 4}$ 3. $\dfrac{h^2 - 9}{h^2 + 6h + 9}$ 4. $\dfrac{y^2 - 6y + 9}{y^2 - 9}$ 5. $\dfrac{x^2 - 16}{2x^2 + 7x - 4}$

6. $\dfrac{3x^2 - 13x + 4}{x^2 - 16}$ 7. $\dfrac{2x^3 + 3x^2}{2x^2 + 5x + 3}$ 8. $\dfrac{3x^4 + 5x^3}{3x^2 + 2x - 5}$ 9. $\dfrac{x^2 + 5x + 6}{x^2 + 6x + 9}$ 10. $\dfrac{x^2 + 8x + 16}{x^2 + 5x + 4}$

11. $\dfrac{6x^2 + x - 2}{3x^2 + 2x}$ 12. $\dfrac{2x^2 + 5x}{4x^2 + 8x - 5}$ 13. $\dfrac{6 + 7x - 3x^2}{x^2 - 2x - 3}$ 14. $\dfrac{3x^2 - 13x + 4}{3x^2 + 11x - 4}$

15. $\dfrac{6(x + 2)^5 (x - 1)^3 - 3(x - 1)^2 (x + 2)^6}{(x - 1)^6}$

16. $\dfrac{2(2x + 1)^2 (3 - 2x) - 4(2x + 1)(3 + 2x)^2}{(2x + 1)^3}$

17. $\dfrac{3(t^2 - 1)^2 2t(t^2 + 1)^3 - (t^2 - 1)^3 (3)(t^2 + 1)^2 \cdot 2t}{\left((t^2 + 1)^3\right)^2}$

18. $\dfrac{4(2t^2 + 1)^3 (t^2 + 2)(t + 5)^3 - 8(2t^2 + 1)^2 (t^2 + 2)(t + 5)^2}{\left[(2t^2 + 1)^2\right]^3}$

19. $\dfrac{(4x - 1)(3x - 4)^3 - 9(3x - 4)^2 (2x^2 - x)}{\left((3x - 4)^3\right)^2}$

20. $\dfrac{3(2x + 3)^2 (5x + 7)^3 + 9(2x + 3)^3 (5x + 7)^2}{\left((2x + 3)^2\right)^5}$

In exercises (21–40), combine the rational expressions into a single rational expression and reduce the result to its simplest form.

21. $\dfrac{x + 4}{x} - \dfrac{2x + 8}{x^2}$ 22. $\dfrac{x + 5}{x^2} - \dfrac{5x + 4}{x^3}$ 23. $\dfrac{2x}{x^2 - 1} - \dfrac{1}{x - 1}$ 24. $\dfrac{5x}{x^2 - 4} + \dfrac{2}{x + 2}$

25. $\dfrac{2}{x - 2} - \dfrac{4}{(x - 2)^2}$ 26. $\dfrac{3}{x + 3} + \dfrac{2}{(x + 3)^2}$ 27. $\dfrac{3}{(x - 1)(x - 2)} - \dfrac{1}{(x - 1)(x + 3)}$

28. $\dfrac{2}{(x + 1)(x - 4)} - \dfrac{5}{(2x - 1)(x + 1)}$ 29. $\dfrac{8}{x^2 + x - 6} - \dfrac{5}{x^2 - x - 2}$ 30. $\dfrac{4}{2x^2 + 7x + 3} + \dfrac{3}{2x^2 - 5x - 3}$

31. $\dfrac{3}{x + 2} + \dfrac{2}{x^2 + 2x} - \dfrac{3x + 1}{x^2}$ 32. $\dfrac{5}{x - 5} - \dfrac{4}{x^2 - 5x} - \dfrac{5x + 2}{x^2}$ 33. $\dfrac{x}{x + 3} + \dfrac{2x - 1}{x^2 + 6x + 9}$

34. $\dfrac{3x + 1}{x^2 - 8x + 16} - \dfrac{2x}{x - 4}$ 35. $\dfrac{x + 2}{2x^2 + 3x + 1} + \dfrac{x - 2}{2x^2 - x - 1}$ 36. $\dfrac{2}{2x^2 + 5x - 3} - \dfrac{4x}{6x^2 - 7x + 2}$

37. $\dfrac{1}{4-4x}+\dfrac{1}{3x-1}+\dfrac{1}{x-1}$

38. $\dfrac{4}{3x-2}+\dfrac{5}{2x-1}-\dfrac{4}{6x-3}$

39. $\dfrac{2}{x^2-x-6}+\dfrac{3}{x^2+3x+2}-\dfrac{1}{x^2-2x-3}$

40. $\dfrac{1}{x^2-3x+2}-\dfrac{4}{x^2-5x+6}+\dfrac{2}{x^2-4x+3}$

In exercises (41–50), simplify the complex fraction.

41. $\dfrac{\dfrac{2}{x-1}-\dfrac{1}{x+2}}{x+5}$

42. $\dfrac{\dfrac{2}{x-1}+\dfrac{1}{x+3}}{3x+5}$

43. $\dfrac{1-\dfrac{3}{x}-\dfrac{10}{x^2}}{1-\dfrac{1}{x}-\dfrac{6}{x^2}}$

44. $\dfrac{1-\dfrac{8}{x}+\dfrac{16}{x^2}}{1-\dfrac{5}{x}+\dfrac{4}{x^2}}$

45. $\dfrac{\dfrac{5}{x+h}-\dfrac{5}{x}}{h}$

46. $\dfrac{\dfrac{7}{x}-\dfrac{7}{x+2h}}{h}$

47. $\dfrac{\dfrac{3}{2(x+h)+1}-\dfrac{3}{2x+1}}{h}$

48. $\dfrac{\dfrac{5}{3(x-h)+2}-\dfrac{5}{3x+2}}{h}$

49. $\dfrac{\dfrac{1}{(x+h)^2}-\dfrac{1}{x^2}}{h}$

50. $\dfrac{\dfrac{1}{(x+2h)^2}-\dfrac{1}{x^2}}{h}$

In exercises (51–62), evaluate the rational expression.

51. $\dfrac{x^2-9}{x^2+6x+9}$, for $x=3$

52. $\dfrac{(x+1)^2}{x^2-4}$, for $x=-1$

53. $\dfrac{x^2-9}{x^2+6x+9}$, for $x=-3$

54. $\dfrac{x^2-16}{x^2-8x+16}$, for $x=4$

55. $\dfrac{x^2-1}{x^2+5x+4}$, for $x=-4$

56. $\dfrac{2x+9}{x^2-6x+5}$, for $x=5$

57. $\dfrac{2x^2+5x+3}{2x^2+x-3}$, for $x=-\dfrac{3}{2}$

58. $\dfrac{5+2x}{-2x^2+3x-1}$, for $x=\dfrac{1}{2}$

59. $\dfrac{2x^2+5x+3}{2x^2+x-3}$, for $x=1$

60. $\dfrac{x^2+6x+5}{2x^2+5x+3}$, for $x=-1$

61. $\dfrac{2x^2+5x+3}{2x^2+x-3}$, for $x=2$

62. $\dfrac{3x^2-5x+7}{6x^2+2x-9}$, for $x=-2$

In exercises (63–74), approximate the value of the rational expression when $x=1850$ (large).

63. $\dfrac{20x^4-8x^3+10x-9}{10x^4-15x+1}$

64. $\dfrac{5x^5-10x^4+9x^2-7}{10x^5+20x^3-7x+16}$

65. $\dfrac{7x^2-3x+5}{2x^2+x-10}$

66. $\dfrac{9x^3+7x^2-4x+2}{x^3-6x^2+14x+15}$

67. $\dfrac{15x^3+8x^2-9x}{8x^4-3x^3-x+10}$

68. $\dfrac{17x^2+9x-8}{9x^3+4x^2-5x+6}$

69. $\dfrac{5x+8}{19x^3-10x+5}$

70. $\dfrac{9x^3+6x^2-7x+6}{7x^5+10x^3-2x^2+9}$

71. $\dfrac{20x^3-8x^2+15}{10x^2-7x+15}$

72. $\dfrac{10x^4+7x^3+2x^2-5x+1}{2x^2+5x+9}$

73. $\dfrac{15x^2+9x+20}{3x^2+10}$

74. $\dfrac{10x^3+7x^2+2x+3}{5x^3-6x^2+9x+1}$

Writing Exercises

75. For large $|x|$, state what the dominant part of a rational expression is, if the degree of the numerator $p(x)$ is equal to the degree of the denominator $q(x)$.

76. For large $|x|$, state what the dominant part of a rational expression is, if the degree of the numerator $p(x)$ is less than the degree of the denominator $q(x)$.

77. For large $|x|$, state what the dominant part of a rational expression is, if the degree of the denominator $q(x)$ is less than the degree of the numerator $p(x)$.

1.5 LONG AND SYNTHETIC DIVISION

Objectives ▶ ▶

In this section you will learn about:

A. Long Division;

B. Synthetic Division;

C. The Remainder Theorem;

D. Complementary Factor; and

E. Evaluating A Rational Expression (Revisited).

We know that an improper rational number, *e.g.* $\dfrac{12}{5}$, can be written as part integer and part a rational number, *e.g.* $2 + \dfrac{2}{5}$. In the sameway we can also express a rational expression $\dfrac{p}{q}$, where the degree of $p \geq$ degree of q, as part a polynomial and part a rational expression. To see how this can be done, we review the division of polynomials, using both **long division** and **synthetic division.**

A. LONG DIVISION

If we want to express a rational expression as part polynomial and part rational expression, then we divide $p(x)$ by $q(x)$. The process of **long division** is explained in the following examples.

Strategy	**Procedure**	**EXAMPLE**
		EXAMPLE 1 Divide $3x^2 - 8x + 12$ by $x - 2$.
Step **1**	Arrange the dividend and divisor in decreasing order of the exponents.	$x - 2 \overline{)\,3x^2 - 8x + 12}$
Step **2**	To find the first term in the quotient, divide the leading term of the dividend by the leading term of the divisor.	$\dfrac{3x^2}{x} = 3x$ $\overset{\displaystyle 3x}{x - 2 \overline{)\,3x^2 - 8x + 12}}$

EXAMPLE

Step **3** Multiply the divisor by this term of the quotient, write the product below the dividend, and align like terms.

$$
\begin{array}{r}
3x \\
x-2\overline{)\,3x^2 - 8x + 12} \\
3x^2 - 6x
\end{array}
$$

Step **4** Subtract the second row from the first row. This can be accomplished by changing the sign of each term in the second row and adding it to the first row.

$$
\begin{array}{r}
3x \\
x-2\overline{)\,3x^2 - 8x + 12} \\
\underset{+}{\underline{-\,3x^2 + 6x}} \\
-2x + 12
\end{array}
$$

Step **5** The last line is the new dividend. Now repeat Step 2 through Step 4. Stop when the degree of the new dividend is less than the degree of the divisor. This is called the **remainder**.

$$
\begin{array}{r}
3x - 2 \\
x-2\overline{)\,3x^2 - 8x + 12} \\
-3x^2 + 6x \\
\underline{-2x + 12} \\
\underset{+}{\underline{\mp\,2x \pm 4}} \\
8 \leftarrow \text{remainder}
\end{array}
$$

Step **6** Write the final answer as

$$
\boxed{\text{Quotient}} + \dfrac{\boxed{\text{Remainder}}}{\boxed{\text{Divisor}}}
$$

↓   ↓   ↓

Polynomial + Rational Expression

$$
\frac{3x^2 - 8x - 12}{x-2} = \underbrace{3x-2}_{\text{quotient}} + \frac{8}{x-2} \begin{array}{l} \leftarrow \text{remainder} \\ \leftarrow \text{divisor} \end{array}
$$

Remark: *In Step 1 if, while arranging terms in decreasing order of exponents, a term with a certain power is missing, then we insert that term with coefficient 0. This is done simply to align like terms.*

EXAMPLE 2 Divide $2x^4 - 3x^3 + 7$ by $x^2 - 2$

Solution:

Step 1 $x^2 + 0x - 2\overline{)\,2x^4 - 3x^3 + 0x^2 + 0x + 7}$ quotient: $2x^2 - 3x + 4$

$\dfrac{2x^4}{x^2} = 2x^2$

Subtract $\underline{2x^4 + 0x^3 - 4x^2}$ ⟵ $2x^2(x^2-2) = 2x^4 - 4x^2 = 2x^4 + 0x^3 - 4x^2$

Step 2-5 $\dfrac{2x^4}{x^2} = 2x^2:$ $-3x^3 + 4x^2 + 0x + 7$ $\dfrac{-3x^3}{x^2} = -3x$

Subtract $\underline{-3x^3 + 0x^2 + 6x}$ ⟵ $-3x(x^2-2) = -3x^3 + 6x = -3x^3 + 0x^2 + 6x$

$4x^2 - 6x + 7$ $\dfrac{4x^2}{x^2} = 4$

Subtract $\underline{4x^2 + 0x - 8}$ ⟵ $4(x^2-2) = 4x^3 - 8 = 4x^2 + 0x - 8$

$-6x + 15$ STOP (why?)

Step 6 Thus, $\dfrac{2x^4 - 3x^3 + 7}{x^2 - 2} = \underbrace{2x^2 - 3x + 4}_{\text{quotient}} + \dfrac{-6x + 15}{x^2 - 2} \begin{array}{l} \leftarrow \text{Remainder} \\ \leftarrow \text{Divisor} \end{array}$

B. SYNTHETIC DIVISION

If the divisor of a polynomial is a linear polynomial of the form $x - r$, then the division can be streamlined by working with only the numerical coefficients of the dividend. This process of division is called **synthetic division.**

We will explain the process of synthetic division by using long division for $\dfrac{2x^3 - 3x^2 - x + 1}{x - 3}$.

By using the step-by-step method we get

$$
\require{enclose}
\begin{array}{r}
2x^2 + 3x + 8 \\
x - 3 \enclose{longdiv}{2x^3 - 3x^2 - x + 1}
\end{array}
$$

Subtract $\quad 2x^3 - 6x^2$

$\qquad\qquad 3x^2 - x + 1$

Subtract $\qquad 3x^2 - 9x$

$\qquad\qquad\qquad 8x + 1$

Subtract $\qquad\qquad 8x - 24$

$\qquad\qquad\qquad\qquad 25$

We notice that in the process of long division, only the coefficients of the dividend and divisor are involved in the computations (because at each step, like terms are aligned and added). Therefore we can develop a scheme that uses only the coefficients and produces the quotient and the remainder. We make the following important observations:

1. The first coefficient 2 of the quotient is the same as that of the dividend.
2. The second coefficient 3 of the quotient is obtained by subtracting -3 times the first coefficient of the quotient from the second coefficient of the dividend.
3. The third coefficient 8 of the quotient is obtained by subtracting -3 times the previous coefficient from the third coefficient of the dividend.
4. The same pattern continues.

We describe the process of synthetic division in the following steps :

Strategy (to divide a polynomial by x – r)

Procedure	**EXAMPLE 3**
	Divide $2x^3 - 3x^2 - x + 1$ by $x - 3$.
Step 1 Write the coefficients of the dividend and the number r of the divisor $x - r$.	$\underline{3|}\ \ 2 \quad -3 \quad -1 \quad 1 \quad (r = 3)$
Step 2 Draw a long horizontal line to separate the coefficients of the dividend and quotient. Bring down the first coefficient of the dividend.	$\begin{array}{r} \underline{3|} \ \ 2 \quad -3 \quad -1 \quad 1 \\ \downarrow \\ \hline 2 \end{array}$

Step 3   Multiply r times the number below the horizontal line and add to the next coefficient above the line.

$$\begin{array}{c|cccc} 3 & 2 & -3 & -1 & 1 \\ & & 6 & & \\ \hline & 2 & 3 & & \end{array}$$

Step 4   Multiply r times the previous number below the line and add to the next number above the line.

$$\begin{array}{c|cccc} 3 & 2 & -3 & -1 & 1 \\ & & 6 & 9 & \\ \hline & 2 & 3 & 8 & \end{array}$$

Step 5   Multiply r times the previous number below the line and add to the next number above the line.

$$\begin{array}{c|cccc} 3 & 2 & -3 & -1 & 1 \\ & & 6 & 9 & 24 \\ \hline & 2 & 3 & 8 & 25 \end{array}$$

To write the final answer, remember that the degree of the quotient is one less than that of the dividend. The numbers below the lines are the coefficients of the quotient and the last number below the line is always the remainder.

$$\frac{2x^3 - 3x^2 - x + 1}{x - 3}$$

$$= \underbrace{2x^2 + 3x + 8}_{\text{quotient}} + \underbrace{\frac{25}{x - 3}}_{\substack{\rightarrow \text{ remainder} \\ \rightarrow \text{ divisor}}}$$

EXAMPLE 4   Use synthetic division to divide $x^3 - 8x + 7$ by $x - 2$

Solution:

    Step 1 $\begin{array}{c|cccc} 2 & 1 & 0 & -8 & 7 \end{array}$ (We write zero coefficient for a missing term)

    Step 2-5 $\begin{array}{c|cccc} 2 & 1 & 0 & -8 & 7 \\ & & 2 & 4 & -8 \\ \hline & 1 & 2 & -4 & -1 \end{array}$

Thus, $\dfrac{x^3 - 8x + 7}{x - 2} = x^2 + 2x - 4 + \dfrac{-1}{x - 2}$ $\begin{array}{l} \longrightarrow \text{remainder} \\ \longrightarrow \text{divisor} \end{array}$

EXAMPLE 5   Use synthetic division to divide $2x^3 + 5x^2 + 9$ by $x + 3$

Solution:

    Step 1 $\begin{array}{c|cccc} -3 & 2 & 5 & 0 & 9 \end{array}$ $x + 3 = x - (-3)$

    Step 2 $\begin{array}{c|cccc} -3 & 2 & 5 & 0 & 9 \\ & & -6 & 3 & -9 \\ \hline & 2 & -1 & 3 & 0 \end{array} \longrightarrow \text{remainder}$

Thus $\dfrac{2x^3 + 5x^2 + 9}{x + 3} = 2x^2 - x + 3$

EXAMPLE 6   Use synthetic division to divide $6x^2 - 5x - 9$ by $2x - 3$

Solution: $$\frac{6x^2 - 5x - 9}{2x - 3} = \frac{3x^2 - \frac{5}{2}x - \frac{9}{2}}{x - \frac{3}{2}}$$ Divide the numerator and the denominator by 2.

We now divide $3x^2 - \frac{5}{2}x - \frac{9}{2}$ by $x - \frac{3}{2}$

$$
\begin{array}{r|ccc}
\frac{3}{2} & 3 & -\frac{5}{2} & -\frac{9}{2} \\
& & \frac{9}{2} & 3 \\
\hline
& 3 & 2 & -\frac{3}{2}
\end{array}
$$

Quotient is $3x + 2$ and the remainder is $-\frac{3}{2}$.

$$\frac{6x^2 - 5x - 9}{2x - 3} = 3x + 2 + \frac{-\frac{3}{2}}{x - \frac{3}{2}} = 3x + 2 - \frac{3}{2x - 3}.$$

C. THE REMAINDER THEOREM

Let us observe an interesting relationship between the value of a polynomial expression $p(x)$ for $x = 2$ and the remainder in the division of $p(x)$ by $x - 2$.

Verify that the value of the polynomial expression $2x^2 - 5x + 8$ for $x = 1$ is equal to the remainder in the division of $2x^2 - 5x + 8$ for $x - 1$.

The value of $2x^2 - 5x + 8$ for $x = 1$ is $2(1)^2 - 5(1) + 8 = 2 - 5 + 8 = 5$. Let us check to see if the remainder in the division of $2x^2 - 5x + 8$ by $x - 1$ is also 5. We use synthetic division.

$$
\begin{array}{r|ccc}
1 & 2 & -5 & 8 \\
& & 2 & -3 \\
\hline
& 2 & -3 & 5
\end{array}
$$

So, we find that the remainder 5 is the same as the value of the polynomial for $x = 1$. We state and prove the general form of this observation known as 'Remainder Theorem'.

Remainder Theorem: The value of a polynomial expression $p(x)$ for $x = r$ is the same as the remainder in the division of $p(x)$ by $x - r$.

Proof: In the long division of $p(x)$ by $x - r$, we have

$$\frac{p(x)}{x - r} = \text{quotient} + \frac{\text{remainder}}{\text{divisor}}$$

$$= q(x) + \frac{R}{x-r}$$

Multiply both sides by $x - r$

$$p(x) = q(x)\,(x - r) + R$$

To evaluate $p(x)$ for $x = r$, we replace x with r. This will make the factor $(x - r)$ zero and consequently we are left with only the remainder R.

The value of the polynomial for $x = r$

$$\begin{aligned} p(r) &= q(r)\,(r - r) + R \\ &= 0 + R \\ &= R, \text{ the remainder} \end{aligned}$$

Thus, it shows that the value of the polynomial expression when $x = r$ is equal to the remainder in the division of $p(x)$ by $x - r$.

D. COMPLEMENTARY FACTOR

Sometimes, we know one factor of a polynomial expression and we want to find the other factor(s). For example, if we know that $(x + 2)$ is a factor of $x^2 + 5x + 6$, then what is the other factor? We call the other factor the complementary factor (CF).

Suppose $(x + 2)(\text{ CF }) = x^2 + 5x + 6$.

Dividing by $x + 2$ gives

$$\frac{(x+2)(\text{ CF })}{(x+2)} = \frac{x^2 + 5x + 6}{x + 2}$$

$$(\text{ CF }) = \frac{x^2 + 5x + 6}{x + 2}$$

This gives us the following rule:

> **Complementary Factor**
>
> If $x - r$ is a factor of a polynomial $p(x)$, then the **complementary factor** of $x - r$ is obtained by dividing $p(x)$ by $x - r$.

EXAMPLE 7   Find the complementary factor of $x + 2$ for the polynomial $x^3 + 8$

Solution: The complementary factor of $x + 2$ is given by $\dfrac{x^3 + 8}{x + 2}$. We can use either long division or synthetic division. If we choose synthetic division we get

$$\begin{array}{r|rrrr} -2 & 1 & 0 & 0 & 8 \\ & & -2 & 4 & -8 \\ \hline & 1 & -2 & 4 & 0 \end{array}$$

Thus, the complementary factor of $(x + 2)$ for the polynomial $x^3 + 8$ is $x^2 - 2x + 4$

In other words, $x^3 + 8 = (x + 2)\left(x^2 - 2x + 4\right)$.

Remark: *We know it is true because* $x^3 + 8 = (x)^3 + (2)^3 = (x + 2)(x^2 - 2x + 4)$.

EXAMPLE 8 Given that $x - 3$ and $x + 5$ are factors of the polynomial $x^4 + 2x^3 - 11x^2 + 8x - 60$, find the complementary factor.

Solution : We first divide $x^4 + 2x^3 - 11x^2 + 8x - 60$ by $x - 3$

$$
\begin{array}{r|rrrrr}
3 & 1 & 2 & -11 & 8 & -60 \\
  &   & 3 & 15 & 12 & 60 \\
\hline
  & 1 & 5 & 4 & 20 & 0
\end{array}
$$

The quotient is $x^3 + 5x^2 + 4x + 20$. We now divide this quotient by the second factor $x + 5$.

$$
\begin{array}{r|rrrr}
-5 & 1 & 5 & 4 & 20 \\
   &   & -5 & 0 & -20 \\
\hline
   & 1 & 0 & 4 & 0
\end{array}
$$

The complementary factors is $x^2 + 0x + 4$ or $x^2 + 4$.

Thus, $x^4 + 2x^3 - 11x^2 + 8x - 60 = (x - 3)(x + 5)(x^2 + 4)$

E. Evaluating A Rational Expression (Revisited)

In the previous section we pointed out that when $\left|x\right|$ is large and $\deg p(x) > \deg q(x)$, then the value of

the rational expression $\dfrac{p(x)}{q(x)}$ is dominated by the quotient of the leading terms of $p(x)$ and $q(x)$. Now,

with long division we can make an improvement in this estimation. Consider the following example:

EXAMPLE 9 Describe the part of the rational expression $\dfrac{x^4 - x^2 + 5}{x^2 + 2x + 1}$ that dominates the value of the

expression when $\left|x\right|$ is large.

Solution: According to the result from the previous section, the answer would have been $\dfrac{x^4}{x^2} = x^2$.

For a better approximation, we divide $x^4 - x^2 + 5$ by $x^2 + 2x + 1$.

$$\begin{array}{r} x^2 - 2x + 2 \\ x^2 + 2x + 1 \overline{\smash{\big)}\ x^4 + 0x^3 - x^2 + 0x + 5} \end{array}$$

Subtract $\qquad x^4 + 2x^3 + x^2$

$\qquad\qquad -2x^3 - 2x^2 + 0x$

Subtract $\qquad -2x^3 - 4x^2 - 2x$

$\qquad\qquad 2x^2 + 2x + 5$

Subtract $\qquad 2x^2 + 4x + 2$

$\qquad\qquad -2x + 3$

Therefore,

$$\frac{x^4 - x^2 + 5}{x^2 + 2x + 1} = x^2 - 2x + 2 + \frac{-2x + 3}{x^2 + 2x + 1}$$

$$= x^2 - 2x + 2 + \frac{\left(\dfrac{-2}{x} + \dfrac{3}{x^2}\right)}{\left(1 + \dfrac{2}{x} + \dfrac{1}{x^2}\right)} \qquad \begin{array}{l}\text{Divide the numerator} \\ \text{and the denominator} \\ \text{by } x^2.\end{array}$$

Using the fact that $\dfrac{1}{x}$ and $\dfrac{1}{x^2}$ are very small (≈ 0) when $|x|$ is large, we get

$$\frac{x^4 - x^2 + 5}{x^2 + 2x + 1} \approx x^2 - 2x + 2 + \left(\frac{0 + 0}{1 + 0 + 0}\right)$$

$$\approx x^2 - 2x + 2$$

$$\approx \text{quotient when we divide the numerator by the denominator.}$$

Thus, the part that dominates the value of $\dfrac{x^4 - x^2 + 5}{x^2 + 2x + 1}$, when $|x|$ is large, is

$x^2 - 2x + 2$.

We state this result as follows.

The part that dominates the value of a rational expression $\dfrac{p(x)}{q(x)}$, when $|x|$ is large

and deg $p(x) >$ deg $q(x)$, is the **quotient** in the division of $p(x)$ by $q(x)$.

EXAMPLE 10 Approximate the value of the rational expression $\dfrac{x^3 - 2x - 1}{x + 2}$ when $x = 1100$.

Solution: Since x is large, so the value of the rational expression is dominated by the **quotient** when we divide the numerator by the denominator. First, we find the quotient, and we replace x in the quotient with 1100.

Dividing $x^3 + 0x^2 - 2x - 1$ by $x + 2$ gives

$$\begin{array}{r|rrrr} -2 & 1 & 0 & -2 & -1 \\ & & -2 & 4 & -4 \\ \hline & 1 & -2 & 2 & -5 \end{array}$$

Therefore, the quotient is $x^2 - 2x + 2$. The approximate value of the rational expression for $x = 1100$ is $(1100)^2 - 2(1100) + 2 = 1207802$

Remark: *Verify with calculator that the value of* $\dfrac{x^3 - 2x - 1}{x + 2}$ *for $x = 1100$ is 1207801.99546. According to*

our earlier approximation, the value of $\dfrac{x^3 - 2x - 1}{x + 2}$ *was given by value of* $\dfrac{x^3}{x} = x^2$ *for $x = 1100$.*

This is 1210000. Compare the two approximations with the exact value, 1207801.995

EXERCISE 1.5

In exercises (1–26), perform division by using long division.

1. $\dfrac{x^2 - 5x + 8}{x - 2}$　　2. $\dfrac{x^2 + 9x - 7}{x + 1}$　　3. $\dfrac{x^3 - 7x^2 + 3x - 5}{x - 3}$　　4. $\dfrac{3x^2 - 11x + 15}{x + 2}$

5. $\dfrac{5x^2 + 3x - 2}{x - 1}$　　6. $\dfrac{x^3 + 5x^2 - 9x + 8}{x + 3}$　　7. $\dfrac{x^4 - 5x^3 + 6x^2 + x - 7}{x - 2}$　　8. $\dfrac{6x^4 - 15x^3 + 7x^2 + 5x - 3}{x + 5}$

9. $\dfrac{5x^3 - x^2 + 9x - 7}{x^2 - x + 1}$　　10. $\dfrac{3x^3 - 2x^2 + 4x - 11}{x^2 - 3x + 2}$　　11. $\dfrac{4x^3 + 2x^2 - 7x - 1}{x^2 + 2x - 1}$　　12. $\dfrac{7x^3 + 5x^2 - 2x + 1}{x^2 + 5x - 3}$

13. $\dfrac{x^3 - x^2 - 10x + 9}{x^3 - x + 3}$　　14. $\dfrac{6x^3 + 5x^2 + 2x - 4}{x^3 + x^2 - 2x + 1}$　　15. $\dfrac{2x^3 - x^2 - 4x + 5}{x^2 + 1}$

16. $\dfrac{3x^3 + 5x + 7}{x^2 + 3x}$　　17. $\dfrac{x^4 - x^3 + x^2 + 2x - 2}{x^3 - x^2}$　　18. $\dfrac{x^4 + x^3 - 2x^2 + 3x + 7}{x^3 + 5x}$

19. $\dfrac{x^3 - 1}{x - 3}$　　20. $\dfrac{x^3 + 5}{x + 2}$　　21. $\dfrac{x^5 - 3}{x^3 - x^2}$　　22. $\dfrac{x^3 + 9x^2}{x - 4}$　　23. $\dfrac{x^3 + x}{x - 1}$

24. $\dfrac{6x^4 - 19x^3 + 19x^2 - 3x - 5}{2x^2 - 5x + 3}$　　25. $\dfrac{10x^6 - 18x^4 + 9x^2 - 7}{2x^2 - 4}$　　26. $\dfrac{5x^6 - 3x^4 + 8x^3 + 7x^2 - 9}{x^3 + x^2 - 2}$

In exercises (27–54), divide using synthetic division.

27. $\dfrac{x^2 - 7x + 2}{x - 3}$　　28. $\dfrac{x^2 + 9x + 16}{x + 5}$　　29. $\dfrac{2x^2 - 8x + 9}{x - 1}$　　30. $\dfrac{3x^2 + 16x - 7}{x + 9}$

31. $\dfrac{4x^2 + x + 10}{x + 1}$　　32. $\dfrac{6x^2 - 3x + 11}{x - 4}$　　33. $\dfrac{3x^2 - 2x + 8}{x + 2}$　　34. $\dfrac{4x^2 + 3x - 5}{x - 7}$

35. $\dfrac{8x^3 - 3x^2 + 4x + 9}{x - 3}$　　36. $\dfrac{x^3 + 1}{x + 1}$　　37. $\dfrac{6x^3 + 2x^2 - 4}{x - 2}$　　38. $\dfrac{5x^3 + 3x - 2}{x + 3}$

39. $\dfrac{x^3 - 1}{x - 1}$　　40. $\dfrac{7x^3 + 2x^2 + 4x}{x + 5}$　　41. $\dfrac{x^3 - 8}{x - 2}$　　42. $\dfrac{x^3 - 27}{x - 3}$

43. $\dfrac{x^3 - 6x + 2}{x + 5}$ **44.** $\dfrac{x^3 - 4x^2 + 7}{x + 4}$ **45.** $\dfrac{2x^3 + 3x^2 + 1}{x - 3}$ **46.** $\dfrac{3x^3 + x - 1}{x - 9}$

47. $\dfrac{5x^3 - 2x^2 + x + 2}{x - \frac{1}{2}}$ **48.** $\dfrac{4x^3 + 3x - 1}{x + \frac{1}{2}}$ **49.** $\dfrac{2x^3 + 3x^2 - 2x + 10}{x + \frac{1}{2}}$ **50.** $\dfrac{x^3 - 2x^2 + 2}{x - \frac{1}{2}}$

51. $\dfrac{7 - x - 2x^2 - x^3}{2 - x}$ **52.** $\dfrac{2 + x - 7x^2 - x^3}{3 - x}$ **53.** $\dfrac{6x^3 - 3x^2 + 1}{3x - 6}$ **54.** $\dfrac{4x^3 - 2x^2 + x - 1}{2x - 6}$

In exercises (55–59), use any method of division to divide $P(x)$ by $S(x)$. Determine the quotient $Q(x)$, the remainder $R(x)$, and verify $P(x) = Q(x)\,S(x) + R(x)$.

55. $P(x) = x^3 + 7x^2 - 2x + 1$, $S(x) = x - 3$

56. $P(x) = 4x^3 - 15x + 2$, $S(x) = x + 2$

57. $P(x) = 3x^3 - 7x^2 + 8x + 9$, $S(x) = x + 3$

58. $P(x) = 7x^3 + 8x^2 - 2x + 1$, $S(x) = x^2 + 2$

59. $P(x) = x^5 + x^3 - 3x^2 + 2x - 5$, $S(x) = x^2 + 1$

In exercises (60–63), find the complementary factor of $(2x + 3)$ for the given polynomial.

60. $-2x^3 - 7x^2 + 8x + 21$ **61.** $2x^3 + 5x^2 - 7x + 15$

62. $2x^4 + 3x^3 - 4x^2 + 4x + 15$ **63.** $2x^4 - 5x^3 - 8x^2 + 2x - 6$

In exercises (64–67), verify the Remainder Theorem, by first dividing synthetically and finding the remainder and then by substituting the value into the polynomial.

64. Divide $6x^2 - 7x + 8$ by $x - 2$ **65.** $2x^3 - 7x^2 + 8x - 9$ by $x + 2$

66. Divide $3x^4 - 5x^3 + 2x - 7$ by $x + 1$ **67.** $-2x^5 + 7x^3 + 8x$ by $x - 3$

In exercises (68–79), find the expression that dominates the value of the rational expression when $|x|$ is large.

68. $\dfrac{x^5 + x + 1}{x^2 + x + 1}$ **69.** $\dfrac{x^5 + x^4 - 2x^3 - 6x^2 + 6x + 8}{x^2 + 3x + 4}$ **70.** $\dfrac{x^6 + x^4 - 5x^2 + 3}{x^2 + 3}$

71. $\dfrac{-4x^3 + 7x - 2}{2x^2 - 3}$ **72.** $\dfrac{x^4 + 2x^3 - 2x^2 + 7x + 2}{x^2 - x + 2}$ **73.** $\dfrac{4x^4 - 2x^2 + 3x - 2}{x^2 - x + 1}$

74. $\dfrac{8x^6 - 3x^2 + 1}{4x^3 - x - 2}$ **75.** $\dfrac{x^5 + x^3 + x^2 - 4}{2x^3 + x - 2}$ **76.** $\dfrac{x^6 - x^2 - 1}{2x^3 - 4}$

77. $\dfrac{x^4 - 9x^2 + 3}{x^2 + 3x - 2}$ **78.** $\dfrac{2x^3 - 4x - 2}{2x + 4}$ **79.** $\dfrac{3x^3 + 5x^2 + 2x - 4}{x^2 - 4x + 5}$

In exercises (80–85), approximate the value of each rational expression for $x = 1200$

80. $\dfrac{10x^6 + 5x^3 - x}{2x^4 - x^2 - 1}$ **81.** $\dfrac{5x^4 - 3x^3 + 7x + 9}{x^2 - 5x + 1}$ **82.** $\dfrac{3x^4 - 2x^3 + x^2 + 2x + 3}{x^2 - x - 1}$

83. $\dfrac{-x^5 + x^3 + 2x^2 - 3x + 1}{x^3 + x^2 - 3}$ **84.** $\dfrac{x^5 - 3x^4 + 5x^2}{x^2 - 3x + 2}$ **85.** $\dfrac{2x^6 + x^5 - x^4 + 8x}{x^4 + x^2 + 2}$

Writing Exercises

86. Distinguish between the processes of reducing a rational expression and dividing the numerator by the denominator.

87. When $|x|$ is large, what part of the rational expression $\dfrac{p(x)}{q(x)}$ dominates its value.

1.6 RADICAL EXPRESSIONS

In this section we will review the algebra of expressions involving square roots, cube roots, and other roots. These expressions are called root expressions or radical expressions.

A. NOTATION FOR RADICALS

The *n*th root of x is denoted as $\sqrt[n]{x}$, where the symbol $\sqrt{}$ is called a **radical**, the number n is the **index** of the radical, and x is the **radicand.**

EXAMPLES

1. When $n = 2$, it is customary to omit the index and use only the radical symbol like $\sqrt{x}$, which is read as the **square root** of x.

2. When $n = 3$, $\sqrt[3]{x}$ is called the **cube root** of x.

Definition:

When n is even, $\sqrt[n]{x} = |a|$ if and only if $x = a^n$.

When n is odd, $\sqrt[n]{x} = a$ if and only if $x = a^n$.

Remark: *When $x = a^n$, $\sqrt[n]{x} = \sqrt[n]{a^n} = a$ or $|a|$ depending upon whether n is odd or even, respectively. In other words, a factor with an exponent the same as the index of the radical can be written without the radical sign. This rule will help us to simplify a root expression.*

B. SIMPLIFYING RADICALS

A radical is said to be in simplified form when each factor whose exponent is the same as the index of the radical is factored out of the radical symbol. We state below the basic rules of radicals that we will use in the process of simplification of radicals.

Rules for Radicals

It is assumed that radicands for an even index are non-negative.

1. $\sqrt[n]{a^n} = \begin{cases} a & \text{if } n \text{ is odd} \\ |a| & \text{if } n \text{ is even} \end{cases}$

2. $\sqrt[n]{ab} = \sqrt[n]{a}\,\sqrt[n]{b}$

3. $\sqrt[n]{\dfrac{a}{b}} = \dfrac{\sqrt[n]{a}}{\sqrt[n]{b}}$

EXAMPLE 1   Simplify $\sqrt{4410}$.

Solution: First we factor 4410 as $2 \cdot 3^2 \cdot 5 \cdot 7^2$.

By using the above rules, we obtain

$$\sqrt{4410} = \sqrt{2 \cdot 3^2 \cdot 5 \cdot 7^2} = 3 \cdot 7 \sqrt{2 \cdot 5} = 21\sqrt{10}$$

Thus, the simplified form of $\sqrt{4410} = 21\sqrt{10}$

EXAMPLE 2   Simplify

a. $\sqrt{16x^3}$ **b.** $\sqrt[3]{-8x^4a^5}$

Solutions: **a.** $\sqrt{16x^3} = \sqrt{4^2 x^2 x} = 4|x|\sqrt{x} = 4x\sqrt{x}$ if $x \geq 0$ Recall $\sqrt{x^2} = |x|$

b. $\sqrt[3]{-8x^4a^5} = \sqrt[3]{(-2)^3 x^3 \cdot x \cdot a^3 \cdot a^2}$

$$= (-2) \, x \, a \sqrt[3]{xa^2} = -2a \, x \sqrt[3]{a^2 x}$$

EXAMPLE 3   Simplify $\sqrt[3]{\dfrac{54ax^4}{16y^6}}$.

Solution: $\sqrt[3]{\dfrac{2 \cdot 3^3 a \cdot x^3 \cdot x}{2 \cdot 2^3 y^3 y^3}} = \dfrac{3x}{2y \cdot y} \sqrt[3]{\dfrac{2ax}{2}} = \dfrac{3x}{2y^2} \sqrt[3]{ax}$

C. Rational Exponents

- If $\dfrac{m}{n}$ is a rational number then by definition $x^{m/n} = \left(\sqrt[n]{x}\right)^m$ or $x^{m/n} = \left(x^m\right)^{1/n} = \sqrt[n]{x^m}$.

- $a^{-n} = \dfrac{1}{a^n}, \quad \dfrac{1}{a^{-n}} = a^n \qquad a \neq 0$

- $\left(\dfrac{a}{b}\right)^{-n} = \left(\dfrac{b}{a}\right)^n, \qquad a \cdot b \neq 0$

EXAMPLES $x^{1/2} = \sqrt[2]{x} = \sqrt{x}, \quad x^{1/3} = \sqrt[3]{x},$

$x^{1/4} = \sqrt[4]{x}, \quad x^{2/3} = \left(\sqrt[3]{x}\right)^2$ or $\sqrt[3]{x^2},$

$4^{-2} = \dfrac{1}{4^2} = \dfrac{1}{16}, \quad \left(\dfrac{2}{3}\right)^{-3} = \left(\dfrac{3}{2}\right)^3 = \dfrac{27}{8},$

$9^{-1/2} = \dfrac{1}{9^{1/2}} = \dfrac{1}{3}, \quad \left(\dfrac{8}{27}\right)^{-1/3} = \left(\dfrac{27}{8}\right)^{1/3} = \dfrac{27^{1/3}}{8^{1/3}} = \dfrac{3}{2}.$

EXAMPLE 4   Rewrite the following expressions in radical form and simplify as far as possible.

   a. $27^{2/3}$ **b.** $\left(16x^4y^{10}\right)^{1/4}$ **c.** $\left(\dfrac{2a}{b}\right)^{-2}$

Solutions:

   a. $27^{2/3} = \sqrt[3]{27^2} = \sqrt[3]{\left(3^3\right)^2} = \sqrt[3]{3^3 \cdot 3^3} = 3 \cdot 3\sqrt[3]{1} = 9$

   or $= \left(\sqrt[3]{27}\right)^2 = 3^2 = 9$

   b. $\left(16x^4y^{10}\right)^{1/4} = \sqrt[4]{16x^4y^{10}} = \sqrt[4]{2^4 x^4 y^8 \cdot y^2}$ Note: $\sqrt[4]{y^8} = y^{8/4} = y^2$

   $= 2\left|x\right|y^2 \sqrt[4]{y^2}$

   $= 2\left|x\right|y^2 \sqrt{y}$ (why?)

   c. $\left(\dfrac{2a}{b}\right)^{-2} = \left(\dfrac{b}{2a}\right)^2$

   $= \dfrac{b^2}{(2a)^2} = \dfrac{b^2}{4a^2}$

EXAMPLE 5   Write each expression without the radical symbol.

   a. $\sqrt{x^3} + \sqrt[3]{(x+2)^2}$ **b.** $\dfrac{5\sqrt{x+9}}{\sqrt[3]{x^2 y^5}}$

Solution: **a.** $\sqrt{x^3} + \sqrt[3]{(x+2)^2} = \left(x^3\right)^{1/2} + \left((x+2)^2\right)^{1/3} = x^{3/2} + (x+2)^{2/3}$

   b. $\dfrac{5\sqrt{x+9}}{\sqrt[3]{x^2 y^5}} = \dfrac{5(x+9)^{1/2}}{\left(x^2 y^5\right)^{1/3}} = \dfrac{5(x+9)^{1/2}}{x^{2/3} y^{5/3}}$

EXAMPLE 6   Write as a single radical: $\sqrt[3]{x^2 y^4}\ \sqrt[4]{x^3 y}$

Solution: $\sqrt[3]{x^2 y^4}\ \sqrt[4]{x^3 y} = \left(x^2\ y^4\right)^{1/3} \left(x^3\ y\right)^{1/4}$

   $= \left(x^2\ y^4\right)^{\frac{4}{12}} \left(x^3\ y\right)^{\frac{3}{12}}$ $\left(\dfrac{1}{3} = \dfrac{4}{12};\ \dfrac{1}{4} = \dfrac{3}{12}\right)$

   $= \left(x^8 y^{16}\right)^{\frac{1}{12}} \left(x^9 y^3\right)^{\frac{1}{12}}$ $x^{m/n} = (x^m)^n$

   $= \left(x^{17} y^{19}\right)^{\frac{1}{12}}$

   $= x\,y\left(x^5 y^7\right)^{\frac{1}{12}} = xy\ \sqrt[12]{x^5 y^7}$

EXAMPLE 7   Multiply

$$\textbf{a.} \quad \left(2\sqrt{5}-3\right)\left(2\sqrt{5}+3\right) \qquad \textbf{b.} \quad \left(\sqrt{x+h}-\sqrt{x}\right)\left(\sqrt{x+h}+\sqrt{x}\right) \qquad \textbf{c.} \quad \left(\sqrt{x+2}-3\right)^2$$

Solution:

a.   By recognizing the pattern $(A - B)(A + B)$, we write

$$\left(2\sqrt{5}-3\right)\left(2\sqrt{5}+3\right) = \left(2\sqrt{5}\right)^2 - (3)^2$$
$$= 4(5) - 9 = 20 - 9 = \mathbf{11}$$

b.   Again, using the pattern $(A - B)(A + B)$, we get

$$\left(\sqrt{x+h}-\sqrt{x}\right)\left(\sqrt{x+h}+\sqrt{x}\right) = \left(\sqrt{x+h}\right)^2 - \left(\sqrt{x}\right)^2$$
$$= x + h - x = \mathbf{h}$$

c.   Replacing A with $\sqrt{x+2}$ and B with -3 in the formula $(A - B)^2 = (A)^2 - 2(A)(B) + (B)^2$ gives

$$\left(\sqrt{x+2}-3\right)^2 = \left(\sqrt{x+2}\right)^2 - 2\left(\sqrt{x+2}\right)(3) + (3)^2$$
$$= x + 2 - 6\sqrt{x+2} + 9 = \mathbf{x + 11 - 6\sqrt{x+2}}$$

D. Rationalizing Denominator

The process of writing a quotient with a radical in the denominator as an equivalent quotient without radical in the denominator is called **rationalizing the denominator.**

For a denominator with a single term, this is accomplished by multiplying both numerator and denominator by an expression that will raise each factor in the radicand of the denominator to a power the same as the index of the radical in the denominator.

For a denominator of the type $a + \sqrt{b}$, rationalization is accomplished by multiplying both numerator and denominator by the **conjugate** of the denominator. The following examples illustrate the procedures:

EXAMPLE 8   Rationalize the denominator:

$$\textbf{a.} \quad \frac{4x}{\sqrt{8x^3 y}} \qquad\qquad \textbf{b.} \quad \sqrt[3]{\frac{16x^3 y}{ab^2}} \qquad\qquad \textbf{c.} \quad \sqrt[4]{\frac{x^{10}}{y^9}}$$

Solutions:

a. $\dfrac{4x}{\sqrt{2^2 \cdot 2 \cdot x^2\, xy}}$. In order for all factors under the radical in the denominator to have even

exponents, we multiply both the numerator and the denominator by $\sqrt{2xy}$.

$$\frac{4x\sqrt{2xy}}{\sqrt{2^2 \cdot 2^2\, x^2\, x^2\, y^2}} = \frac{4x\sqrt{2xy}}{2 \cdot 2\left|x\right|\left|x\right|\left|y\right|} \qquad\qquad |x||x| = |x|^2 = \left|x^2\right| = x^2$$

$$= \frac{4x\sqrt{2xy}}{4x^2|y|} = \frac{\sqrt{2xy}}{x|y|}$$

b. $\quad \sqrt[3]{\dfrac{2^3 \cdot 2x^3 y}{ab^2}} = 2x\sqrt[3]{\dfrac{2y}{ab^2}} = \dfrac{2x\sqrt[3]{2y}}{\sqrt[3]{ab^2}}$

To raise each factor of the radicand in the denominator to an exponent 3, we multiply both the numerator and the denominator by $\sqrt[3]{a^2 b}$.

$$= \frac{2x\sqrt[3]{2y}\ \sqrt[3]{a^2 b}}{\sqrt[3]{ab^2}\ \sqrt[3]{a^2 b}} = \frac{2x\sqrt[3]{2ya^2 b}}{\sqrt[3]{a^3 b^3}} = \frac{2x\sqrt[3]{2ya^2 b}}{ab}$$

c. $\quad \sqrt[4]{\dfrac{x^{10}}{y^9}} = \dfrac{\sqrt[4]{x^{10}}}{\sqrt[4]{y^9}} = \dfrac{\sqrt[4]{x^8 \cdot x^2}}{\sqrt[4]{y^8 \cdot y}} = \dfrac{x^2 \sqrt[4]{x^2}}{y^2 \sqrt[4]{y}} = \dfrac{x^2}{y^2}\sqrt[4]{\dfrac{x^2}{y}}$ $\qquad$ Note: $\sqrt[4]{x^8} = \sqrt[4]{\left(x^2\right)^4} = x^2$

$$= \frac{x^2}{y^2}\sqrt[4]{\frac{x^2 y^3}{y^4}} \qquad \text{Rationalize the denominator}$$

$$= \frac{x^2}{y^3}\sqrt[4]{x^2 y^3}$$

EXAMPLE 9 $\quad$ Rationalize the denominator: $\dfrac{x-4}{2-\sqrt{x}}$, $x \neq 4$

Solution: $\quad$ Multiply the numerator and the denominator by the * conjugate of $2 - \sqrt{x}$. We get

> * $a - \sqrt{b}$ and $a + \sqrt{b}$ are conjugates of each other.

$$\frac{(x-4)\left(2+\sqrt{x}\right)}{\left(2-\sqrt{x}\right)\left(2+\sqrt{x}\right)} .$$

To simplify the denominator, we use the pattern $(A - B)(A + B) = (A)^2 - (B)^2$.

$$\frac{(x-4)\left(2+\sqrt{x}\right)}{(2)^2 - \left(\sqrt{x}\right)^2} = \frac{(x-4)\left(2+\sqrt{x}\right)}{4-x} = \frac{-(4-x)\left(2+\sqrt{x}\right)}{4-x}$$

Since $x \neq 4$, we cancel $4 - x$. Hence, $\dfrac{-(4-x)\left(\sqrt{x}+2\right)}{(4-x)} = -(2+\sqrt{x})$.

- The process of rationalizing the numerator is done in a similar manner. This is illustrated by the following example.

EXAMPLE 10 $\quad$ Rationalize the numerator $\dfrac{\sqrt{x+h} - \sqrt{x}}{h}$, $x > 0$, $x + h > 0$, and $h > 0$

Solution: $\quad$ Multiplying the numerator and the denominator by the conjugate of the numerator gives:

$$\frac{\left(\sqrt{x+h}-\sqrt{x}\right)\left(\sqrt{x+h}+\sqrt{x}\right)}{h\left(\sqrt{x+h}+\sqrt{x}\right)}$$

Using the pattern $(A-B)(A+B)$ in the numerator we simplify as :

$$\frac{\left(\sqrt{x+h}\right)^2-\left(\sqrt{x}\right)^2}{h\left(\sqrt{x+h}+\sqrt{x}\right)}=\frac{x+h-x}{h\left(\sqrt{x+h}+\sqrt{x}\right)}$$

$$=\frac{h}{h\left(\sqrt{x+h}+\sqrt{x}\right)}=\frac{1}{\sqrt{x+h}+\sqrt{x}}$$

E. EVALUATING A RADICAL EXPRESSION

To evaluate a root expression for $x = a$, we replace x with a in the root expression, just as we do with polynomials and rational expressions.

EXAMPLE 11   Evaluate $\sqrt{x-13}$, for

a. $x = 21$ **b.** $x = 5$

Solutions :   **a.**   **For $x = 21$,**
$$\sqrt{x-13}=\sqrt{21-13}=\sqrt{8}$$
$$=\sqrt{2^2\cdot 2}=2\sqrt{2}$$

b.   **For $x = 5$,**
$$\sqrt{x-13}=\sqrt{5-13}=\sqrt{-8} \quad *$$

$\sqrt{-8}$ does not exist in the set of real numbers.

> * The square root of a negative number is not a real number. We say that $\sqrt{-1}$ is imaginary. We write $\sqrt{-1}=i$. This gives
> $$\sqrt{-8}=\sqrt{-1\cdot 8}.$$
> $$=\sqrt{-1}\sqrt{8}=i\sqrt{8}$$
> $$=i2\sqrt{2}$$
> (For more details about imaginary or complex numbers, see Appendix A.)

Dominating part when $|x|$ is large

When $|x|$ is large, the dominant part of a radical expression is found exactly in the same way as for a polynomial or rational expression. The following example illustrates the procedure.

EXAMPLE 12   Describe the part of $\dfrac{8x+3}{\sqrt{4x^2+9}}$ that dominates in evaluating the expression when $|x|$ is large.

Solution: In order to use the fact that $\dfrac{1}{x}$, $\dfrac{1}{x^2}$ and $\dfrac{1}{x^3}$ very small (almost zero) when $|x|$ is large, we write the given expression as

* Factor x^2 out of 9.

Consider $9 = x^2 \times \dfrac{9}{x^2}$.

In general, to factor A out of B, write

$B = A \cdot \dfrac{B}{A}$

$$\frac{8x+3}{\sqrt{4x^2+9}} = \frac{x\left(8+\dfrac{3}{x}\right)}{*\sqrt{x^2\left(4+\dfrac{9}{x^2}\right)}} = \frac{x\left(8+\dfrac{3}{x}\right)}{\sqrt{x^2}\,\sqrt{4+\dfrac{9}{x^2}}} = \frac{x\left(8+\dfrac{3}{x}\right)}{|x|\sqrt{4+\dfrac{9}{x^2}}}$$

When $|x|$ is large, we have

$$\frac{x\left(8+\dfrac{3}{x}\right)}{|x|\sqrt{4+\dfrac{9}{x^2}}} = \frac{x(8+0)}{|x|\sqrt{4+0}} = \frac{8x}{|x|\sqrt{4}} = \frac{8x}{2|x|} = \frac{4x}{|x|}$$

Thus, $\dfrac{4x}{|x|}$ dominates the value of $\dfrac{8x+3}{\sqrt{4x^2+9}}$ when $|x|$ is large.

Notice that

$$\frac{4x}{|x|} = \frac{8x}{2|x|} = \frac{8x}{2\sqrt{x^2}} = \frac{8x}{\sqrt{4x^2}} = \frac{\text{leading term of the numerator}}{\sqrt{\text{leading term of the radicand}}}$$

Remark: *For a large x such as 50,000, the value of the expression is approximately* $\dfrac{4(50,000)}{|50,000|} = 4$.

When x = −50,000 then value of the given expression is approximately −4.

EXERCISE 1.6

In exercises (1–21), simplify the radical.

1. $\sqrt{128}$ 2. $\sqrt{243}$ 3. $\sqrt[3]{-128}$ 4. $\sqrt[4]{81}$ 5. $\sqrt{\dfrac{32}{25}}$

6. $\sqrt{12x^2y^5}$ 7. $\sqrt{24x^5y^2}$ 8. $\sqrt[3]{216x^3y^7}$ 9. $\sqrt[3]{81x^5y^6}$ 10. $\sqrt{3y^2}\,\sqrt{12y^4}$

11. $\sqrt{6x^2}\,\sqrt{8x^2y^2}$ 12. $\sqrt[3]{4xy^2}\,\sqrt[3]{2x^5y^2}$ 13. $\sqrt[3]{4x^3z^2}\,\sqrt[3]{4x^5z^4}$ 14. $\sqrt{\dfrac{12a^3b^5}{c^4}}$

15. $\sqrt{\dfrac{12p^4q^3}{3r^2}}$ 16. $\sqrt[4]{\dfrac{32x^5y^8}{z^8}}$ 17. $\sqrt[3]{\dfrac{125x^8}{8y^2z^4}}$ 18. $\sqrt{(x+2)^2}$

19. $\sqrt[3]{(3x-5)^3}$ 20. $\sqrt{4x^2+24x+36}$ 21. $\sqrt{9y^2-18y+9}$

In exercises (22–37), evaluate the expression.

22. $9^{3/2}$ 23. $36^{-3/2}$ 24. $8^{-2/3}$ 25. $(125)^{4/3}$ 26. $\left(64x^2y^4\right)^{1/2}$ 27. $\left(25x^6y^{12}\right)^{\frac{1}{2}}$

28. $\left(\dfrac{8}{27}\right)^{-2/3}$ 29. $\left(\dfrac{25}{9}\right)^{-\frac{3}{2}}$ 30. $\left(8a^6\right)^{2/3}$ 31. $(-64)^{\frac{5}{3}}$ 32. $(-243)^{3/5}$

33. $\left(125a^6b^3c^9\right)^{2/3}$ **34.** $\left(16x^2y^4\right)^{3/2}$ **35.** $\left(64x^6y^3\right)^{2/3}$ **36.** $\left(-125a^6\right)^{2/3}$ **37.** $\left(32x^{10}y^5\right)^{2/5}$

In exercises (38–49), write the expression without the radical symbol.

22. $9^{3/2}$ **23.** $36^{-3/2}$ **24.** $8^{-2/3}$ **25.** $(125)^{4/3}$

38. $\sqrt{\dfrac{2x-1}{2x+1}}$ **39.** $\sqrt[3]{\dfrac{5x+7}{5x-3}}$ **40.** $\left(5x^2+3\right)\sqrt{2x+3}$ **41.** $(x+2)\sqrt{x^2+4}$

42. $\sqrt[3]{x^2(x+2)}$ **43.** $\sqrt[5]{y^3(y+1)}$ **44.** $\sqrt{4x^3(x-3)}$ **45.** $\sqrt[3]{3y^3(y+7)}$

46. $\dfrac{\sqrt{2x+5}}{\sqrt[3]{5x+2}}$ **47.** $\dfrac{\sqrt[5]{3x-4}}{\sqrt[3]{4x+3}}$ **48.** $4\sqrt{x}\,\sqrt[3]{y^2}$ **49.** $\sqrt[3]{6x^2}\,\sqrt[5]{y^2}$

In exercises (50–61), factor the expression and simplify.

50. $10x(2x+3)^{1/2}+\left(5x^2+3\right)(2x+3)^{-1/2}$

51. $(3x+5)^{-\frac{1}{2}}(5x+4)^{\frac{1}{2}}+2\,(3x+5)^{\frac{1}{2}}(5x+4)^{-\frac{1}{2}}$

52. $6x(4x+3)^{3/2}+6\left(3x^2+2\right)(4x+3)^{1/2}$

53. $12x(x+5)^{\frac{3}{2}}+(4x^2+3)\,(x+5)^{\frac{1}{2}}$

54. $\dfrac{(x+2)^{1/2}-(x+2)^{-1/2}}{\left((x+2)^{1/2}\right)^2}$

55. $\dfrac{7x(x-3)^{-1/2}+(x-3)^{1/2}}{\left((x-3)^{1/3}\right)^2}$

56. $\dfrac{(3x+2)^{-2/3}\,x-(3x+2)^{1/3}}{\left((3x+2)^{1/3}\right)^2}$

57. $\dfrac{(3x+4)^{3/2}+4\,(3x+4)^{1/2}}{\left((3x+4)^{-1/3}\right)^4}$

58. $\dfrac{18x(2x+7)^{1/2}-\left(9x^2+2\right)(2x+7)^{-1/2}}{\left((2x+7)^{1/2}\right)^2}$

59. $\dfrac{20\,(3x+5)^{-1/2}-(x+4)\,(3x+5)^{1/2}}{\left((3x+5)^{1/2}\right)^2}$

60. $\dfrac{(2x+5)^{-1/2}\,(3x+7)^{1/3}-(3x+7)^{-2/3}\,(2x+5)^{1/2}}{\left((3x+7)^{1/3}\right)^2}$

61. $\dfrac{(x+2)^{-1/2}\,(x+5)^{-2/3}+(x+2)^{1/2}\,(x+5)^{1/3}}{\left((x+5)^{1/3}\right)^2}$

In exercises (62–71), multiply and simplify.

62. $\left(9\sqrt{x}-2\right)\left(9\sqrt{x}+2\right)$ **63.** $\left(3-5\sqrt{x}\right)\left(3+5\sqrt{x}\right)$ **64.** $\left(2\sqrt{x+3}-5\right)\left(2\sqrt{x+3}+5\right)$

65. $\left(3\sqrt{x-5}-4\right)\left(3\sqrt{x-5}+4\right)$ **66.** $\left(2\sqrt{x+1}-3\right)\left(2\sqrt{x+1}+3\right)$ **67.** $\left(3\sqrt{2x-3}-5\right)\left(3\sqrt{2x-3}+5\right)$

68. $\left(2\sqrt{x+3}+3\right)^2$ **69.** $\left(\sqrt{2x+3}+5\right)^2$ **70.** $\left(\sqrt{x+h}-\sqrt{x}\right)^2$ **71.** $\left(\sqrt{x+2h}+\sqrt{x}\right)^2$

In exercises (72–79), rationalize the denominator.

72. $\dfrac{16x}{\sqrt{2x}}$ **73.** $\dfrac{5x}{\sqrt{3x}}$ **74.** $\dfrac{5ax}{\sqrt[3]{25a^2x}}$ **75.** $\dfrac{2bx^2y}{\sqrt[3]{9bxy^2}}$

76. $\dfrac{x-9}{\sqrt{x}-3}$ **77.** $\dfrac{2}{\sqrt{x}+2}$ **78.** $\dfrac{4x-100}{2\sqrt{x}-10}$ **79.** $\dfrac{9x-25}{3\sqrt{x}+5}$

In exercises (80–89), rationalize the numerator.

80. $\dfrac{\sqrt{x+h+2}-\sqrt{x+2}}{h}$ **81.** $\dfrac{\sqrt{x+h+1}-\sqrt{x+1}}{h}$ **82.** $\dfrac{\sqrt{2x+2h+3}-\sqrt{2x+3}}{h}$ **83.** $\dfrac{\sqrt{3x+3h-5}-\sqrt{3x-5}}{h}$

84. $\dfrac{\dfrac{1}{\sqrt{x+h}}-\dfrac{1}{\sqrt{x}}}{h}$ **85.** $\dfrac{\dfrac{1}{\sqrt{x+2h+1}}-\dfrac{1}{\sqrt{x+1}}}{h}$ **86.** $x-\sqrt{2x+x^2}$

87. $x+\sqrt{5x+x^2}$ **88.** $2x-\sqrt{3x+4x^2}$ **89.** $\sqrt{x^2+9x}-4x$

In exercises (90–97), evaluate the expression for the given x value.

90. $\sqrt{x-9}$, when $x=13$ **91.** $\sqrt{8-x}$, when $x=-1$ **92.** $\sqrt{x-9}$, when $x=5$

93. $\sqrt{13-2x}$, when $x=-6$ **94.** $\sqrt{12-x^2}$, when $x=2$ **95.** $\sqrt{x^2-18}$, when $x=3$

96. $\sqrt{12-x^2}$, when $x=6$ **97.** $\sqrt[3]{x^2+2}$, when $x=5$

In exercises (98–101), describe the part that dominates the value of the expression when $|x|$ is large.

98. $\dfrac{4x+5}{\sqrt{16x^2+25}}$ **99.** $\dfrac{7x-8}{\sqrt{4x^2+1}}$ **100.** $\dfrac{12x-7}{\sqrt{9x^2+49}}$ **101.** $\dfrac{5x+13}{\sqrt{8x^2+13x}}$

Writing Exercises

102. When can a factor in the radicand be taken out of the radical symbol?

103. Sometimes a factor that comes out of radical symbol is written with absolute value symbols. Explain when and why?

1.7 CHAPTER SUMMARY

1. A **real number** is a number that can be expressed in a decimal form.

2. The real number that requires an infinite number of non-zero digits in its decimal expression is called a **non-terminating decimal.**

3. A non-terminating decimal is called a **repeating decimal** if it has a repeating pattern after some finite number of decimal places.

4. A decimal expression without a repeating pattern is called a **non-repeating decimal.**

5. If all digits to the right of the decimal point are zero, then the real number is called an **integer.**

   For example, … $-3, -2, -1, 0, 1, 2, 3, 4,$ … are integers.

6. A quotient $\dfrac{p}{q}$ of two integers p and q, where $q\neq 0$, is called a **rational number.**

7. A rational number in its decimal form is either a **terminating** or a **repeating non-terminating** decimal.

8. A real number that is not a rational number is called an **irrational number.**

9. An irrational number in its decimal form is a non-terminating decimal **without a repeating block.**

10. There is a **one-to-one correspondence** between the real numbers and points on the **number line.**

11. "*n* **is positive**" is equivalent to *n* > 0. "*n* **is negative**" is equivalent to *n* < 0. "*n* **is non-negative**" is equivalent to *n* ≥ 0. "*n* **is non-positive**" is equivalent to *n* ≤ 0.

12. A continuous portion of the number line is called an **interval.**

13. The portion of the number line between real number *a* and *b*, where *a* < *b*, is called an **open interval** and it consists of all real numbers *x* such that *a* < *x* < *b*. An open interval between **a** and **b** is also written as (*a*, *b*).

14. If the end points of the portion of the number line between *a* and *b* are also included, then it is called a **closed interval** and is written as: *a* ≤ *x* ≤ *b* or [*a*, *b*].

15. The portion of the number line that extends indefinitely, to either direction, is called an **unbounded interval.** For example, $(5, \infty)$ or $(-\infty, -1]$.

16. The **union** of two intervals *I* and *J* is written as $I \cup J$.

17. The **intersection** of two interval *I* and *J* is written as $I \cap J$.

18. The **absolute value** of a **real number** *x*, written as $|x|$, is the distance on the number line from *x* to the origin.

19. The **absolute value** of quantity *K* is defined as: $|K| = \begin{cases} K, & \text{if } K \geq 0 \\ -K, & \text{if } K < 0 \end{cases}$.

20. $\sqrt{x^2} = |x|$.

21. **Properties of Absolute Value:**

For any real numbers *a* and *b*,

(i) the distance between *a* and *b* is $|a-b|$ or $|b-a|$

(ii) $|ab| = |a||b|$

(iii) $\left|\dfrac{a}{b}\right| = \dfrac{|a|}{|b|}$ (*b* ≠ 0)

(iv) $|a+b| \leq |a|+|b|$ (Triangle Inequality)

(v) $|a| = p \quad \rightarrow \quad a = p \text{ or } a = -p$

(vi)   For $p > 0$, $\left| a \right| < p \;\rightarrow\; -p < a < p$

(vii) For $p \geq 0$, $\left| a \right| > p \;\rightarrow\; a < -p$ or $a > p$

22. An **expression** obtained by applying operations such as addition, subtraction, multiplication, division or taking roots to variables and real numbers is called an **algebraic expression.**

23. An algebraic expression that consists of a variable raised to a constant power like x^n is called a **power expression.**

24. In a power expression like x^n, x is said to be the **base** and n is called the **exponent** or **power.**

25. The law of exponents are:

(i) $x^m \cdot x^n = x^{m+n}$, (ii) $\dfrac{x^m}{x^n} = x^{m-n}$, (iii) $\left(x^m \right)^n = x^{mn}$,

(iv) $(xy)^n = x^n y^n$ (v) $\left(\dfrac{x}{y} \right)^n = \dfrac{x^n}{y^n}$, (vi) $x^{-m} = \dfrac{1}{x^m}$,

(vii) $x^0 = 1$, (viii) $x^1 = x$

26. A **polynomial expression** is obtained by applying any combination of operations like addition, subtraction, or constant multiples of power expressions with non-negative powers. The general form of a polynomial expression is $a_n x^n + a_{n-1} x^{n-1} + \ldots + a_1 x + a_0$, where a_n, a_{n-1}, $\ldots$ a_1, a_0 are real numbers $\left(a_n \neq 0 \right)$, and n is a non-negative integer.

27. The **degree** of a polynomial is the highest exponent of the variable.

28. Polynomials of degree 1, 2, and 3, are called **linear**, **quadratic** and **cubic** polynomials respectively.

29. If the terms of a polynomial are arranged in descending order of the exponents of the variable, then the first term is called the **leading term** of the polynomial and its coefficient is called the **leading coefficient.**

30. The constants a_0, a_1, a_2, $\ldots$, a_n are called the **coefficients** of the polynomial expression.

31. A polynomial with all coefficients equal to zero is called the **zero polynomial**.

32. The constant multiples of power expressions like $a_n x^n$, $a_{n-1} x^{n-1}, \ldots, a_1 x$, a_0 are called **terms** of the polynomial.

33. A polynomial with only one term is called a **monomial.**

34. A polynomial with only two terms is called a **binomial.**

35. A polynomial with exactly three terms is known as a **trinomial.**

36. Special products:
(i) $(A - B)(A + B) = A^2 - B^2$,

(ii) $(A \pm B)^2 = A^2 \pm 2AB + B^2$, and

(iii) $(A + B)^3 = A^3 + 3A^2B + 3AB^2 + B^3$

(iv) $(A - B)^3 = A^3 - 3A^2B + 3AB^2 - B^3$

(v) $(A - B)(A^2 + AB + B^2) = A^3 - B^3$

(vi) $(A + B)(A^2 - AB + B^2) = A^3 + B^3$

37. The process of writing a given expression as a product of polynomials is called **factoring.**

38. The strategy for factoring is:

Step **1**   Identify common factors

Step **2**   If one of the factors is a Binomial then use

$$(A)^2 - (B)^2 = (A - B)(A + B), \text{ or}$$

$$(A)^3 - (B)^3 = (A - B)(A^2 + AB + B^2), \text{ or}$$

$$\text{and} \quad (A)^3 + (B)^3 = (A + B)(A^2 - AB + B^2).$$

Step **3**   If one of the factors is a trinomial $(ax^2 + bx + c)$, then proceed as follows.

    a. $\dfrac{(ax\ \ )(ax\ \ )}{a}$

    b.   Look for two numbers α and β whose product $\alpha\beta = ac$ and sum $\alpha + \beta = b$.

    c.   Use the number (α) in the first factor and the other number (β) in the second factor

        like $\dfrac{(ax + \alpha)(ax + \beta)}{a}$.

    d.   Factor out common factors and cancel out the number in the denominator.

Step **4**   If one of the factors is a polynomial with four terms, then use the method of grouping terms.

39. For $x = a$, the value of expression is obtained by replacing x with a in the expression.

40. For large $|x|$; $\dfrac{1}{x}, \dfrac{1}{x^2}, \dfrac{1}{x^3}, \ldots$ are very small, almost negligible. In short, $\dfrac{1}{x} \to 0$ as $|x| \to \infty$.

41. For large $|x|$, the value of a polynomial expression is **dominated** by the **leading term** of the polynomial.

42. An algebraic expression $\dfrac{p(x)}{q(x)}$ where $p(x)$ and $q(x)$ are polynomial expressions is called a **rational expression.**

43. Removing common factors from the numerator and denominator of a rational expression is called **reducing** of a **rational expression.**

44. A **complex** expression can be reduced to a rational expression by multiplying each term at the top and bottom by the lowest common denominator of all denominators.

45. If on substituting a for x in the rational expression $\dfrac{f(x)}{g(x)}$, the denominator is zero but the numerator is not, then $\dfrac{f(x)}{g(x)}$ is said to be **undefined** for $x = a$. If numerator and denominator are both zero, $\dfrac{f(x)}{g(x)}$ is said to be **indeterminate** for $x = a$.

For $a > 0$, $\dfrac{a}{0} \to \infty$ (**undefined**). For $a < 0$, $\dfrac{a}{0} \to -\infty$ (**undefined**), and $\dfrac{0}{0}$ is **indeterminate**.

46. For large $\left| x \right|$, the value of a rational expression $\dfrac{p(x)}{q(x)}$ is dominated by

    (i)   the quotient of leading coefficients, if $\deg p(x) = \deg q(x)$;

    (ii)   0, if $\deg p(x) < \deg q(x)$; and

    (iii)   the quotient when we divide $p(x)$ by $q(x)$ if $\deg p(x) > \deg q(x)$.

47. A rational expression $\dfrac{p(x)}{q(x)}$, with $\deg p(x) > \deg q(x)$ can be expressed as part polynomial and part rational expression by using **long division.**

48. The value of a polynomial expression $p(x)$ for $x = r$ is the same as the remainder in the division of $p(x)$ by $x - r$. This result is known as the **remainder theorem.**

49. When $q(x) = x - r$, then the division of polynomials $\dfrac{p(x)}{q(x)}$ is done faster by **synthetic** division.

50. If $x - r$ is a factor of a polynomial $p(x)$, then the **complementary factor** of $x - r$ is obtained by dividing $p(x)$ by $x - r$.

51. When n is **even**, $\sqrt[n]{x} = \left| a \right|$ if and only if $x = a^n$ and $x \geq 0$

52. When n is **odd**, $\sqrt[n]{x} = a$ if and only if $x = a^n$

53. A radical is said to be in simplified form when each factor inside the radical has an exponent less than the index, and there is no fraction under the radical.

54. $\sqrt{x} = x^{1/2}$, $\sqrt[3]{x} = x^{1/3}$ and in general $\left(\sqrt[n]{x}\right)^m = x^{m/n}$.

55. The process of writing a quotient with a radical in the denominator as an equivalent quotient with no radical in the denominator is called **rationalizing the denominator.**

56. For a denominator with a **single term**, rationalization of the denominator is accomplished by multiplying both numerator and denominator by an expression that will raise each factor in the radicand in the denominator to a power which is the same as the index of the radical.

57. When the denominator is of the type $a + \sqrt{b}$, rationalization of the denominator is accomplished by multiplying both numerator and denominator by the **conjugate** $a - \sqrt{b}$ of the denominator.

1.8 CHAPTER REVIEW

In exercises (1–4), consider the following numbers

$$-\frac{1}{5}, 0, 3, 2\pi, 5.93, 2.\overline{17}, \sqrt{25}, \sqrt{7}, 5\%, -\frac{5}{7}, 3.1223157\ldots, -2.8$$

List the numbers for the indicated classification.

1. integers   2. rationals   3. irrationals   4. reals

In exercises (5–10), indicate the approximate location of the number on the number line.

5. $\dfrac{\pi}{6}$ 6. $-\dfrac{\pi}{12}$ 7. $\sqrt{7}+2$ 8. $\sqrt{5}-6$ 9. $\dfrac{8}{3}$ 10. $-\dfrac{7}{5}$

In exercises (11–22), graph the interval on the number line and write the interval without inequalities.

11. $-1 < x \le 3$ 12. $-2 \le x < 1$ 13. $2 \le x \le 5$ 14. $5 < x < 8$

15. $x \ge -1$ 16. $x \le 4$ 17. $2 > x$ 18. $-1 < x$

19. $x \ge 7$ or $x < 1$ 20. $x > -1$ or $x < -5$ 21. $x > 2$ and $x \le 6$ 22. $x \ge -1$ and $x \le 4$

In exercises (23–40), write without absolute value symbols.

23. $\left| 11 - 15 \right|$ 24. $\left| 2 - 12 \right|$ 25. $\left| 5 - \sqrt{26} \right|$ 26. $\left| \sqrt{32} - 4 \right|$

27. $\left| 2\pi - 8 \right|$ 28. $\left| 3\pi - \sqrt{7} \right|$ 29. $\left| \sqrt{x+5} \right|$, if $x \ge -5$ 30. $\left| \sqrt{2x-3} \right|$, $x \ge \dfrac{3}{2}$

31. $\left| -2 - t^2 \right|$ 32. $\left| x^2 + 5 \right|$ 33. $\left| y - 1 \right|$, if $y \ge 1$ 34. $\left| 2 - x \right|$ if $x \ge 2$

35. $\left| y - 1 \right|$, if $y < 1$ 36. $\left| y + 7 \right|$, $y < -7$ 37. $\left| x - 5 \right|$ 38. $\left| x + 12 \right|$

39. $\left| x \right| + \left| x - 1 \right|$, if $0 < x < 1$ 40. $\left| x - 2 \right| + \left| x \right|$, if $0 < x < 2$

In exercises (41–46), write the expression with absolute value symbols.

41. $\sqrt{(x+20)^2}$ 42. $\sqrt{(x-11)^2}$

43. The distance between x and -1 44. The distance between x and 5.

45. The distance between x and 2 is at least 5 46. The distance between x and -4 is at most 12.

In exercises (47–52), use $\left| x - 3 \right| = \delta$ and express the given expression in terms of δ.

47. $\left| 5x - 15 \right|$ 48. $\left| \dfrac{1}{3}x - 1 \right|$ 49. $\left| \dfrac{2x-6}{5} \right|$ 50. $\left| \dfrac{3x-9}{4} \right|$ 51. $\left| x - 2 \right|$ 52. $\left| x - 1 \right|$

In exercises (53–57), simplify and write the answer with positive exponents.

53. $\left(25x^5 y \right)^{1/2}$ 54. $\left(9x^3 + 1 \right)\sqrt{5x+9}$ 55. $9(x+3)^0 + 5^0$ 56. $\left(27x^3 y^6 \right)^{2/3}$ 57. $\left(25 \cdot x^4 y^2 \right)^{3/2}$

In exercises (58–62), use appropriate formula to multiply.

58. $\left(\sqrt{2x+3} - 5 \right)\left(\sqrt{2x+3} + 5 \right)$ 59. $\left(\sqrt{x+h+7} - \sqrt{x+7} \right)\left(\sqrt{x+h+7} + \sqrt{x+7} \right)$

60. $\left(\sqrt{x+c} + \sqrt{x} \right)^2$ 61. $\left(\sqrt{x+7} - \sqrt{x} \right)^2$ 62. $(x+5)^3$

In exercises (63–74), factor completely.

63. $3x^2 - 12x^4$

64. $8x^3 - 27t^3$

65. $x^4 - 81$

66. $x^4 - 16y^4$

67. $x^2 - 5x - 6$

68. $x^2 - 2x - 48$

69. $12x^2 - 31x + 20$

70. $x^4 - 4$

71. $2x^3 + x^2 - 18x - 9$

72. $(x+5)^3 (x+1)^2 + (x+5)^4 (x+1)$

73. $(5x+3)^{-1/2}(x+2)^{1/2} + (5x+3)^{1/2}(x+2)^{-1/2}$

74. Approximate the value of $8x^3 - 7x^2 - 50x + 1$ when $x = 900$

In exercises (75–77), reduce the rational expression to its simplest form.

75. $\dfrac{2x^2 + x - 3}{5x^2 - 3x - 2}$

76. $\dfrac{6x^2 + 7x - 5}{4x^2 - 1}$

77. $\dfrac{3(x+1)^2 (x-3)^5 - 5(x-3)^4 (x+1)^3}{\left((x-3)^5\right)^2}$

In exercises (78–81), combine the rational expressions into a single rational expression and reduce them.

78. $\dfrac{3}{(x+h)^2} - \dfrac{3}{x^2}$

79. $\dfrac{5}{2x-3} - \dfrac{3x+2}{2x^2 - 7x + 6}$

80. $\dfrac{7}{2x+1} + \dfrac{2x+5}{2x^2 - x - 1}$

81. **Simplify the compound expression:** $\dfrac{\dfrac{5}{x+h+3} - \dfrac{5}{x+3}}{h}$

In exercises (82–85), evaluate the rational expression for the given value of x.

82. $\dfrac{x^2 + x - 6}{x^2 + 8x + 15}$, for $x = 3$

83. $\dfrac{x^2 + x - 6}{x^2 + 8x + 15}$, for $x = -3$

84. $\dfrac{25x - 50}{x^2 - 6x + 9}$, for $x = 3$

85. $\dfrac{2x^2 - x - 1}{5x^2 - 2x - 3}$, for $x = 1$

In exercises (86–90), indicate the dominant part of the rational expression when $|x|$ is large.

86. $\dfrac{18x^3 - 10x^2 + 7x + 3}{6x^3 + 5x + 11}$

87. $\dfrac{4x^2 - 3x - 12}{6x^6 - 10x^5 + 7x^3 + x + 10}$

88. $\dfrac{2x^4 + 5x^3 + 8x^2 + 7x + 2}{x^2 + x + 2}$

89. $\dfrac{3x^3 + 9x^2 - 5}{x^2 - 2x + 9}$

90. $\dfrac{9x^2 + 5x + 24}{6x^4 + 3x^3 + 12x + 13}$

In exercises (91–92), divide by long division.

91. $\dfrac{x^4 + 3x^2 - 6x - 10}{x^2 + 3x - 5}$

92. $\dfrac{20x^4 - 3x^2 + 9}{5x^2 - 2}$

In exercises (93–96), divide using synthetic division.

93. $\dfrac{3x^3 - 8x^2 + 7x + 2}{x - 2}$

94. $\dfrac{4x^3 - 2x + 3}{x + 1}$

95. $\dfrac{7x^3 - 9x^2 + 2x - 11}{x - 1}$

96. $\dfrac{5x^3 + 6x^2 - 20}{x + 2}$

In exercises (97–98), simplify by factoring.

97. $\dfrac{(2x+1)^{-1/2} (4x+5)^{1/2} - 2(4x+5)^{-1/2} (2x+1)^{1/2}}{\left((4x+5)^{1/2}\right)^2}$

98. $\dfrac{(x+7)^{-1/2} (x+1)^{1/3} - (x+7)^{1/2} (x+1)^{-2/3}}{\left((x+1)^{1/3}\right)^2}$

In exercises (99–100), rationalize the denominator.

99. The denominator in $\dfrac{x - 25}{\sqrt{x} - 5}$.

100. The numerator in $\sqrt{x^2 + 5x} - x$.

1.9 CHAPTER TEST

1. Consider the numbers: $\frac{2}{7}, \sqrt{4}, -\sqrt{3}, \frac{\pi}{2}, -2.98, 2\%, 5.\overline{32}, -1.731523\ldots$ and list the numbers that are;

   a. integer   **b.** rational numbers   **c.** irrational numbers

2. Show the interval $x \geq 10$ or $x < 2$ on the number line and write the interval without inequalities.

3. Write each of the following expressions without absolute value symbols.

   a. $\left| \pi - 5 \right|$ **b.** $\left| -9 - x^2 \right|$ **c.** $\left| x - 4 \right|$

4. Given that $\left| x - 1 \right| = \delta$, write the following in terms of δ.

   a. $\left| x + 3 \right|$ **b.** $\left| 5x - 5 \right|$

5. Use formulas to simplify each of the following expressions.

   a. $\left(3 - \sqrt{x+9} \right)^2$ **b.** $\left(\sqrt{x+h+5} - \sqrt{x} \right)\left(\sqrt{x+h+5} + \sqrt{x} \right)$ **c.** $(x-2)^3$

6. Factor each of the following polynomials.

   a. $2x^4 - 32$ **b.** $24x^2 + 2x - 15$ **c.** $3x^3 + 24$ **d.** $3x^3 + x^2 - 12x - 4$

7. Reduce each rational expression.

   a. $\dfrac{5x^2 - 13x - 6}{3x^2 - 4x - 15}$ **b.** $\dfrac{2(x+2)^{-2/3}(x+3)^{1/2} - (x+2)^{1/3}(x+3)^{-1/2}}{\left((x+3)^{1/2} \right)^2}$

8. Simplify each compound expression.

   a. $\dfrac{\dfrac{9}{(x+h)^2} - \dfrac{9}{x^2}}{}$ **b.** $\dfrac{\dfrac{11}{x+h+2} - \dfrac{11}{x+2}}{h}$

9. Evaluate $\dfrac{x^2 + x - 12}{x^2 - 4x + 3}$ for :   **a.** $x = 1$ **b.** $x = 6$ **c.** $x = 3$

10. Indicate the dominant part of each rational expression when $\left| x \right|$ is large.

    a. $\dfrac{10x^3 - 9x^2 - 10x + 12}{5x^3 + 7x^2 + 5x - 1}$ **b.** $\dfrac{x^4 - 3x^3 + 2x - 5}{x^2 - x + 1}$ **c.** $\dfrac{4x^2 - 7x + 8}{x^3 - 8}$

11. Divide using synthetic division $\dfrac{2x^3 - 5x^2 - 4x + 1}{x - 3}$.

12. Rationalize the numerator $\dfrac{\sqrt{2x + 2h + 3} - \sqrt{2x + 3}}{h}$.

Functions

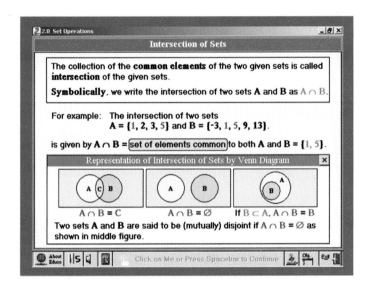

Functions

2 FUNCTIONS

Mathematics is an exact science and has a language that facilitates precision and logic. Mathematical language has words and phrases with special meaning, just like any other language. In this chapter we will discuss key words and definitions related to two very important concepts in mathematics namely sets and functions. We will recall the concept of a set, introduce the concept of a function, and study a variety of terms associated with these concepts.

The discussion in this chapter is divided into six sections:

2.1 SETS - A REVIEW

In this section, we run a quick review of sets. We recall a few important definitions and terms. Some examples are also given to facilitate the review.

> **Objectives** ▶ ▶
>
> In this section you will learn about:
> A. Definition of a Set;
> B. Describing Sets;
> C. Operations on Sets;
> D. Venn Diagrams; and
> E. Cartesian Product.

A. DEFINITION OF A SET

The notion of a set is basic to most mathematical concepts. We often talk about a collection of objects. Such collections, if **well defined**, are called sets.

> **Set**
>
> A set is a **well defined** collection of objects.

By the phrase 'well defined' we mean that there is a rule or a property which can be used to identify the members of the set.

There are, however, some collections whose members may be difficult to identify, for example, the collection of all students in a class who are almost six feet tall. This collection does not define a set because "almost six feet tall" is not well defined. Collections must be **well defined.**

EXAMPLES:

- Set of all counting members
- Set of all integers
- Set of all prime numbers
- Set of all rational numbers
- Set of all real numbers
- Set of all vowels in English alphabet
- Set of all words in Webster's Dictionary (Edition 9) that start with alphabet A, D or P.

Notation: A set is usually denoted by an upper case letter. As a convention, N is used for the set of all natural numbers, I for the set of all integers, Q for the set of all rational numbers, and R for the set of all real numbers. W is often used to denote the set of whole numbers.

Element of a set

An object that belongs to a set is called its element or member.

Notation: If 'a' is an element of a set X, we often express this by writing '$a \in X$', where $\in$ stands for 'belongs to' or 'is a member of'. $\notin$ stands for 'does not belong to' or 'is not a member of'.

For example, $3 \in N$ and $\sqrt{2} \notin N$.

Remark: *A collection that does not contain any object is also well defined by stating that "it has no member." This set is called the **null set** or **empty set** and is denoted by ϕ.*

B. DESCRIBING SETS

In mathematics, sets are described in two ways:

a. by listing all of its elements called **listing method.**

b. by including the property that identifies its elements called **set builder method.**

Listing Method

To describe a set by the listing method, we list either all the elements or all elements with a suggestive pattern and enclose them in a pair of braces.

EXAMPLES:

- $\{1, 2, 3, 4, 5, 6, 7, 8, 9, 10\}$ = set of all counting numbers between 1 and 10, both inclusive.
- $\{1, 2, 3, 4, \ldots, 99\}$ = set of all counting numbers between 1 and 100, including 1.
- $\{3, 5, 7, 9, 11\}$ = set of all odd numbers between 1 and 13.
- $\{2, 4, 6, 8, 10, \ldots, 76\}$ = set of all even numbers between 1 and 77.
- $\{0, 1, 4, 9, 16, 25, 36, \ldots\}$ = set of squares of all integers.
- $\{1, 3, 5, 7, 9, 11, \ldots\}$ = set of all positive odd numbers.

Remarks: *1.   The fact that a set is a well defined collection confirms that an element may not be repeated.*

2.   The order in which the elements are listed does not matter.

Set Builder Method

To describe a set by the set builder method, we mention a generic element followed by the identifying property of the elements of the set. $\{x|$ property satisfied by $x\}$.

EXAMPLES:

- The set of all counting numbers between 1 and 10, both inclusive = $\{x|x$ is a natural number and $1 \leq x \leq 10\}$.
  This set is alternatively written as
  $\{x|x \in N, 1 \leq x \leq 10\}$, it being understood that N denotes the set of all natural (counting) numbers.

- The set of all counting numbers between 1 and 100, including 1.
  $= \{x|x \in N, \ 1 \leq x < 100\}$ or $\{x|x \in N, 1 \leq x \leq 99\}$

- The set of all odd numbers between 1 and 13.
  $= \{x|x \in N, 1 < x < 13$ and x is odd$\}$.

- The set of all even numbers between 1 and 77 both inclusive
  $= \{x|x \in N, 1 \leq x \leq 77$ and x is even$\}$

- The set of squares of whole numbers
  $= \{x|x$ is square of a whole number$\}$
  or $\{x^2|x$ is a whole number$\}$

- The set of all odd numbers
  $= \{x|x$ is an odd number$\}$

C. OPERATIONS ON SETS

In mathematics, a set of objects is given an algebraic structure by defining rules of operations that produce new objects of the same kind in the same way as adding two integers produces a new integer. In this section, we define the following three rules of operations on sets.

1. Union of Two Sets   **2.** Intersection of Two Sets   **3.** Complement of a Set B in a Set A.

1.   Union of Two Sets

If A and B are two sets, then their union, denoted by $A \cup B$, is the set of all those elements that are either in A or in B or in both.

Since elements of A and B can be identified, elements of $A \cup B$ can also be identified. Therefore, $A \cup B$ is a set. In the set-builder notation,

$$A \cup B = \{x \,|\, x \in A \ \textbf{or} \ x \in B\}.$$

Remark: *In mathematical logic, $x \in A$ or $x \in B$ means "**if x is not** in A then **it is** in B". It does not exclude the possibility of x being in both A and B.*

> **2. Intersection of Two Sets**
>
> If A and B are two sets, then their intersection, denoted by $A \cap B$, is the set of all the elements which are common to both A and B.

Once again, elements of $A \cap B$ can be identified since elements of A and B can be identified. Therefore, $A \cap B$ is a set. In the set builder notation,

$$A \cap B = \{x \mid x \in A \text{ and } x \in B\}.$$

> **3. Complement of Set B in a Set A**
>
> If A and B are two sets then the complement of B in A, denoted by $A \backslash B$, is the set of those elements of A that are not in B. Written in set-builder notation,
>
> $$A \backslash B = \{x \mid x \in A \text{ and } x \notin B\}.$$

EXAMPLE 1   Let P be the set of all letters in the word 'algebra' and Q the set of all letters in the word 'geometry'.

Determine   **a.** $P \cup Q$ **b.** $P \cap Q$ **c.** $P \backslash Q$ **d.** $Q \backslash P$

Solution: $P = \{x \mid x \text{ is a letter in the word "algebra"}\}$

$\qquad = \{a, l, g, e, b, r\}$ 　　　　The letter a to be listed only once.

$Q = \{x \mid x \text{ is a letter in the word "geometry"}\}$

$\qquad = \{g, e, o, m, t, r, y\}$ 　　　　The letter e to be listed only once.

a. 　$P \cup Q = \{x \mid x \in P \text{ or } x \in Q\}$

$\qquad\qquad = \{a, l, g, e, b, r, o, m, t, y\}$

Process: List all the distinct members of P and then add to this list all members of Q which are not already listed.

b. 　$P \cap Q \quad = \{x \mid x \in P \text{ and } x \in Q\}$

$\qquad\qquad = \{g, e, r\}$

Process: List all the members common to P and Q.

c. 　$P \backslash Q \quad = \{x \mid x \in P \text{ and } x \notin Q\}$

$\qquad\qquad = \{a, l, b\}$

Process: List all the members of P which are not in Q.

d. 　$Q \backslash P \quad = \{x \mid x \in Q \text{ and } x \notin P\}$

$\qquad\qquad = \{o, m, t, y\}$

Process: List all the members of Q which are not in P.

D. VENN DIAGRAMS

Algebra of real numbers has many properties. Real numbers are visualized by plotting them on a number line. Similarly, algebra of sets has many properties that are visualized by using diagrams called Venn Diagrams.

Venn Diagram

A Venn diagram consists of closed regions drawn inside a rectangle. The closed regions, often circular, represent sets.

EXAMPLES:

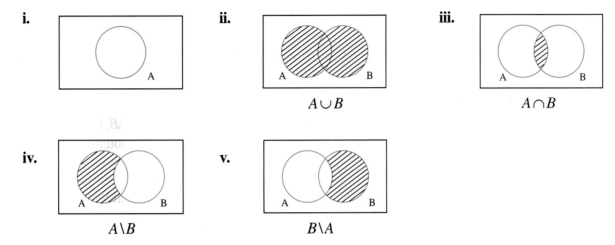

i.

ii.

$A \cup B$

iii.

$A \cap B$

iv.

$A \setminus B$

v.

$B \setminus A$

Venn diagrams can be utilized to visualize algebraic properties of sets. Examine the following properties and illustrations using Venn diagrams.

a. Among three sets, union $\cup$ is associative *i.e.* $(A \cup B) \cup C = A \cup (B \cup C)$

Illustration through Venn diagrams:

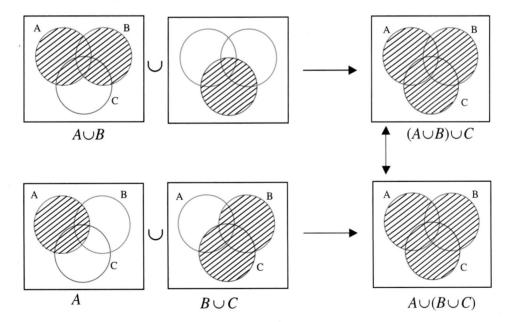

$A \cup B$

$\cup$

$(A \cup B) \cup C$

A

$B \cup C$

$A \cup (B \cup C)$

b. Among three sets, intersection $\cap$ is associative *i.e.* $(A \cap B) \cap C = A \cap (B \cap C)$.

Illustration through Venn diagrams:

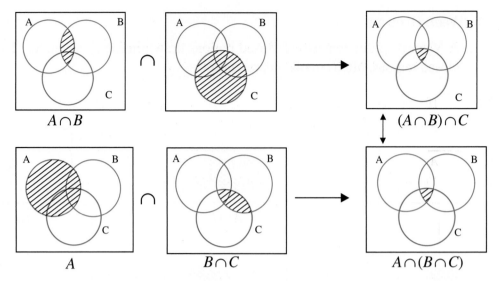

$$A \cap B \qquad \cap \qquad \qquad \rightarrow \qquad (A \cap B) \cap C$$

$$A \qquad \cap \qquad B \cap C \qquad \rightarrow \qquad A \cap (B \cap C)$$

c.   Intersection ($\cap$) is distributive over union ($\cup$) in sets *i.e.* $A \cap (B \cup C) = (A \cap B) \cup (A \cap C)$
Illustration through Venn diagrams:

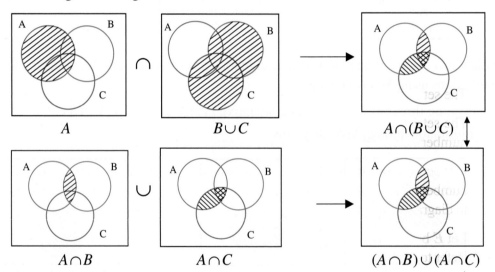

$$A \qquad \cap \qquad B \cup C \qquad \rightarrow \qquad A \cap (B \cup C)$$

$$A \cap B \qquad \cup \qquad A \cap C \qquad \rightarrow \qquad (A \cap B) \cup (A \cap C)$$

d.   Union ($\cup$) is distributive over intersection ($\cap$) in sets *i.e.* $A \cup (B \cap C) = (A \cup B) \cap (A \cup C)$.
Illustration through Venn diagrams:

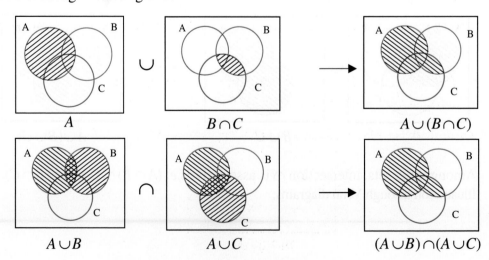

$$A \qquad \cup \qquad B \cap C \qquad \rightarrow \qquad A \cup (B \cap C)$$

$$A \cup B \qquad \cap \qquad A \cup C \qquad \rightarrow \qquad (A \cup B) \cap (A \cup C)$$

Subset

A set *A* is said to be a subset of a set *B* if every element of *A* is also an element of B, that is, $x \in A$ implies $x \in B$.

Notation: If *A* is a subset of *B*, then we write this as '$A \subseteq B$'. The statement '$A \nsubseteq B$' means *A* is not a subset of *B*, *i.e.* there is some element *x* in *A* which is not in *B*.

Remark: *$A \nsubseteq B$ even if there is one element in A that is not in B. 'Subset of' and 'not a subset of' can be depicted by the following Venn diagrams:*

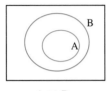

$A \subseteq B$

(i)

All $x \in A$ are in *B*.

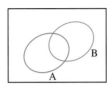

$A \nsubseteq B$

(ii)

Some elements in *A* are not in *B*.

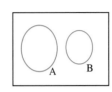

$A \nsubseteq B$

(iii)

Some elements in *A* are not in *B*.

$A \nsubseteq B$

(iv)

Some elements in *A* are not in *B*.

EXAMPLES

- The set *N* of natural numbers is a subset of the set *I* of integers. In symbols $N \subseteq I$.

- The set *W* of whole numbers is not a subset of the set *N* of all natural numbers. Recall the number zero is in *W* but not in *N*. Refer to diagram (iv).

- If *P* denotes the set of all prime numbers and *O* the set of all odd integers, then $P \not\subset O$ since the number 2 is in *P* but not in *O*. Likewise $O \not\subset P$ since the number 9 is odd but not prime. Refer to diagram (ii).

- Let *E* be the set of all even numbers and *O* the set of all odd numbers. Then $E \not\subset O$ and $O \not\subset E$. Refer to diagram (iii).

- The null set ϕ is a subset of every set because there is nothing in ϕ which is not in any set. In symbols $\phi \subseteq A$ for every set *A*.

- Every set *A* is a subset of itself because $x \in A$ implies $x \in A$ and this is always true.

Disjoint Sets

Two sets *A* and *B* are said to be disjoint if $A \cap B = \phi$, that is *A* and *B* do not have any *common elements*.

Disjoint sets *A* and *B* can be depicted in a Venn diagram as follows:

Disjoint sets

EXAMPLES:

- If E is the set of even numbers and O is the set of odd numbers, then E and O are disjoint.

- If I^+ is the set of positive integers and I^- is the set of negative integers, then I^+ and I^- are disjoint. Remember that the integer zero is neither positive nor negative.

- If E is the set of even numbers and P is the set of prime numbers, then E and P are not disjoint because $E \cap P = \{2\}$.

E. CARTESIAN PRODUCT OF TWO SETS

A typical example of Cartesian product is the Cartesian plane.

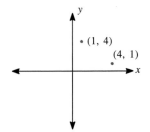

We know that the cartesian coordinates (1, 4) and (4, 1) do not represent the same point of the Cartesian plane, because the order in which two numbers 1 and 4 are paired is important. Such pairs are called ordered pairs.

> **Ordered Pair**
>
> A pair of elements a, b in which the first member is a and the second member is b is called an **ordered pair** denoted by (a, b)

EXAMPLES:

- (3, 4) represents an ordered pair of numbers 3 and 4 where 3 occurs before 4.

- (7, –3) represents an ordered pair of numbers 7 and –3, where 7 occurs before –3.

- (2, 2) represents an ordered pair of numbers 2 and 2.

Remark: *Two ordered pairs (a, b) and (c, d) are equal if and only if a = c and b = d, that is if and only if the respective components of the two ordered pairs are equal.*

> **Cartesian Product**
>
> Cartesian product X×Y of two sets X and Y is the set consisting of all ordered pairs (a, b) where a, the first component, is an element of X and b, the second component, is an element of Y.

EXAMPLES:

a. The Cartesian plane is the Cartesian product of **R** with itself, where **R** is the set of real numbers.

b. If $A = \{x, y\}$, $B = \{2, 3, 4\}$, then
$A{\times}B = \{(x, 2), (x, 3), (x, 4), (y, 2), (y, 3), (y, 4)\}$
$B{\times}A = \{(2, x), (2, y), (3, x), (3, y), (4, x), (4, y)\}$

In general, $A{\times}B \neq B{\times}A$.

We give below two results relating the Cartesian product of the union or intersection of two sets with a third set.

a. $(A \cup B) \times C = (A \times C) \cup (B \times C)$

b. $(A \cap B) \times C = (A \times C) \cap (B \times C)$

EXAMPLE 2   Let $A = \{2, 3, 4, -1\}$, $B = \{a, b, c\}$, $C = \{c, p, q\}$

Compute   **i.** $A \times B$ **ii.** $A \times C$ **iii.** $A \times (B \cup C)$

iv. $A \times (B \cap C)$ **v.** $(A \times B) \cup (A \times C)$ **vi.** $(A \times B) \cap (A \times C)$

Verify that: $A \times (B \cup C) = (A \times B) \cup (A \times C)$
$A \times (B \cap C) = (A \times B) \cap (A \times C)$

Solutions:

i. $A \times B = \{(x, y) \mid x \in A, y \in B\}$

$= \{(2, a), (2, b), (2, c), (3, a), (3, b), (3, c),$
$(4, a), (4, b), (4, c), (-1, a), (-1, b), (-1, c)\}$

ii. $A \times C = \{(x, y) \mid x \in A, y \in C\}$

$= \{(2, c), (2, p), (2, q), (3, c), (3, p), (3, q),$
$(4, c), (4, p), (4, q), (-1, c), (-1, p), (-1, q)\}$

iii. $B \cup C = \{a, b, c\} \cup \{c, p, q\} = \{a, b, c, p, q\}$
Therefore,

$A \times (B \cup C) = \{(2, a), (2, b), (2, c), (2, p), (2, q), (3, a),$
$(3, b), (3, c), (3, p), (3, q), (4, a), (4, b) (4, c), (4, p),$
$(4, q), (-1, a), (-1, b) (-1, c), (-1, p), (-1, q)\}$

iv. $B \cap C = \{a, b, c\} \cap \{c, p, q\} = \{c\}$
Therefore

$A \times (B \cap C) = \{(2, c), (3, c), (4, c), (-1, c)\}$

v.   Using (i) and (ii),

$(A \times B) \cup (A \times C) = \{(2, a), (2, b), (2, c), (3, a), (3, b), (3, c), (4, a), (4, b), (4, c),$
$(-1, a), (-1, b), (-1, c)\} \cup \{(2, c), (2, p), (2, q), (3, c), (3, p),$
$(3, q), (4, c), (4, p), (4, q), (-1, c), (-1, p), (-1, q)\}$

$= \{(2, a), (2, b), (2, c), (3, a), (3, b), (3, c), (4, a), (4, b), (4, c),$
$(-1, a), (-1, b), (-1, c), (2, p), (2, q), (3, p), (3, q), (4, p),$
$(4, q), (-1, p), (-1, q)\}.$

vi. Using (i) and (ii),

$(A \times B) \cap (A \times C) = \{(2, a), (2, b), (2, c), (3, a), (3, b), (3, c), (4, a), (4, b), (4, c),$
$(-1, a), (-1, b), (-1, c)\} \cap \{(2, c), (2, p), (2, q), (3, c), (3, p),$
$(3, q), (4, c), (4, p), (4, q), (-1, c), (-1, p), (-1, q)\}$
$= \{(2, c), (3, c), (4, c), (-1, c)\}$

From (iii) and (v), we find that

$$A \times (B \cup C) = (A \times B) \cup (A \times C)$$

From (iv) and (vi), we find that

$$A \times (B \cap C) = (A \times B) \cap (A \times C)$$

EXERCISE 2.1

In exercises (1-10), identify whether the given collection is a set or not? Justify your answer.

1.	The collection of all consonants in English alphabet.

2.	The collection of all numbers approximately equal to 2.

3.	The collection of all numbers that equal 2 when rounded to the nearest hundredth.

4.	The collection of all rational numbers with prime number denominators.

5.	The collection of all real numbers greater than -3.

6.	The collection of all students in your school who are approximately eighteen years old.

7.	The collection of all employees of World Com who do not live far from their office.

8.	The collection of all integers that satisfy the equation $x^2 + 1 = 0$.

9.	The collection of all mathematics majors in your school who graduated in the year 2000.

10.	The collection of all voters in your county registered for the presidential election in the year 2000.

In exercises (11-20), write the sets by the listing method.

11.	$\{x \mid x$ is a non-negative integer$\}$.

12.	$\{x \mid x$ is a non-positive integer$\}$.

13.	$\{x \mid x$ is a natural number and a multiple of $3\}$.

14.	$\{x \mid x$ is a vowel in the English alphabet$\}$.

15.	$\{x \mid x$ is a letter in the word 'aeroplane'$\}$.

16.	$\{x \mid x$ is a rational number whose square is $2\}$.

17.	$\{x \mid x$ is the first letter of a weekday$\}$.

18.	$\{x \mid x$ is a positive rational number, the sum of whose numerator and denominator is $7\}$.

19.	$\{x \mid x$ is a positive rational number, whose denominator exceeds the numerator by one$\}$.

20.	$\{x \mid x$ is a natural number lying between 5 and 30 and is divisible by $5\}$.

In exercises (21-25), write the sets using the set-builder method.

21.	$\{3, 6, 9, 12, 15, 18\}$

22.	$\{3, 5, 7, 11, 13, ..., 29\}$.

23.	$\{..., -6, -4, -2, 0, 2, 4, 6, ...\}$

24.	$\{$January, March, May, July, August, October, December$\}$.

25.	$\{-1, 1\}$

In exercises (26-30), compute A∪B, A∩B, A\B, and B\A.

26. $A = \{x, y, z, l, m, n\}$, $B = \{x, y, p, q, n\}$ **27.** $A = \{1, 2, 3, 4, 5\}$, $B = \{0, 1, 2, 3, 4, 5\}$

28. $A = \{x | x$ is an even number$\}$, $B = \{x | x$ is an odd number$\}$

29. $A = \{$Sunday, Tuesday, Thursday, Saturday$\}$ $B = \{$Monday, Tuesday, Wednesday, Saturday$\}$

30. $A = \{$English, Mathematics, Physics, Chemistry$\}$ $B = \{20, 40, 25, 60\}$

In exercises (31-35), check whether A⊆B or B⊆A or neither.

31. $A =$ Set of whole numbers, $B =$ Set of natural numbers.   **32.** $A = \{a, b, c, d\}$, $B = \{l, m, n\}$

33. $A = \{$Sunday, Monday, Tuesday, Saturday$\}$ $B =$ Set of all weekdays

34. $A = \{x | x$ is a multiple of 2$\}$, $B = \{x | x$ is a multiple of 4$\}$.

35. $A = \{x | x$ is a prime number$\}$, $B = \{x | x$ is a natural number$\}$.

In exercises (36-40), compute A × B, B × A, and A × A.

36. $A = \{1, 2, 5, 10\}$, $B = \{-1, 0, 4, 7\}$ **37.** $A = \{x, y, u, v\}$, $B = \{l, m, a, b\}$

38. $A =$ Set of natural numbers   **39.** $A = \{$Sunday, Tuesday, Friday$\}$
$B =$ Set of integers $B = \{20, 40, 30\}$

40. $A =$ Set of letters in the word 'train'
$B =$ Set of letters in the word 'aeroplane'

In exercises (41-45), compute (i) (A∪B)∪C   (ii) A∪(B∪C)   (iii) (A∩B)∩C   (iv) A∩(B∩C).
Verify that: (A∪B)∪C = A∪(B∪C),   (A∩B)∩C = A∩(B∩C).

41. $A = \{a, b, c, l\}$, $B = \{l, x, y\}$, $C = \{a, l, x\}$ **42.** $A = \{1, 3, 5, 7\}$, $B = \{2, 4, 6\}$, $C = \{1, 2, 3, 4, 5\}$

43. $A =$ Set of natural numbers, $B =$ Set of whole numbers, $C =$ Set of integers

44. $A = \{x | x$ is a multiple of 2$\}$, $B = \{x | x$ is a multiple of 4$\}$, $C = \{x | x$ is a multiple of 8$\}$

45. $A = \{$Sunday, Tuesday, Thursday, Saturday$\}$,
$B = \{$Monday, Tuesday, Wednesday, Saturday$\}$
$C = \{$Sunday, Tuesday, Friday$\}$

In exercises (46-48), verify that   (i) (A∪B)×C = (A×C) ∪ (B×C)   (ii) (A∩B)×C = (A×C) ∩ (B×C)

46. $A = \{a, b, c\}$, $B = \{c, l, m\}$, $C = \{l, p, q\}$ **47.** $A = \{1, 4, 7\}$, $B = \{2, 4, 6\}$, $C = \{7, 8, 9\}$

48. $A = \{x, y, z\}$, $B = \{1, 2, 3\}$, $C = \{1, 2, x, p\}$

Writing Exercises

49. Distinguish between the two methods of describing sets.

50. Explain the significance of Venn Diagrams.

2.2 FUNCTIONS

Objectives ▶ ▶

In this section you will learn about:

A. The definition of a Function.

B. Elementary Functions.

The concept of a function is another important part of mathematics. Mathematical language depends more on sets and functions than anything else. Suppose that an electronic store makes a profit of $50 when it sells a DVD player of a particular brand. How much profit does the storekeeper make when 2 or 8 or 15 DVD players are sold?. We know that the profit depends upon the number (x) of DVD players sold and can be calculated by using a certain expression, **50x** in this case. This situation can be described mathematically in the following statement.

"If the store sells x DVD players then the profit will be $50x$ dollars". Mathematicians formalized this kind of association which relates an object in a collection (numbers that signify DVD players sold in this case) to an object in another collection (numbers that signify the profit), and called the relationship a **function.**

A. THE DEFINITION OF A FUNCTION

Function

A function is a rule which describes how to associate elements of a set X with elements of a set Y in an unambiguous manner.

Notation   A function may be described as follows.

$f: X \rightarrow Y$ [indicates elements of X are associated with elements of Y].

$f(x) = $ Rule   [describes the rule that associates a generic element x of X with unique element of Y].

Two things to Remember

1. **Every** element of X is associated with an element of Y.

2. Every element of X is associated with exactly one element of Y. This is required for the association to be unambiguous.

Explanation of the Notation of a Function

$f: X \rightarrow Y$

a. f is the **name** of the function

b. X is called **domain** of the function f.

c. $\rightarrow$ indicates the direction of association.

d. $f(x) = $ Rule defines the rule written as an **expression** for a generic element x of X, if possible.

e.   Set of all elements of Y associated with the elements of X is called the **Range** of the function f.

Remark: *As examples will show in the next section, some functions may not be represented by an expression. In such a case a complete description of association is necessary.*

Function as an Input-Output Machine

A function is like an input-output machine. Suppose a function $f: R \rightarrow R_+$ described by $f(x) = x^2 + 1$ takes any real number x (element of R) and produces a positive number (element of R_+) by adding 1 to the square of x. Thus, under f

$\quad$ 2 $\quad$ is associated with $2^2 + 1 = 5$,

$\quad$ -1 $\quad$ is associated with $(-1)^2 + 1 = 2$,

$\quad$ 0 $\quad$ is associated with $0^2 + 1 = 1$,

and so on.

Thus the function f acts like an input machine which takes the input x and produces the output $f(x) = x^2 + 1$ in this case.

Pictorially,

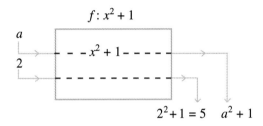

Remark: *An example of a relation is an association between the elements of X and elements of Y, where one or both of the "Two things to remember" are possibly violated. A relation may or may not be a function, but a function is certainly a relation. A relation is simply an association or correspondence between the elements of two sets.*

If $f: X \rightarrow Y$ is a function then

1. $f(a)$ is called the image of a under f or the f-image of a, and

2. a is called a pre-image of $f(a)$ under f.

Remark: *By the definition of a function every element of its domain has exactly one image. An element of the set Y may have none, one, or more pre-images.*

EXAMPLES:

a. f is not a function. Although all elements of X are associated with elements of Y, the element b is associated with two elements 7 and 8. Therefore f is a relation and not a function.

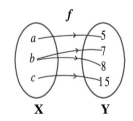

b. g is not a function because at least one element of X is not associated with an element of Y. Here c is not associated with any element of Y. So, g is not a function, but it is a relation.

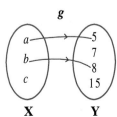

c. **_u_** is a function from X to Y because

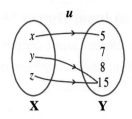

    i. All elements of X are associated with exactly one element of Y.

    ii. No element of X is associated with more than one element of Y.

d. **_v_** is a function from X to Y because

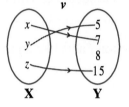

    i. All elements of X are associated with exactly one element of Y.

    ii. No element of X is associated with more than one element of Y.

e. **_w_** is a function from X to Y because

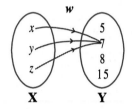

    i. All elements of X are associated with exactly one element of Y.

    ii. No element of X is associated with more than one element of Y.

When the domain X of a function is a finite set and no pattern is visible in the association or correspondence between the elements of the domain X and the set Y, it is best to describe the function with diagrams or by listing the output to each input.

EXAMPLE 1 $X = \{a, b, c, d\}$, $Y = \{0, -1, 1\}$

$f: X \rightarrow Y$ is defined by the following association:

$f(a) = -1$, $f(b) = 1$, $f(c) = -1$, $f(d) = 1$

The function may be described alternatively by using the diagram:

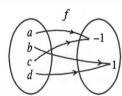

EXAMPLE 2   Find a function f that describes the rule of correspondence between X and Y,

    where: $X = \{1, 2, 3, 4, 5, 6\}$

              Y = the set of integers.

Suppose $f: X \rightarrow Y$ is defined by

    $f(1) = 1$, $f(2) = 4$, $f(3) = 9$, $f(4) = 16$, $f(5) = 25$, and $f(6) = 36$.

Notice that f squares the input. Thus this function $f: X \rightarrow Y$ may be described by the rule $f(x) = x^2$.

Remark: *We may describe the rule in example 1 by simply listing the images.*
Thus we will say that for the function in example 1, the rule is:

$$a \to -1$$
$$b \to 1$$
$$c \to -1$$
$$d \to 1$$

An alternative definition of a function

Consider the function in Example 2 above. We may describe the function as a subset of $X \times Y$ where the elements of the subset have the format (input, output). Thus the function in example 2 may be defined by the subset

$$\{(1, 1), (2, 4), (3, 9), (4, 16), (5, 25), (6, 36)\}$$

Recall that a subset of $X \times Y$ is called a relation from X to Y. Under this definition the condition "to *each* input assign a *unique* output" translate into the following two conditions:

A.   Each element of the domain occurs as a first component..

B.   No two second components share the same first component.

Thus, a function $f: X \to Y$ may be defined as a relation from X to Y (equivalently a subset of $X \times Y$) with the above two conditions.

EXAMPLE 3   Express area A of a circle as a function of its radius.

Solution: This simply means that we write A as an expression in x (the radius) and then write A in the function form.

We know that area of a circle is $\pi(\text{radius})^2$. Thus, if the radius of a circle is x, then its area in the function form is:

$$A(x) = \pi x^2$$

EXAMPLE 4   To encourage bulk buying a company reduces the list price of $ 1000 per unit by four cents, times the number of units bought. Express company's revenue (R) as a function of units (x) bought from a particular distributor.

Solution: Notice that the company's revenue (R) is linked to the number of units (x) bought. Thus, if x units are bought, then the price per unit is reduced by $.04x$ (4 cents or .04 dollar per unit bought). So the discounted price per unit would become $\$(1000 - .04x)$.

Since x units are bought, the revenue from x units equals $x(1000 - .04x)$.

Hence revenue can be written as a function of the number of units (x) bought as follows:

$$R(x) = x(1000 - .04x)$$

Remark: *Here $R: N \to R$ is a function from the set of counting numbers*
to the set of real numbers, and the function is given by the rule

$$R(x) = x(1000 - .04x)$$

EXAMPLE 5   The following table gives the price per unit of different volume purchases.

Number bought	2	3	4	5	6
Price per unit	3	2	5/3	3/2	7/5

a.   Find a suitable function which gives the price per unit when certain number of units is bought.

b.   Determine the price per unit when 21 units are purchased.

Solutions: **a.**   On observing the table carefully, we find a pattern (relationship) in the price per unit for the number of units bought.

Number of Units Bought x	Price per unit p	Pattern
6	7/5	$\dfrac{6+1}{6-1}$
5	$3/2 = 6/4$	$\dfrac{5+1}{5-1}$
4	5/3	$\dfrac{4+1}{4-1}$
Lets us try this pattern for 2 and 3 units		
3	$2 = \dfrac{4}{2}$	$\dfrac{3+1}{3-1}$
2	$3 = \dfrac{3}{1}$	$\dfrac{2+1}{2-1}$

So, the pattern shows that if x units were bought, then the price per unit will be $\dfrac{x+1}{x-1}$. Hence price p can be expressed as a function of the number of units (x) bought by the following function

$$p(x) = \frac{x+1}{x-1}.$$

b.   The price per unit when the number of units brought is 21 is given by:

$$p(21) = \frac{21+1}{21-1} = \frac{22}{20} = \frac{11}{10} = 1.10$$

Remark: *Notice that the rule of association in the above example is not applicable for the purchase of a single unit ($x = 1$). $p(1) = \dfrac{1+1}{1-1} = \dfrac{2}{0}$ (undefined).*

EXAMPLE 6   Express the distance d of a point x on the number line from the point O, the origin, as a function of x.

Solution: We know that distance of a point on the number line from the origin (the point zero) is expressed in terms of the absolute value of the number.

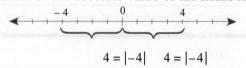

$$4 = |-4| \qquad 4 = |-4|$$

In other words, the distance d of a point x on a number line from the origin is $|x|$. This can be written in the function form $d(x) = |x|$.

EXAMPLE 7   A shipping company charges \$5 per pound for packages weighing five pounds or less. The charge is \$ 3.50 per pound if a package weighs more than five pounds. Determine a function r that gives rate per pound if a package weighs x pounds.

Solution: It is clear that the rates are different for two different weight categories. This is the case of a function that has different rule for a different value of the input. If r denotes the rate per pound then

$r(x) = 5$ when the weight (x) is up to five pounds.

$r(x) = 3.5$ when the weight, $f(x)$ is more than five pounds.

Thus, we write the two pieces of the rule as follows to describe the function $r: N \to R$:

$$r(x) = \begin{cases} 5 & \text{if } x \le 5 \\ 3.5 & \text{if } x > 5 \end{cases}$$

Remark: *A function that is described by more than one rule depending upon the value of the input is called a piecewise function. A piecewise function is written in the following format:*

$$f(x) = \begin{cases} rule\ 1,\ condition\ 1 \\ rule\ 2,\ condition\ 2 \\ \dots, \qquad \dots \\ \dots, \qquad \dots \end{cases}$$

B. ELEMENTARY FUNCTIONS

As we have seen, a function is defined by an expression (or a set of expressions) in the input. Many of the functions are classified or categorized based on the format of the rule.

Functions may be classified as:

1. Power Function   **2.** Polynomial Function   **3.** Rational Function

4. Absolute Value Function   **5.** Root Function   **6.** Piecewise Function

 Note   Later, we will add **logarithmic**, **exponential**, and **circular** (trigonometric) functions to the list.

1. Power Function

A power function is a function whose algebraic expression consists of the input variable raised to a constant non-negative integral power. In general, a **power function** is of the form.

$f(x) = cx^n$,   where c is a constant and n is a non-negative integer.

EXAMPLES

- The area A of a circle of radius r is given by $A(r) = \pi r^2$.

- The volume V of a cube of side x is given by $V(x) = x^3$.

2. Polynomial Function

A polynomial function is obtained by applying any combination of the operations like addition, subtraction, or constant multiple to power functions. In general, a polynomial function $f(x)$ is defined as follows:

$f(x) = a_n x^n + a_{n-1} x^{n-1} + \ldots + a_1 x + a_0$, where a_n, a_{n-1}, $\ldots$ a_1, a_0 are real numbers $\left(a_n \neq 0 \right)$ and n is a non-negative integer.

In a special case when $n = 0$, $f(x)$ is a constant function.

EXAMPLES

- Since in the function $f(x) = 5x - 7$, the polynomial $5x - 7$ is of degree one, we call this a **linear function.**

- The polynomial in $f(x) = 2x^2 - 7x + 10$ is of degree **two**, so we call this a **quadratic function.**

- $f(x) = 7$ is an example of a constant function.

3. Rational Function

A **rational function is a ratio of two polynomial functions.** In general, a rational function is defined as follows

$f(x) = \dfrac{p(x)}{q(x)}$, where $p(x)$ and $q(x)$ are polynomials in x and $q(x) \neq 0$

EXAMPLES

- The reciprocal function $f(x) = \dfrac{1}{x}$
- $g(x) = \dfrac{3x - 2}{x^2 - 16}$

4. Absolute Value Function

If the 'expression' part of a function contains an absolute value, the function is said to be an **absolute value function.**

EXAMPLES

- $f(x) = \left| x - 2 \right|$
- $g(x) = 3 - \left| x + 1 \right|$
- $h(x) = x + \left| x^2 + 1 \right|$

5. Radical Function

A function whose 'expression' part contains a radical of the variable is called a radical function.

EXAMPLES

- $f(x) = \sqrt{x}$, a square root function
- $g(x) = \sqrt[3]{x}$, a cube root function.

6. Piecewise Function

Sometimes a single expression can not completely describe the function. As in Example 7, the shipping rate function was expressed in two parts (pieces). Such a function is called .

EXAMPLES

* **First-class mailing cost function** $f(x)$,

where x represents the weight in ounces, $f(x) = \begin{cases} \$.37 & if \ 0 < x \le 1 \\ \$.55 & if \ 1 < x \le 2 \\ \$.78 & if \ 2 < x \le 3 \end{cases}$

* $f(x) = \begin{cases} x^2 & if \ -2 \le x < 2 \\ 4 & if \ x \ge 2 \end{cases}$

* $g(x) = \begin{cases} x^2 & if \ -2 \le x < 2 \\ 6 & if \ x = 2 \\ x & if \ x > 2 \end{cases}$

⬤ **Note**

$f(0) = 0^2 = 0$ since $-2 \le 0 \le 2$

$f(3) = 4$ since $3 \ge 2$

$f(-3)$ is undefined since -3 does not satisfy eiher $-2 \le x < 2$ or $x \ge 2$.

$g(2) = 6$ since 2 satisfies $x = 2$.

$g(-1) = (-1)^2$ since -1 satisfies $-2 \le x < 2$.

$g(3) = 3$ since 3 satisfies $x > 2$.

$g(-4)$ is undefined since $x = -4$ does not satisfy any of the conditions.

EXERCISE 2.2

In exercises (1-12), write an expression that describes one of the variables in terms of the other.

1. The surface area (S) of a sphere in terms of its radius r.

2. The total cost (C) of purchasing printers at the rate of \$450 per unit in terms of the number (x) of printers bought.

3. The volume (V) of a sphere in terms of its radius r.

4. The revenue (R) of a company that sells an item for \$5.00 in terms of the items (x) sold by the company.

5. The area (A) of a square in terms of its side (a).

6. The surface area (S) of a cube in terms of its edge (x).

7. The volume (V) of a cube in terms of its edge (x).

8. The perimeter (p) of a square in terms of its side (a).

9. The perimeter (p) of an equilateral triangle in terms of its base (x).

10. The length (L) of a part of the number line segment between 2 and 5 in terms of n, the number of equal parts into which it is divided.

11. The temperature (C) in Celsius in terms of temperature (F) in Fahrenheit.

12. The cost (C) of x units if each unit is marked \$1.5, given the sales tax is 7.25%.

Which picture in exercises (13-20) represents a function? Explain.

13.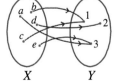

14.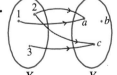

15.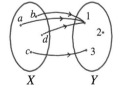

16.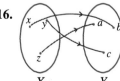

17.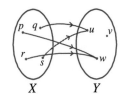

18.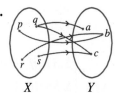

19.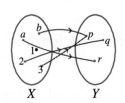

20.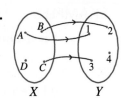

Which rule in exercises (21-30) defines a function?

21. From set S to set A, where S = set of all states of USA ;
A = the set of all letters in the English alphabet.

Rule: To each state associate the first letter in the name of the state.

22. From set A to set P, where

A = set of all letters in the English alphabet;

P = the set of the last names of letters in all the presidents of USA.

Rule: To each letter in the English alphabet associate the last name (of the president) that starts with the letter.

23. From the set N of counting numbers to the set N of counting numbers.

Rule: To every counting number associate the square of the number.

24. From the set S of squares of whole numbers to the set Z of all integers.

Rule: To each whole number s in S associate an integer whose square is s.

25. Let $X = \{a, b\}$, $Y = \{\phi, \{a\}, \{b\}, \{a, b\}\}$

Rule: To each element of X associate an element of Y that contains the chosen element of X.

26. Let $X = \{a\}$, $Y = \{\phi, \{a\}\}$

Rule: To each element of X associate an element of Y that contains the chosen element of X.

27. From the set N of natural numbers to the set N of natural numbers.

Rule: To every natural number associate its successor.

28. From the set N of natural numbers to the set N of natural numbers.

Rule: To every natural number associate its predecessor.

29. X = set of all students in your class.

Y = set of all real numbers between 0 and 1.

Rule: To each student associate the number obtained by dividing his/her social security number by 10^9.

30. From N to the set $\{0, 1\}$, where N is the set of counting numbers.

Rule: If n is odd, associate 0.

If n is even, associate 1.

In exercises (31-40), determine if the given rule defines a function.

31. Input: x, output = $1 - x^2$

32. Input x, output = $2 - \sqrt{x}$

33. Input: x, output = $1 \pm \sqrt{x}$

34. Input t, output = $\pm\sqrt{t-1}$

35. Input: x, output = $\left| \pm(x+2) \right|$

36. Input x, output = $\pm|x+2|$

37. Input: x, output $= \dfrac{3x-1}{x+2}$

38. Input t, output $= 2t^2 - 1$

39. Input s, output $= \dfrac{-3 \pm \sqrt{s^2+4}}{2}$

40. Input x, output $= \dfrac{2-3x}{x^2+1}$

In exercises (41-48), determine if the table defines a function or not.

41.

x	0	1	2	3	4	5
$f(x)$	3	2	1	3	5	2

42.

x	1	2	3	2	5	6
$g(x)$	5	1	2	3	0	7

43.

x	3	10	5	8	7	2
$h(x)$	100	90	80	90	70	50

44.

x	2	4	6	8	6	10
$f(x)$	5	3	2	7	2	9

45.

x	−3	2	0	1	4	5
$s(x)$	−1	1	0	0	3	4

46.

t	1	2	3	3	4	5	6
$h(t)$	6	5	4	0	3	2	1

47.

x	2	3	4	5	6	7	8
$p(x)$	2	3	3	5	5	7	7

48.

x	1	2	1	3	4	5
$f(x)$	3	4	3	9	8	15

In exercises (49-56), determine whether the relation defines a function. In case it does, find the domain and the range.

49. $\{(x, 1), (y, 3), (x, 4), (z, 7)\}$

50. $\{(x, 2), (y, 3), (z, 3), (t, 7)\}$

51. $\{(a, -10), (b, 0), (c, 20), (d, 20), (a, 10)\}$

52. $\{(-2, 3), (-1, 0), (0, 1), (1, 0), (2, 0)\}$

53. $\{(4, -4), (3, -3), (1, -1), (0, 0), (1, 1), (2, -2)\}$

54. $\{(1, A), (2, B), (3, C), (a, A), (b, B), (c, C)\}$

55. $\left\{ \left(2, \sqrt{2}\right), \left(3, \sqrt{3}\right), \left(5, \sqrt{5}\right), \left(2, -\sqrt{2}\right), \left(3, -\sqrt{3}\right), \left(5, -\sqrt{5}\right) \right\}$

56. $\left\{ (-2, 4), (0, 0), (1, 2), (3, 6), (4, 8), (5, 10) \right\}$

In exercises (57-75), classify the function as a power, polynomial, rational, absolute value, radical, or a piecewise function.

57. $f(x) = -\left| 3x+2 \right|$

58. $g(x) = 3 - 5x + x^3$

59. $h(x) = 5x^{-2}$

60. $f(x) = x(100 - 0.02\,x)$

61. $C(x) = \sqrt{(100 - 3x)}$

62. $R(x) = \sqrt[3]{100 + 2x - x^2}$

63. $C(x) = \sqrt{(100 - 3x)^2}$

64. $f(x) = \left| x - 5 \right|$

65. $f(x) = \begin{cases} x^2 & \text{if } x > 2 \\ -2x+1 & \text{if } x \le 2 \end{cases}$

66. $f(x) = 3x^{2/3}$

67. $g(x) = (x^3 - 3x)(x + 1)^2$

68. $P(x)$ = postage charged by united States Postal Services on the regular shipping of a package that weighs x pounds.

69. $I(x)$ = Income tax that one pays to IRS (Internal Revenue Service) for a taxable income of x dollars.

70. $f(x) = \left| 3x + 1 \right| - 4\left| 2x + 5 \right|$.

71. The cost function $C(x)$ for a purchase of x items when a whole seller sells an item for \$5 each for a purchase of less than 10 items, and \$4 each for a purchase of ten or more items.

72. $h(x) = \dfrac{|2x+7|}{x^2+1}$ **73.** $p(x) = |3x^2 - 7| + x^2 - 2x$ **74.** $f(x) = \dfrac{4x^2 - 1}{2 - 3x}$ **75.** $g(x) = \dfrac{2x-3}{5x+9}$

In exercises (76-82), write the polynomial function in factored form.

76. $f(x) = 9 - 18x$ **77.** $g(x) = 12x - 4$ **78.** $g(x) = 25x^2 - 9$ **79.** $f(x) = 5x^2 - 20$

80. $f(x) = -5x^2 + 7x - 2$ **81.** $h(x) = 3x^2 - 5x + 2$ **82.** $H(x) = 54x^3 - 2$

In exercises (83-90), write the absolute value function as a piecewise function without absolute value bars.

83. $f(x) = |2 + x^2|$ **84.** $g(x) = |(x+1)^4|$ **85.** $h(x) = |x-5|$

86. $f(x) = |2x-7|$ **87.** $H(x) = |x-3| + |x-4|$ **88.** $f(x) = |2x-1| - |x+2|$

89. $f(x) = |\sqrt{x+9}|$ **90.** $p(x) = |\sqrt{2x-5}|$

In exercises (91-95), write the rational function in reduced form.

91. $f(x) = \dfrac{x^2 - 4}{x^2 - x - 2}$ **92.** $s(x) = \dfrac{x^3 - 1}{x^2 + x + 1}$ **93.** $h(x) = \dfrac{x^2 - 5x}{x^3 + 5x^2 + 6x}$

94. $g(x) = \dfrac{x^2 - 2x + 1}{x^2 - 1}$ **95.** $f(x) = \dfrac{x^2 - 1}{x^3 - 1}$

In exercises (96-100), write the radical function without the radical form.

96. $f(x) = \sqrt[3]{(x+1)^4}$ **97.** $g(x) = \dfrac{3x}{\sqrt{x^2(x+1)}}$ **98.** $h(x) = \sqrt{x^2(x+2)^2}$

99. $b(x) = \left(\sqrt[5]{(x+3)}\right)^2$ **100.** $p(x) = \sqrt[4]{(2x-3)^2}$

Writing Exercises

101. Give a list of a special functions.

102. Distinguish between a function and a relation.

2.3 DOMAIN AND RANGE OF A FUNCTION

In the previous section we defined a function as a rule that assigns to each element of a non-empty set **A**, **a** unique (exactly one) element of a set B. Functional notation was given as $f: A \rightarrow B$; A was called the domain of **f**. An element **b** assigned to the element **a** of A was called the image of **a** or *f*-image of **a**. In this section we explore how to find image of an element and learn how to determine domain and range of a function.

Objectives ▶ ▶

In this section you will learn about:

A. Evaluating a Function;

B. The Domain of A Function; and

C. The Range of a Function.

A. EVALUATING A FUNCTION

The element x of the set A is called an **input** and the corresponding element $f(x)$ of the set B is called the **output.**

This terminology makes more sense if we regard the **"function f"** as a **'machine f'** that changes x into $f(x)$.

$$\xrightarrow[\text{input}]{x} \quad \boxed{f(x)} \quad \xrightarrow[\text{output}]{f(x)}$$

Suppose John pledges \$5 more than what Don pledges, then the amount $A(x)$ of John's pledge is described in terms of the amount x of Don's pledge as

$$\xrightarrow[\text{input}]{x} \quad \boxed{A(x)} \quad \xrightarrow[\text{output}]{x+5}$$

If Don pledges \$2, then the amount of John's pledge is given as

$$\xrightarrow[\text{input}]{2} \quad \boxed{A(2)} \quad \xrightarrow[\text{output}]{2+5=7}$$

Technically speaking, the output 7 is the value of the function $A(x)$ when $x = 2$. In short, we write it as $A(2) = 7$.

We generalize the notation as follows :

> **Evaluating a Function**
>
> If the function $f: A \rightarrow B$ assigns the element y of B to the element x of A, then $f(x) = y$.

EXAMPLE 1   Numerical Form of a function.

Use the following table and find the values, if possible.

Time (t)	Noon	1	2	3	4	5
Temp (T)	70	73	74	74	76	78

    a. T(1)   **b.** T(3)   **c.** T(6)

Solutions:

a.   When $t = 1$, $T = 73$, so   T(1) = **73**

b.   Similarly, T(3) = **74**

c.   Usually a numerical form of a function does not describe a function as completely as an algebraic (formula) form. Therefore, in the present form we cannot answer the question. However, if we can find a corresponding algebraic form, then we will be able to answer the question. For this, we have to wait until we learn how to change a numerical representation into a formula representation of a function.

When the output $f(x)$ is defined in terms of an expression or a formula, we substitute (replace) 'a' for x in the expression or the formula and simplify to get the value $f(a)$.

EXAMPLE 2   Polynomial Function

For $f(x) = 5x^2 - 2x + 8$, find

    a. $f(0)$ **b.** $f(1)$ **c.** $f(-2)$

    d. $f(a + 1)$ **e.** $f(x + h)$

Solutions:

a.   *$f(0)$ = the value of the expression for $x = 0$

          <small>Substitute the 'input' $x = 0$ in the expression</small>

       $= 5(0)^2 - 2(0) + 8 = 5(0) - 0 + 8 = 0 - 0 + 8 = $ **8**

Thus, the value of the output $f(x)$ when $x = 0$ is 8.

> *   Assuming that f is the cost function, then 8 is the fixed cost. In other words, if the company makes zero number of items, the cost is $8.

b.   ** $f(1)$ = the value of the expression for $x = 1$

          <small>Substitute the 'input' $x = 1$ in the expression</small>

       $= 5(1)^2 - 2(1) + 8 = 5(1) - 2 + 8 = 5 - 2 + 8 = $ **11**

> **   If f is the cost function, then $f(1)$ gives the cost of producing one unit.

c. $f(-2) = 5(-2)^2 - 2(-2) + 8$ <small>The 'input' is -2</small>

       $= 5(4) + 4 + 8$

       $= 20 + 4 + 8 = $ **32**

d. $f(a + 1) = $ value of the expression for $x = a + 1$ <small>Substitute the 'input' $x = a + 1$ in the expression</small>

       $= 5(a + 1)^2 - 2(a + 1) + 8$

       $= 5\left(a^2 + 2a + 1\right) - 2a - 2 + 8$

       $= 5a^2 + 10a + 5 - 2a + 6$

       $= $ **$5a^2 + 8a + 11$**

e. $f(x + h) = $ value of the expression for $x + h$ <small>Substitute the input $x + h$ for x</small>

       $= 5(x + h)^2 - 2(x + h) + 8$

       $= 5\left(x^2 + 2xh + h^2\right) - 2x - 2h + 8$

       $= $ **$5x^2 + 10xh + 5h^2 - 2x - 2h + 8$**

EXAMPLE 3   Polynomial Function

If $f(x) = -3x^2 + 4x$, find

    a. $f(-2)$ **b.** $f(x + h) - f(x)$

Solutions:

    a. $f(-2)$:   We replace x with -2 in the expression $f(x) = -3x^2 + 4x$.

       $f(-2) = -3(-2)^2 + 4(-2) = -3(4) - 8 = -12 - 8 = -20$

    b. $f(x + h) - f(x)$

$$= -3(x + h)^2 + 4(x + h) - \left(-3x^2 + 4x\right)$$

$$= -3\left(x^2 + 2xh + h^2\right) + 4x + 4h + 3x^2 - 4x$$

$$= -3x^2 - 6xh - 3h^2 + 4x + 4h + 3x^2 - 4x = -6xh - 3h^2 + 4h$$

EXAMPLE 4   Rational Function

If $f(x) = \dfrac{x^2 - 5x + 6}{x + 4}$, find   **a.** $f(1)$ **b.** $f(3)$

Solutions:

    a. $f(1)$: We replace x with 1, so $f(1) = \dfrac{(1)^2 - 5(1) + 6}{1 + 4} = \dfrac{1 - 5 + 6}{5} = \dfrac{2}{5}$

    b. $f(3)$: We replace x with 3, so $f(3) = \dfrac{(3)^2 - 5(3) + 6}{3 + 4} = \dfrac{9 - 15 + 6}{7} = \dfrac{0}{7} = 0$

EXAMPLE 5   Absolute Value Function

If $f(x) = |2x - 3|$, find   **a.** $f(1)$ **b.** $f(a + h)$

Solutions:

    a. $f(1)$: We replace x with 1 in the expression.

       $f(1) = |2(1) - 3| = |2 - 3| = |-1| = 1$

    b. $f(a + h)$: We replace x with $a + h$ in the expression.

       $f(a + h) = |2(a + h) - 3| = |2a - 2h - 3|$

EXAMPLE 6   Absolute Value Function

If $f(x) = \dfrac{|x - 2|}{x - 2}$, find

    a. $f(2 + h)$, $h > 0$ **b.** $f(2 + h)$, $h < 0$

Solutions:

a. $f(2 + h)$: We replace x with $2 + h$ in the expression.

$$f(2+h) = \frac{|2+h-2|}{2+h-2} = \frac{|h|}{h} = \frac{h}{h}, \text{ because } |h| = h \text{ when } h > 0$$
$$= 1$$

b. $f(2 + h) = \dfrac{|h|}{h} = \dfrac{-h}{h}$, because $|h| = -h$ when $h < 0$
$$= -1$$

EXAMPLE 7   Piecewise Function

If $f(x) = \begin{cases} \dfrac{x^2-4}{x-2} & if \quad x \neq 2 \\ 5 & if \quad x = 2 \end{cases}$

find   **a.** $f(2)$ **b.** $f(0)$ **c.** $f(-3)$

Solutions:

a.   Since $x = 2$, use the lower piece of the rule.
$$f(2) = 5$$

* **b.**   Since $x \neq 2$, use the upper piece of the rule

and replace x with 0 in the expression $\dfrac{x^2-4}{x-2}$.

$$f(0) = \frac{0^2-4}{0-2} = \frac{-4}{-2} = 2$$

> * To evaluate a piecewise function, first select the appropriate piece and then substitute the **input**.

c.   Since $x \neq 2$, use the upper piece of the rule and

replace x with -3 in $\dfrac{x^2-4}{x-2}$.

$$f(-3) = \frac{(-3)^2-4}{(-3)-2} = \frac{9-4}{-5} = \frac{5}{-5} = -1$$

EXAMPLE 8   Rational Function

If $f(x) = \dfrac{x^2+x-2}{x^2+2x-3}$, find   **a.** $f(-3)$ **b.** $f(1)$

Solutions:

a. $f(-3)$: We replace x with -3.

$$f(-3) = \frac{(-3)^2+(-3)-2}{(-3)^2+2(-3)-3} = \frac{9-3-2}{9-6-3} = \frac{4}{0} \quad \text{(undefined)}$$

b. $f(1)$: We replace x with 1

$$f(1) = \frac{(1)^2+(1)-2}{(1)^2+2(1)-3} = \frac{1+1-2}{1+2-3} = \frac{0}{0} \quad \text{(indeterminate)}$$

EXAMPLE 9   Radical Function

If $f(x) = \sqrt{x - 13}$, find   **a.** $f(21)$ **b.** $f(5)$

Solutions:

   a. $f(21):$ We replace x with 21 in the expression.

$$f(21) = \sqrt{21 - 13} = \sqrt{8} = \sqrt{2^2 \cdot 2} = 2\sqrt{2}$$

   b. $f(5):$ We replace x with 5 in the expression.

$$f(5) = \sqrt{5 - 13} = \sqrt{-8}$$ does not exist in the set of real numbers because there is no real number whose square is -8.

B. THE DOMAIN OF A FUNCTION

Examples 8 and 9 above show that there may be numbers that can **not** be used for inputs in a given function. Compare this with the case of a machine where there can be restrictions on the raw material (input). Generally, a machine comes with a WARNING label indicating such restrictions. For a function, the restrictions on inputs are indicated in the description of its **domain.**

> **Domain of a Function**
>
> The domain of a function is the set of all possible inputs. If $f(x)$ is given by a formula, the domain is the set of all real numbers for which $f(x)$ has a unique real number value.

Sometimes a function comes with its stated domain, while at other times we need to determine the domain. For this we develop some guiding principles. The first guiding principle has been indicated in Example 8. We state the principle as follows.

> **First Guiding Principle For the Domain**
>
> We do not include those inputs, or those values of x in the domain, that make the denominator of the expression, which defines the function, equal to zero.

For example, $x = 2$ and $x = -2$ are **not** in the domain of the function $f(x) = \dfrac{2x + 7}{x^2 - 4}$.

EXAMPLE 10   Find the domain of the following functions:

   a. $\dfrac{x^2 + 3x - 1}{x - 4}$ **b.** $\dfrac{3x^3 + 5x - 7}{2x^2 - 18}$

Solutions:

   a. $\dfrac{x^2 + 3x - 1}{x - 4}:$ $x = 4$ makes the denominator 0, and all other value of x are acceptable

inputs. Therefore, by the first guiding principle, the domain of this function is the set of all real numbers except 4.

b. $\dfrac{3x^3 + 5x - 7}{2x^2 - 18}$:   To find the values of x that make the denominator of the expression zero,

we equate the denominator to zero and solve for the variable.

$$2x^2 - 18 = 0 \ \rightarrow \ 2\left(x^2 - 9\right) = 0 \ \longrightarrow \ x^2 = 9$$

$$\longrightarrow \ x = -3, \ \text{or} \ x = 3$$

Thus, by first guiding principle, $x = -3$ and $x = 3$ are not acceptable inputs and all other inputs are acceptable. Therefore, the domain of the function is the set of all real numbers except $x = -3$ and $x = 3$.

Remarks: *1.*   *The domain of a rational function is the set of all real numbers, except the real numbers that make the denominator zero.*

       2.   *The numbers that make the denominator zero are called zeros of the denominator.*

Another restriction on the domain of a function arises out of the situations indicated in example 9(b) (above). Do not include those input values, or values of x, for which the value(s) of $f(x)$ **are not real numbers.** We state this as a second guiding principal for the domain.

> **Second Guiding Principle for the Domain**
>
> We do not include those inputs, or those values of x in the domain that make the radicand of an even root a negative number.

For example, $x = 5$ for $f(x) = \sqrt[4]{x^2 - 49}$ is not an acceptable input. In fact any number x where $-7 < x < 7$ is not an acceptable input and therefore not to be included in the domain.

EXAMPLE 11   Find the domain of the following functions

     a. $f(x) = \sqrt{x-5}$ **b.** $f(x) = \dfrac{2x^2 + 4}{\sqrt{4-x}}$

Solutions:

   a. $f(x) = \sqrt{x-5}$:

By the second guiding principle the radicand must be non-negative for any value of x in the domain.

That is, $x - 5 \geq 0$ or $x \geq 5$

Therefore, the domain is $[5, \infty)$.

   b. $f(x) = \dfrac{2x^2 + 4}{\sqrt{4-x}}$:

By the second guiding principle the radicand must be non-negative, or $4 - x \geq 0$. Also by the first guiding principle the denominator must be non-zero. Therefore, since the radical is in the denominator, the radicand must be strictly positive, or $4 - x > 0$.

$$4 - x > 0 \ \longrightarrow \ 4 > x \ \text{or} \ x < 4.$$

Therefore, the domain is an **open interval** $(-\infty, 4)$.

EXAMPLE 12   Piecewise Function

If $f(x) = \begin{cases} 2x+3 & \text{if } x < 1 \\ 15 & \text{if } x = 1 \end{cases}$, find

a. $f(0)$ **b.** $f(-2)$ **c.** $f(3)$ **d.** $f(1)$

Solutions:

a. $f(0)$:   We replace x with 0 in the expression. But there are two pieces in the expression. In which piece should we substitute $x = 0$? Since $0 < 1$, first piece "$2x + 3$" if $x < 1$ is applicable. So we replace x with 0 in $2x + 3$.

$f(0) = 2(0) + 3 = 0 + 3 = \mathbf{3}$

b. $f(-2)$:   We replace x with -2 in $2x + 3$, the piece (with the condition $x < 1$, since $-2 < 1$) whose domain contains -2.

$f(-2) = 2(-2) + 3 = -4 + 3 = \mathbf{-1}$

c. $f(3)$:   Not defined since 3 does not satisfy either condition, the domain is $(-\infty, 1]$.

d. $f(1)$:   We find from the second piece.

$f(1) = \mathbf{15}$

These examples emphasize the need for a conditional statement with every piece that constitutes the function.

To be able to construct a domain statement we have stated two guiding principles. In order to use the first principle, we need to know all inputs (x-values) that make the denominator of the expression part zero *i.e.*, zeros of the denominator. Such inputs are to be excluded from the domain. The other principle stated that the radicand of an even root cannot be negative. For example, in $f(x) = \sqrt{x-4}$, x must be 4 or more than 4. For simple expressions, zeros of the denominator, or values of x such that radicand is non-negative can be obtained by inspection. But for more general expressions, we will discuss new methods for finding the domain in the next chapter.

C. THE RANGE OF A FUNCTION

The term **range** is associated with the values (outputs) of a function.

> **Range of a Function**
>
> The **range** of a function is the set of all possible outputs (function values).
>
> That is, if D is the domain of a function f, then the range of f is collection of $f(x)$ values for all x in D.

Since outputs of a function depend on the inputs, we need to keep in focus the domain, in order to determine the range of the function.

EXAMPLE 13   Find the domain and range of $f(x) = 5x - 7$.

Solution: Since the expression part of the function $(5x - 7)$ has neither denominator nor an even radical, the two guiding principles do not impose any restrictions on inputs.

Consequently, we make the following domain statement:

Domain :   Whole set of real numbers or $(-\infty, \infty)$.

Also, the outputs (function values) have no restrictions ; therefore, the **range** is $(-\infty, \infty)$.

EXAMPLE 14   Find the domain and range of $f(x) = x^2 + 4$.

Solution: Because there is neither a denominator nor an even root in the expression part of the function, therefore the guiding principles impose no restrictions.

Thus, the **domain** is $(-\infty, \infty)$.

The outputs are given by $x^2 + 4$. Since x^2 is always non-negative, therefore, $x^2 + 4$ is 4 or more than 4*.

> * $x^2 \geq 0$ implies $x^2 + 4 \geq 4$

Thus, the **range** is $[4, \infty)$.

EXAMPLE 15   Find the domain and range of $f(x) = \sqrt{x-2}$.

Solution: By the second guiding principle no input can be less than 2.

Thus, the **domain** is $[2, \infty)$.

If inputs (x-values) are greater than or equal to 2, then $\sqrt{x-2}$ is always defined and non- negative (why?).

Thus, the **range** is $[0, \infty)$.

EXAMPLE 16   Find the domain and range of $f(x) = \dfrac{x+1}{x-3}$.

Solution: By the first guiding principle, the denominator of the expression part must not become zero. So, the input $x = 3$ is unacceptable.

Thus, the **domain** is the set of all real numbers except $x = 3$ or $(-\infty, 3) \cup (3, \infty)$.

For inputs as all real numbers except 3, the outputs will be all real numbers except 1 (why?).

This gives the **range** as $(-\infty, 1) \cup (1, \infty)$.

This example indicates that finding the range can be more difficult than finding the domain. We will see later (Example 11, section 2.4) that all real numbers except 1 can be an output. Here we note only that if we try to find an x that corresponds to $y = 1$, we have

$$1 = \frac{x+1}{x-3} \longrightarrow x - 3 = x + 1 \longrightarrow -3 = 1$$

This is never true. Hence, there is no x-value corresponding to $y = 1$.

EXERCISE 2.3

In exercises (1-10), find   a. $f(0)$ b. $f(3)$ c. $f(-2)$ d. $f(a+1)$ e. $f(x+h)-f(x)$

1. $f(x)=7x+8$ **2.** $f(x)=3x-5$ **3.** $f(x)=10$ **4.** $f(x)=-3$

5. $f(x)=7-2x^2$ **6.** $f(x)=-3x^2+1$ **7.** $f(x)=7x^2+3x$ **8.** $f(x)=5x^2-3x+1$

9. $f(x)=\sqrt{15-x}$ **10.** $f(x)=\sqrt{2x+9}$

In exercises (11-20), find   a. $f(0)$ b. $f(1)$ c. $f(3)$ d. $f(2)$

11. $f(x)=\dfrac{5}{x-2}$ **12.** $f(x)=\dfrac{4}{x+3}$ **13.** $f(x)=\dfrac{x}{x+1}$ **14.** $f(x)=\dfrac{x+2}{x-2}$

15. $f(x)=\dfrac{2x-1}{x-5}$ **16.** $f(x)=\dfrac{2x+1}{4x+5}$ **17.** $f(x)=\dfrac{x-3}{x^2-25}$ **18.** $f(x)=\dfrac{x-1}{x^2+1}$

19. $f(x)=\dfrac{x-2}{x^2-4}$ **20.** $f(x)=\dfrac{x^2}{2x^2+3}$

In exercises (21-28), find   a. $f(3)$ b. $f(5)$ c. $f(2)$ d. $f(3+h)$; $h>0$

21. $f(x)=\left|x\right|+2$ **22.** $f(x)=\left|x\right|-4$ **23.** $f(x)=\left|x-1\right|$ **24.** $f(x)=\left|3x-2\right|$

25. $f(x)=\dfrac{\left|x\right|}{x}$ **26.** $f(x)=\dfrac{\left|x-2\right|}{x-2}$ **27.** $f(x)=\dfrac{x-3}{\left|x-3\right|}$ **28.** $f(x)=\dfrac{3x-2}{\left|x+1\right|-1}$

In exercises (29-36), find   a. $f(-1)$ b. $f(0)$ c. $f(5)$ d. $f(2+h)$; $h>0$

29. $f(x)=\begin{cases}x+2, & x<1\\2-x, & x\ge1\end{cases}$ **30.** $f(x)=\begin{cases}\dfrac{2x-1}{x+2}, & x>3\\3, & x\le3\end{cases}$ **31.** $f(x)=\begin{cases}2x-1, & x<0\\5, & x=0\\x^2, & x>0\end{cases}$

32. $f(x)=\begin{cases}x^2, & x<1\\3x-2, & x\ge1\end{cases}$ **33.** $f(x)=\begin{cases}\dfrac{1}{x}, & x<0\\x^2, & x\ge0\end{cases}$ **34.** $f(x)=\begin{cases}-5, & x\le0\\6, & 0<x<4\\1/2, & x\ge4\end{cases}$

35. $f(x)=\begin{cases}-2, & x<2\\3, & x=2\\2, & x>2\end{cases}$ **36.** $f(x)=\begin{cases}\left|3x-5\right|+2, & x\le0\\\dfrac{2}{x+1}, & x>0\end{cases}$

37. The following is the 1994 United State income tax rate schedule for a single taxpayer. It is a 5-part piecewise function:

If taxable income (x) is

Over	But not over	Tax owed is	Of the amount over
$0	$22,750	15%	$0
22,750	55,100	$3,412.50 + 28%	22,750
55,100	115,000	12,470.50 + 31%	55,100
115,000	250,000	31,039.50 + 36%	115,000
250,000	…	79,639.50 + 39.6%	250,000

Find the federal income tax for a single taxpayer whose taxable income is

a. $15,000   **b.** $50,000   **c.** $115,000   **d.** $300,000

38. The cost (C), Revenue (R), and Profit (P) on x items are as follows:

$C(x) = 4000 + 1.5x$, $R(x) = 5x$, and $P(x) = R(x) - C(x) = 3.5x - 4000$

What will be the cost, revenue, and profit if the company produces 20,000 items?

39. The cost (C), Revenue (R), and Profit (P) on x items are as follows:

$C(x) = 2500 + 2.5x$, $R(x) = 8x$, and $P(x) = R(x) - C(x) = 5.5x - 2500$

What will be the cost, revenue, and profit if the company produces 15,000 items.

40. A wholesaler can sell each VCR for $150 - \dfrac{x}{5000}$, if x units are sold. Write an expression for the company's revenue function. Evaluate the revenue and price per VCR if the wholesaler sells 500 such VCR's.

41. A wholesaler can sell each DVD for $300 - \dfrac{x}{4000}$, if x units are sold. Write an expression for the company's revenue function. Evaluate the revenue and sale price per DVD if the wholesaler sells 400 such DVD's.

42. The time T taken to harvest x tons of apples is given by $T(x) = \dfrac{x+1}{50-x}$ days ($x < 50$). Show that the time taken to harvest 10 tons of apples in the beginning of the job is less than the time taken in harvesting 10 tons near the end of the job. (Economists refer to this as the Law of Diminishing Returns.)

43. If we plant "x more than 24" trees per acre, then the yield per tree is $600 - 12x$. Write the total yield (Y) function. Find the total yield (Y) if we plant 29 trees per acre.

44. If we plant "x more than 30" trees per acre, then the yield per tree is $800 - 15x$. Write the total yield (Y) function. Find the total yield (Y) if we plant 35 trees per acre.

45. The price (p) per bushel of corn after x number of weeks of the harvest is given by

$$p(x) = 2 + .01x - .02x^2$$

Should the farmer sell this crop after 2 weeks or 3 weeks?

46. The price (p) per bushel of corn after x number of weeks of the harvest is given by

$$p(x) = 4 + .02x - .01x^2$$

Should the farmer sell the crop after 3 weeks or 4 weeks.

In exercises (47-59), find the domain and range of the function.

47. $f(x) = 3x + 2$

48. $f(x) = 6x - 5$

49. $g(x) = 3x^2 + 2x + 1$

50. $f(x) = -2x^2 + 3x - 5$

51. $f(x) = |x - 5| + 1$

52. $f(x) = x^4 + 5$

53. $h(x) = x^3$

54. $g(x) = \dfrac{2x}{x^2 - 1}$

55. $f(x) = \sqrt{x+1}$

56. $h(x) = \dfrac{4}{\sqrt{3-x}}$

57. $K(x) = \dfrac{x+5}{x-8}$

58. $g(x) = \dfrac{4x+3}{x+7}$

59. $f(x) = |2 - 3x| - 3$

2.4 GRAPHICAL REPRESENTATION OF A FUNCTION

In addition to the two different representations of a function, namely, numerical and algebraic, a function can be represented in graphical form. There are two reasons for the early introduction of graphs. First, a picture helps in visual thinking. Secondly, the available technology of a graphing calculator or computer software such as Derive, Maple, Mathcad or Mathematical has made graphing so fast and easy that we do not need to wait. We start this section with the intermediate step of writing a function in a numerical form.

Objectives ▶ ▶

In this section you will learn about:

A. The numerical form of a function;

B. The rectangular coordinate system;

C. The graph of a function;

D. Interpreting a graph; and

E. The Vertical Line Test.

A. THE NUMERICAL FORM OF A FUNCTION

The picture (graph) of a function shows the way inputs and outputs of the function behave. Algebraically, this behavior is shown by a formula such as

$A(x) = x + 5$ (The amount of John's pledge)

If we use different values for the input (x), we can record the corresponding outputs in a table form.

x	0	1	2	3	4	5
$A(x)$	5	6	7	8	9	10

(why not negative values?)

Thus, the algebraic form $A(x) = x + 5$ has been displayed in numerical form.

In general, an algebraic form of a function

$f(x) =$ **expression**

can be changed to a numerical (table) form as described in the following strategy.

Strategy for Changing Algebraic Form To Numerical Form

Step **1**   Select different inputs (x-values) from the domain of the function. In the absence of a stated domain, use inputs in accordance with the guiding principles of the domain.

Step **2**   Substitute each input (x-value) in the expression (formula) part of the function and evaluate the expression.

Step **3**   Compute the $f(x)$ – row (column).

EXAMPLE 1   The price (p) per bushel of corn after x number of weeks of the harvest is given by

$p(x) = 2 + .01x - .02x^2$

Write the function $p(x) = 2 + .01x - .02x^2$ ($x \geq 0$) in a numerical form

Solution:

Step 1   Since x is the number of weeks after the harvest, x cannot be negative.

x	0	1	2	3	4	5

Step 2   We evaluate the price function $p(x)$ at each input (x-value).

x	0	1	2	3	4	5
$p(x)$	2	1.99	1.94	1.85	1.72	1.55

EXAMPLE 2   Write $f(x) = x^3 + 1$ in its numerical form.

Solution:

Step 1   According to the * guiding principles for the domain all input (x-values) are acceptable.

x	−3	−2	−1	0	1	2

Step 2   Evaluate the function $f(x)$ at each input (x-value).

x	−3	−2	−1	0	1	2
$f(x)$	−26	−7	0	1	2	9

> **Graphical Representation**
>
> * Guiding Principles for the Domain
>
>   1. Do not use an input (x-value) that makes the denominator of the expression zero.
>
>   2. Do not use an input (x-value) that makes the radicand of an even root negative.

EXAMPLE 3   Write $f(x) = \sqrt{x-1}$ in its numerical (table) form. Round off calculations to two decimal places.

Solution:

Step 1   According to the second guiding principle, we cannot use an input (x-value) less than 1.

x	1	2	3	4	5	6

Step 2   Evaluate the function $f(x)$ at each input (x-value).

x	1	2	3	4	5	6
$f(x)$	0	1	1.41	1.73	2	2.24

The table gives an approximation of the function $f(x)$.

EXAMPLE 4   Change $f(x) = |x-2|$ to a numerical (table) form.

Solution:

Step 1   All inputs (x-values) are acceptable. (why?)

x	−1	0	1	2	3	4

Step 2   Evaluate the function $f(x)$ at each input (x-value).

x	−1	0	1	2	3	4
$f(x)$	3	2	1	0	1	2

EXAMPLE 5   Change the following piecewise function to an equivalent numerical (table) form.

$$* \quad f(x) = \begin{cases} 2-x & , \text{ if } x < 1 \\ 3 & , \text{ if } x = 1 \\ 4 & , \text{ if } x > 1 \end{cases}$$

> * Three pieces of the function are joined at $x = 1$, so use a few x-values on the left and a few values on the right of $x = 1$.

Solution:

Step 1   All inputs are acceptable.

x	−1	0	1	2	3	4

Step 2   Evaluate the function at each x value.

x	−1	0	1	2	3	4
$f(x)$	3	2	3	4	4	4

Remarks:

1. The numerical form of a function does not describe a function completely. The algebraic form does. It only suggests a pattern which, in turn, leads to a possible algebraic form. In fact, a table of values may suggest more than one algebraic expressions that may describe the table. In order to avoid this confusion, it is advised that a sufficiently large number of x-values covering different possibilities may be included in a table.

2. The concept of a relation was briefly introduced in Section 2.2. A relation can be expressed in tabular form with no restrictions on the inputs or outputs. In the tabular form of a relation, the x-values (inputs) can be repeated but in the tabular form for a function each x-value can appear only once.

Relation:

x	0	1	4	9	16	1	4	9	16
$R(x)$	0	1	2	3	4	−1	−2	−3	−4

Function:

x	0	1	4	9	16
$f(x)$	0	1	2	3	4

If somehow we can plot one point for each ordered pair (input, output), then we can visualize the relationship between the inputs and outputs. This connection between algebra and geometry was first introduced by Rene Descartes, a great French mathematician of 17th century, and is based on the rectangular coordinate system.

B. THE RECTANGULAR COORDINATE SYSTEM

Consider two perpendicular number lines (Figure 2.1) which intersect at their zero points. These two lines are usually pictured as horizontal and vertical lines with their positive directions to the right and upward, respectively. The point of intersection is called the **origin.** The horizontal line is called the **input-axis** or x-axis in case x is the independent variable. The vertical line is called the **output-axis.** The outputs are function values and the function may represent various quantities like cost, revenue, profit etc. Therefore we select the letter "y" to denote output values and the output axis is also called the y-axis.

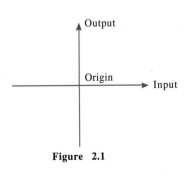

Figure 2.1

Notation : x denotes **input.**

y denotes **output.**

0 denotes the **origin.**

* Using this notation, Figure 2.1 becomes Figure 2.2. To plot a point *P* for the ordered pair (*x*, *y*), we measure *x* units along the *x*-axis and *y* units along the *y*-axis. (Figure 2.3)

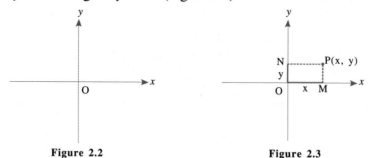

Figure 2.2   **Figure 2.3**

(*OM* = *PN* = *x*-coordinate, *PM* = *ON* = *y*-coordinate of *P*)

* The two axes divide the plane into four parts. We refer to these parts as quadrants. We number them in counter clockwise direction as follows.

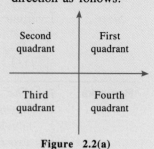

Figure 2.2(a)

Remark: *According to the description of the coordinate system, the signs of the x and y-coordinates in various quadrants can be described in the following tabular form.*

Co-ordinates	First Quadrant	Second Quadrant	Third Quadrant Quadrant	Fourth Quadrant
x	+	−	−	+
y	+	+	−	−

EXAMPLE 6   Plot the points *A*(3, 2), *B*(−2, 3), *C*(−1, −2), *D*(5, −1), *E*(4, 0), *F*(0, −3) and *G*(0, 0).

Solution:

The points *A*, *B*, *C*, *D*, *E* and *G* are shown in Figure 2.4.

Now we are ready to give the graphical representation of a function.

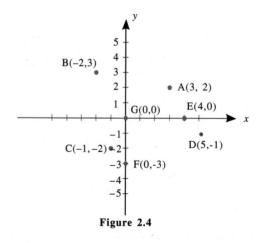

Figure 2.4

C. THE GRAPH OF A FUNCTION

The **graph** of a function $f(x)$ consists of all those points (*x*, *y*) such that *x* = input and $y = f(x)$ = output. In symbols, the graph is the set $\{(x, f(x))$ where $x \in$ domain of $f\}$.

To Draw The Graph of A Function

We will discuss two methods to draw the graph of a function.

1. By hand (paper and pencil method)   2. By calculator or computer.

Method 1   Paper and pencil method

Strategy:

Step 1   Write the function $f(x)$ = expression as *y* = expression.

Step 2   State the domain of the function by using the guiding principles.

Step 3   Choose a few x-values in the domain, evaluate the function (expression) at each x-value, and write the function in a numerical (table) form as

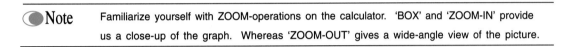

x	
y	

Step 4   Plot each pair (x, y) according to the rectangular coordinate system.

Step 5   Join the points by smooth curve(s).

Method 2   Graphing Calculator

Step 1   Press GRAPH   *Step* 2   Select $y1 =$

Step 3   Let $y1 =$ expression   *Step* 4   Select a suitable RANGE

Step 5   Press GRAPH

⬤Note   Familiarize yourself with ZOOM-operations on the calculator. 'BOX' and 'ZOOM-IN' provide us a close-up of the graph. Whereas 'ZOOM-OUT' gives a wide-angle view of the picture.

EXAMPLE 7   Sketch the graph of the function $f(x) = x + 5$ that represents the amount of John's pledge.

Solution: First, we do this by hand (paper and pencil method).

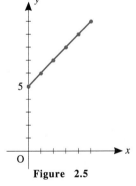

Step 1   Let $y = x + 5$.

Step 2   Since x is the amount of Don's pledge, so x cannot be negative.

Step 3

x	0	1	2	3	4	5
y	5	6	7	8	9	10

Step 4   Plot the points. (Figure 2.5)

Figure 2.5

Step 5   Join the points. In this case, all the points are on a straight line (Figure 2.5).

With Graphing Calculator

Step 1   Press GRAPH

Step 2   Select $y(x) =$

Step 3   Let $y1 = x + 5$

Step 4   Select RANGE (x min = 0, x max = 15, y min = 0, and y max = 15)

Step 5   Press GRAPH.

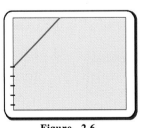

Figure 2.6

Remark: *The set of all ordered pairs (x, y) where x is associated with y under a relation, defines the relation. The set of points obtained by plotting these ordered pairs is called the graph of the relation.*

D. INTERPRETING A GRAPH

Before we give more examples on graphing functions, we first learn how to interpret a graph.

The graphical representation of a function gives visual information. From the graph that is drawn to the scale, we can determine all of the following visually.

1.   The value of the function for a given x-value and the x-value(s) for a given y-value.

2.   Where the function **increases** or **decreases**,

3.   The outputs (y) for the zero input (x), and

4.   The outputs (x) that give zero output (y).

Interpretation of the Graph

1.   The heights (y) represent the values of the function, the amount of John's pledge (Example 7).

2.   Given a value x^* of x (the amount of Don's pledge) we can find the corresponding height (y^*) (amount of John's pledge).
      (Use TRACE in Graphing Calculator)

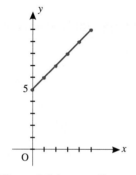

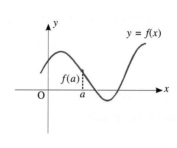

> *   The height at any point x is given by $f(x)$.

Figure 2.5 (repeated)   **Figure 2.7**

⬤ Note   Label the x-axis and the y-axis with the quantities they represent, if possible.

Through x^* move toward the curve on a vertical line until it meets the curve. Let this point be P (Figure 2.8). From the point P move horizontally toward the y-axis until it meets the y-axis. The y-coordinate of y^* is the value of the function when x is x^*.

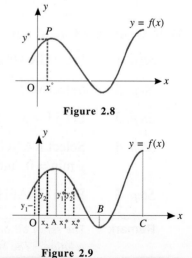

> *   For an increasing graph, the output (y) increases as the input (x) increases

*   **3.**   Look at the heights y_1 and y_2 of the graph for $x = x_1$ and $x = x_2$ respectively where $x_2 > x_1$. We observe that the height y_2 is also greater than height y_1 (Figure 2.9). In other words, as x **increases**, y **also increases.**

Figure 2.8

In Figure 2.9, the graph is increasing up to A, then it decreases between A and B, and it again increases when x is between B and C.

Figure 2.9

4.   The function $y = x + 5$ (Figure 2.5) is **linear** and its graph is **straight line**.

5. The output (y) for zero input (x) can have many meanings. (For a cost function, it is the fixed cost). A common name is the y-**intercept.** In example 7, the y-intercept (or the amount of John's pledge when Don pledges zero dollars) is 5. (Figure 2.5). In Figure 2.10, the y-intercept is represented by the point R.

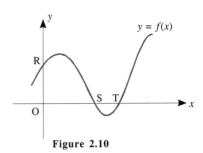

Figure 2.10

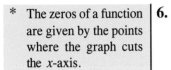

6. The input(s) (x) that give zero output (y) also have special meanings.

*   In general, we call them **zeros of the function.**

Since the function values are represented by the heights (y), therefore at the zeros of a function the heights (y) are zeros. This means the points on the graph that are on the x-axis are the zeros of the function. Such points are also known as **x-intercepts.** On Figure 2.10 the x-intercepts are represented by S and T.

The graph in Figure 2.5 has no x-intercept. This means the amount of John's pledge is never zero.

Zeros of a Function

The zeros of a function are the x-intercepts of the graph of the function.

EXAMPLE 8   A piece of equipment with an original cost of eight million dollars is depreciating every year. The book value V after x years is given by $V(x) = 8 - 2x$ in millions of dollars. Sketch the graph and interpret.

Solution: By hand   (paper and pencil)

Step 1   Write $y = 8 - 2x$.

Step 2   Since x is the number of years after the date of purchase, x cannot be negative.

Step 3   We write the function in a table.

x	0	1	2	3	4
y	8	6	4	2	0

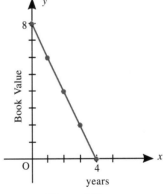

Figure 2.11

Step 4   Plot each pair (input, output) or (x, y).

Step 5   Join the points. We get a line as in (Figure 2.11).

With Graphing Calculator

Step 1   Press 'GRAPH'

Step 2   Select $y(x) =$

Step 3   Let $y1 = 8 - 2x$

Step 4   Select a suitable RANGE (x min = 0, x max = 10, y min = 0 and y max = 10 or Standard Range) or Zoom-STD

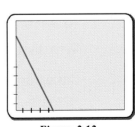

Figure 2.12

Step 5   Press GRAPH.

Interpretation of the Graph

1. The height (y) represents the book value of the equipment.

* **2.** After x^* years, the book value (y^*) is obtained by moving x^* vertically toward the graph until it meets the graph at P. Now move horizontally toward the y-axis until it meets the y-axis at y^* (Figure 2.13). (Use TRACE in Graphing Calculator.)

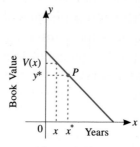

Figure 2.13

* If the graph is not drawn to the scale, then the height at any point $x = x^*$ is given by $V(x^*)$.

* **3.** Look at the heights (Figure 2.14) y_1 and y_2 for $x = x_1$ and $x = x_2$ where $x_2 > x_1$. We see that $y_2 < y_1$. In this case as x **increases**, y **decreases**. Such a graph is called a **falling (decreasing) graph**.

* For a decreasing graph, the output (y) decreases as the input (x) increases.

4. The function $V(x)$ is **linear** and its graph is a **straight line.** (Figure 2.15).

5. The y-intercept (the initial value) is 8 (Figure 2.15).

6. There is only one zero of the function, that is $x = 4$ (Figure 2.15). In other words, after 4 years the book value of the equipment becomes zero.

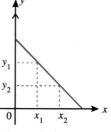

Figure 2.14

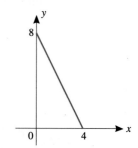

Figure 2.15

Remarks:

1. *We notice that if we factor $8 - 2x$ as $2(4 - x)$, then the number 4 in the factor $4 - x$ indicates the zero of the function. Is it always true that factors of the function indicate the zeros? Check the next example.*

2. *In the above example one hash mark on the x-axis denotes one year and one hash mark on the y-axis denotes one million dollars.*

EXAMPLE 9 An object is thrown upward with a velocity of 64 ft/s. The height (h) at any time (t) is given by $h(t) = 64t - 16t^2$. Sketch the graph of the height function and interpret.

Solution: By hand

    Step 1 Write the height function as $y = 64x - 16x^2$.

    Step 2 Since x is the time after the object is shot upwards, x cannot be negative.

    Step 3

x	0	1	2	3	4
y	0	48	64	48	0

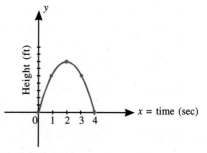

Figure 2.16

Step 4   Since the *y*-values are quite large, therefore we make an adjustment in the scale. Let each space represent 10 units of height (*ft*). We plot the points.

Step 5   Join the points by a smooth curve. (Figure 2.16)

With Graphing Calculator

Step 1   Press GRAPH   *Step* 2   Select *y*(*x*) =

Step 3   Let $y1 = 64x - 16x^2$

Step 4   Select a suitable 'RANGE'
(*x* min = 0, *x* max = 10 with scl = 1
y min = 0 and *y* max = 70 with scl = 10)

Step 5   Press Graph

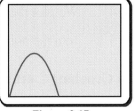

Figure 2.17

Interpretation of the Graph

1.   The height (*y*) represents the height of the object.

* 2.   After any time *x** sec the height of the object is given by *y** (Use TRACE) (Figure 2.18).

3.   Is it an **increasing** or a **decreasing** graph? The graph **increases** from *x* = 0 to 2 and **decreases** from *x* = 2 to 4. In other words, the object is rising (the height is increasing) during the first 2 seconds, then it is falling (the height is decreasing) during the last 2 seconds. (Figure 2.19).

4.   The function *h*(*t*) is a second degree (quadratic) polynomial function and its graph has the shape of an inverted bowl or a **parabola.**

5.   The *y*–intercept (initial height of the object) = 0 (Figure 2.19).

6.   There are two zeros of the function; at *x* = 0 and *x* = 4. This makes sense because the object starts from the ground level and comes back to the ground after 4 seconds (Figure 2.19).

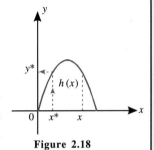

Figure 2.18

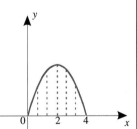

Figure 2.19

*   Even if the graph is not drawn to the scale, still the height at any point *x* = *x** is given by *h*(*x**).

*   The zeros of the function and the factors of its expression are related. (Now you know why you studied factoring in elementary algebra.)

Remark: *If we factor $64t - 16t^2$ as $16t(4 - t)$ or $16(t - 0)\,(4 - t)$, then, the factors **t – 0** and **4 – t** indicate the zeros 0 and 4 of the function. We will investigate this further in the next chapter.*

EXAMPLE 10   Graph $f(x) = x^3 + 1$ and interpret.

Solution: By hand

Step 1   Let $y = x^3 + 1$.

Step 2, 3   Refer to Example 2 of this section.
We have a numerical form of the function.

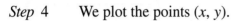

x	−3	−2	−1	0	1	2
y	−26	−7	0	1	2	9

Step 4   We plot the points (x, y).

Step 5   Join the points (Figure 2.20).

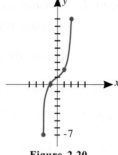

Figure 2.20

With Graphing Calculator

Step 1   Press GRAPH   *Step* 2   Select $y(x) =$

Step 3   Let $y1 = x^3 + 1$

Step 4   Select a suitable RANGE
(x min $= -10$, x max $= 10$,
y min $= -10$, and y max $= 10$ or ZOOM-std)

Step 5   Press GRAPH

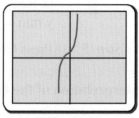

Figure 2.21

Interpretation

1.   The height (y-value) represents the value of the function

2.   For any $x = x^*$, the corresponding value of the function is given by y^* (Use TRACE) (Figure 2.22).

3.   It is an increasing graph (why?)

4.   The function $f(x)$ is a **cubic** function and its graph is given in Figure 2.22.

5.   The y-intercept $= 1$ because when $x = 0$, $y = 1$ (Figure 2.22).

6.   There is only one zero of the function and it is at $x = -1$.

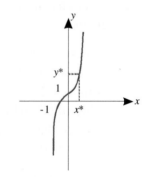

Figure 2.22

EXAMPLE 11   Sketch a graph of $f(x) = \dfrac{x+1}{x-3}$.

Solution: By hand

Step 1   Let $y = \dfrac{x+1}{x-3}$.

Step 2   Since $x = 3$ makes the denominator of $f(x)$ zero, $x = 3$ does not belong to the domain of the function.

Step 3   We choose a few x-values on the left and a few on the right of $x = 3$. By computing the corresponding y-values we get

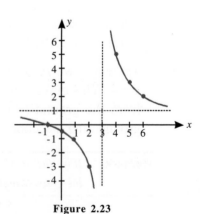

Figure 2.23

x	−1	0	1	2	4	5	6
y	0	$-\dfrac{1}{3}$	−1	−3	5	3	$\dfrac{7}{3}$

Step 4   We plot these points (Figure 2.23).

Step 5   By joining the points we get the graph of the function (Figure 2.23).

With Graphing Calculator

Step 1   Press GRAPH

Step 2   Select $y1$ or $y(x)$

Step 3   Let $y1 = \dfrac{x+1}{x-3}$

Step 4   Select a suitable RANGE

Step 5   Press GRAPH

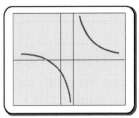

Figure 2.24

Interpretation

The graph gets closer to the vertical line $x = 3$ as x gets closer to 3. Such a vertical line is called a **vertical asymptote.** Note that the range (set of outputs) consists of all real numbers except 1, see example 16 of section 2.3.

EXAMPLE 12   Sketch the graph of $f(x) = \sqrt{x-1}$

Solution: By hand

Step 1   Write the function as $y = \sqrt{x-1}$

Steps 2, 3   Refer to Example 3 of section 2.4. x-values can not be less than 1.

x	1	2	3	4	5	6
y	0	1	1.41	1.73	2	2.24

Step 4   We plot the ordered pairs (x, y).

* *Step* 5   By joining the points we get the graph of the function (Figure 2.25).

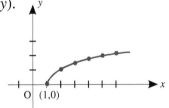

Figure 2.25

*   The graph of a square root function is above the x-axis and is an increasing graph.

With Graphing Calculator

Step 1   Press **Graph**

Step 2   Select $y1 =$

Step 3   Let $y1 = \sqrt{(x-1)}$

Step 4   Let the **range** be
x min = 0, x max = 10, y min = 0, y max = 10

Step 5   Press Graph

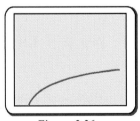

Figure 2.26

EXAMPLE 13   Sketch and interpret the graph of $f(x) = \left| x-2 \right|$.

Solution: By hand

Step 1   Let $y = |x - 2|$

Steps 2, 3 Refer to Example 4 of section 2.4.

x	−1	0	1	2	3	4
y	3	2	1	0	1	2

Step 4   We plot the points (Figure 2.27).

Step 5   By joining the points we get the graph of the function (Figure 2.27).

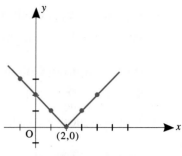

Figure 2.27

With Graphing Calculator

Let $y1 = \text{abs}(x - 2)$ and set the

RANGE: x min = −10, x max = 10,
y min = −10, and y max = 10

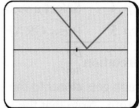

Figure 2.28

Interpretation

1. The heights (y) represent the values of $f(x)$.

2. For any $x = x^*$ the corresponding value of the function is given by y^* (Figure 2.29).

3. The graph is both increasing and decreasing; it increases on the interval $(2, \infty)$ and decreases on $(-\infty, 2)$ (Figure 2.29).

4. The function is an **absolute value** function and its graph has a sharp **corner**.

5. The y-intercept of the graph is 2.

6. $x = 2$ is only zero of the function.

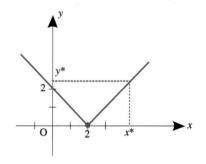

Figure 2.29

EXAMPLE 14   Sketch and interpret $f(x) = \begin{cases} 2 - x & if & x < 1 \\ 3 & if & x = 1 \\ 4 & if & x > 1 \end{cases}$

Solution: By hand

Step 1   Let $y = \begin{cases} 2 - x & if & x < 1 \\ 3 & if & x = 1 \\ 4 & if & x > 1 \end{cases}$

Steps 2, 3 Refer to Example 5 of section 2.4.

x	−1	0	1	2	3	4
y	3	2	3	4	4	4

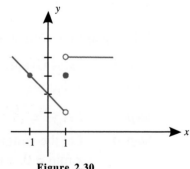

Figure 2.30

Step 4   Plot the points (Figure 2.30).

Step 5   Join the points and draw the graph of each piece of the function (the first part is **linear**, so its graph is a straight line; the second piece is the point (1, 3) and third part $y = 4$ is a *horizontal line*) (Figure 2.30).

Notice that there are open circles (Figure 2.30) at the right end of part 1 of the graph and left end of part 3 of the graph because $x = 1$ is not included in either of these two parts, first and third. We show the exclusion by open circle and inclusion by a solid dot.

* Notice the special format for entering a piecewise function.	**With Graphing Calculator**

* Let $y1 = (2 - x)(x < 1) + (3)(x = 1) + (4)(x > 1)$. By selecting a suitable range, the graph is drawn under 'DRAW DOT' format.

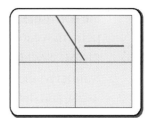

Figure 2.31

Remark: *Do not expect to see either open circles or a single point on the screen. A single point can, however, be seen by suitably setting the RANGE parameters. In this case set xmin = −6.3, xmax = 6.3, ymin = −5 and ymax = 5.*

Interpretation

1. The heights (y) represent the values of $f(x)$.

2. For any $x = x^*$ the corresponding value of the function is given by y^* (Figure 2.32).

3. The graph is **decreasing** on $(-\infty, 1)$. Also, the graph of the function is **not continuous** at $x = 1$. Finally, the function is constant $(= 4)$ on $(1, \infty)$.

4. The graph of a piecewise function is drawn in pieces.

5. The y-intercept $= 2$ (Figure 2.32).

6. There is no x-intercept or zeros of the function.

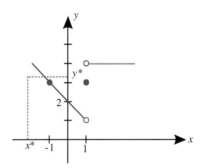

Figure 2.32

EXAMPLE 15   Figure 2.33 shows the Dow Jones Industrial Average during the month of May 8 to June 8, 2004.

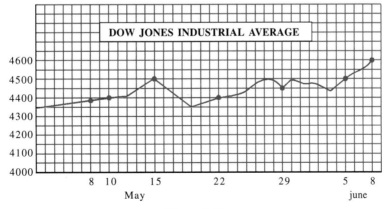

Figure 2.33

Examine the graph and answer each of the following:

a. What were the Dow Jones Industrial Average on May 10, May 15, May 22, May 29 and June 8?

b. When was the average highest? lowest?

c. Did the average increase during the week of May 8 - May 15?

Solutions:

a. May 10 is shown on the horizontal axis and is considered as an "*x*-value". From that point on the horizontal axis go toward the graph on a vertical line until the line meets the graph. From this point move toward the vertical axis on a horizontal line until the line meets the vertical axis. The measurement 4400 of this point is the Dow Jones Industrial Average on May 10, 2004.

Similarly, the values of the average on May 15, May 22, May 29, and June 8 are 4500, 4400, 4450, and 4600, respectively.

b. The highest average is reached at the highest point on the graph; it is on June 8. Similarly, on May 18, the average reached the lowest (between May 18 and 19 on the Graph).

c. The average increases from May 8 - May 15.

EXAMPLE 16 It is possible to * approximate the area under the curve $y = 6x - x^2$ from $x = 0$ to $x = 2$ and bounded by *x*-axis as the sum of the areas of the shaded rectangles (Figure 2.34). Find the approximate area.

> * For the exact area under the curve, we need calculus.

Solution: The height of the first rectangle = the value of the function

at $\dfrac{1}{2}$ = $6\left(\dfrac{1}{2}\right) - \left(\dfrac{1}{2}\right)^2 = \dfrac{11}{4}$.

The height of the second rectangle = the value of the function at $1 = 6(1) - (1)^2 = 5$.

The height of the third rectangle = the value of the

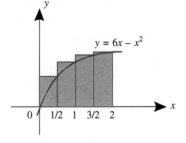

Figure 2.34

function at $\dfrac{3}{2}$ = $6\left(\dfrac{3}{2}\right) - \left(\dfrac{3}{2}\right)^2 = 9 - \dfrac{9}{4} = \dfrac{27}{4}$.

Similarly, the height of the fourth rectangle = $6(2) - (2)^2 = 8$.

By applying the formula for the area of a rectangle, we get the

area of the first rectangle = (base)(height) = $\dfrac{1}{2} \cdot \dfrac{11}{4} = \dfrac{11}{8}$

area of the second rectangle = $\dfrac{1}{2}(5) = \dfrac{5}{2}$

area of the third rectangle = $\dfrac{1}{2}\left(\dfrac{27}{4}\right) = \dfrac{27}{8}$, and

area of the fourth rectagle = $\dfrac{1}{2}(8) = 4$.

Thus the estimated area = sum of the four rectangles = $\dfrac{11}{8} + \dfrac{5}{2} + \dfrac{27}{8} + 4 = \dfrac{45}{4}$.

E. THE VERTICAL LINE TEST

Recall that a function associates a unique output to each input from its domain. Let us see what it means when a function is given in its graphical form. If $x = x^*$ is any input, then the corresponding output y^* is given by moving x^* on x-axis vertically toward the curve (graph) until it meets the graph at P and then by continuing horizontally towards the y-axis until it meets the y-axis at y^*. In short, the output y^* is the y-coordinate of the point where the **vertical line** through x^* meets the graph. If the vertical line through x^* crosses the graph in more than one point, there would be at least two different outputs associated with x^*. In this situation, the graph will not represent a function. However, the graph **will** represent a relation. We use this fact to test whether or not a graph is that of a function.

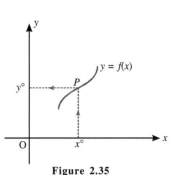

Figure 2.35

| Remark: | *It is possible that a vertical line may not meet the graph at any point (why?).* |

Vertical Line test

A graph represents a function provided that
any vertical line intersects the graph in at most one point.

Remarks: *1.*   *A graph does not represent a function if there is at least one vertical line that meets the graph in two or more points.*

          2.   *No part of the graph of a function can be a vertical line segment because then you can draw a vertical line that meets the graph in many points (infinite number of points indeed).*

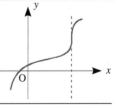

EXAMPLE 17   Determine whether each graph in Figure 2.36 represents a function.

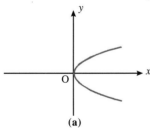

(a)   (b)

Figure 2.36

Solutions:

   a.   There is a vertical line drawn through the graph that cuts the graph in two points P and Q (Figure 2.37(a)). Therefore, the graph does not represent a function.

   b.   Any vertical line drawn through the graph meets the graph in only one point (Figure 2.37(b)). Therefore, the graph represents a function.

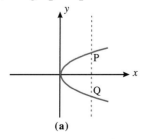
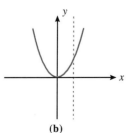

(a)   (b)

Figure 2.37

EXERCISE 2.4

In exercises (1-54), sketch the graph of each by hand and then verify by using a graphing calculator.

1. $f(x) = 2x - 1$ **2.** $g(x) = 4 - 5x$ **3.** $f(x) = 3x - 2$ **4.** $f(x) = 7 - x$

5. $g(x) = 2$ **6.** $f(x) = 0$ **7.** $h(x) = -3$ **8.** $g(x) = -\dfrac{3}{2}$

9. $f(x) = x^2 - 1$ **10.** $f(x) = x^2 - 3$ **11.** $g(x) = x^2 + 1$ **12.** $g(x) = x^2 + 4$

13. $h(x) = 2x^2 - 1$ **14.** $g(x) = 3x^2 - 2$ **15.** $f(x) = 4x^2 - 8x$ **16.** $f(x) = 3x^2 + 6x$

17. $f(x) = 1 - x^2$ **18.** $f(x) = 4 - 2x^2$ **19.** $g(x) = 4 - x^2$ **20.** $g(x) = -x^2 + 2x + 1$

21. $f(x) = x^3$ **22.** $f(x) = x^3 - 1$ **23.** $f(x) = x^3 - 8$ **24.** $g(x) = 1 - x^3$

25. $f(x) = 8 - x^3$ **26.** $f(x) = \sqrt{x} - 1$ **27.** $g(x) = \sqrt{x} - 3$ **28.** $g(x) = \sqrt{x} + 1$

29. $f(x) = \sqrt{x} + 2$ **30.** $f(x) = \sqrt{x-2}$ **31.** $g(x) = \sqrt{x+3}$ **32.** $g(x) = \sqrt{x+1}$

33. $h(x) = \sqrt{x-4}$ **34.** $f(x) = |x-1|$ **35.** $f(x) = |x+4|$ **36.** $g(x) = |x+1|$

37. $g(x) = |x-3|$ **38.** $f(x) = \begin{cases} 2 & ; \ x \le 1 \\ -2 & ; \ x > 1 \end{cases}$ **39.** $f(x) = \begin{cases} 1 & ; \ x \le 0 \\ 2 & ; \ x > 0 \end{cases}$

40. $g(x) = \begin{cases} 0 & ; \ x \le 0 \\ 1 & ; \ x > 0 \end{cases}$ **41.** $g(x) = \begin{cases} -4 & ; \ x \le -1 \\ 3 & ; \ x > -1 \end{cases}$ **42.** $f(x) = \begin{cases} x & ; \ x \le 1 \\ 2 & ; \ x > 1 \end{cases}$

43. $f(x) = \begin{cases} 3 & ; \ x \le 2 \\ x & ; \ x > 2 \end{cases}$ **44.** $g(x) = \begin{cases} x^2 & ; \ x < 2 \\ 2x & ; \ x \ge 2 \end{cases}$ **45.** $f(x) = \begin{cases} 3x+1 & ; \ x \le -1 \\ 5 & ; \ x > -1 \end{cases}$

46. $f(x) = \begin{cases} |x| & ; \ x \le 1 \\ 1 & ; \ x > 1 \end{cases}$ **47.** $g(x) = \begin{cases} -2x & ; \ x < 3 \\ x^2 & ; \ x \ge 3 \end{cases}$ **48.** $g(x) = \begin{cases} |x-1| & ; \ x \le 2 \\ 1 & ; \ x > 2 \end{cases}$

49. $g(x) = \begin{cases} 0 & ; \ x \le -2 \\ |x| & ; \ x > -2 \end{cases}$ **50.** $f(x) = \begin{cases} |x| & ; \ x \le 1 \\ \sqrt{x} & ; \ x > 1 \end{cases}$ **51.** $h(x) = \begin{cases} \sqrt{x} & ; \ 0 \le x < 3 \\ |x| & ; \ x \ge 3 \end{cases}$

52. $g(x) = \begin{cases} 2 & ; \ x < 0 \\ x & ; \ 0 \le x \le 2 \\ 1 & ; \ x > 2 \end{cases}$ **53.** $h(x) = \begin{cases} -2 & ; \ x \le 1 \\ 1 & ; \ 1 < x < 4 \\ 3 & ; \ x \ge 4 \end{cases}$ **54.** $f(x) = \begin{cases} 3x-2 & ; \ x < 3 \\ 4 & ; \ x = 3 \\ 10-x & ; \ x > 3 \end{cases}$

In exercises (55-70), examine the graph and identify the function as **(a)** linear function **(b)** quadratic function, **(c)** cubic function, or **(d)** absolute value function.

55. 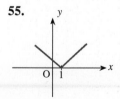   **56.** 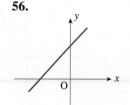   **57.** 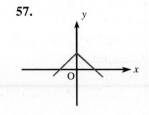   **58.**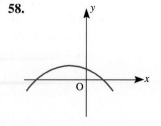

59.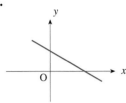

60.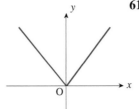

61.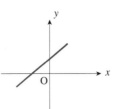

62.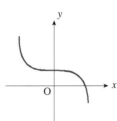

63.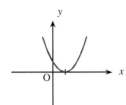

64.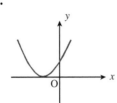

65.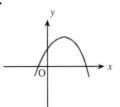

66.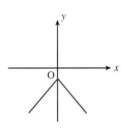

67.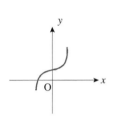

68.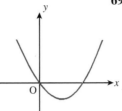

69.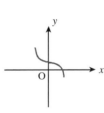

70.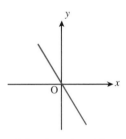

In exercises (71-78), examine each graph and identify   **a.** the *y*-intercept, if any **b.** zeros of the function, if any
c. the *x*-values where the graph is increasing or decreasing   **d.** the domain   **e.** the range.

71.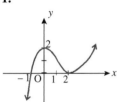

72.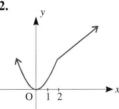

73.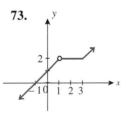

74.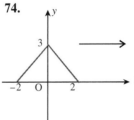

75.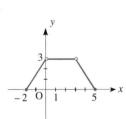

76.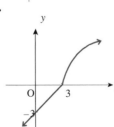

77.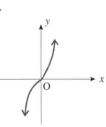

78.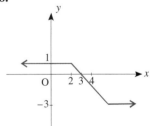

79.   Figure 2.38 shows the height of a stone thrown
up in the air from a height of 20 feet above ground
level. Examine the graph and give

    a.   the time (in seconds) when it reaches its highest point.

    b.   the maximum height reached,

    c.   the time when it strikes the ground.

    d.   the height at the 2nd second, 7th second, and 10th second.

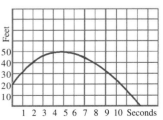

Figure 2.38

80. The daytime temperatures at an airport on
August 8, 1994 were recorded in Figure 2.39.

    a. When did it reach the maximum temperature reach?

    b. Give the interval when the temperature was rising.

    c. Give the interval when the temperature was falling.

    d. What was the temperature at 3 PM? 6 PM?

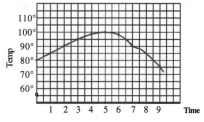

Figure 2.39

81. In Figures 2.40 (a) and (b) the area under the curve is approximated by the sum of the areas of the shaded
rectangles. **Find the estimated area in each case.**

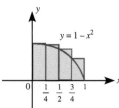

Figure 2.40 (a)

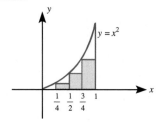

Figure 2.40 (b)

In exercises (82-93), apply the vertical line test to determine whether or not the graph is a function.

82.

83.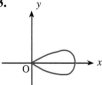

84.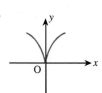

85.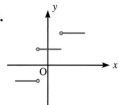

86.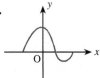

87.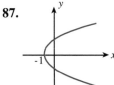

88.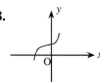

89.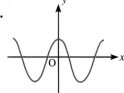

90.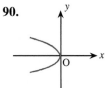

91.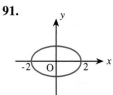

92.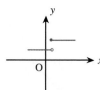

93.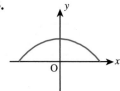

2.5 DISTANCE AND SLOPE

In this section we will use the rectangular coordinate system and coordinates of points to find the length, the coordinates of the midpoint, and the slope (steepness) of the line segment that joins two points.

Objectives ▶ ▶

In this section you will learn to find:

A. The Distance between two points;

B. The Midpoint of a line segment; and

C. The Slope of a line.

A. THE DISTANCE BETWEEN TWO POINTS

There will be many situations where we will need to measure the **exact** distance between two points. Using a ruler will generally give an approximate measure. However, the rectangular system of coordinates can help us to find the **exact** measure. Suppose we wish to find the **exact** distance between the points $P(1, 2)$ and $Q(6, 5)$. We plot the points on the rectangular system of coordinates. We drop perpendiculars PM and QN on the x-axis from points P and Q, respectively. Then we draw a horizontal line PK from point P toward the line QN (Figure 2.41).

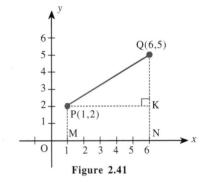

Figure 2.41

* The **horizontal distance** between the points P and Q
  $= PK = ON - OM = 6 - 1 = 5$

* The **vertical distance** between the points P and Q
  $= QK = QN - KN = QN - PM = 5 - 2 = 3$

* The **horizontal distance** between two points is equal to the difference between their x-coordinates.

* The **vertical distance** between two points is equal to the difference between their y-coordinates.

By applying the Pythagorean theorem to the right triangle PKQ, we get

$$(PQ)^2 = (PK)^2 + (QK)^2$$
$$= \text{(horizontal distance)}^2 + \text{(vertical distance)}^2$$
$$= \quad 5^2 \quad + \quad 3^2 \quad = 25 + 9 = 34$$

Therefore, the distance $PQ = \sqrt{34}$

To generalize the above procedure, we consider any two points $P(x_1, y_1)$ and $Q(x_2, y_2)$ (Figure 2.42). The **horizontal distance** between P and Q

$$= PK = \left| ON - OM \right| = \left| x_2 - x_1 \right|$$

and the **vertical distance** between points P and Q

$$= QK = \left| QN - KN \right| = \left| QN - PM \right| = \left| y_2 - y_1 \right|.$$

The Pythagorean Theorem gives

$$(PQ)^2 = (PK)^2 + (QK)^2 = \left(\left|x_2 - x_1\right|\right)^2 + \left(\left|y_2 - y_1\right|\right)^2$$

$$= \left(x_2 - x_1\right)^2 + \left(y_2 - y_1\right)^2$$

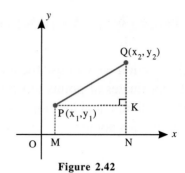

Figure 2.42

Thus, if d is the distance between the points P and Q, then

$$* \quad d = \sqrt{\left(x_2 - x_1\right)^2 + \left(y_2 - y_1\right)^2}$$

The Distance Formula

The distance d between the points $\left(x_1, y_1\right)$

and $\left(x_2, y_2\right)$ is given by

$$* \quad d = \sqrt{\left(x_2 - x_1\right)^2 + \left(y_2 - y_1\right)^2}$$

$$* \quad d = \sqrt{(\text{horizontal distance})^2 + (\text{vertical distance})^2}$$

*   To find the distance between two points

Step 1   Label the points as $\left(x_1, y_1\right)$ and

$$\left(x_2, y_2\right).$$

EXAMPLE 1   Find the distance between the points $(3, -7)$ and $(5, -3)$.

Solution:

     Step 1   Labeling the points as $\left(x_1, y_1\right)$ and $\left(x_2, y_2\right)$ we get

$$\begin{array}{ccc} \left(x_1, y_1\right) & & \left(x_2, y_2\right) \\ (3, -7) & \text{and} & (5, -3) \end{array}$$

     Step 2   Substituting $x_1 = 3$, $y_1 = -7$, $x_2 = 5$ and $y_2 = -3$ in the formula gives

$$d = \sqrt{(5-3)^2 + \left(-3 - (-7)\right)^2} = \sqrt{(5-3)^2 + (-3+7)^2}$$

$$= \sqrt{2^2 + 4^2} = \sqrt{4 + 16} = \sqrt{20} = 2\sqrt{5}$$

EXAMPLE 2   Is the triangle with vertices $A(2, 4)$, $B(0, 4)$ and $C(1, 3)$ a right triangle?

Solution:

For triangle ABC to be a right triangle, the square of the length of one side must be equal to the sum of the squares of the lengths of other two sides, by Pythagorean Theorem. To check this, we first find the lengths AB, BC, and AC.

AC = distance between $A(2, 4)$ and $C(1, 3)$

$$= \sqrt{(1-2)^2 + (3-4)^2} = \sqrt{(-1)^2 + (-1)^2} = \sqrt{1+1} = \sqrt{2}$$

BC = distance between $B(0, 4)$ and $C(1, 3)$

$$= \sqrt{(1-0)^2 + (3-4)^2} = \sqrt{(1)^2 + (-1)^2} = \sqrt{1+1} = \sqrt{2}$$

AB = distance between $A(2, 4)$ and $B(0, 4)$

$$= \sqrt{(0-2)^2 + (4-4)^2} = \sqrt{(-2)^2 + (0)^2}$$

$$= \sqrt{4+0} = \sqrt{4} = 2$$

Since, $(AC)^2 + (BC)^2 = \left(\sqrt{2}\right)^2 + \left(\sqrt{2}\right)^2 = 2^2 = (AB)^2$, the triangle ABC is a right triangle with side AB as the hypotenuse and the right angle at C (Figure 2.43).

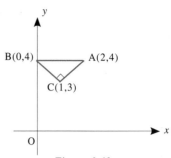

Figure 2.43

Remark: *We will do this problem again after we review the concept of **slope** (Example 6 section 4.1).*

EXAMPLE 3 Find the horizontal and vertical distances between the points $P\left(x, 64x - 16x^2\right)$ and $Q\left(x, \sqrt{x-1}\right)$, $x > 1$ as shown in Figure 2.44.

Solution:

The horizontal distance between points P and Q

= the difference between the x-coordinates of P and Q

$= \left|x - x\right| = \left|0\right| = 0$

The vertical distance between points P and Q

= the difference between the y-coordinates of P and Q

$= \left|64x - 16x^2 - \sqrt{x-1}\right|$

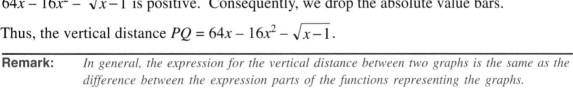

Figure 2.44

Since the point P is higher than point Q, so the expression $64x - 16x^2 - \sqrt{x-1}$ is positive. Consequently, we drop the absolute value bars.

Thus, the vertical distance $PQ = 64x - 16x^2 - \sqrt{x-1}$.

Remark: *In general, the expression for the vertical distance between two graphs is the same as the difference between the expression parts of the functions representing the graphs.*
Vertical distance = (function value above) − (function value below).

EXAMPLE 4 In Figure 2.45, find general expressions for the vertical distances PQ and RS.

Solution:

The vertical distance PQ

= the difference between the y-coordinates of points P and Q

= function above − function below

$= \qquad \sqrt{x} \qquad - \qquad x^2$

where x is the x-coordinate of P (or Q)

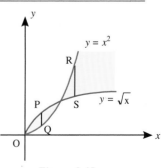

Figure 2.45

Similarly, the distance RS

= function above – function below

= x^2 – $\sqrt{x}$

where x is the x-coordinate of R (or S)

B. THE MIDPOINT OF A LINE SEGMENT

Consider the line segment that joins the points $P\left(x_1 , y_1\right)$ and

$Q\left(x_2 , y_2\right)$ in (Figure 2.46).

To find the **exact** coordinates of the midpoint R of the line segment PQ, we draw perpendiculars PM, QN, and PK. Let the coordinates of R be (a, b). We drop a perpendicular RS from the point R to the x-axis, the point S is the midpoint of the segment MN, the horizontal distance MS must be equal to the horizontal distance SN.

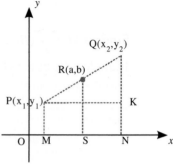

Figure 2.46

This gives

$$a - x_1 = x_2 - a$$

or $\quad 2a = x_2 + x_1$

$$\rightarrow \quad a = \frac{x_2 + x_1}{2} = \frac{x_1 + x_2}{2}$$

Similarly, we can show that $b = \dfrac{y_1 + y_2}{2}$.

Thus, the coordinates of the midpoint R are $\left(\dfrac{x_1 + x_2}{2} , \dfrac{y_1 + y_2}{2}\right)$.

> **The Midpoint Formula**
>
> The coordinates of the midpoint of the line segment that joins (x_1, y_1) and (x_2, y_2) are
>
> $$\left(\frac{x_1 + x_2}{2} , \frac{y_1 + y_2}{2}\right)$$

EXAMPLE 5 Find the coordinates of the midpoint of the line segment that joins $(5, -7)$ and $(-3, 9)$.

Solution: According to the formula, the midpoint of the line segment is given by

$$\left(\frac{x_1 + x_2}{2} , \frac{y_1 + y_2}{2}\right) = \left(\frac{5 + (-3)}{2} , \frac{-7 + 9}{2}\right)$$

> *Step 2* Substitute the values of x_1 , x_2, y_1 and y_2 into the formula and simplify.

$$= \left(\frac{2}{2}, \frac{2}{2}\right) = (1, 1)$$

EXAMPLE 6   Figure 2.47 shows the graphs of two functions $y = 3x$ and $y = x^2$. A vertical line at $x = 2$ cuts the graph of $y = 3x$ at the point P and it meets the graph of $y = x^2$ at Q. Find the coordinates of the midpoint M of the line segment PQ.

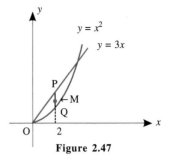

Figure 2.47

Solution: First, we find the coordinates of the endpoints P and Q of the line segment.

The x-coordinates of both P and Q are 2. To find the y-coordinates of the point P, we substitute $x = 2$ in $y = 3x$. This gives $y = 3(2) = 6$. Therefore, the coordinates of the point P are $(2, 6)$.

Similarly, the y-coordinate of point Q is obtained by substituting 2 for x in $y = x^2$.

We get $y = (2)^2 = 4$

Therefore, the coordinates of the point Q are $(2, 4)$.

By applying the formula, the midpoint M is located at

$$\left(\frac{2+2}{2}, \frac{6+4}{2} \right) = \left(\frac{4}{2}, \frac{10}{2} \right) = (2, 5).$$

EXAMPLE 7   In Figure 2.48, the line PQ is vertical and M is the midpoint of the segment PQ. Find the general expression for the coordinates of the point M.

Solution: From Figure 2.48, the x-coordinates of both P and Q are equal to x.

The y-coordinate of point P is given by $y = 3x$.

Therefore, the coordinates of point P are $(x, 3x)$.

Similarly, the coordinates of point Q are $\left(x, x^2 \right)$.

Using the midpoint formula gives the coordinates of the point M as

$$\left(\frac{x+x}{2}, \frac{3x+x^2}{2} \right) \text{ or } \left(x, \frac{3x+x^2}{2} \right).$$

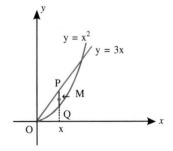

Figure 2.48

C. THE SLOPE OF A LINE

The slope of a line measures the steepness or slant or direction of the line.

The slope of the line PQ (Figure 2.49)

$$= \frac{\text{Rise}}{\text{Run}} = \frac{\text{change in } y}{\text{change in } x}$$

We write this in a formula form as follows :

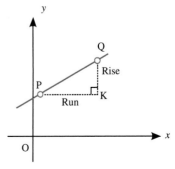

Figure 2.49

The Slope Formula

The **slope** of the line that joins two points $P(x_1, y_1)$ and $Q(x_2, y_2)$

is the number m given by $\quad m = \dfrac{y_2 - y_1}{x_2 - x_1}$.

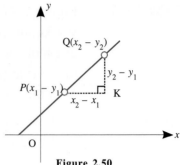

Figure 2.50

Remarks: 1. *The vertical distance $y_2 - y_1$ is the **change** in y as we move from point $P(x_1, y_1)$ to point $Q(x_2, y_2)$ along the line. This change in y is more frequently denoted by Δy (read as delta y). Similarly, by writing $\Delta x = x_2 - x_1$, we have*

the slope $(m) = \dfrac{\Delta y}{\Delta x}$ (Figure 2.51)

2. m = *average rate of change in y*
= *rate of change in y, because for a straight line the slope is constant.*

Slope = rate of change

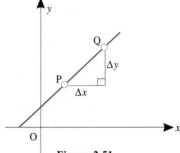

Figure 2.51

EXAMPLE 8   Compute the slope of the line that joins

    a. $(-2, -1)$ and $(-1, 5)$ **b.** $(-1, -5)$ and $(1, -8)$

    c. $(9, 3)$ and $(-9, 3)$ **d.** $(2, 5)$ and $(2, -4)$

Solutions:

a. We label the points as $(-2, -1)$ and $(-1, 5)$.

By applying the formula, we get

  * $m = \dfrac{y_2 - y_1}{x_2 - x_1} = \dfrac{5 - (-1)}{-1 - (-2)} = \dfrac{5 + 1}{-1 + 2} = \dfrac{6}{1} = 6$

Figure 2.52(a)

* A line with positive slope slants upward to the right.

b. The formula gives the slope of the line through the points $(-1, -5)$ and $(1, -8)$ as

  * $m = \dfrac{-8 - (-5)}{1 - (-1)} = \dfrac{-8 + 5}{1 + 1} = \dfrac{-3}{2}$

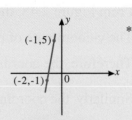

Figure 2.52(b)

* A line that has negative slope will slant downwards to the right.

c. Similarly, the slope of the line joining $(9, 3)$ and $(-9, 3)$ is

  * $m = \dfrac{3 - 3}{-9 - 9} = \dfrac{0}{-18} = 0$

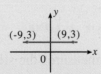

Figure 2.52(c)

* A horizontal line has slope = 0.

d. The slope of the line containing the points $(2, 5)$ and $(2, -4)$ is

  * $m = \dfrac{5 - (-4)}{2 - 2} = \dfrac{9}{0}$ (undefined)

Figure 2.52(d)

* The slope of a vertical line is undefined.

EXAMPLE 9   The *x*-coordinates of points *P* and *Q* on the graph of $y = x^2$ are 2 and 5 respectively. Find the slope of the secant line *PQ* (Figure 2.53).

Solution: First, we find the coordinates of the point *P* and *Q*.

When $x = 2$, $y = (2)^2 = 4$.

Therefore, the coordinates of the point *P* are (2, 4).

Similarly, when $x = 5$, $y = (5)^2 = 25$.

So, the coordinates of the point *Q* are (5, 25).

Now by applying the formula, we find

the slope of the secant line $PQ = \dfrac{25-4}{5-2} = \dfrac{21}{3} = 7$

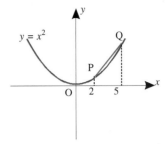

Figure 2.53

The following example is the generalization of this example.

EXAMPLE 10   The *x*-coordinates of points *P* and *Q* on the graph of $y = x^2$ are *x* and *x* + *h* respectively. Find the slope of the secant line *PQ* (figure 2.54).

Solution: For the coordinates of the point *P*.

x-coordinate = *x* and *y*-coordinate = x^2.

Thus point *P* has the coordinates $\left(x, x^2\right)$.

For the coordinates of the point *Q*,

x-coordinate = *x* + *h* and *y*-coordinate = $(x + h)^2 = x^2 + 2xh + h^2$.

Thus point *Q* has the coordinates $Q\left(x + h, x^2 + 2xh + h^2\right)$.

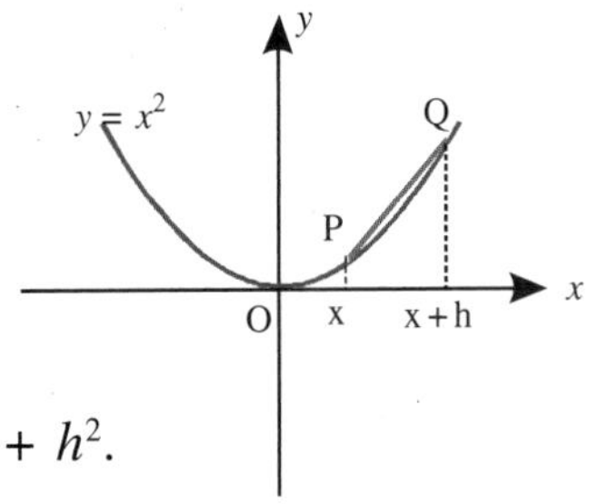

Figure 2.54

By using the formula, we get the

slope of the secant line $PQ = \dfrac{x^2 + 2xh + h^2 - x^2}{x + h - x}$

$$= \dfrac{2xh + h^2}{h} = \dfrac{\boldsymbol{h}\,(2x + h)}{\boldsymbol{h}} = 2x + h$$

Thus, the slope of the secant line $PQ = 2x + h$.

EXAMPLE 11   Suppose *C*(*x*), the cost in dollars of manufacturing *x* television sets, is given by $C(x) = 150x + 500$.

    a. Find the cost of producing 20 television sets.

    b. Find the marginal cost.

    c. Find the cost of producing 21 *TV* sets by using the information from parts (a) and (b).

Solutions:

    a.   Evaluating the cost function when $x = 20$, we get $C(20) = 150(20) + 500 = 3500$

    b.   The marginal cost is the additional cost to produce one more unit. Therefore, it is the rate of change of the cost function. Since the rate of change for a linear function is given by the slope, so we have marginal cost = 150 *.

> * Recall slope of a line $y = mx + c$ is *m*, the coefficient of *x*.

c. From part (a), the cost of making 20 *TV* sets is $3500 and part(b) gives the cost $150 of each additional *TV* set. Therefore, the cost of 21 *TV* sets = 3500 + 150 = $3,650.

EXERCISE 2.5

In exercises (1-10), find the exact distance between the points *P* and *Q*.

1. $P(-1, 5)$, $Q(4, -2)$ **2.** $P(-5, 1), Q(2, 1)$ **3.** $P(2, -3)$, $Q(-1, 1)$

4. $P(0, 0)$, $Q(3, 7)$ **5.** $P(x, \sqrt{x})$, $Q(x, x^2)$ **6.** $P(a, 2a + 1), Q(a, 3 - 4a)$

7. $P(x, x^2)$, $Q(x, x^3)$ **8.** $(x, 3x - 1), Q(x, x^3 - 1)$ **9.** $P(c, 0)$, $Q(x, y)$

10. $P(x, 2x + 1), Q(x + h, 2(x + h) + 1)$

In exercises (11-20), *A*, *B*, and *C* are the vertices of a triangle. Determine whether the triangle ABC is a right triangle.

11. $A(2, 0)$, $B(2, 4)$, and $C(5, 0)$ **12.** $A(3, 5)$, $B(2, -4)$, and $C(0, 1)$ **13.** $A(3, 1)$, $B(6, 3)$, and $C(-1, 2)$

14. $A(-2, 4)$, $B(1, 1)$, and $C(5, -3)$ **15.** $A(2, 2)$, $B(6, 4)$, and $C(4, 8)$ **16.** $A(3, 0)$, $B(0, 5)$, and $C(8, 3)$

17. $A(2, 6)$, $B(-4, 2)$, and $C(-4, 6)$ **18.** $A(1, 3)$, $B(4, 3)$, and $C(1, -6)$

19. $A(5, 3)$, $B(3, 5)$, and $C(7, 9)$ **20.** $A(0, 2)$, $B(4, 10)$, and $C(-1, 0)$

In exercises (21-30), find an expression for the vertical distance between points *P* and *Q*.

21.
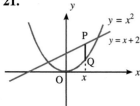

22.
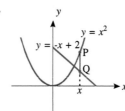

23.
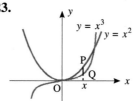

24.
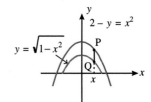

25.
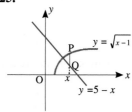

26.
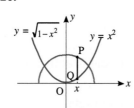

27.
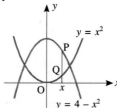

28.
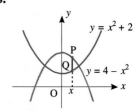

29.
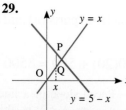

30.
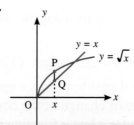

In exercises (31-41), find the coordinates of the midpoint of the line segment *PQ*.

31. $P(-1, 7), Q(5, 9)$ **32.** $P(-3, 5), Q(5, -3)$ **33.** $P(-1, 5), Q(4, -2)$

34. $P(2, -3), Q(-5, 2)$ **35.** $P(2, -3), Q(-1, 1)$ **36.** $P(-4, 5), Q(3, 8)$

37. $P\left(x, \sqrt{x}\right), Q\left(x, x^2\right)$ **38.** $P(x, x^2), Q(x, 2x + 1)$ **39.** $P\left(x, x^2\right), Q\left(x, x^3\right)$

40. $P(x, 3 - 2x), Q(x, 2x - 1)$ **41.** $P(x, x^2 + 1), Q(x, 1 - x^3)$

In exercises (42-51), find the coordinates of the midpoint of the line segment *PQ* **in exercises (21-30).**

42. Exercise 21 **43.** Exercise 22 **44.** Exercise 23 **45.** Exercise 24 **46.** Exercise 25

47. Exercise 26 **48.** Exercise 27 **49.** Exercise 28 **50.** Exercise 29 **51.** Exercise 30

In exercises (52-63), find the slope of the line segment that joins points *P* **and** *Q*.

52. $P(-1, 3), Q(5, -2)$ **53.** $P(3, 7), Q(-3, 7)$ **54.** $P(2, 1), Q(-5, 1)$

55. $P(-2, 5), Q(5, -2)$ **56.** $P(3, -1), Q(3, -7)$ **57.** $P(-7, 1), Q(-7, 9)$

58. $P(-1, 5), Q(4, -2)$ **59.** $P(-2, -3), Q(4, 5)$ **60.** $P\left(x, \sqrt{x}\right), Q\left(x, x^2\right)$

61. $P(x, 4x - 3), Q(x, -4x + 7)$ **62.** $P\left(x, x^2\right), Q\left(x + h, (x+h)^2\right)$ **63.** $P(x, x^2), Q(x - h, (x - h)^2)$

In exercises (64-73), find the slope of the secant line PQ in the simplest form.

64.
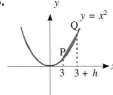

65.
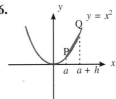

66.
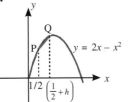

67.
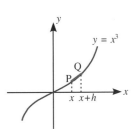

68.
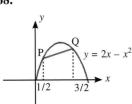

69.
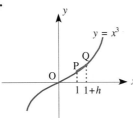

70.
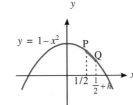

71.
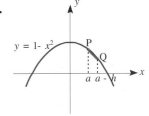

72.
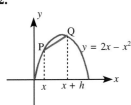

73.
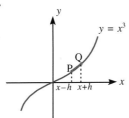

74. The sales of a company rose from two million to five million during the period 1989 to 1991. Assuming that the growth during this period was linear, find the rate of growth.

75. The sales of a company rose form five million to ten million during the period 1991 to 1995. Assuming that the growth during this period was linear, find the rate of growth.

76. Suppose that the cost $C(x)$ in dollars of producing x graphing calculators is given by
$$C(x) = 30x + 20$$
a. Find the cost of producing 10 calculators. **b.** Find the marginal cost.
c. Use parts (a) and (b) to find the cost of producing 11 calculators.

77. Suppose that the cost $C(x)$ in dollars of producing x recliners is given by
$$C(x) = 80x + 35$$
a. Find the cost of producing 50 recliners. **b.** Find the marginal cost.
c. By using parts (a) and (b), compute the cost of producing 51 recliners.

78. Suppose $f(x) = 1.32x + 3.72$ is a possible formula form of the following numerical form of the function f.

x	5	4	2	9	3
$f(x)$	12	8	5	15	9

a. Predict the value of the function when $x = 10$. **b.** Find the rate of change in $f(x)$.

79. Suppose $f(x) = -0.7x + 92.67$ is a possible formula form of the following numerical form of the function f.

x	55	65	75	95	105	115
$f(x)$	60	47	35	20	18	19

a. Predict the value of the function when $x = 100$. **b.** What is the rate of change in $f(x)$?

80. Suppose $f(x) = .2x + 4.15$ is a possible formula form of the following numerical form of the function f.

x	16	12	23	45	3
$f(x)$	8	6	9	14	4

a. Predict the value of the function when $x = 20$. **b.** Find the rate of change in $f(x)$.

81. Suppose $f(x) = 0.5x + 33.8$ defines the following relationship between the height (in inches) of fathers and their oldest sons:

Father's Height	70	67	63	64	65	68	69	70	72	68	71	69	73
Son's Height	68	68	66	65	66	70	65	67	73	72	69	68	70

a. Predict the oldest son's height if his father is 74 inches tall.
b. For every one inch increase in Father's height, what is the increase in his oldest son's height.

Writing Exercises

82. Explain why the slope of a straight line is constant.

83. Can you find the slope of a parabola? Why or why not?

2.6 OPERATIONS ON FUNCTIONS

We have seen how operations of addition and multiplication of numbers make algebra more rich and meaningful for solving real life problems. The operations of union and intersection of sets make the concept of sets more meaningful for applications. Similarly, we can define operations on functions. These operations help us use functions in a variety of applications.

Objectives ▸ ▸

In this section you will learn about:

A. The Basic Operations; and

B. Composite Functions.

In this section we will study operations with functions. Also, we will discuss the composition of two functions when the outputs of one function become the inputs of the other.

A. THE BASIC OPERATIONS

The basic operations of sum, difference, product and quotient of two functions are defined for those functions whose outputs can be added, subtracted, multiplied and divided. This is clearly possible when the outputs are numbers.

We start with two functions $f(x) = 5x^2$ and $g(x) = \sqrt{3x+5}$. The elementary operations like addition, subtraction, multiplication, and division with these functions are defined as follows:

$$(f + g)\,(x) = f(x) + g(x) = 5x^2 + \sqrt{3x+5}\,, \qquad (f - g)\,(x) = f(x) - g(x) = 5x^2 - \sqrt{3x+5}$$

$$(f \cdot g) = f(x) \cdot g(x) = 5x^2\,\sqrt{3x+5}\,, \qquad \left(\frac{f}{g}\right)(x) = \frac{f(x)}{g(x)} = \frac{5x^2}{\sqrt{3x+5}}$$

In general, these operations on functions are defined as follows:

Sum, Difference, Product and Quotient of Functions

If f and g are two functions, then their

sum is:	$(f + g)\,(x) = f(x) + g(x),$
difference is:	$(f - g)\,(x) = f(x) - g(x),$
product is:	$(f \cdot g)\,(x) = f(x) \cdot g(x),$ and
quotient is:	$\left(\dfrac{f}{g}\right)(x) = \dfrac{f(x)}{g(x)}, \; g(x) \neq 0$

Remark: *The inputs x must be from the intersection of the domains of f and g so that f(x) and g(x) are both defined.*

Multiplication of a Function and a Real Number

The product of a function f and a number 'a' is defined as follows:

Let a be a real number and f a function. Then the function 'af' is defined by

$$(af)\,(x) = a\,f(x)$$

Equality of Functions

It is very important to be able to distinguish one function from another. To this end it helps if we know when two functions are equal or the same. Equality of two functions are defined as follows:

> Two functions f and g are equal, $f = g$, if;
>
> **a.** Domain of f = Domain of g
>
> **b.** $f(x) = g(x)$ **for all** x in the domain.

EXAMPLE 1 If $f(x) = x^2 + 1$ and $g(x) = 3x - 5$, find

    a. $(f + g)(x)$ **b.** $(f - g)(x)$,   **c.** $(f \cdot g)(x)$

    d. $\left(\dfrac{f}{g}\right)(x)$ **e.** $(-2f)(x)$ **f.** $(2f - 5g(x)$

and indicate the domain in each case.

Solutions:

    a. $(f + g)(x) = f(x) + g(x) = x^2 + 1 + 3x - 5$

                      $= x^2 + 3x - 4$

The domain of this function is the set of all real numbers, since the domain of each of f and g is the set of all real numbers.

    b. $(f - g)(x) = f(x) - g(x) = x^2 + 1 - (3x - 5)$

                      $= x^2 + 1 - 3x + 5 = x^2 - 3x + 6$

The domain of the function is again the set of all real numbers, since the domain of both f and g is the set of all real numbers.

    c. $(f \cdot g)(x) = f(x) \cdot g(x) = \left(x^2 + 1\right)(3x - 5)$

                    $= 3x^3 - 5x^2 + 3x - 5$

The domain is the set of all real numbers (**why?**).

    d. $\left(\dfrac{f}{g}\right)(x) = \dfrac{f(x)}{g(x)} = \dfrac{x^2 + 1}{3x - 5}$

The domain consists of all real numbers except $x = \dfrac{5}{3}$ (**why?**), or simply

$$\left\{x : x \neq \frac{5}{3}\right\}, \text{ or } \left(-\infty, \frac{5}{3}\right) \cup \left(\frac{5}{3}, \infty\right).$$

    e. $(-2f)(x) = -2f(x) = -2(x^2 + 1) = -2x^2 - 2$

The domain is the set of all real numbers, since domain of f is set of all real numbers.

f. $(2f - 5g)(x) = (2f)(x) - (5g)(x) = 2f(x) - 5g(x)$
$$= 2(x^2 + 1) + (-5)(3x - 5)$$
$$= 2x^2 + 2 - 15x + 25 = 2x^2 - 15x + 27$$

The domain is the set of all real numbers (why?)

EXAMPLE 2   Suppose the functions f and g are given in their numerical (table) forms as:

x	-2	-1	0	1	2	3
$f(x)$	8	2	7	-1	-5	-3

x	-2	-1	0	1	2	3
$g(x)$	-1	-5	-11	7	8	9

Find the numerical (table) forms of   **a.** $(f + g)(x)$ **b.** $(f - g)(x)$

c. $(f \cdot g)(x)$ **d.** $\left(\dfrac{f}{g}\right)(x)$ **e.** $(f - 3g)(x)$

Solutions:

We start with the given tables and extend them to answer each part.

	x	-2	-1	0	1	2	3
	$f(x)$	8	2	7	-1	-5	-3
	$g(x)$	-1	-5	-11	7	8	9
a.	$(f + g)(x)$	7	-3	-4	6	3	6
b.	$(f - g)(x)$	9	7	18	-8	-13	-12
c.	$(f \cdot g)(x)$	-8	-10	-77	-7	-40	-27
d.	$\left(\dfrac{f}{g}\right)(x)$	-8	$-\dfrac{2}{5}$	$-\dfrac{7}{11}$	$-\dfrac{1}{7}$	$-\dfrac{5}{8}$	$-\dfrac{1}{3}$
e.	$(f - 3g)(x)$	11	17	40	-22	-29	-30

EXAMPLE 3   Suppose $f(x) = 2x - 1$, $g(x) = x + 1$, and $h(x) = x$. Verify that the functions $f + g$ and $3h$ are equal.

Solution: We verify the two conditions for equality of functions.

a.   Domain of each of f, g, and h is the set of all real numbers. Therefore, domain of $f + g$ is the set of all real numbers. Also, domain of $3h$ is the set of all real numbers.

b. $(f + g)(x) = f(x) + g(x)$
$$= (2x - 1) + (x + 1)$$
$$= 3x$$
$$(3h)(x) = 3h(x) = 3x$$

Therefore, $(f + g)(x) = (3h)(x)$ for all x in the domain.

Since both conditions for equality of $f + g$ and $3h$ are satisfied, we conclude that $f + g = 3h$.

B. COMPOSITE FUNCTIONS

Suppose that the profit (P) of a retail store depends upon the sales (S) and the sales (S) in turn depend upon the average daytime temperature (T). This chain of dependency is $P(S(T))$ and it is called the **composition of function** P with function S. In this method of combining functions, the output of one function becomes the input of the other.

In the machine analogy, if f and g are two machines (functions), then the composition of f with g represents an assembly line set up, where the output $g(x)$ of the first machine (g) becomes the input of the second machine (f) (Figure 2.55).

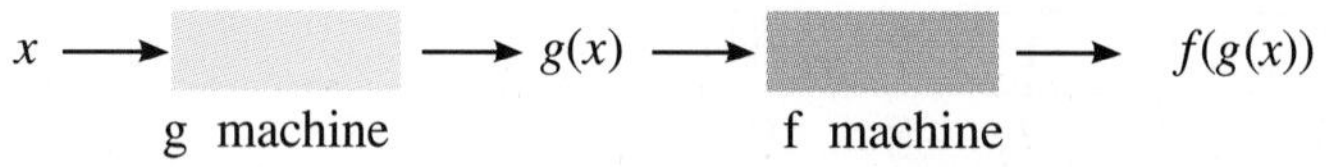

$$x \longrightarrow \boxed{} \longrightarrow g(x) \longrightarrow \boxed{} \longrightarrow f(g(x))$$

g machine   f machine

Figure 2.55

For example, if $f(x) = 5x - 3$ and $g(x) = x^2$, then $f(g(x)) = f\left(x^2\right) = 5x^2 - 3$.

Notation: The **composition** of f with g is written as $f \circ g$.

> **Composition of Functions**
>
> The composition of f with g is defined as
>
> $$(f \circ g)(x) = f(g(x)).$$
>
> The domain of $f \circ g$ consists of all x in the domain of g for which $g(x)$ is in the domain of f.

EXAMPLE 4   If $f(x) = \sqrt{x-1}$ and $g(x) = 2x^2 - 7$, find

a. $(f \circ g)(x)$ **b.** $(g \circ f)(x)$

Give the domain in each case.

Solutions:

a.   By definition

$$(f \circ g)(x) = f(g(x)) = f\left(2x^2 - 7\right)$$

Now replace x with $2x^2 - 7$ in the expression for $f(x)$. We get

$$(f \circ g)(x) = f\left(2x^2 - 7\right) = \sqrt{2x^2 - 7 - 1} = \sqrt{2x^2 - 8}.$$

Domain of $f \circ g$:

The domain of g is the set of all real numbers but the domain of $f \circ g$ consists of only those x values for which $g(x)$ is in the domain of f. For the domain of $f(g(x))$, the input $g(x)$ must be greater than or equal to 1, since the domain of f consists of all those real numbers that are greater than or equal to 1. Therefore,

$$2x^2 - 7 \geq 1 \quad \text{or} \quad 2x^2 - 8 \geq 0 \quad \text{or} \quad 2\left(x^2 - 4\right) \geq 0 \quad \text{or} \quad 2(x - 2)(x + 2) \geq 0$$

> * $ab \geq 0$ implies either both a and b are non-negative or both are non-positive.

$2(x - 2)(x + 2) \geq 0$ implies

$x - 2 \geq 0$ and $x + 2 \geq 0$ $\quad \rightarrow \quad$ $x \geq 2$ and $x \geq -2 \rightarrow$ $\quad x \geq 2$

or $\; x - 2 \leq 0$ and $x + 2 \leq 0$ $\rightarrow$ $\quad x \leq 2$ and $x \leq -2 \rightarrow$ $\quad x \leq -2$

Thus, the domain of $f \circ g$ is $(-\infty, -2] \cup [2, \infty)$.

b. By definition

$$(g \circ f)(x) = g(f(x)) = g\left(\sqrt{x-1}\right).$$

We replace x with $\sqrt{x-1}$ in the expression of $g(x)$. This gives

$$(g \circ f)(x) = g\left(\sqrt{x-1}\right) = 2\left(\sqrt{x-1}\right)^2 - 7.$$
$$= 2(x-1) - 7 = 2x - 2 - 7$$
$$= 2x - 9$$

Domain of $g \circ f$:

Similarly, the domain of $g \circ f$ consists of those x in the domain of f for which $f(x)$ is in the domain of g. Since the domain of f consists of all $x \geq 1$ and the domain of g accepts every real number, the domain of $g \circ f$ is $[1, \infty)$.

EXAMPLE 5 Write the function $f(x) = \sqrt[3]{9 + \sqrt{1+x}}$ as a composition of two functions.

Solution:

Let $U(x) = \sqrt{1+x}$ and $V(x) = \sqrt[3]{9+x}$

Now $\left(V \circ U\right)(x) = V(U(x)) = V\left(\sqrt{1+x}\right)$

$$= \sqrt[3]{9 + \sqrt{1+x}} = f(x).$$

⬤ Note There can be other choices for the functions U and V. For example, we can take $U(x) = 9 + \sqrt{1+x}$ and $V(x) = \sqrt[3]{x}$.

EXAMPLE 6 Given the functions f and g in numerical (table) forms as

x	−1	0	1	2	3	4
$f(x)$	3	1	2	−1	5	7

x	1	2	3	4	5	7
$g(x)$	0	4	10	3	1	2

Compute **a.** $(f \circ g)(2)$ and **b.** $(g \circ f)(-1)$

Solutions:

a. $(f \circ g)(2) = f(g(2)) = f(4) = 7$

b. $(g \circ f)(-1) = g(f(-1)) = g(3) = 10$

EXAMPLE 7 Compute **a.** $(f \circ g)(1)$ and **b.** $(g \circ f)(2)$ where the graphs of f and g are shown in Figure 2.56.

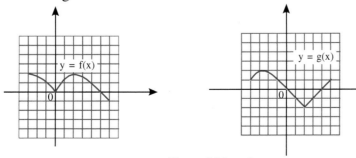

Figure 2.56

Solutions:

a. $(f \circ g)\,(1) = f(\,g(1)) = f(-1) = 1$

b. $(g \circ f\,)\,(2) = g(f(2)) = g(2) = -2$

Exercise 2.6

In exercises (1-14), use the given function f and g to find (a) $(f+g)$ (b) $(f-g)$ (c) fg (d) f/g (e) ef (f) $3g$
(g) $2f+3g$ (h) $2f-3g$. Also state the domain of each.

1. $f(x) = x^2 - x + 1,\ g(x) = 2x - 1$

2. $f(x) = 2x - 3,\ g(x) = x + 7$

3. $f(x) = x^2 - 5x - 7,\ g(x) = x^2 - 4$

4. $f(x) = -4x,\ g(x) = 1 + x^2$

5. $f(x) = 7x - 25,\ g(x) = x - 2$

6. $f(x) = 2x^2 - 1,\ g(x) = x^2 - 4$

7. $f(x) = x^2 - x - 3,\ g(x) = x$

8. $f(x) = x^3 - 1,\ g(x) = 9$

9. $f(x) = -4,\ g(x) = 1 - x^2$

10. $f(x) = -4x,\ g(x) = x^2 + 4$

11. $f(x) = \sqrt{x-2},\ g(x) = x$

12. $f(x) = \sqrt{x-5},\ g(x) = -3x$

13. $f(x) = \sqrt{x},\ g(x) = \sqrt{9-x^2}$

14. $f(x) = \sqrt{x^2-9},\ g(x) = x - 3$

In exercises (15-35), compute (a) $(f \circ g)\,(x)$ (b) $(g \circ f)\,(x)$

15. $f(x) = 4,\ g(x) = 5$

16. $f(x) = 4x - 1,\ g(x) = 2$

17. $f(x) = -5,\ g(x) = 3 - 7x$

18. $f(x) = 5x - 2,\ g(x) = 2 - x$

19. $f(x) = 13x - 9,\ g(x) = 9x + 13$

20. $f(x) = 9x + 2,\ g(x) = 2x - 3$

21. $f(x) = 5 - 2x,\ g(x) = 2x - 5$

22. $f(x) = x^2 - 9,\ g(x) = 2x - 3$

23. $f(x) = x^2 + 2x - 5,\ g(x) = x + 3$

24. $f(x) = x^2 - 19x,\ g(x) = x + 1$

25. $f(x) = \sqrt{x+5},\ g(x) = 2x - 7$

26. $f(x) = 4x - 2,\ g(x) = \sqrt{x+2}$

27. $f(x) = \dfrac{3}{x+2},\ g(x) = 2x + 5$

28. $f(x) = 2x + 1,\ g(x) = \dfrac{3}{x^2-1}$

29. $f(x) = 5x - 2,\ g(x) = |x-1|$

30. $f(x) = |x+3|,\ g(x) = |x|$

31. $f(x) = |x+1|,\ g(x) = |x-1|$

32. $f(x) = |2x - 1|,\ g(x) = |x+4|$

33. $f(x) = \sqrt{x},\ g(x) = \sqrt{9-x}$

34. $f(x) = \sqrt{x - 10},\ g(x) = \sqrt{x+1}$

35. $f(x) = \sqrt{5+x},\ g(x) = \sqrt{x}$

In exercises (36-39), compute (a) $(f \circ g)\,(x)$ (b) $(g \circ f)\,(x)$ and state the domain.

36. $f(x) = \dfrac{2}{x-1},\ g(x) = \dfrac{1}{x^2}$

37. $f(x) = x^2 + 4,\ g(x) = \dfrac{1}{x}$

38. $f(x) = \sqrt{x},\ g(x) = \sqrt{2-x}$

39. $f(x) = |1-5x|,\ g(x) = |3x-2|$

In exercises (40-47), compute   (a) $(f \circ g)(1)$ (b) $(g \circ f)(-2)$

40. $f(x) = 3x + 5, \ g(x) = x - 3$

41. $f(x) = 4x + 1, \ g(x) = \dfrac{1}{x}$

42. $f(x) = 3x + 7, \ g(x) = 2$

43. $f(x) = \dfrac{3x - 2}{x + 5}, \ g(x) = x^2$

44. $f(x) = \sqrt{x^2 + 1}, \ g(x) = 4x - 1$

45.

x	−2	−1	0	1	5	6
$f(x)$	1	5	2	−1	8	10

x	1	2	3	4	5
$g(x)$	5	−1	3	5	7

46.

x	−3	−2	0	1	2
$f(x)$	7	5	1	−3	−5

x	1	2	3	4	5
$g(x)$	0	1	2	3	4

47.

x	−5	−4	−3	−2	−1
$f(x)$	4	3	2	3	2

x	−2	0	1	3	5
$g(x)$	3	−3	−5	0	1

In exercises (48 to 50), the graphs of functions $y = f(x)$ and $y = g(x)$ are given. Find the value of:
(a) $(f \circ g)(1)$ (b) $(g \circ f)(-2)$.

48.
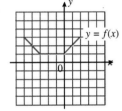
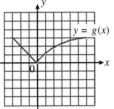

49.
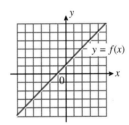

Figure 2.57

Figure 2.58

50.
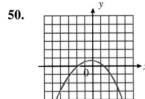

Figure 2.59

Writing Exercises

51.   Explain what is meant by the composition of functions.

52.   Distinguish between $f \circ g$ and $g \circ f$.

2.7 CHAPTER SUMMARY

1.   "A function can be defined as a rule that associates a unique output to each permissible input."

2.   A function f is described by its rule in the format
$$f(x) = \text{expression in } x.$$

3.   In the notation $f(x)$, x is called the independent variable.

4.   If in the statement $f(x) =$ expression, the expression part gives more than one value for some x value, then the statement does not describe a **function**, it is a relation.

5.   A function whose algebraic expression consists of the independent variable raised to a constant power is called a **power function**. In general a power function looks like,
$$f(x) = ax^n,$$
where a is any real number and n is a positive integer.

6.   **A polynomial function** is obtained by applying any combination of the operations: addition, subtraction, to constant multiple of power functions. In general, a polynomial function has the form $f(x) = a_n x^n + a_{n-1} x^{n-1} + \ldots + a_1 x + a_0$, where a_n, a_{n-1}, $\ldots$, a_1, a_0 are real numbers and n is a non-negative integer. Note that when $n = 0$, the polynomial is reduced to one term, $f(x) = a_0$, and is called **constant function.**

7.   A polynomial function of degree one is known as a **linear function.**

8.   A polynomial function of degree two is known as a **quadratic function.**

9.   A quotient of two polynomials function is called a rational function. In short $f(x) = \dfrac{p(x)}{q(x)}$ where $p(x)$ and $q(x)$ are polynomial functions and $q(x)$ is not a zero polynomial, is called a **rational function.**

10.   If the 'expression' part of a function contains an absolute value, the function is called an **absolute value function.** In short, an **absolute value function** has the form, $f(x) = \left| p(x) \right| + a(x)$, where $p(x)$ and $a(x)$ are polynomials.

11.   A function whose 'expression' part contains a radical of the variable is called a **radical function.**

12.   A function that is described by more than one expression is called a **piecewise function.**

13.   In the notation $f(x)$, x is also referred to as the **input** and $f(x)$ is called the **output.**

14.   If $f(x)$ is given by an expression in x, then the value of the function $f(x)$ when $x = k$, where k is the input and $f(x)$ is the output, is written as $f(k)$.

15.   The **domain** of a function consists of all possible inputs.

16. The **first guiding principle for the domain** says that the inputs that make the denominator of the expression part of the function equal to zero are not acceptable.

17. According to the **second guiding principle** for the domain, the inputs that make the radicand of an even radical negative are not acceptable.

18. The **range** of a function consists of all possible outputs.

19. A **function** can be written in three different forms :
     1. algebraic (formula) form,
     2. numerical (table) form, and
     3. graphical form.

20. A **numerical form** (or representation) of a function is written as a table

x	
$f(x)$	

where the x-row contains some x-values from the domain and the $f(x)$ – row has the corresponding function values.

21. For the **graphical representation** of a function we use the **rectangular system of coordinates**.

22. In the rectangular system of coordinates the horizontal axis represents the **input-axis** and the vertical axis represents the **output-axis.**

23. The **graph** of a function $f(x)$ consists of all those points (x, y) such that x equals the input and $f(x)$ $(= y)$ equals the output.

24. The graph of a **linear function** is always a **straight line.**

25. In a graph the **value** of the function for $x = k$ is the same as the **height** of the graph at $x = k$.

26. If the outputs (y values) increase as the inputs (x values) increase, then the graph (function) is **increasing** (rising).

27. If the outputs decrease as the inputs increase, then the graph (function) is **decreasing** (falling).

28. If the value of the function $f(x)$ is equal to zero at $x = k$, then $x = k$ is called a **zero of the function.**

29. In a graph **the zeros** of the function are given by the x-intercepts of the graph.

30. The value (output) of the function $f(x)$ when the input is zero is given by the y-intercept of the graph.

31. A graph represents a function provided that any vertical line intersects the graph in at most one point (**vertical line test**).

32. The **horizontal distance** between two points equals the absolute value of the difference between their x-coordinates.

33. The **vertical distance** between two points equals the absolute value of the difference between their y-coordinates.

34. The **distance** between two points (x_1, y_1) and (x_2, y_2) is

$$= \sqrt{(\text{horizontal distance})^2 + (\text{vertical distance})^2}$$

$$= \sqrt{(x_2 - x_1)^2 + (y_2 - y_1)^2}$$

35. The coordinates of the **midpoint** of the line segment that joins (x_1, y_1) and (x_2, y_2) are

$$\left(\frac{x_1 + x_2}{2}, \frac{y_1 + y_2}{2} \right).$$

36. The **slope** of the line that joins two points (x_1, y_1) and (x_2, y_2) is the number m defined by

$$m = \frac{y_2 - y_1}{x_2 - x_1} = \frac{\text{vertical change}}{\text{horizontal change}}$$

$$= \frac{\Delta y}{\Delta x}$$

37. Slope = rate of change

38. The **sum, difference, product, and quotient of functions** f and g are defined as follows :
$(f + g)(x) = f(x) + g(x), \quad (f - g)(x) = f(x) - g(x),$

$(f \cdot g) = f(x) \cdot g(x),$ and $\left(\dfrac{f}{g} \right)(x) = \dfrac{f(x)}{g(x)} \quad g(x) \neq 0$

The domain of each of these functions is the intersection of the domains of f and g.

39. The composition of functions f and g is written as $(f \circ g)$ and is defined as
$(f \circ g)(x) = f(g(x)).$

40. The domain of $f \circ g$ consists of all x in the domain of g for which $g(x)$ is in the domain of f.

2.8 CHAPTER REVIEW

In exercises (1-5), compute A∪B, A∩B, A/B and B/A.

1. $A = \{1, 2, x, l, p\}$, $B = \{x, 1, 5, t\}$.   **2.** $A = \{x | x \text{ is a multiple of } 5\}$, $B = \{x | x \text{ is a multiple of } 10\}$.

3. $A = \{x | x \text{ is a prime number}\}$, $B = \{x | x \text{ is an odd prime number}\}$.

4. $A = \{-2, -4, -6, \dots\}$, $B = \{-1, -3, -5, \dots\}$.

5. $A = $ Set of rational numbers, $B = $ Set of irrational numbers.

In exercises (6-9), write an expression that describes one of the variables in terms of the other.

6.   The perimeter (p) of a circle in terms of its radius.

7.   The total cost (c) of purchasing x VCR's at the rate of \$150 per VCR.

8.   Length (L) of a part of the number line segment between 5 and 12 in terms of n, the number of equal parts into which it is divided.

9.   Cost (C) of x units if each unit is marked \$2, given that the sales tax is 5%.

In exercises (10-17), write the absolute value function without the absolute value bars.

10. $f(x) = |x^2 + 1|$ **11.** $f(x) = |-(x^2 + 4)|$ **12.** $g(x) = |x - 10|$ if $x < 10$

13. $f(x) = |x + 12|, \ x > -12$ **14.** $h(x) = |x - 1| + 2|x - 3|$ if $x > 3$

15. $g(x) = 2|x + 1| + 5|x + 5|, \ x < -5$ **16.** $H(x) = |x - 7|$ **17.** $h(x) = |3x - 2|$

In exercises (18-25), write the function without the radical symbol.

18. $f(x) = \sqrt{2x + 1}$ **19.** $f(x) = \sqrt[3]{3x + 7}$ **20.** $g(x) = \sqrt{(x + 5)^2}$ **21.** $g(x) = \sqrt{(9x - 2)^2}$

22. $h(x) = \sqrt{x^2(x + 1)^2}$ **23.** $g(x) = \sqrt{x^2(5x + 6)}$ **24.** $f(x) = \sqrt[3]{(x + 9)^2}$ **25.** $g(x) = \sqrt[3]{x^2(8 + 4x)}$

In exercises (26-33), find (a) $f(-2)$,   (b) $f(a + 1)$ and   (c) $f(x + h) - f(x)$.

26. $f(x) = 4x - x^2$ **27.** $f(x) = 12$ **28.** $f(x) = 7$ **29.** $f(x) = 2x^2 + 3x - 9$

30. $f(x) = 3x - 2$ **31.** $f(x) = 7x + 11$ **32.** $f(x) = \sqrt{8 - x}$ **33.** $f(x) = \sqrt{7 - 9x}$

In exercises (34-39), find $f(3)$, $f(2)$, and $f(1)$.

34. $f(x) = \dfrac{2x - 1}{x + 2}$ **35.** $f(x) = \dfrac{2x + 5}{x^2 - 9}$ **36.** $f(x) = \dfrac{x^2 + 1}{x - 2}$

37. $f(x) = \dfrac{8x - 16}{3x^2 - 12}$ **38.** $f(x) = \dfrac{x^2 - x}{x^2 - 1}$ **39.** $f(x) = \dfrac{2x^2 + 3x + 5}{x^2 + 7}$

In exercises (40-45), find (a) $f(5)$ and (b) $f(2 + h)$; $h > 0$.

40. $f(x) = |x - 2|$ **41.** $f(x) = |x^2 - 4|$ **42.** $f(x) = \dfrac{|x - 2|}{x - 2}$

43. $f(x) = |4 - x^2|$ **44.** $f(x) = |2 - x|$ **45.** $f(x) = \dfrac{x^2 - 4}{|x - 2|}$

In exercises (46-49), find   (a) $f(-2)$,   (b) $f(1)$ (c) $f(1+h)$, $h > 0$.

46. $f(x) = \begin{cases} x+1 & if \quad x \leq 1 \\ 2x & if \quad x > 1 \end{cases}$

47. $f(x) = \begin{cases} 2x+5 & if \quad x < 1 \\ 8 & if \quad x = 1 \\ -x^2 & if \quad x > 1 \end{cases}$

48. $f(x) = \begin{cases} 2x+3 & if \quad x < 0 \\ 7 & if \quad x = 0 \\ x^2 & if \quad x > 0 \end{cases}$

49. $f(x) = \begin{cases} x^2 - 2 & if \quad x < 0 \\ x^2 + 2 & if \quad x \geq 0 \end{cases}$

In exercises (50-57), find the domain and range of the function.

50. $f(x) = 10x - 7$

51. $g(x) = x^2 - 9$

52. $g(x) = 2 + |x-1|$

53. $f(x) = -5 + |x^2 - 1|$

54. $h(x) = \dfrac{x+1}{x+3}$

55. $g(x) = \dfrac{x+10}{3x-5}$

56. $f(x) = \sqrt{x-10}$

57. $f(x) = \sqrt{x+15}$

In exercises (58-61), determine whether or not each is a function.

58. $g(x) = \pm\sqrt{x}$

59. $g(x) = x^3 - 3x + 5$

60.

x	−1	0	1	2	3	4
$f(x)$	5	0	6	9	6	1

61.

x	−2	0	1	0	2	1	3
$f(x)$	2	5	−17	−12	−27	5	12

In exercises (62-73), sketch the graph.

62. $f(x) = 5x - 2$

63. $f(x) = -3x + 5$

64. $f(x) = 2x - x^2$

65. $f(x) = x^2 + 4x$

66. $f(x) = x^3 + 2$

67. $f(x) = x^3 - 3$

68. $f(x) = |x-3|$

69. $f(x) = |x+5|$

70. $f(x) = \sqrt{x+2}$

71. $f(x) = \sqrt{x-5}$

72. $f(x) = \begin{cases} x^2 & ; \ x \leq 2 \\ 1 & ; \ x > 2 \end{cases}$

73. $f(x) = \begin{cases} |x| & ; \ x \leq 1 \\ \frac{1}{2}x & ; \ x > 1 \end{cases}$

In exercises 74-77, identify the function as a   (a) linear function   (b) quadratic function
(c) cubic function   (d) absolute value function.

74.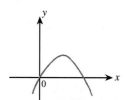

75.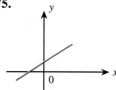

76.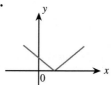

77.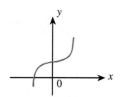

In exercises (78-81), examine each graph and find (a) y-intercept, if any   (b) zeros of the function, if any
(c) the x-values where the graph increases   (d) the domain (e) the range.

78.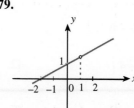

79.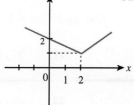

80.

81.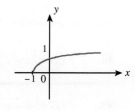

82. A person on a special diet records the
weight every week as in Figure 2.60.
Examine the graph and find

(a) the weeks when the weight increases,

(b) the weeks when the weight decreases, and

(c) the weeks when the weight is constant.

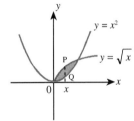

weeks

Figure 2.60

83. The area under the curve $y = 1 - x^2$
is estimated by the sum of the areas
of the shaded rectangles. Find the estimated
area (Figure 2.61)

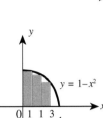

Figure 2.61

In exercises (84-85), apply the vertical line test to determine whether or not it is a function.

84.

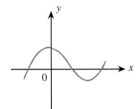

85.

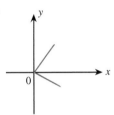

In exercises (86-89), find (a) the distance PQ   (b) the coordinates of the midpoint of PQ, and (c) the slope of the line PQ.

86. $P(-3, 9)$, $Q(2, 7)$ **87.** $P(6, -12)$, $Q(-4, -7)$ **88.** $P(x, 3x)$, $Q\left(x, x^2\right)$ **89.** $P(x, -5x)$, $Q(x, x^3)$

In exercises (90-91), find   (a) the vertical distance PQ   (b) the coordinates of the midpoint of the segment PQ.

90.

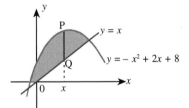

91.

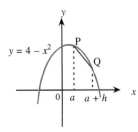

In exercises (92-93), find the slope of the secant line PQ in the simplest form.

92.

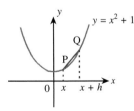

93.

In exercises (94-97), use the given functions f and g to find

(a) $f + g$ (b) $f - g$ (c) fg (d) f/g (e) $f \circ g$ (f) $g \circ f$ (g) $3f$ (h) $-5g$

94. $f(x) = 5x - 7$, $g(x) = x^2 - 9$ **95.** $f(x) = x^3 - 3x + 1$, $g(x) = -3x + 4$

96. $f(x) = \sqrt{x}$, $g(x) = 2x^2 - 3x$ **97.** $f(x) = \sqrt{x+3}$, $g(x) = x^2$

98. If $f(x) = \dfrac{x+1}{x-2}$ and $g(x) = \dfrac{2}{x^2}$, compute

   (a) $(f \circ g)(x)$ **(b)** $(g \circ f)(x)$ and state the domain of each.

In exercises (99-104), compute   **(a)** $(f \circ g)(2)$ **(b)** $(g \circ f)(-1)$

99. $f(x) = \dfrac{2x-1}{x+2}$, $g(x) = x^2$ **100.** $f(x) = 1$, $g(x) = 2x - 5$ **101.** $f(x) = \sqrt{x+3}$, $g(x) = x^2$

102.

x	-1	0	1	2	3
$f(x)$	2	3	-1	5	4

x	-1	1	2	3	4	5
$g(x)$	0	1	3	6	5	-7

103.

x	-2	-1	0	1	2	3
$f(x)$	2	1	0	1	2	-1

x	-1	0	1	2	3
$g(x)$	0	1	2	3	4

104.

x	-1	0	1	2	3	4
$f(x)$	0	1	-2	3	2	1

x	-2	-1	0	1	2	3
$g(x)$	-2	3	4	-4	1	2

Writing Exercises

105. Describe how the following can be broken up into simpler function.

   $S(p) = (3p+2)\sqrt{p^2 + 2}$.

106. Explain the difference between the functions $f \circ g$ and $g \circ f$.

2.9 CHAPTER TEST

1. Write a function statement for each of the following:

   a. The surface area (S) of a cube as a function of the length (x) of its edge.

   b. The cost (C) of manufacturing VCRs depends on the number (x) of VCRs produced plus the fixed cost of $1000. (assume that the cost per VCR is $100).

2. Write each function without the absolute value or radical symbols.

   a. $f(x) = 3|x-2| - 5|x-4|$ if $x < 2$ **b.** $g(x) = \sqrt{4x^2(x-2)^2}$ **c.** $h(x) = \sqrt[3]{x^3(x-1)^2}$

3. Evaluate $f(2)$ and $f(2+h)$, $h > 0$.

   a. $f(x) = \sqrt{6-x}$ **b.** $f(x) = 3x - x^2$ **c.** $f(x) = |2-x|$

   d. $f(x) = \dfrac{x^2 - 4}{x+3}$ **e.** $f(x) = \dfrac{x+4}{x^2 - 2x}$ **f.** $f(x) = \begin{cases} 3 & \text{if } x < 0 \\ 2-x & \text{if } 0 \le x < 2 \\ x^2 & \text{if } x \ge 2 \end{cases}$

4. Determine whether or not each is a function.

    a.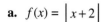

x	-5	0	2	1	3	7
$f(x)$	0	1	0	2	3	5

    b. $f(x) = \pm x$ c.

    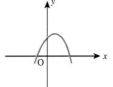

5. Sketch the graph of each function:

    a. $f(x) = |x+2|$ b. $f(x) = 3x - x^2$ c. $f(x) = \sqrt{x+3}$ d. $f(x) = \begin{cases} x^2 & \text{if } x \le 1 \\ 2 & \text{if } x > 1 \end{cases}$

6. Examine the graph of the function $f(x)$ and give

    a. the y-intercept,   b. zero of the function,

    c. the x-values where the graph increases or, decreases

    d. the domain, and   e. the range.

    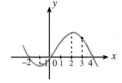

7. The area under the curve $y = x^2$ is estimated by the sum of the areas of the shaded rectangles. Find the estimated area.

    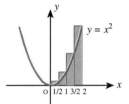

8. Find (a) vertical distance PQ and (b) the coordinates of the midpoint of the segment PQ.

    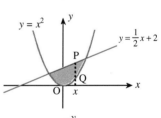

9. Find the slope of the secant line PQ in the simplest form.

    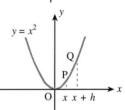

10. A pathologist records the growth of a particular bacteria in a dish. When it reaches a certain count, she drops a dose of antibiotics and then records the drop in the bacteria count. By examining a copy of her chart (Figure 2.62) find

    a. the bacteria count at 11 AM.

    b. the time when the count was 700,

    c. the initial count,

    d. the time when she dropped the antibiotics in the dish,

    e. the count at that time, and

    f. the count at the time she stopped recording.

11. If $f(x) = \sqrt{x-3}$ and $g(x) = x^2 - 6$, compute

    (a) $(f \circ g)(x)$ (b) $(g \circ f)(x)$.

    State the domain of each.

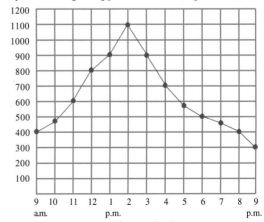

Figure 2.62

Equations and Inequalities

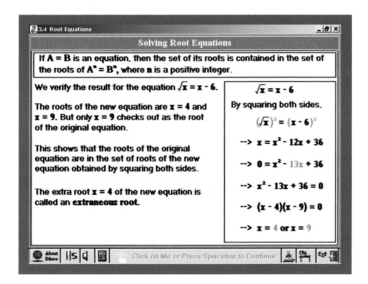

3.4 Root Equations

Solving Root Equations

If $A = B$ is an equation, then the set of its roots is contained in the set of the roots of $A^n = B^n$, where n is a positive integer.

We verify the result for the equation $\sqrt{x} = x - 6$.

The roots of the new equation are $x = 4$ and $x = 9$. But only $x = 9$ checks out as the root of the original equation.

This shows that the roots of the original equation are in the set of roots of the new equation obtained by squaring both sides.

The extra root $x = 4$ of the new equation is called an **extraneous root**.

$\sqrt{x} = x - 6$

By squaring both sides,

$(\sqrt{x})^2 = (x - 6)^2$

$\rightarrow x = x^2 - 12x + 36$

$\rightarrow 0 = x^2 - 13x + 36$

$\rightarrow x^2 - 13x + 36 = 0$

$\rightarrow (x - 4)(x - 9) = 0$

$\rightarrow x = 4 \text{ or } x = 9$

Click on Me or Press Spacebar to Continue

3

EQUATIONS AND INEQUALITIES

The notation $f(x)$ represents some quantity that depends on an input x. It is important from application point of view to know the inputs that give an output or a function value of zero. Such inputs (x-values) are called the **zeros** of the function. The zeros of the function $f(x)$ are the same as the solutions of the equation $f(x) = 0$.

Thus, we devote major part of this chapter in exploring the **solutions** of **equations** $f(x) = 0$, when $f(x)$ is a polynomial, rational, absolute value, or a radical function. We will also look into the sign behavior of the function near a zero. In other words, we would like to know the signs of the function on both sides of a zero of the function. This probe leads us to the **solutions of inequalities** such as

$$f(x) > 0 \ \text{ or } \ f(x) \geq 0 \ \text{ or } \ f(x) < 0 \ \text{ or } \ f(x) \leq 0.$$

Lastly, by using the new tools of this chapter and with the guiding principles of Chapter 2, we will give a more efficient way of finding the domain of a function.

The discussion in this chapter is organized in seven sections.

3.1   *Polynomial Equations;*

3.2   *Rational Equations;*

3.3   *Absolute Value Equations;*

3.4   *Root Equations;*

3.5   *Inequalities;*

3.6   *Domain of a Function (Revisited); and*

3.7   *Roots of Polynomial Equations (Revisited).*

3.1 POLYNOMIAL EQUATIONS

In this section we will investigate the solutions of polynomial equations of different degrees. Before we start the discussion, recall that the statement that "α is a solution of the equation" is equivalent to the statement that "α is a root of the equation".

In order to use the graphical method (technology), it is important to learn how to translate an equation into a form that connects the **roots** of the equation with the **zeros** of the function. The following rule explains how to get the function whose zeros are the same as the roots of the given equation.

Objectives ▶ ▶

In this section you will learn about:

A. First Degree (Linear) Equations;

B. Second Degree (Quadratic) Equations;

C. The Factor Theorem;

D. Higher Degree Equations; and

E. Forming Equations.

From Roots of an Equation to Zeros of a Function

The roots of an equation $p(x) = q(x)$ are the same as the zeros of the function $f(x) = p(x) - q(x)$.

To find the roots of an equation, we use the above rule in two steps:

Step 1   Transfer all terms to one side of the equation; the other side becomes zero.

Step 2   The roots of the equation are the zeros of the function $f(x)$, where

$f(x)$ is the non-zero side of the equation.

EXAMPLE 1   Find the function whose zeros are the same as the roots of the equation

$$x^2 - 5x = 6.$$

Solution:

Step 1   Transferring terms over to the left side of the equation gives

$$x^2 - 5x - 6 = 0.$$

Step 2   The roots of the equation are the same as the zeros of the function

$$f(x) = x^2 - 5x - 6.$$

Now we proceed to solve polynomial equations. We will give both the algebraic and the graphical methods. Since a polynomial equation can be of degree one or two or higher, we consider each case separately. Let us begin with a polynomial equation of degree one.

A. FIRST DEGREE (LINEAR) EQUATIONS

Recall that the **degree** of a polynomial is the highest exponent of the variable. Therefore, in a linear equation the highest exponent of the unknown is always one. To solve a linear equation algebraically, we give the following strategy. There are two different kinds of first degree equations: those with one unknown, whose solution is a number, and those with more than one unknown, whose solutions are expressions. The steps to solve the two kinds of equations are essentially the same. The solution to the first type can be obtained graphically by finding the zero of the related function $f(x)$.

To Solve a Linear Equation

Algebraically (Roots)

EXAMPLE 2   Solve $\dfrac{1}{2}x - \dfrac{2}{5} = 1 - \dfrac{x}{3}$

Equation in one unknown

> * lcd is the abbreviation for **least common denominator**.

Procedure

Step 1   Remove fractions (How?)

Multiply each term on both sides, by the * lcd. Also remove parentheses, if any, using the distributive rule.

Solution :

⟶ Multiplying by the lcd, 30 gives

$$30\left(\frac{1}{2}x\right) - 30\left(\frac{2}{5}\right) = 30(1) - 30\left(\frac{x}{3}\right)$$

$$15x - 12 = 30 - 10x$$

Step **2** Transfer the terms with the unknown over to one side and everything else to the other side by adding or subtracting the same quantity to both sides of the equation. $\longrightarrow$ $15x + 10x = 30 + 12$

Step **3** Simplify both sides. $\longrightarrow$ $25x = 42$

Step **4** Divide both sides by the coefficient of the unknown. $\longrightarrow$ Dividing by 25 gives $x = \dfrac{42}{25}$

Graphically (Zeros)

To solve the equation graphically, *we first find a function* whose zeros are the same as the roots of the equation. Then we graph the function either by hand or with a graphing calculator. The *x*-intercept(s) of the graph give the zeros of the function, which are the roots of the equation. We illustrate this method as follows:

Step **1** Transfer all terms of the equation over to one side. Simplify (optional). $\longrightarrow$ $\dfrac{1}{2}x - \dfrac{2}{5} - 1 + \dfrac{x}{3} = 0$ or

$$\dfrac{5}{6}x - \dfrac{7}{5} = 0$$

Step **2** Let the expression for the function $f(x)$ be the expression on the non-zero side of the equation. $\longrightarrow$ $f(x) = \dfrac{5}{6}x - \dfrac{7}{5}$

Step **3** Sketch the graph of the function and find its *x*-intercepts. $\longrightarrow$ To sketch the graph of

$y = f(x) = \dfrac{5}{6}x - \dfrac{7}{5}$ we can either use the paper and pencil method or a graphing calculator.

By Hand (paper pencil method)

a. We write the function as

$$y = f(x) = \dfrac{5}{6}x - \dfrac{7}{5}$$

b. To write this function in a numerical form, we attempt to find only two points because the graph of a linear function is always a straight line. We may however, plot three points to ensure that the graph is correct (why?).

x	0	1	2
y	$\dfrac{-7}{5}$	$\dfrac{-17}{30}$	$\dfrac{4}{15}$

With Graphical Calculator

a. Let $y1 = \dfrac{5}{6}x - \dfrac{7}{5}$

b. Select a suitable RANGE and press GRAPH

c. Plot the points and draw the line by joining the points

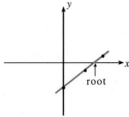

Figure 3.1(a)

d. The zero of the function or the root of the equation is given by the *x*-intercept.

> *Comment:* It is hard to read an *x*-intercept like $\dfrac{42}{25}$ on a graph paper.

c. ZOOM-IN near the *x*-intercept and use TRACE. Successive repetition of ZOOM-IN and TRACE will improve the approximation of the **root** of the equation.

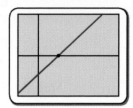

Figure 3.1(b)

Check that the root of the equation is ≈ 1.67658

EXAMPLE 3
Literal Equation

Solve $5y - 2x = 7$ for y.

Solution: Since the highest exponent of the unknown (y) is one, the equation is a linear equation.

Algebraically

Step 1   There are no fractions or parentheses.

Step 2   Transferring terms without the unknown (y) over to the right side of the equation becomes $5y = 7 + 2x$.

Step 3   Each side is in simplified form.

Step 4   Dividing both sides by the coefficient of the unknown y gives $y = \dfrac{7}{5} + \dfrac{2}{5}x$.

Thus, we solved the equation $5y - 2x = 7$ for y.

Graphically   Not applicable.

EXAMPLE 4
Literal Equation

Solve $C = 2\pi r$ for r.

Solution: The highest exponent of the unknown (r) is 1. Therefore, it is a linear equation.

Algebraically

Step 1   Not applicable, because there are no fractions or parentheses.

Step 2   The term with the unknown r is already on one side and the term without the unknown is on the other side.

Step 3   Both sides are in simplified forms.

Step 4   Dividing both sides by the coefficient (2π) of the unknown gives

$$\frac{C}{2\pi} = \frac{2\pi r}{2\pi} \quad \text{or} \quad \frac{C}{2\pi} = r$$

Graphically   Not applicable.

B. SECOND DEGREE (QUADRATIC) EQUATIONS

In a quadratic equation, the highest exponent of the unknown is 2. A quadratic equation in standard form is $ax^2 + bx + c = 0$. We can solve the equation algebraically and graphically.

1. To solve a Quadratic Equation   Algebraically (Roots)

Procedure

EXAMPLE 5   Solve $x^2 - 6x = -5$

Solution:

Step 1   Remove all fractions and parentheses. $\longrightarrow$ There are no fractions or parentheses.

Step 2   Transfer all terms over to one side and simplify. $\longrightarrow$ $x^2 - 6x + 5 = 0$

Step 3   Either use the **factoring method** or the **quadratic formula method.**

Factoring Method

a.   Factor the nonzero side. $\longrightarrow$ $(x - 5)(x - 1) = 0$

b.   Set each factor to zero $\longrightarrow$ $x - 5 = 0 \mid x - 1 = 0$

c.   Solve each equation $\longrightarrow$ $x = 5 \mid x = 1$

Thus, the two roots of $x^2 - 6x = -5$ are 1 and 5.

Formula Method

> **Quadratic Formula**
> Two roots of the equation $ax^2 + bx + c = 0$ are
> given by $x = \dfrac{-b \pm \sqrt{b^2 - 4ac}}{2a}$.

Step 1   Compare with the standard form $ax^2 + bx + c = 0$ and list the values of a, b and c. $\longrightarrow$ Comparing $x^2 - 6x + 5 = 0$ with $ax^2 + bx + c = 0$ gives $a = 1$, $b = -6$, and $c = 5$.

Step 2   Substitute the values of a, b, and c in the formula: $\longrightarrow$

$$x = \frac{-b \pm \sqrt{b^2 - 4ac}}{2a}$$

$$x = \frac{-b \pm \sqrt{b^2 - 4ac}}{2a}$$

$$= \frac{-(-6) \pm \sqrt{(-6)^2 - 4(1)(5)}}{2(1)}$$

$$= \frac{6 \pm \sqrt{36 - 20}}{2}$$

Step 3   Simplify the radical.   ⟶

$$= \frac{6 \pm \sqrt{16}}{2} = \frac{6 \pm 4}{2}$$

Step 4   Separate the two roots and   ⟶
simplify.

$$= \frac{6+4}{2}, \frac{6-4}{2} = 5 , 1$$

Thus, the two roots of
$x^2 - 6x + 5 = 0$ are 5 and 1.

> *Comment:*   Factoring may not always be easy or even possible. The quadratic formula
> can be applied in all cases. Recall that $ax^2 + bx + c$ can be factored if it is
> possible to find two numbers p and q such that $p + q = b$ and $pq = ac$.

2. To Solve the Quadratic Equation Graphically

A function whose zeros are the same as the roots of the
equation $x^2 - 6x = -5$ is $f(x) = x^2 - 6x + 5$.

Let $y1 = x^2 - 6x + 5$. Press GRAPH after selecting
a suitable range. Use ZOOM-IN and TRACE for each
x-intercept and approximate the roots.

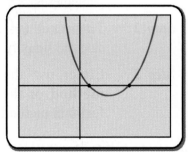

Figure 3.2

> **Remark:**   *The zero $x = 1$ of the function $f(x) = x^2 - 6x + 5$ corresponds to the factor $x - 1$, and the zero*
> *$x = 5$ corresponds to the factor $x - 5$. This means that if we can find the zeros of a function*
> *$f(x) =$ expression, then we can also find the factors of the 'expression'. This relationship*
> *between the zero of a polynomial function and the factor of its expression deserves a special*
> *mention and is discussed in the next objective as the factor theorem.*

C. THE FACTOR THEOREM

> **Factor Theorem**
>
> If $x = r$ is a zero of the polynomial function $f(x)$, then
> $x - r$ is a factor of $f(x)$. Conversely, if $x - r$ is a factor of
> $f(x)$, then $x = r$ is a zero of $f(x)$.

Proof of the Factor Theorem

Recall the remainder theorem in section 1.5C.

"The value of the polynomial for $x = r$ is the same as the remainder in the division of the polynomial by
$x - r$".

We use the same result to prove the factor theorem. Let $q(x)$ be the quotient and R the remainder, when
we divide $f(x)$ by $x - r$.

Then $f(x) =$ (Quotient)(Divisor) + Remainder

$$f(x) = q(x)(x - r) + R \qquad\qquad\qquad \textbf{(1)}$$

Substitute $x = r$ in this equation:

$$f(r) = q(r)(r - r) + R$$
$$f(r) = R$$

But $f(r) = 0$, since $x = r$ is a zero of the function $f(x)$.

Therefore, $R = 0$, and we get from (**1**)

$$f(x) = q(x)(x - r) \longrightarrow (x - r) \text{ is a factor of } f(x).$$

Conversely: If $x = r$ is a factor of $f(x)$ then $f(x) = q(x)(x - r)$

$$\longrightarrow \quad f(r) = q(r)(r - r) = 0$$
$$\longrightarrow \quad x = r \text{ is a zero of } f(x)$$

EXAMPLE 6   For the equation $x^2 - 2x = 2$ find

    a.   the **exact** roots, and

    b.   the **approximate** values of the roots by using a graphical method.

Solutions: **a.**   For the **exact** roots of the equation, we use one of the algebraic methods.

    Step 1   There are no fractions or parentheses.

    Step 2   Collecting all terms on one side of the equation gives $x^2 - 2x - 2 = 0$

    Step 3   The factoring method is not applicable. (why?) We use the quadratic formula.

Comparing the equation with the standard equation $ax^2 + bx + c = 0$ gives $a = 1$, $b = -2$, and $c = -2$.

Substituting the values of a, b, and c in the formula $x = \dfrac{-b \pm \sqrt{b^2 - 4ac}}{2a}$ gives

$$x = \frac{-(-2) \pm \sqrt{(-2)^2 - 4(1)(-2)}}{2(1)}$$

$$* \sqrt{12} = \sqrt{2^2 \cdot 3} = 2\sqrt{3}$$

$$* \qquad = \frac{2 \pm \sqrt{4 + 8}}{2} = \frac{2 \pm \sqrt{12}}{2}$$

Simplifying the radical, we get $x = \dfrac{2 \pm 2\sqrt{3}}{2} = \dfrac{2(1 \pm \sqrt{3})}{2} = 1 \pm \sqrt{3}$

The two **exact** roots of the equation are $1 + \sqrt{3}$ and $1 - \sqrt{3}$.

⬤Note $\sqrt{3} \approx 1.7320508$ so the roots are approximately 2.7320508 and $-.7320508$.

---

    b.   Approximate the value of the roots using a calculator

A function whose zeros are the same as the roots of the equation is

$$f(x) = x^2 - 2x - 2$$

Let $y1 = x^2 - 2x - 2$. Press GRAPH after selecting a suitable range (The standard range; $x - \min = -10, x - \max = 10, y - \min = -10,$ and $y - \max = 10$ is one suitable range).

Use ZOOM-IN and TRACE for each x-intercept and check the roots are

$$\approx 2.7380957 \text{ and } -.7142851$$

More accurate answers can be obtained by changing the range and getting y as close to 0 as possible on the *trace*.

EXAMPLE 7   Solve the equation $x^2 = 4x - 4$.

       a. algebraically   **b.** graphically

Solutions: **a.**   **Algebraically**

Formula Method	

Step 1   Not applicable, because there are no fractions or parentheses.

Comparing the equation with

$ax^2 + bx + c = 0$ gives
$a = 1, b = -4, c = 4$

Step 2   By collecting all terms on the left of the equality sign gives $x^2 - 4x + 4 = 0$.

Substituting the values of a, b, and c in the formula gives

Step 3   **Factoring Method**

Factoring the nonzero side gives
$(x - 2)(x - 2) = 0$

$$x = \frac{4 \pm \sqrt{16 - 16}}{2}$$

$$x = \frac{4 \pm 0}{2}$$

Setting each factor to zero gives
$x - 2 = 0, \; x - 2 = 0$

By separating the roots we get

Step 4   Solving the equations gives

$$x = 2, \; x = 2$$

$$x = \frac{4 + 0}{2}, \frac{4 - 0}{2} = 2, 2.$$

In this case, the two roots of the equation are equal.

---

* Remark: *Since the root $x = 2$ is repeated twice, the root is of **multiplicity** two.*

---

*   In general if a root of an equation is repeated k times, we call it a root of **multiplicity k.**

b. Graphically

A function whose zeros are the same as the roots of the equation is $f(x) = x^2 - 4x + 4$.

Let $y1 = x^2 - 4x + 4$. Graph the function on a suitable range, use ZOOM-IN and TRACE repeatedly, and estimate the zeros of the function. The result will be $x \approx 2$.

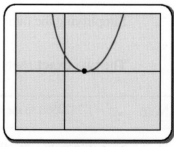

Figure 3.3

Comment: Since $x = 2, 2$ are roots of $f(x) = 0$, therefore, by the factor theorem, $x - 2$ and $x - 2$ are the factors of $f(x)$.

EXAMPLE 8   Solve $\dfrac{3x^2}{2} = 2(x-2)$ algebraically and check the answer graphically.

Solution:

a. Algebraically

Step 1   Multiplying the equation by 2 gives
$$3x^2 = 4(x-2) \text{ or } 3x^2 = 4x - 8$$

Step 2   Collecting terms on the left side gives
$$3x^2 - 4x + 8 = 0.$$

Step 3   The factoring method is not applicable.(why?) Therefore, we use the quadratic formula method.

By comparing the equation with
$$ax^2 + bx + c = 0, \text{ we get } a = 3, \ b = -4, \text{ and } c = 8.$$

Substituting the values for *a*, *b,* and *c* in the formula, we get

$$x = \frac{4 \pm \sqrt{16 - 96}}{6} = \frac{4 \pm \sqrt{-80}}{6}$$

* $= \dfrac{4 \pm i\sqrt{80}}{6} = \dfrac{4 \pm 4i\sqrt{5}}{6}$

$$= \frac{2(1 \pm i\sqrt{5})}{3}$$

$$= \frac{2(1 + i\sqrt{5})}{3} \text{ and } \frac{2(1 - i\sqrt{5})}{3}$$

Thus, the equation $\dfrac{3x^2}{2} = 2(x-2)$ has no **real** root

Let us confirm this graphically.

* $\sqrt{-80} = \sqrt{(-1)80}$

$= \sqrt{-1} \times \sqrt{80} = i\sqrt{80}$

$= i\sqrt{2^2 \cdot 2^2 \cdot 5}$

$= 2 \cdot 2i\sqrt{5}$

$= 4i\sqrt{5}$

See appendix A for more details of imaginary numbers.

b. Graphically

A function whose zeros are the same as the roots of the equation is $f(x) = \dfrac{3x^2}{2} - 2(x-2)$.

Let $y1 = \dfrac{3x^2}{2} - 2(x-2)$. Select a suitable range and graph the function (Figure 3.4).

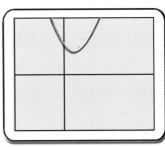

(Figure 3.4)

The graph has no *x*-intercept. In other words, the function has no zeros. Equivalently, the equation has no real roots.

EXAMPLE 9   Approximate the roots of the equation $x^2 - 2.25x - 0.625 = 0$ and use the factor theorem to give approximate factors of the trinomial.

Solution: **Graphical**

For approximate roots of the equation, we find approximate zeros of the function $f(x) = x^2 - 2.25x - 0.625$.

In a graphing calculator, let $y1 = x^2 - 2.25x - 0.625$. On the standard range the graph is as shown on the screen (Figure 3.5).

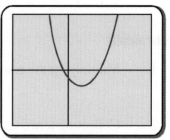

Figure 3.5

By using ZOOM-IN and TRACE, it can be verified that the approximate locations of the zeros (x-intercepts) are

$$-0.238095 \text{ and } 2.5$$

Using the factor theorem, the factors of the polynomial are given approximately by

$$x^2 - 2.25x - 0.625 \approx (x - 2.5)(x + 0.238)$$

Algebraically

$$x^2 - 2.25x - 0.625 = 0 \longrightarrow x^2 - \frac{9}{4}x - \frac{5}{8} = 0 \longrightarrow 8x^2 - 18x - 5 = 0$$

$$\longrightarrow (2x - 5)(4x + 1) = 0$$
$$\longrightarrow 2x - 5 = 0 \quad \text{or} \quad 4x + 1 = 0$$
$$\longrightarrow x = \frac{5}{2} = 2.5 \quad \text{or} \quad x = -\frac{1}{4} = -.25$$

Note   The algebraic answer is exact whereas the graphical answer is approximate. A better approximation can be obtained by zooming in several times.

D. HIGHER DEGREE EQUATIONS

Now we consider equations of degree higher than two. The easiest form of a higher degree equation, when solving, is the factored form such as

$$(x - 2)(x + 3)^2 (x - 10) = 0$$

To solve this, we extend the factoring method used for a quadratic equation. Set each factor to zero.

$$x - 2 = 0 \quad \text{or} \quad (x + 3)^2 = 0 \quad \text{or} \quad x - 10 = 0$$

Solving these equations gives

$$x = 2 \quad \text{or} \quad x + 3 = 0, \quad x + 3 = 0 \quad \text{or} \quad x = 10$$
$$x = -3, \qquad x = -3$$

Therefore, $x = 2, x = -3, x = -3$ and $x = 10$ are the roots of the equation. The root -3 is of multiplicity 2.

Suppose, the equation is not in factored form. We will explain the algebraic method with a cubic equation. However, the procedure can also be used for other higher degree equations. Graphically, this procedure is the same as for quadratic or linear equations.

To Solve a Higher Degree Equation

EXAMPLE 10   Solve $2x^3 + x^2 - 13x + 6 = 0$

Procedure   *Solution:*

Step 1   Find one of the roots of the $\longrightarrow$ Substituting $x = 1$ gives:
equation by inspection. ($x = k$ is $2(1)^3 + (1)^2 - 13(1) + 6$
a root if it satisfies the equation, $= 2 + 1 - 13 + 6 \neq 0.$
so try $x = \pm 1, \pm 2, \pm 3, \ldots$).

Substituting $x = -1$ gives:
$2(-1)^3 + (-1)^2 - 13(-1) + 6$
$= -2 + 1 + 13 + 6 \neq 0$

Substituting $x = 2$ gives:
$2(2)^3 + (2)^2 - 13(2) + 6$
$= 16 + 4 - 26 + 6 = 0.$

Step 2   Suppose $x = k$ is a root in $\longrightarrow$ Since $x = 2$ satisfies the equation, so
Step 1. By factor theorem $x - k$ $x = 2$ is a root of the equation.
is a factor of the polynomial.
Divide the polynomial by the   By factor theorem $x-2$ is a factor of
factor $x - k$. (Synthetic division $2x^3 + x^2 - 13x + 6$
is faster).

Dividing

> * The remainder $2x^3 + x^2 - 13x + 6$ by $x - 2$ gives
> was expected to
> be zero (why?)

$$\begin{array}{r|rrrr} 2 & 2 & 1 & -13 & 6 \\ & & 4 & 10 & -6 \\ \hline & 2 & 5 & -3 & 0 \end{array} \ \ *$$

Hence,

Step 3   Use the quotient to write an $\longrightarrow$ $2x^3 + x^2 - 13x + 6$
equation of degree one less than $= (x - 2)(2x^2 + 5x - 3)$
the original equation. $2x^2 + 5x - 3 = 0$

Step 4   If the equation in Step 3 is of $\longrightarrow$ The equation in Step 3 is of degree 2, so
degree 2, then use the factoring   we use either factoring or the formula
method or the quadratic formula   method. We prefer the factoring method,
method. If it is still a polynomial   if possible.
equation of degree more than 2, $2x^2 + 5x - 3 = 0$
then repeat Steps 1-3. $(2x - 1)(x + 3) = 0$

$$\begin{array}{c|c} 2x - 1 = 0 & x + 3 = 0 \\ 2x = 1 & x = -3 \\ x = \dfrac{1}{2} & \end{array}$$

Thus, the roots of $2x^3 + x^2 - 13x + 6 = 0$

are $x = 2,\ \dfrac{1}{2}$, and -3.

Graphically

A function whose zeros are the same as the roots of the equation is $f(x) = 2x^3 + x^2 - 13x + 6$.

Graph $y1 = 2x^3 + x^2 - 13x + 6$ on the standard range and use ZOOM-IN and TRACE to locate the zeros of the function.

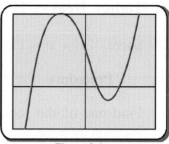

Figure 3.6

EXAMPLE 11   Solve $x^3 - x^2 + 3x + 5 = 0$.

Solution: **Algebraically**

Step 1   We check that $x = -1$ is a root of the equation, because

$$(-1)^3 - (-1)^2 + 3(-1) + 5 = -1 - 1 - 3 + 5 = 0$$

Step 2   Divide $x^3 - x^2 + 3x + 5$ by $x + 1$.

(By factor theorem, if $x = -1$ is a root then $x + 1$ is a factor of the polynomial)

```
-1|  1   -1   3    5
         -1   2   -5
   ─────────────────
     1   -2   5    0
```

Thus, $x^3 - x^2 + 3x + 5 = (x + 1)(x^2 - 2x + 5)$

Step 3   The quotient gives the equation $x^2 - 2x + 5 = 0$

Step 4   Since the factoring method is not applicable, we use the quadratic formula method. Comparing the equation with $ax^2 + bx + c = 0$ gives $a = 1$, $b = -2$, and $c = 5$. The quadratic formula gives

$$x = \frac{-(-2) \pm \sqrt{(-2)^2 - 4(1)(5)}}{2(1)} = \frac{2 \pm \sqrt{4 - 20}}{2} = \frac{2 \pm \sqrt{-16}}{2} = \frac{2 \pm 4i}{2} = 1 \pm 2i$$

*   Thus, the equation has only one real root (-1) and two imaginary roots $(1 + 2i$ and $1 - 2i)$.

* We notice that the imaginary roots occur in pairs. One root is the conjugate of the other. Conjugates have the form, $a + ib$ and $a - ib$.

Graphically

Let $y1 = x^3 - x^2 + 3x + 5$. Graph $y1$ on the standard range (Figure 3.7).

The graph shows only one x-intercept (zero of the function). By using ZOOM-IN and TRACE we can estimate the real root of the equation.

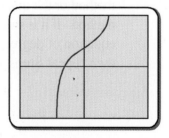

Figure 3.7

EXAMPLE 12   By using a graphical calculator estimate the roots of the equation

$$x^4 - 4x^3 - 8x^2 + 12 = 0$$

Solution: A function whose zeros are the same as the roots of the equation is

$$f(x) = x^4 - 4x^3 - 8x^2 + 12$$

Let $y1 = x^4 - 4x^3 - 8x^2 + 12$. Graph the function on the standard range (or any other suitable range).

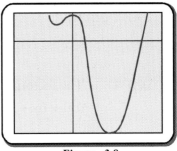

Figure 3.8

The graph of the function has only two *x*-intercepts. This means that the equation has only two real roots. Using ZOOM-IN AND TRACE, we estimate the zeros of the function at **1.04 and 5.4.**

Thus, the two real roots of the equation are $\approx$ **1.04 and 5.4.**

> **Important Result**
> In general a polynomial equation of degree *n* has exactly *n* roots, if we count a root repeated *k* times as *k* roots and also count imaginary roots.

Remarks: 1. *Imaginary roots always occur in conjugate pairs.*

2. *In example 12, above, we got only two real roots. The other two roots must be imaginary.*

EXAMPLE 13 Find all roots of the equation $x^4 - x^3 - x + 1 = 0$

Solution: **Algebraically**

Step 1 We check that $x = 1$ is a root of the equation, because

$$1^4 - 1^3 - 1 + 1 = 1 - 1 - 1 + 1 = 0$$

Step 2 Divide $x^4 - x^3 - x + 1$ by $x - 1$.

(By factor theorem, if $x = 1$ is a root of $x^4 - x^3 - x + 1 = 0$, then $x - 1$ is a factor of the polynomial $x^4 - x^3 - x + 1$).

$$
\begin{array}{r|rrrrr}
1 & 1 & -1 & 0 & -1 & 1 \\
  &   & 1 & 0 & 0 & -1 \\
\hline
  & 1 & 0 & 0 & -1 & 0
\end{array}
$$

Thus, $x^4 - x^3 - x + 1 = (x - 1)(x^3 - 1)$.

Step 3 The quotient gives the equation

$$x^3 - 1 = 0$$

This is still an equation of degree greater than 2. So, we repeat steps 1 through 3.

- We check that $x = 1$ is a root of the equation $x^3 - 1 = 0$, because

$$1^3 - 1 = 1 - 1 = 0$$

- Divide $x^3 - 1$ by $x - 1$

$$
\begin{array}{r|rrrr}
1 & 1 & 0 & 0 & -1 \\
  &   & 1 & 1 & 1 \\
\hline
  & 1 & 1 & 1 & 0
\end{array}
$$

Thus, $x^3 - 1 = (x - 1)(x^2 + x + 1)$.

• The quotient gives the equation

$$x^2 + x + 1 = 0$$

The resulting equation is a quadratic. So, we go to step 4.

Step 4   The factoring method is not applicable to $x^2 + x + 1 = 0$. Comparing this equation with $ax^2 + bx + c = 0$, we get $a = 1$, $b = 1$, $c = 1$. The quadratic formula gives

$$x = \frac{-1 \pm \sqrt{1^2 - 4(1)(1)}}{2(1)}$$

$$= \frac{-1 \pm \sqrt{1-4}}{2}$$

$$= \frac{-1 \pm \sqrt{-3}}{2}$$

$$= \frac{-1 \pm i\sqrt{3}}{2}$$

Hence, the roots of the given equation $x^4 - x^3 - x + 1 = 0$ are

$$x = 1, 1, \frac{-1 - i\sqrt{3}}{2}, \frac{-1 + i\sqrt{3}}{2}.$$

Graphically

Let $y_1 = x^4 - x^3 - x + 1$. Graph y_1 on the standard range (Fig. 3.9). Use TRACE to explore the graph. The graph touches the x-axis at $x = 1$.

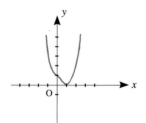

Figure 3.9

Since the given equation is of degree 4 and complex roots occur in pairs, one of the following must happen.

a. $x = 1$ is a root that is repeated four times.

b. $x = 1$ is a root that is repeated two times.

a.   If $x = 1$ is a root that is repeated four times, then the graph of the $x^4 - x^3 - x + 1$ must be the same as the graph of $(x - 1)(x - 1)(x - 1)(x - 1)$, that is $(x-1)^4$.
[$x - 1$ is a factor of $x^4 - x^3 - x + 1$ four times]
Let $y_2 = (x - 1)^4$

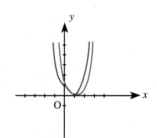

Figure 3.10

Now graph both y_1 and y_2 on the standard range. The graphs are shown in Fig. 3.10.

They are not identical. Hence $x = 1$ is not a root that is repeated four times.

b.   So, it follows that the root $x = 1$ is repeated two times only. By the factor theorem $(x - 1)^2$ is a factor of $x^4 - x^3 - x + 1$. The other two roots must come from the quotient

$$\frac{x^4 - x^3 - x + 1}{(x-1)^2}$$

Let $y_3 = y_1/(x-1)^2$ or $(x^4 - x^3 - x + 1)/(x-1)^2$. Graph only y_3 on the standard range. The graph (Fig. 3.11) shows that y_3 has no x-intercepts. This means that the remaining roots of $x^4 - x^3 - x + 1 = 0$ are complex numbers.

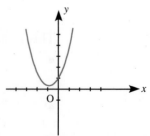

Figure 3.11

To complete the solution repeat the last two steps of the algebraic solution.

Comment: When a graph does not have x-intercepts, the graphical method fails to give the imaginary roots.

E. FORMING EQUATIONS

So far we have been discussing how to find roots of equations. Now we look at the reverse problem of finding an equation with given roots. The 'Factor theorem' comes in very handy for this purpose. In fact, by repeatedly * applying Factor Theorem we get the following result:

Factorization Theorem

Let $f(x) = a_n x^n + a_{n-1} x^{n-1} + \ldots + a_1 x + a_0$ be a polynomial of degree n (≥ 1). Then $f(x)$ can be written as

$$f(x) = a_n(x - r_1)(x - r_2) \ldots (x - r_n)$$

where $r_1, r_2, \ldots, r_n$ may be real or complex, repeated or distinct.

> * $f(x) = (x - r_1)\ g(x)$
>
> $g(x) = (x - r_2)\ h(x)$
> .
> .
> .
>
> where $r_1, r_2, \ldots$ are the zeros of the polynomials $f(x), g(x), \ldots$

The result stated as Factorization Theorem is made possible by the application of the following theorem known as 'Fundamental Theorem of Algebra'.

Fundamental Theorem of Algebra

Every polynomial equation has at least one root, real or complex.

In general, there can be many equations with given roots. For example,

$$(x - 1)(x + 1) = 0 \;\rightarrow\; x^2 - 1 = 0$$
$$2(x - 1)(x + 1)(x + 2) = 0 \;\rightarrow\; 2x^3 + 4x^2 - 2x - 4 = 0$$
$$(x - 1)(x + 1)(x^2 + x + 1) = 0 \;\rightarrow\; x^4 + x^3 - x - 1 = 0$$

are **all equations** with 1 and −1 as two roots. However, $x^2 - 1 = 0$ has just 1 and −1 as roots and no more. In other words, $x^2 - 1 = 0$ is an equation of lowest degree with 1 and −1 as its roots.

Remark: $x^2 - 1 = 0$ and $ax^2 - a = 0$ $(a \neq 0)$ both have 1 and −1 as their roots. However, coefficient of the highest degree term in $x^2 - 1$ is 1. Two equations are said to be equivalent if they have same roots.

EXAMPLE 13   Form an equation of lowest degree with roots −2, 3, and 5.

Solution:

Step 1	Root $x = -2$ gives us $x - (-2) = x + 2$ as a factor
	Root $x = 3$ gives us $x - 3$ as a factor
	Root $x = 5$ gives us $x - 5$ as a factor Write a linear factor corresponding to each root.
Step 2	$(x + 2)(x - 3)(x - 5)$ Multiply all the linear factors.
	$= x^3 - 6x^2 - x + 30$
Step 3	The desired equation is $x^3 - 6x^2 - x + 30 = 0$ Equate the resulting polynomial to zero.

Obtain the equation by equating the resulting polynomial to zero.

EXAMPLE 14 Form an equation of lowest degree with roots 2, 2, and –1.

Solution:

Step 1 The linear factors are:
$$x - 2, \ x - 2, \ \text{and} \ x - (-1) = x + 1$$

Step 2 Multiplying the linear factors, we get
$$(x - 2)(x - 2)(x + 1)$$
$$= x^3 - 3x^2 + 4$$

Step 3 The desired equation is
$$x^3 - 3x^2 + 4 = 0$$

EXAMPLE 15 Form an equation of lowest degree with roots $-1, \sqrt{2}$, and $-\sqrt{2}$.

Solution:

Step 1 The linear factors are:

$$x - (-1) = x + 1, \ x - \sqrt{2}, \ \text{and} \ x - \left(-\sqrt{2}\right) = x + \sqrt{2}$$

Step 2 Multiplying the linear factors, we get

$$(x + 1)\left(x - \sqrt{2}\right)\left(x + \sqrt{2}\right)$$
$$= (x + 1)(x^2 - 2)$$
$$= x^3 + x^2 - 2x - 2$$

> $(a + b)(a - b)$
> $= a^2 - b^2$

Step 3 The desired equation is
$$x^3 + x^2 - 2x - 2 = 0$$

EXAMPLE 16 Form an equation of lowest degree that has $3, 1 + i, 1 - i, -2$ as its roots.

Solution:

Step 1 The linear factors are:
$$x - 3,$$
$$x - (1 + i) = \mathbf{x - 1 - i},$$
$$x - (1 - i) = \mathbf{x - 1 + i}, \text{ and}$$
$$x - (-2) = \mathbf{x + 2.}$$

Step 2 Multiplying the linear factors, we get
$$(x - 3)(x - 1 - i)(x - 1 + i)(x + 2)$$
$$= (x - 3)(x + 2)(x - 1 - i)(x - 1 + i)$$
$$= (x^2 - x - 6)(x^2 - 2x + 2)$$
$$= x^4 - 3x^3 - 2x^2 + 10x - 12$$

> Use the rule for difference of squares.
> $(x - 1 - i)(x - 1 + i)$
> $= ((x - 1) - i)((x - 1) + i)$
> $= (x - 1)^2 - i^2$
> $= (x - 1)^2 - (-1)$
> $= x^2 - 2x + 2$

Step 3 The desired equation is
$$x^4 - 3x^3 - 2x^2 + 10x - 12 = 0$$

3.16

EXAMPLE 17 Find an equation that has **just** $2 - \sqrt{3}$, $2 + \sqrt{3}$, $-i$, i, and 4 as its roots.

Solution:

Step 1   The linear factors are:

$$x - \left(2 - \sqrt{3}\right) = x - 2 + \sqrt{3},$$

$$x - \left(2 + \sqrt{3}\right) = x - 2 - \sqrt{3},$$

$$x - (-i) = x + i,$$

$$x - i, \text{ and}$$

$$x - 4$$

Step 2   Multiplying the linear factors, we get

$$\left(x - 2 + \sqrt{3}\right)\left(x - 2 - \sqrt{3}\right)(x + i)(x - i)(x - 4)$$

$$= \left(x^2 - 4x + 1\right)^* \left(x^2 + 1\right)^{**} (x - 4)$$

$$= \left(x^4 - 4x^3 + 2x^2 - 4x + 1\right)(x - 4)$$

$$= x^5 - 8x^4 + 18x^3 - 12x^2 + 17x - 4$$

Step 3   The desired equation is

$$x^5 - 8x^4 + 18x^3 - 12x^2 + 17x - 4 = 0$$

Use the rule for difference of squares.

* $(x - 2 + \sqrt{3})(x - 2 - \sqrt{3})$

$= ((x - 2) + \sqrt{3})((x - 2) - \sqrt{3})$

$= (x - 2)^2 - \left(\sqrt{3}\right)^2$

$= (x - 2)^2 - 3$

$= x^2 - 4x + 1$

** $(x + i)(x - i)$

$= x^2 - (i)^2$

$= x^2 - (-1)$

$= x^2 + 1$

EXERCISE 3.1

In exercises (1-8), solve the linear equation, algebraically and graphically.

1. $3(x + 1) = 2(x - 5)$
2. $\dfrac{x-1}{5} = \dfrac{2x-1}{7}$
3. $\dfrac{x+1}{3} = \dfrac{5x+3}{4}$
4. $\dfrac{3x-4}{2} = \dfrac{2x+1}{5}$

5. $\dfrac{3x+7}{3} = \dfrac{7x+2}{5}$
6. $\dfrac{2}{3}x + 7 = \dfrac{x}{2} + \dfrac{1}{3}$
7. $2x + \dfrac{1}{3} = \dfrac{x}{2} + \dfrac{8}{3}$
8. $-\dfrac{x}{4} + 4 = \dfrac{2}{3}x + \dfrac{3}{2}$

In exercises (9-18), solve for the indicated unknown.

9. $V = \pi r^2 h$, for h
10. $S = \pi r l$, for l
11. $V = \dfrac{1}{3}\pi r^2 h$, for h
12. $V = l\, b\, h$, for h

13. $2y = 3x - 7$, for x
14. $-2x + 4y = 9$, for x
15. $5x - 7y = 15$, for y
16. $7x - 5y - 11 = 0$, for y

17. $5x + a = ax - b$, for x
18. $3x + 2a = 4ax - 3$, for a

In exercises (19–38), solve the quadratic equation algebraically and graphically.

19. $x^2 - 5x = -6$
20. $x^2 = 7x - 12$
21. $x^2 - 3x = 4$
22. $x^2 + 5x = -6$

23. $15x^2 = 13x + 2$
24. $3x^2 + 8x + 5 = 0$
25. $2x^2 = x + 3$
26. $8x^2 + 2x = 1$

27. $9x^2 - 12x + 4 = 0$
28. $25x^2 + 10x + 1 = 0$
29. $2x^2 + 12x + 18 = 0$
30. $16x^2 - 24x = -9$

31. $x(x + 1) = 4$
32. $3x(x + 2) - 2 = 0$
33. $x(2x + 5) = 1$
34. $2x(3x - 1) = 1$

35. $x(x - 5) = -10$
36. $x(2x + 3) + 2 = 0$
37. $2x^2 + x = -2$
38. $3x^2 - 2x = -2$

In exercises (39–42), use a graphing calculator to factor the trinomial approximately.

39. $x^2 - 2x - 1$ **40.** $x^2 - 4x - 3$ **41.** $2x^2 - 3x - 1$ **42.** $3x^2 - 5x + 1$

In exercises (43–58), solve algebraically and graphically.

43. $x^3 - 4x^2 - x + 4 = 0$ **44.** $x^3 - 3x^2 = 9x - 27$ **45.** $x^3 - 4x^2 = 11x + 6$ **46.** $x(x^2 - 4x - 17) = -60$

47. $x^2(x - 3) = -4$ **48.** $2x^3 - 5x^2 - 14x + 8 = 0$ **49.** $x^2(x^2 - 2) = -4$ **50.** $x^2(x^2 - 5) = 2(x^2 + 9)$

51. $x^3 - 5x^2 = 4(4x + 1)$ **52.** $x^2(x - 5) = 3(2 - 3x)$ **53.** $x^3 - 3x^2 + 2 = 0$ **54.** $x^3 - 8 = x(7 - 2x)$

55. $x^4 - 3x^3 - 27x^2 - 13x + 42 = 0$ **56.** $x^4 + 10x^3 + 8x^2 - 106x - 105 = 0$

57. $x^4 - 15x^2 + 10x + 24 = 0$ **58.** $x^4 - 2x^3 - x + 2 = 0$

In exercises (59–64), solve the equation graphically.

59. $0.5x^2 = 5x + 2$ **60.** $1.5x^2 = 4 - 3x$ **61.** $x^3 + 2x^2 = 5x - 8$ **62.** $2x^3 - x^2 = 7.5 - 2.5x$

63. $2x^3 - 2.64x^2 = 8.82x - 11.6424$ **64.** $x^4 - 2.1x^4 + 3.2x^3 = 2x^2 + 10x - 3$

65. The profit (P) of a company after selling x units of an item is given by $P(x) = x(-2 + x)$ (in millions). How many units (x) of the item should be sold so that the profit becomes 8 million dollars?

66. The profit (P) of a company after selling x units of an item is given by $P(x) = 1.2x(5 - x^2)$ (in millions). For what sales (x) will the profit become 5 million dollars?

67. A farmer has a roll of 100 ft of fencing to enclose a rectangular patch. Find the dimensions of the rectangular patch so that its area is 600 ft^2.

68. A farmer wants to fence a rectangular patch with a roll of 120 ft wire. What should be the sides of the rectangular patch so that its area is 800 ft^2?

69. A page of print is supposed to contain 100 in^2 of the printed region. The dimensions of the page are 16 in by 12 in. What should the margin be if all the four margins are the same?

70. The dimensions of a page are 12 in by 10 in and it is supposed to contain 80 in^2 of the printed region. What should be the margin if all the margins are the same?

71. If 24 trees are planted per acre, then each tree produces 600 apples per year. Each additional tree planted per acre reduces the yield of each tree by 12 apples per year. Let x represent the number of trees above 24 planted per acre. For what x-values will the total yield become 15660 apples?

In exercises (72-92), find the equation of lowest degree whose roots are given below.

72. $3, 2$ **73.** $5, 4$ **74.** $2, -5$ **75.** $5, -2$ **76.** $3, 0$ **77.** $0, -8$

78. $-2, -2$ **79.** $1, 1$ **80.** $-3, 4, 7$ **81.** $2, 5, -1$ **82.** $-1, -2, 3$ **83.** $3, -5, 0, 0$

84. $3, -1, 0, 3$ **85.** $3, 2, 4, 4$ **86.** $-2, 3 - \sqrt{7}, 3 + \sqrt{7}$ **87.** $0, 1 - 2\sqrt{5}, 1 + 2\sqrt{5}$

88. $2i, -2i, -\sqrt{3}, \sqrt{3}$ **89.** $2 - i, 2 + i, \sqrt{5}, -\sqrt{5}$ **90.** $-1 + 2i, -1 - 2i, 2 + \sqrt{7}, 2 - \sqrt{7}, -3$

91. $3 + 5i, 3 - 5i, 3, 3, 3$ **92.** $-3 - \sqrt{2}, -3 + \sqrt{2}, -2, 2, 0$

Writing Exercises

93. Explain why the roots of the equation $p(x) = q(x)$ are same as the zeros of the function $f(x) = p(x) - q(x)$.

94. Describe the procedure for finding zeros of a polynomial function.

3.2 EQUATIONS WITH RATIONAL EXPRESSIONS

Objective ▶ ▶

In this section you will learn about:

A. Solving Equations with Rational expressions.

In this section we will discuss the roots of an equation containing rational expressions. Such equations are usually called **Rational Equations.** We will use both algebraic and graphical methods to find the zeros of rational functions.

While solving polynomial equations we did not emphasize checking the roots of the equation. However, for a rational equation we must check each root for the possibility that it may make a denominator of the equation zero and thus become unacceptable. Such unacceptable values of x indicate special behaviors of the graph of the rational function that corresponds to the given rational equation. We will discuss this behavior in the next chapter.

A. SOLVING RATIONAL EQUATIONS

To solve a rational equation, we first transform the equation to a polynomial equation, and then use the method(s) discussed in section 3.1. We explain the strategy with the following example.

Algebraically

Strategy

EXAMPLE 1   Solve $\dfrac{x^2-4}{x-2}=0$

Solution:

Step 1   Remove the denominator by multiplying each term by the lcd. Also remove the parentheses, if any, using the distributive law.

$\longrightarrow$ $\dfrac{x^2-4}{x-2}\,(x-2)=0\,(x-2)$

$x^2-4=0$

Step 2   Solve the resulting polynomial equation and find all **possible** roots of the equation.

$\longrightarrow$ To solve this quadratic equation we use the factoring method.

$$(x-2)(x+2)=0$$

$$x-2=0 \quad | \quad x+2=0$$
$$x=2 \quad | \quad x=-2$$

Therefore, $x=2$ and -2 are **possible** roots.

Step 3   Check each possible root. A root is acceptable if it does not make any denominator of the equation zero.

$\longrightarrow$ To check $x=2$, we replace x with 2 in the equation. The denominator $x-2$ becomes zero, and therefore $x=2$ is not acceptable.

Since $x=-2$ does not make the denominator zero, it is the only root of the equation.

Graphically

A function whose zeros are same as the roots
of the equation is

$$f(x) = \frac{x^2 - 4}{x - 2}$$

Let $y1 = \dfrac{x^2 - 4}{x - 2}$. The graph of the function on

the standard range is shown in Figure 3.12.

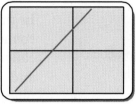

Figure 3.12

⬤ Note   The graph may not show that $x = 2$ is excluded from the domain.

The zero of the function is at the x-intercept. We use ZOOM-IN and TRACE to estimate the
x-intercept.

EXAMPLE 2   Solve $\dfrac{12}{x^2 - 9} + \dfrac{5}{x + 3} = \dfrac{8}{x - 3}$.

Solution: **Algebraically**

Step 1   The * lcd of denominators

$(x - 3)(x + 3)$, $x + 3$ and $x - 3$, is $(x - 3)(x + 3)$.

Multiplying the equation by $(x - 3)(x + 3)$ gives

$12 + 5(x - 3) = 8(x + 3)$

$12 + 5x - 15 = 8x + 24$

$5x - 3 = 8x + 24$

> * To find lcd.
>
> ***Step* 1**   Factor each denominator.
> $x^2 - 9 = (x - 3)\ (x + 3)$
>
> ***Step* 2**   Take the product of all
> different factors; each factor
> comes with the highest
> exponent.

Step 2   Solving the first degree equation gives

$5x - 3 = 8x + 24 \longrightarrow 5x - 8x = 24 + 3$

$\longrightarrow \quad -3x = 27$

$\longrightarrow \quad x = -9$

Step 3   Since $x = -9$ does not make any of the

denominators of the equation equal to
zero, it is an acceptable root of the equation.

Graphically

A function whose zeros are the same as the roots of the equation is

$$f(x) = \frac{12}{x^2 - 9} + \frac{5}{x + 3} - \frac{8}{x - 3} .$$

Let $y1 = \dfrac{12}{x^2 - 9} + \dfrac{5}{x + 3} - \dfrac{8}{x - 3}$. The graph on a suitable range is

shown in Figure 3.13.

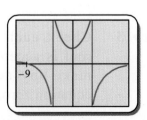

Figure 3.13

Using ZOOM-IN and TRACE gives an approximate value of the zero of
the function or the root of the equation. Note that the x-intercept is -9.

EXAMPLE 3   Solve $\dfrac{5}{2x+1} = \dfrac{2}{x-1}$

Solution: **Algebraically**

- Multiplying the equation by the lcd, $(2x + 1)(x - 1)$, gives

$$\dfrac{5}{2x+1} = \dfrac{2}{x-1} \longrightarrow 5(x - 1) = 2(2x + 1)$$

$$\longrightarrow 5x - 5 = 4x + 2 \longrightarrow 5x - 4x = 2 + 5$$

$$\longrightarrow x = 7$$

- Since $x = 7$ does not make any of the denominators of the equation zero, it is an acceptable root of the equation.

Graphically

A function whose zeros are the same as the roots of the equation is

$f(x) = \dfrac{5}{2x+1} - \dfrac{2}{x-1}$.

Let $y1 = \dfrac{5}{2x+1} - \dfrac{2}{x-1}$. The graph on a suitable range is shown in Figure 3.14.

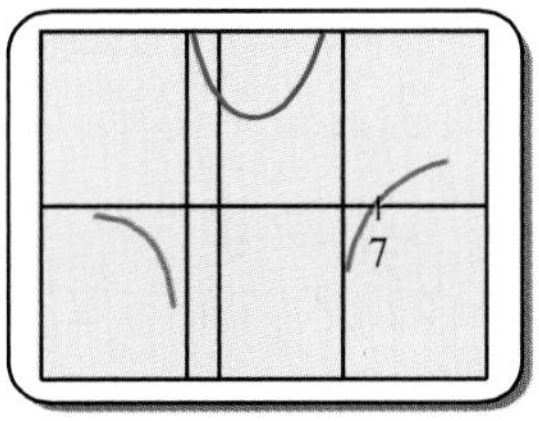

An approximate location of the zero of the function is obtained by using ZOOM-IN and TRACE. Note that the x-intercept is $x = 7$.

Figure 3.14

EXAMPLE 4   Solve $\dfrac{5}{x-2} - \dfrac{2}{x+3} = \dfrac{25}{x^2+x-6}$.

Solution: **Algebraically**

- Multiplying the equation by the lcd $(x - 2)(x + 3)$ $x^2 + x - 6 = (x + 3)(x - 2)$

$$\dfrac{5}{x-2}(x-2)(x+3) - \dfrac{2}{x+3}(x-2)(x+3) = \dfrac{25}{(x-2)(x+3)}(x-2)(x+3)$$

$$\longrightarrow 5(x + 3) - 2(x - 2) = 25 \longrightarrow 5x + 15 - 2x + 4 = 25$$

- Solving the linear equation gives

$$5x - 2x = 25 - 15 - 4 \longrightarrow 3x = 6 \longrightarrow x = 2$$

- Since $x = 2$ makes one of the denominators of the equation zero, it is **not** a root of the equation.

Thus the equation has no root.

Graphically

A function whose zeros are same as the roots of the equation is

$$f(x) = \frac{5}{x-2} - \frac{2}{x+3} - \frac{25}{x^2+x-6}.$$

Let $y1 = \frac{5}{x-2} - \frac{2}{x+3} - \frac{25}{x^2+x-6}$. On a suitable range the graph of $y1$ looks like Figure 3.15.

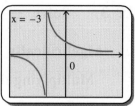

Figure 3.15

The graph does not intersect the x-axis. Thus, the equation has no root.

EXERCISE 3.2

In exercises (1-10), solve the equation both algebraically and graphically.

1. $\dfrac{8}{x^2-4} + \dfrac{3}{x-2} = \dfrac{5}{x+2}$

2. $\dfrac{3}{x+3} - \dfrac{5}{x-3} = -\dfrac{8}{x^2-9}$

3. $\dfrac{20}{x^2-4} + \dfrac{3}{x+2} = \dfrac{5}{x-2}$

4. $\dfrac{18}{x^2-9} + \dfrac{3}{x+3} = \dfrac{2}{x-3}$

5. $\dfrac{8}{2x-1} - \dfrac{3}{x+2} = 1$

6. $\dfrac{3}{x-2} - \dfrac{8}{2x+1} = 1$

7. $\dfrac{2}{x-3} + \dfrac{1}{x-2} = 1$

8. $\dfrac{1}{x-4} + \dfrac{1}{2x+1} = 1$

9. $\dfrac{x}{x+2} - \dfrac{1}{x-1} = \dfrac{4}{x^2+x-2}$

10. $\dfrac{2x}{x+3} + \dfrac{3}{x+1} = \dfrac{6}{x^2+4x+3}$

In exercises (11-29), find all zeros of the function both algebraically and graphically.

11. $f(x) = \dfrac{x^2-16}{x-2}$

12. $f(x) = \dfrac{x^2-9}{x+3}$

13. $f(x) = \dfrac{x(x-3)}{x+1}$

14. $f(x) = \dfrac{x(x+5)}{x-2}$

15. $g(x) = \dfrac{x^2-x-2}{x^2-9}$

16. $h(x) = \dfrac{x^2+3x+2}{x^2-16}$

17. $g(x) = \dfrac{x^2-3x-4}{x^2-4x}$

18. $g(x) = \dfrac{x^2-2x-3}{x^2-3x}$

19. $f(x) = \dfrac{x+1}{x^2-3x-4}$

20. $g(x) = \dfrac{x-5}{x^2-4x-5}$

21. $f(x) = \dfrac{4}{x^2-9}$

22. $h(x) = \dfrac{12}{x^2+4}$

23. $g(x) = \dfrac{9}{2x-3}$

24. $f(x) = \dfrac{7}{3x+5}$

25. $f(x) = \dfrac{5x^2}{x^2+2}$

26. $g(x) = \dfrac{-3x^2}{x^2-9}$

27. $h(x) = \dfrac{x^2+4}{x^2-16}$

28. $f(x) = \dfrac{x^2+16}{x^2-7}$

29. $f(x) = \dfrac{2x^2+2}{x-1}$

30. $g(x) = \dfrac{2x^2+3}{x+4}$

31. If the cost $c(x)$ of removing $x\%$ of the waste in a city is given by

$$c(x) = \frac{500}{100-x} \qquad \text{(million)}$$

then what percent of the waste can be removed if the city spends 30 million dollars?

32. In exercise 31, find the percent of waste that can be removed if the city spends 40 million dollars.

Writing Exercises

33. Explain why the roots of the equation $\dfrac{p(x)}{q(x)} = 0$ are the same as the zeros of the function $p(x)$ if these are different from the zeros of $q(x)$.

3.3 ABSOLUTE VALUE EQUATIONS

Recall that the absolute value of a quantity K is given by

$$|K| = \begin{cases} K & \text{if } K \geq 0 \\ -K & \text{if } K < 0 \end{cases}$$

In this section we will use the above rule to transform an absolute value equation into two equations without having any absolute value symbols. The roots of the resultant equations can be found by using methods in the previous sections. We will also find the zeros of an absolute value function graphically.

> **Objectives ▶▶**
>
> In this section you will learn about:
>
> A. Solving an Absolute Value Equation; and
>
> B. Writing an Absolute Value Function without Absolute Value symbols.

A. SOLVING AN ABSOLUTE VALUE EQUATION

Algebraically	Procedure

EXAMPLE 1 Solve $|3x-7|-2=0$

Solution:

Step 1 Write the equation in the standard form: $\longrightarrow$ $|3x-7| = 2$

$$|K| = \text{number}$$

* Recall the rule $|x| = p$ if and only if $x = p$ or $x = -p$. (section 1.2C)

Step 2 Write two equations without absolute value bars: $\longrightarrow$ $3x - 7 = 2$ or $3x - 7 = -2$

* $K =$ number or $K = -$number

Step 3 Solve the resulting equations. $\longrightarrow$

$$3x - 7 = 2 \qquad 3x - 7 = -2$$
$$3x = 9 \qquad\quad 3x = 5$$
$$x = 3 \qquad\quad x = \frac{5}{3}$$

Step 4 Check each solution in Step 3. $\longrightarrow$

We can verify that both these values of x satisfy the original equation.

Therefore, $x = \frac{5}{3}$ and $x = 3$ are the roots of the absolute value equation.

Graphically

A function whose zeros are the same as the roots of the equation is

$$f(x) = |3x-7| - 2 .$$

Let $y1 = \text{abs}(3x - 7) - 2$. On the standard range, the graph of the function looks like Figure 3.16.

Use ZOOM-IN and TRACE to locate the zeros of the function. Note that the x-intercepts are 1.67 and 3.

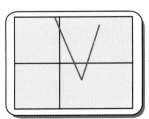

Figure 3.16

EXAMPLE 2   Find the zeros of the function $f(x) = \left| x^2 - 4 \right|$.

Solution: For zeros of the function, we solve the equation $\left| x^2 - 4 \right| = 0$.

This is an absolute value equation. First, we solve the equation algebraically.

Algebraically

Step 1   The equation in the standard form looks like $\left| x^2 - 4 \right| = 0$.

Step 2   * Writing the equation without absolute value symbols gives

$x^2 - 4 = 0$ or $x^2 - 4 = -0$

> * $|K|$ = number is equivalent to
> K = number or
> K = – number

Step 3   Solving the resultant equations gives

$(x - 2)(x + 2) = 0$

$\longrightarrow$ $x - 2 = 0$ or $x + 2 = 0$

$\longrightarrow$ $x = 2$ or $x = -2$

Step 4   We may check that both the values of x satisfy the given equation.

Therefore, $x = 2$ and -2 are the roots of the equation.

Thus, $x = 2$ and -2 are the zeros of the function $f(x) = \left| x^2 - 4 \right|$.

Graphically

Let $y1 = \text{abs}(x^2 - 4)$. The graph on the standard range looks like Figure 3.17.

The graph shows two zeros of the function. We can find their approximate values by using ZOOM-IN and TRACE.

The x-intercepts are -2 and 2.

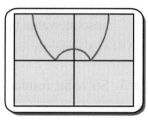

Figure 3.17

EXAMPLE 3   Solve $\left| x - 3 \right| = \left| 3x + 1 \right|$.

Solution:

Algebraically

- Dividing both sides by $\left| 3x + 1 \right|$ gives $\dfrac{\left| x - 3 \right|}{\left| 3x + 1 \right|} = \dfrac{\left| 3x + 1 \right|}{\left| 3x + 1 \right|} = 1$ $(3x + 1 \neq 0)$

$\longrightarrow$ $\dfrac{\left| x - 3 \right|}{\left| 3x + 1 \right|} = 1$ $\left(\dfrac{|A|}{|B|} = \left| \dfrac{A}{B} \right| \right)$

- Writing the equation without absolute value symbols gives two equations:

$\dfrac{x - 3}{3x + 1} = 1$ or $\dfrac{x - 3}{3x + 1} = -1$

- Solving these equations gives

$$x - 3 = 3x + 1$$
$$-3 - 1 = 3x - x$$
$$-4 = 2x$$
$$-2 = x$$

$$x - 3 = -3x - 1$$
$$x + 3x = 3 - 1$$
$$4x = 2$$
$$x = \frac{2}{4} = \frac{1}{2}$$

- We may verify that both these values of x satisfy the original equation.

Checking for $x = -2$

$$|-2 - 3| = |3(-2) + 1|$$

$$|-5| = |-5|$$

$$5 = 5 \quad \text{True}$$

Checking for $x = \frac{1}{2}$

$$\left|\left(\frac{1}{2}\right) - 3\right| = \left|3\left(\frac{1}{2}\right) + 1\right|$$

$$\left|-\frac{5}{2}\right| = \left|\frac{5}{2}\right| \qquad \text{True}$$

Therefore, $x = -2$ and $x = \frac{1}{2}$ are the two roots of the equation.

Graphically

A function whose zeros are the same as the roots of the equation is

$$f(x) = |x - 3| - |3x + 1| .$$

Let $y1 = \text{abs}(x - 3) - \text{abs}(3x + 1)$. On the standard range the graph of $y1$ looks like Figure 3.18.

Use ZOOM-IN and TRACE to locate the zeros of the function. The x-intercepts are -2 and $.5$

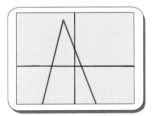

Figure 3.18

B. WRITING AN ABSOLUTE VALUE FUNCTION WITHOUT ABSOLUTE VALUE SYMBOLS

In Section 1.2 we learned how to write a simple absolute value expression without absolute value symbols. Now, with the methods of solving equations we can attempt the problem in a more general and efficient way.

To write an absolute value function without absolute value symbols, we will first find the zeros of the function, then write expressions of the function without absolute value on both sides of each zero. This is done by using the definition

$$|K| = \begin{cases} K & \text{if } K \geq 0 \\ -K & \text{if } K < 0 \end{cases}$$

Procedure

EXAMPLE 4   Write $f(x) = \left|\frac{x}{2} - \frac{1}{3}\right|$ without absolute value bars.

Solution:

Step 1   Find the zeros of the absolute value expressions by solving equations such as

$$|g(x)| = 0 \quad \text{or} \quad g(x) = 0.$$

Let $x = \alpha$ be a root.

For the zeros of the function we solve

$$\frac{x}{2} - \frac{1}{3} = 0 \quad \longrightarrow \quad x = \frac{2}{3}$$

3.25

Step 2 Determine the sign of $g(x)$ for $x < \alpha$. $\longrightarrow$ $x < \dfrac{2}{3} \longrightarrow \dfrac{x}{2} < \dfrac{1}{3} \longrightarrow \dfrac{x}{2} - \dfrac{1}{3} < 0$, so

If the sign is non-negative, then write

$|g(x)| = g(x)$ for $x < \alpha$. $\dfrac{x}{2} - \dfrac{1}{3}$ is **negative**,

If the sign is negative, then write

$|g(x)| = -g(x)$ for $x < \alpha$. therefore $\left|\dfrac{x}{2} - \dfrac{1}{3}\right| = -\left(\dfrac{x}{2} - \dfrac{1}{3}\right)$ or $\dfrac{1}{3} - \dfrac{x}{2}$.

Step 3 Repeat Step 2 for $x \geq \alpha$. $\longrightarrow$ $x \geq \dfrac{2}{3} \longrightarrow \dfrac{x}{2} \geq \dfrac{1}{3} \longrightarrow \dfrac{x}{2} - \dfrac{1}{3} \geq 0$, so

$\dfrac{x}{2} - \dfrac{1}{3}$ is **non-negative**, and $\left|\dfrac{x}{2} - \dfrac{1}{3}\right| = \dfrac{x}{2} - \dfrac{1}{3}$

Step 4 Use the expressions in Steps 2 and 3 $\longrightarrow$ $\left|\dfrac{x}{2} - \dfrac{1}{3}\right| = \begin{cases} \dfrac{1}{3} - \dfrac{x}{2} & \text{if } x < \dfrac{2}{3} \\ \dfrac{x}{2} - \dfrac{1}{3} & \text{if } x \geq \dfrac{2}{3} \end{cases}$
to write the absolute value function as
a piecewise function.

EXAMPLE 5 Write $f(x) = |2x - 3| - 3$ without the absolute value symbols.

Solution:

Step 1 To find the zeros of the absolute value expression $|2x - 3|$, we solve the equation

$$|2x - 3| = 0 \quad \text{or} \quad 2x - 3 = 0 \quad \longrightarrow \quad x = \dfrac{3}{2}$$

Step 2 **For** $x < \dfrac{3}{2}$, $2x - 3$ is **negative**, and therefore $x < \dfrac{3}{2} \ \rightarrow \ 2x < 3 \ \rightarrow \ 2x - 3 < 0$

$$\begin{aligned} f(x) &= |2x - 3| - 3 \\ &= -(2x - 3) - 3 \\ &= -2x + 3 - 3 = -2x \end{aligned}$$

Step 3 **For** $x \geq \dfrac{3}{2}$, $2x - 3$ is **non-negative**, so $x \geq \dfrac{3}{2} \ \rightarrow \ 2x \geq 3 \ \rightarrow \ 2x - 3 \geq 0$

$$\begin{aligned} f(x) &= |2x - 3| - 3 \\ &= 2x - 3 - 3 = 2x - 6 \end{aligned}$$

Step 4 Writing the function as a piecewise function, we get

$$|2x - 3| - 3 = \begin{cases} -2x & \text{if } x < \dfrac{3}{2} \\ 2x - 6 & \text{if } x \geq \dfrac{3}{2} \end{cases}.$$

EXERCISE 3.3

In exercises (1-12), solve the equation both algebraically and graphically.

1. $\left| 8x - 7 \right| = 9$

2. $\left| 7x + 4 \right| = 5$

3. $\left| 2x - 9 \right| = -5$

4. $\left| 3x + 5 \right| = -7$

5. $\left| \dfrac{x+2}{x-2} \right| = 4$

6. $\left| \dfrac{x-3}{2x+1} \right| = 2$

7. $\left| 2x + 3 \right| = \left| 2 - 3x \right|$

8. $\left| 3x - 7 \right| = \left| 2 - 5x \right|$

9. $\left| x - 2 \right| = \dfrac{x^2}{4}$

10. $\left| 2x - 3 \right| = x^2$

11. $\left| x - 2 \right| = x^2$

12. $\left| x + 1 \right| = x^2$

In exercises (13-24), find the zeros of the function.

13. $f(x) = \left| 2x - 1 \right| - 3$

14. $g(x) = \left| 3x - 1 \right| - 5$

15. $g(x) = \left| 5 - 3x \right| - 2$

16. $f(x) = \left| 5x + 2 \right| - 2$

17. $h(x) = \left| x - 2 \right| + 1$

18. $g(x) = \left| 2x + 3 \right| + 4$

19. $f(x) = \left| x + 1 \right| + 2$

20. $f(x) = \left| x - 1 \right| - 9$

21. $g(x) = \left| x^2 - 9 \right|$

22. $g(x) = \left| x^2 + 9 \right|$

23. $f(x) = \left| x^2 - 2 \right|$

24. $f(x) = \left| x^2 - 6 \right|$

In exercises (25-36), write the expressions for the function without absolute value symbols.

25. $f(x) = \left| x - 5 \right|$

26. $f(x) = \left| x + 7 \right|$

27. $f(x) = \left| 2x - 3 \right|$

28. $f(x) = \left| 3x + 5 \right|$

29. $f(x) = \left| \dfrac{x}{3} - \dfrac{4}{5} \right|$

30. $f(x) = \left| \dfrac{x}{4} - 2 \right|$

31. $f(x) = \left| x - 4 \right| - 2$

32. $f(x) = \left| x + 5 \right| + 3$

33. $f(x) = \left| 2x - 9 \right| - 5$

34. $f(x) = \left| 3x + 4 \right| - 3$

35. $f(x) = \left| x^2 - 4 \right| - 5$

36. $f(x) = \left| x^2 - 9 \right| + 5$

3.4 RADICAL EQUATIONS

A **radical equation** is an equation involving radicals of the unknown. The equation is solved algebraically by rationalizing the equation. Some roots of the new equation may not be the roots of the original equation. The extra roots are called the **extraneous roots**. Root equations are sometimes called radical equations.

Objective ▶ ▶

In this section you will learn about:

A. Solving a Radical Equation.

Before we give the details of the method for solving a radical equation, we state and demonstrate the use of the following simple fact.

Fact: If $A = B$ is an equation, then the set of its roots is contained in the set of the roots of $A^n = B^n$, where n is a positive integer. In other words, the roots of the equation $A = B$ are among the roots of the equation $A^n = B^n$ for any positive integer n.

We verify this fact for the equation $\sqrt{x} = x - 6$.

By squaring both sides, we get

$$\left(\sqrt{x}\right)^2 = (x - 6)^2 \longrightarrow x = x^2 - 12x + 36$$
$$\longrightarrow 0 = x^2 - 13x + 36$$
$$\longrightarrow (x - 4)(x - 9) = 0 \longrightarrow x = 4 \text{ and } x = 9$$

The roots of the new equation are $x = 4$, and $x = 9$. Now $\sqrt{9} = 9 - 6$ is true while $\sqrt{4} = 4 - 6$ is false. So only $x = 9$ checks out as the root of the original equation. This shows that the roots of the original equation are in the set of roots of the new equation obtained by squaring both sides.

The extra root $(x = 4)$ of the new equation is called an **extraneous root.**

A. SOLVING A RADICAL EQUATION

To solve a root equation, first we rationalize the equation by using the above fact, and then solve the resulting equation. We check each root of the new equation for the roots of the original equation. We state the strategy in the following steps:

Procedure

EXAMPLE 1   Solve $\sqrt{x+8} - \sqrt{x} = 2$.

Solution:

Step 1   Keep only one radical on one side and transfer all the remaining terms to the other side of the equation.

$\longrightarrow$ $\sqrt{x+8} = 2 + \sqrt{x}$

Step 2   Square both sides, if the equation has a square root. Cube both sides if it has a cube root. In general, raise both sides to nth power if it has an nth root $\sqrt[n]{\ }$.

$\longrightarrow$ Squaring both sides gives

$$\left(\sqrt{x+8}\right)^2 = \left(2 + \sqrt{x}\right)^2$$

$$x + 8 = 4 + 4\sqrt{x} + x$$

$$x + 8 - 4 - x = 4\sqrt{x} \longrightarrow 4 = 4\sqrt{x}$$

Step 3   Repeat Step 1 and 2 until the equation has no radical.

$\longrightarrow$ $4 = 4\sqrt{x}$ or $1 = \sqrt{x}$

or $1 = x \longrightarrow x = 1$

Step 4 & 5   Solve the new equation, and check each root obtained in Step 4 for the roots of the original equation.

$\longrightarrow$ Checking $x = 1$:

$$\sqrt{1+8} - \sqrt{1} = 2 \quad \text{or} \quad 2 = 2$$

Since $x = 1$ checks as a root of the original equation, it is the only root.

Graphically

A function whose zero are the same as the roots of the equation is
$f(x) = \sqrt{x+8} - \sqrt{x} - 2$.

Let $y1 = \sqrt{x+8} - \sqrt{x} - 2$. The graph of $y1$ on the standard range looks like Figure 3.19.

The graph shows only one zero of the function. By using ZOOM-IN and TRACE, we can find an approximate value of the zero. The x-intercept is 1.

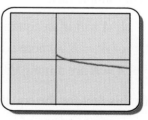

Figure 3.19

EXAMPLE 2   Solve $\sqrt{5x+11} - \sqrt{3x+10} = 1$.

Solution: **Algebraically**

- Keeping only one radical on the left side gives $\sqrt{5x+11} = 1 + \sqrt{3x+10}$

- Squaring both sides gives $\left(\sqrt{5x+11}\right)^2 = \left(1+\sqrt{3x+10}\right)^2$

   $$\longrightarrow \quad 5x + 11 = 1 + 2\sqrt{3x+10} + 3x + 10$$

- Repeating Steps 1 and 2 gives $5x + 11 - 1 - 3x - 10 = 2\sqrt{3x+10}$

   $$2x = 2\sqrt{3x+10}$$

   $$x = \sqrt{3x+10}$$

   Squaring both sides gives $x^2 = 3x + 10$

- Solving the quadratic equation gives $x^2 - 3x - 10 = 0$

   $$(x - 5)(x + 2) = 0$$

   $$x - 5 = 0 \;\middle|\; x + 2 = 0$$

   $$x = 5 \;\middle|\; x = -2$$

- Check for the roots of the original equation.

$x = 5$	$x = -2$
$\sqrt{5(5)+11} - \sqrt{3(5)+10} = 1$	$\sqrt{5(-2)+11} - \sqrt{3(-2)+10} = 1$
$\sqrt{25+11} - \sqrt{15+10} = 1$	$\sqrt{-10+11} - \sqrt{-6+10} = 1$
$\sqrt{36} - \sqrt{25} = 1$	$\sqrt{1} - \sqrt{4} = 1$
$6 - 5 = 1$	$1 - 2 = 1$
$1 = 1$	$-1 \neq 1$
Therefore, $x = 5$ **is a root** of the equation.	Therefore, $x = -2$ **is not a root** of the equation.

Thus, the original equation has only one root, $\boldsymbol{x = 5}$.

Graphically

A function whose zeros are the same as the roots of the equation is

$f(x) = \sqrt{5x+11} - \sqrt{3x+10} - 1$.

Let $y1 = \sqrt{5x+11} - \sqrt{3x+10} - 1$.

The graph of $y1$ on the standard range looks like Figure 3.20.

The graph shows that there is only one zero of the function. ZOOM-IN and TRACE will help to locate that zero of the function, namely 5.

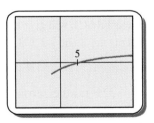

Figure 3.20

EXAMPLE 3   Solve $(3x - 1)^{2/3} = 4$

Solution: Since $(3x-1)^{2/3} = \sqrt[3]{(3x-1)^2}$, so the equation is a root equation.

   Algebraically

- Writing the radical on the left side gives $\sqrt[3]{(3x-1)^2} = 4$.

- By cubing both sides, we get $\left(\sqrt[3]{(3x-1)^2}\right)^3 = (4)^3 \longrightarrow (3x-1)^2 = 64$

- Solving the quadratic equation gives:

$$(3x-1)^2 - (8)^2 = 0 \longrightarrow (3x-1-8)(3x-1+8) = 0$$
$$\longrightarrow (3x-9)(3x+7) = 0$$
$$\longrightarrow 3x-9 = 0 \quad \text{or} \quad 3x+7 = 0$$
$$\longrightarrow x = 3 \quad \text{or} \quad x = -\frac{7}{3}$$

- Check each root for the solution of the original equation.

$x = 3$	$x = -\dfrac{7}{3}$
$(3(3)-1)^{2/3} = 4$	$\left(3\left(-\dfrac{7}{3}\right)-1\right)^{2/3} = 4$
$(9-1)^{2/3} = 4$	$(-7-1)^{2/3} = 4$
$8^{2/3} = 4$	$(-8)^{2/3} = 4$
$\left(\sqrt[3]{8}\right)^2 = 4$	$\left(\sqrt[3]{-8}\right)^2 = 4$
$2^2 = 4$	$(-2)^2 = 4 \quad \text{or} \quad 4 = 4$
$4 = 4$	
Therefore, $x = 3$ is a root of the original equation.	Therefore, $x = -\dfrac{7}{3}$ is a root of the original equation.

Thus, the equation has two roots: $\boldsymbol{x = 3}$ and $\boldsymbol{x = -\dfrac{7}{3}}$.

Graphically

A function whose zeros are the same as the roots of the equation is

$f(x) = (3x-1)^{2/3} - 4$.

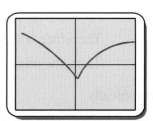

Let $y1 = \left((3x-1)^2\right)^{1/3} - 4$. The graph of $y1$ on the standard range looks like Figure 3.21. The intercepts indicate that there are two zeros of the function. ZOOM-IN and TRACE will give approximate values of the zeros (roots). The two x-intercepts are 3 and -2.333.

Figure 3.21

EXAMPLE 4   Find the zeros of the function $f(x) = \sqrt{2x-3} + 3 - x$.

Solution: The zeros of the function $f(x)$ are the same as the roots of the equation

$$\sqrt{2x-3} + 3 - x = 0 \qquad\qquad (1)$$

To solve this equation we use the above strategy.

- By keeping the radical on the left side and transferring $3 - x$ to the right side we get

$\sqrt{2x-3} = x - 3$.

- Squaring both sides we get $\left(\sqrt{2x-3}\right)^2 = (x-3)^2$

  or $2x - 3 = x^2 - 6x + 9$

- Solving the quadratic equation gives

  $2x - 3 = x^2 - 6x + 9 \longrightarrow x^2 - 8x + 12 = 0$

  $\longrightarrow (x-6)(x-2) = 0 \longrightarrow x = 6$ or $x = 2$

- Check each root for the solution of the original equation (1).

$x = 6$	$x = 2$
$\sqrt{2(6)-3} + 3 - 6 = 0$	$\sqrt{2(2)-3} + 3 - 2 = 0$
$\sqrt{12-3} + 3 - 6 = 0$	$\sqrt{4-3} + 3 - 2 = 0$
$3 + 3 - 6 = 0$	$\sqrt{1} + 3 - 2 = 0$
$0 = 0$	$1 + 3 - 2 \neq 0$
Therefore, $x = 6$ is a root of equation (1).	Therefore, $x = 2$ is not a root of equation (1).

Thus, $x = 6$ is the only root of equation (1).

Consequently, $x = 6$ is the only zero of the function $f(x)$.

Graphically

To find the zeros of the function $f(x) = \sqrt{2x-3} + 3 - x$,

we let $y1 = \sqrt{2x-3} + 3 - x$.

The graph of $y1$ on the standard range looks like Figure 3.22.
The graph shows that there is only one zero of the function.
Use ZOOM-IN and TRACE to find its approximate location.
The x-intercept is 6.

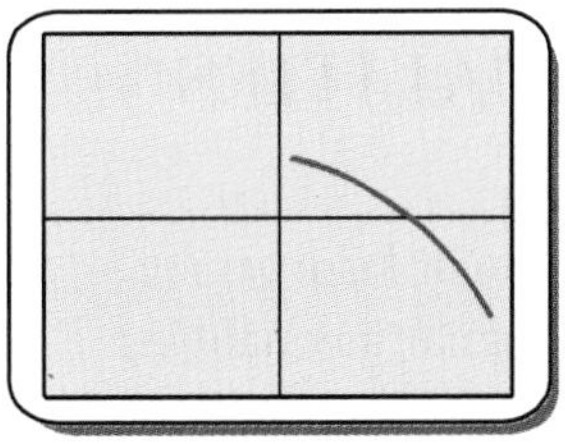

Figure 3.22

EXERCISE 3.4

In exercises (1-12), solve the equation algebraically and graphically.

1. $\sqrt{x-2} = 2 - x$ 2. $\sqrt{x+5} = 5 + x$ 3. $(x-1)^{2/3} = 9$ 4. $(x+3)^{2/3} = 4$

5. $(x+2)^{2/3} = 16$ 6. $(x-5)^{2/3} = 25$ 7. $(x+1)^{3/2} = 8$ 8. $(x-3)^{3/2} = 27$

9. $\sqrt{3x-5} = 1 + \sqrt{x+2}$ 10. $\sqrt{x-3} = 1 - \sqrt{x+1}$ 11. $\sqrt{4\sqrt{2x-3}} = \sqrt{x+2}$ 12. $\sqrt{\sqrt{2}\sqrt{x+2}} = \sqrt{x-2}$

In exercises (13-40), find the zeros of the function.

13. $f(x) = \sqrt{x-3} - 4$ 14. $f(x) = \sqrt{x+5} - 6$ 15. $g(x) = \sqrt{x-8} - 4$ 16. $g(x) = \sqrt{x+6} - 4$

17. $h(x) = \sqrt{x+2} - x$ 18. $g(x) = \sqrt{x+2} + x$ 19. $f(x) = \sqrt{x+6} - x$ 20. $g(x) = \sqrt{x+6} + x$

21. $g(x) = \sqrt{3x+1} - 2x + 1$ 22. $f(x) = \sqrt{2x+1} - x + 1$ 23. $h(x) = \sqrt{2x+5} + x - 5$ 24. $f(x) = \sqrt{3x-5} + x - 1$

25. $f(x) = \sqrt{x^2 - 5x - 2} - 2$ **26.** $g(x) = \sqrt{x^2 + 3x + 5} - 3$ **27.** $g(x) = \sqrt{x^2 - x - 2} - 2$

28. $h(x) = \sqrt{-x^2 + 6x - 7} - 1$ **29.** $h(x) = \sqrt{x + 2} + 2 - x$ **30.** $f(x) = \sqrt{2x - 7} + x - 5$

31. $f(x) = \sqrt{x + 2} + 4 - x$ **32.** $g(x) = \sqrt{x + 17} + x - 3$ **33.** $f(x) = \sqrt{x - 7} - \sqrt{x + 7} + 1$

34. $g(x) = \sqrt{x + 5} - \sqrt{x - 5} + 1$ **35.** $g(x) = \sqrt{x - 5} - \sqrt{x + 7} + 1$ **36.** $f(x) = \sqrt{x + 5} - \sqrt{x - 5} - 1$

37. $f(x) = \sqrt{x + 2} - \sqrt{2x - 3} - 1$ **38.** $f(x) = \sqrt{x + 1} - \sqrt{2x + 5} - 1$ **39.** $g(x) = \sqrt{x + 1} - \sqrt{2x - 5} - 1$

40. $f(x) = \sqrt{2x + 3} - \sqrt{2x + 7} + 1$

41. The cost and revenue of x items for a small manufacturing company are

$$C(x) = \frac{x + 10}{\sqrt{x} + 2}, \quad R(x) = \sqrt{x}, \text{ respectively.}$$

How many items must the company produce in order to break even?

Writing Exercises

42. Describe the procedure for solving root equations.   **43.** Explain what are extraneous roots.

3.5 INEQUALITIES

Objectives ▶▶

In this section you will learn about:

A. Solving Polynomial Inequalities;

B. Solving Rational Inequalities; and

C. Solving Absolute Value Inequalities.

In this section we will learn how to solve polynomial, rational, and absolute value inequalities. Graphically, the solution of the inequality $f(x) > 0$ gives the interval where the graph of the function $f(x)$ is above the x-axis. Similarly, the solution of $f(x) < 0$ gives the interval where the graph of $f(x)$ is below the x-axis.

A. SOLVING POLYNOMIAL INEQUALITIES

A polynomial inequality can be of degree 1, 2 or higher. The following method is applicable to all three kinds.

To solve a polynomial inequality, write the inequality in the standard form like $f(x) > 0$ or $f(x) < 0$, find the roots of the equation $f(x) = 0$, plot these values on the number line thus dividing the number line into parts, and finally check each interval for the solution of the inequality. We write this strategy in steps as follows.

EXAMPLE 1   Solve $4x + 5 > 9x - 15$

Algebraically

         Procedure

                             Solution:

Step **1**   Transfer all terms over to the ⟶ $4x + 5 - 9x + 15 > 0$
left side and simplify. $-5x + 20 > 0$

Step **2**   Set the nonzero side to zero ⟶ $-5x + 20 = 0$ or
and find the roots of the $4 = x$
equation.

> **Alternative Method for solving linear inequality.**
> Use the same method as for linear equations. Recall, the inequality symbol reverses when both sides of the inequality are divided or mulitiplied by a negative number.

Step 3 Plot the roots in Step 2 on the number line, thus dividing the number line into intervals.

The number line is divided into two intervals A and B. Interval A is $(-\infty, 4)$ and interval B is $(4, \infty)$.

For example,
$$4x + 5 > 9x - 15$$
$$4x - 9x > -15 - 5$$
$$-5x > -20$$

Dividing by -5 gives
$$\frac{-5x}{-5} < \frac{-20}{-5}$$

(The inequality is reversed)
$$x < 4$$

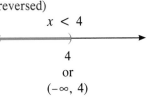

or
$(-\infty, 4)$

Step 4 Select a test number in each interval. If it satisfies the given inequality, then the interval belongs to the solution of the inequality and write yes (Y) above the interval. Otherwise, write no (N).

To check the interval A we select $x = 0$ as the test number. Substituting in the original inequality gives
$$4(0) + 5 > 9(0) - 15$$
$$5 > -15$$

This is a true statement, so we write 'Y' above the interval A.

Similarly, we select $x = 5$ as the test number for the interval B.

Substituting $x = 5$ in the original inequality gives
$$4(5) + 5 > 9(5) - 15$$
$$25 > 30$$

This is not a true statement, so we write 'N' above the interval B.

A(Y)   B(N)

4

Thus, the solution of the inequality is $(-\infty, 4)$.

Step 5 Shade in the 'Y' interval(s). Include the end points if the inequality symbol is either $\geq$ or $\leq$. Exclude the end points for a strict inequality ($>$ or $<$).

Graphically

From Step 1, let $y1 = $ nonzero side. Graph $y1$ on the standard range or any other suitable range.

$$y1 = -5x + 20$$

Locate the zero of the graph and write the interval where the graph is above the x-axis.

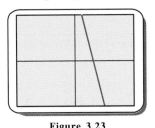

Figure 3.23

The graph shows the x-intercept at $x \approx 4$ and the graph is above the x-axis on the left of 4. Therefore, the solution of the inequality is $(-\infty, 4)$.

EXAMPLE 2   Solve $-8 < 2x - 5 < 3$.

Solution: **Algebraically**

The double inequality $-8 < 2x - 5 < 3$ is equivalent to two inequalities.

$$-8 < 2x - 5 \text{ and } 2x - 5 < 3.$$

Therefore, the solution of the given inequality is the conjunction (intersection) of the solutions of these two inequalities. Solving each linear inequality by the alternative method gives

$$-8 < 2x - 5 \qquad\qquad\qquad 2x - 5 < 3$$

$$-2x < 3 \longrightarrow x > -\frac{3}{2} \qquad\qquad 2x < 8 \longrightarrow x < 4$$

The conjunction of these intervals is

$$-\frac{3}{2} < x < 4 \quad \text{or} \quad \left(-\frac{3}{2}, 4\right)$$

or

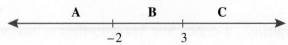

-3/2   4

Alternative Method

We can solve a double inequality by keeping only the variable (unknown) in the middle expression.

$$-8 < 2x - 5 < 3.$$

Adding 5 to all sides will eliminate -5 in the middle expression.

$$-8 + \mathbf{5} < 2x - 5 + \mathbf{5} < 3 + \mathbf{5}$$
$$-3 < 2x < 8$$

Dividing by 2 will leave only x in the middle expression.

$$-\frac{3}{2} < x < 4$$

Graphically

Let $y1 = 2x - 5 \quad \rightarrow \quad y2 = 3 \quad \rightarrow \quad y3 = -8$.

Graph $y1$, $y2$, and $y3$, simultaneously on the standard range. Use ZOOM-IN and TRACE to approximate the x-values where the graph $y1$ intersects $y2$ and $y3$. Then determine the approximate interval the graph of $y1$ lies between the graphs of $y2$ and $y3$. This interval should be in approximation to $\left(-\frac{3}{2}, 4\right)$.

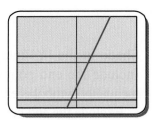

Figure 3.24

Remark: *Use ZOOM-IN and TRACE repeatedly to get a more accurate x-value where y1 intersects y2 or y3. Each x-value of the point of intersection is found separately.*

EXAMPLE 3   Solve $x^2 - x \geq 6$

Solution: **Algebraically**

     Step 1   Transferring all terms to the left side gives: $x^2 - x - 6 \geq 0$

     Step 2   Solving the equation $x^2 - x - 6 = 0$ gives

               $(x - 3)(x + 2) = 0 \longrightarrow x = 3$ and $x = -2$

     Step 3   Plotting the roots on the number line divides the line into three intervals A, B, and C.

                       A   B   C

                           -2   3

Interval A is $(-\infty, 2)$, interval B is $(-2, 3)$ and interval C is $(3, \infty)$.

-

Interval A	**Interval B**	**Interval C**
Test number $x = -3$	Test number $= 0$	Test number $= 4$
$(-3)^2 - (-3) \geq 6$	$(0)^2 - 0 \geq 6$	$(4)^2 - 4 \geq 6$
$9 + 3 \geq 6$	$0 \geq 6$	$16 - 4 \geq 6$
$12 \geq 6$		$12 \geq 6$
This is a true statement. So write **Y** above interval A.	This is not a true statement. So write **N** above the interval B.	This is a true statement. So write **Y** above interval C.

- Shade in the "Y" intervals and include the end points. The solution of the inequality is

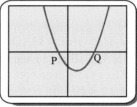

Thus, the solution of $x^2 - x \geq 6$ is $(-\infty, -2] \cup [3, \infty)$.

Remark: *For inequalities of the type '$\leq$' and '$\geq$' we include the end points of the intervals that form solution. This is done to accomodate 'equal to' part in the equalities '$\leq$' and '$\geq$'.*

Graphically

The graph of $y1 = x^2 - x - 6$ (Figure 3.25) shows two zeros. Use ZOOM-IN and TRACE to find their approximate locations (P and Q). The graph is above the x-axis on the left of P and on the right of Q.

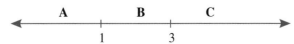

Figure 3.25

EXAMPLE 4 An object is thrown vertically upward from the ground level with an initial velocity of 64 ft/sec. The height (h) after time t seconds is given by

$$h(t) = 64t - 16t^2$$

Find when the object will be more than 48 feet above the ground level.

Solution: We want to find values of t when the height (h) is more than 48. For this, we solve $64t - 16t^2 > 48$.

Algebraically

- Transferring all terms to the left gives

$$64t - 16t^2 - 48 > 0$$

- Solving the equation $64t - 16t^2 - 48 = 0$, we get

$$-16t^2 + 64t - 48 = 0 \quad \longrightarrow \quad -16(t^2 - 4t + 3) = 0$$
$$\longrightarrow \quad -16(t - 3)(t - 1) = 0$$
$$\longrightarrow \quad t = 1 \quad \text{or} \quad t = 3$$

- By plotting these values on the number line divides the line into three intervals A, B, and C.

Here interval A is $(-\infty, 1)$, interval B is $(1, 3)$ and interval C is $(3, \infty)$.

Interval A	**Interval B**	**Interval C**
Test number $= 0$	Test number $= 2$	Test number $= 4$
$64(0) - 16(0)^2 > 48$	$64(2) - 16(2)^2 > 48$	$64(4) - 16(4)^2 > 48$
$0 > 48$	$128 - 64 > 48$	$256 - 256 > 48$
	$64 > 48$	$0 > 48$
This is not true. Therefore, the interval A is not part of the solution. We write "N" above the interval A.	This is true ; we write "Y" above interval B.	This is not true. So we write "N" above the interval C.

- Shading in the 'Y' interval and excluding the end points gives

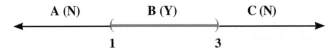

Thus, the object is more than 48 ft above the ground level during time interval $(1, 3)$.

Graphically

From Step 1, let $y1 = 64x - 16x^2 - 48$. On the standard range the graph looks like Figure 3.26. Estimate the interval where the graph is above the x-axis. Since the x-intercepts are 1 and 3, the graph is above the x-axis for $1 < x < 3$.

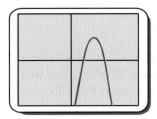

Figure 3.26

B. SOLVING RATIONAL INEQUALITIES

A rational inequality is an inequality involving rational expressions. The method to solve a rational inequality is almost same as the method for solving a polynomial inequality. We explain the strategy in the steps shown in the following example.

EXAMPLE 5   Solve $\dfrac{3x+1}{x-2} \geq 1$.

Solution: **Algebraically**

- Transfer all terms to the left side: $\dfrac{3x+1}{x-2} - 1 \geq 0$.

- Write the nonzero side as a single rational expression.

$$\frac{3x+1}{x-2} - \frac{x-2}{x-2} \geq 0 \longrightarrow \frac{3x+1-x+2}{x-2} \geq 0 \longrightarrow \frac{2x+3}{x-2} \geq 0$$

- Set the numerator and denominator equal to zero and solve each equation.

$$
\begin{array}{c|c}
2x + 3 = 0 & x - 2 = 0 \\
2x = -3 & x = 2 \\
x = -\dfrac{3}{2} &
\end{array}
$$

- Plot the roots on the number line.

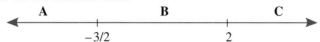

The two solutions divide the number line into three intervals A, B, and C namely $(-\infty, -3/2)$, $(-3/2, 2)$, and $(2, \infty)$.

- Select a test number in each part and check whether the interval is part of the solution. Use "Y" for yes and "N" for no.

Using the test number $x = -2$ for the interval A, we get

$$\frac{3(-2)+1}{-2-2} \ge 1 \longrightarrow \frac{-6+1}{-4} \ge 1 \longrightarrow \frac{-5}{-4} \ge 1 \text{ or } \frac{5}{4} \ge 1$$

This is a true statement. So we write "Y" above the interval A.

Using the test number $x = 0$ for the interval B, we get

$$\frac{3(0)+1}{0-2} \ge 1 \longrightarrow \frac{1}{-2} \ge 1 \longrightarrow -\frac{1}{2} \ge 1$$

This is not a true statement. So we write "N" above the interval B.

Use test number $x = 3$ for interval C. We get

$$\frac{3(3)+1}{3-2} \ge 1 \quad \text{or} \quad \frac{10}{1} \ge 1$$

This is a true statement. So we write "Y" above the interval C.

- Shade in the "Y" intervals and include the end points if the inequality symbol is $\le$ or $\ge$ provided the denominator does not become zero.

Even though the original inequality is $\ge$, we do not include $x = 2$, because it makes the denominator of the rational expression $\frac{3x+1}{x-2}$ zero, which means $\frac{3x+1}{x-2}$ is not defined at $x = 2$. Equivalently $x = 2$ is not in the domain of $\frac{3x+1}{x-2}$.

Thus, the solution of the rational inequality is $\left(-\infty, -\frac{3}{2}\right] \cup (2, \infty)$.

Graphically

From Step 2, let $y1 = \dfrac{2x+3}{x-2}$. The graph on the standard range looks like Figure 3.27.

Estimate the intervals where the graph is above the x-axis. The x-intercept is $-\dfrac{3}{2}$ and the graph is undefined at $x = 2$.

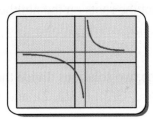

Figure 3.27

EXAMPLE 6   Solve $\dfrac{3}{x-3} < \dfrac{1}{x+1}$.

Solution: **Algebraically**

- Transferring all terms to left side gives: $\dfrac{3}{x-3} - \dfrac{1}{x+1} < 0$.

- Writing the left side as a single rational expression gives

$$\frac{3(x+1)}{(x-3)(x+1)} - \frac{1(x-3)}{(x-3)(x+1)} < 0$$

$$\frac{3x+3-x+3}{(x-3)(x+1)} < 0 \quad \longrightarrow \quad \frac{2x+6}{(x-3)(x+1)} < 0$$

- Setting the numerator and the denominator equal to zero separately and solving the resulting equations give

$$
\begin{array}{c|c|c}
2x + 6 = 0 & (x-3)(x+1) = 0 & \\
2x = -6 & x - 3 = 0 & x + 1 = 0 \\
x = -3 & x = 3 & x = -1
\end{array}
$$

- Plotting these roots on the number line divides the number line into four intervals A, B, C and D.

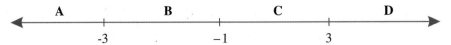

Interval A is $(-\infty, -3)$, interval B is $(-3, -1)$, interval C is $(-1, 3)$, and interval D is $(3, \infty)$.

- By selecting a test number $x = -4$ in interval A, we get

$$\frac{3}{-4-3} < \frac{1}{-4+1} \quad \longrightarrow \quad \frac{3}{-7} < \frac{1}{-3} \quad \longrightarrow \quad -9 < -7 \quad \text{\small Multiply both sides by the lcd = 21}$$

This is a true statement. We write "Y" above interval A.

Checking the interval B with test number $x = -2$, we get

$$\frac{3}{-2-3} < \frac{1}{-2+1} \quad \longrightarrow \quad \frac{3}{-5} < \frac{1}{-1} \quad \longrightarrow \quad \frac{-3}{5} < -1$$

This is not true. So we write "N" above interval B.

Similarly, we can examine intervals C and D and find "Y" and "N", respectively.

- Shading in the "Y" intervals and excluding the end points we get

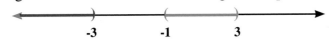

Thus the solution of the inequality is $(-\infty, -3) \cup (-1, 3)$.

Graphically

Let $y1 = \dfrac{3}{x-3} - \dfrac{1}{x+1}$ or $\dfrac{2x+6}{(x-3)(x+1)}$.

Graph $y1$ on the standard range or any other suitable range. We are looking for the intervals where the graph is below the x-axis. If we use ZOOM-IN and TRACE to find the x-intercept (zero), it will be approximately at $x = -3$. Thus, the graph is below the x-axis on $(-\infty, -3)$. Also, the graph is below the x-axis for the middle part. Use ZOOM-IN and TRACE to locate the vertical lines containing the middle part. This interval will be $(-1, 3)$.

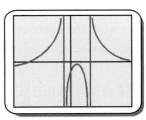

Figure 3.28

C. SOLVING ABSOLUTE VALUE INEQUALITIES

An inequality involving absolute value expressions is called **absolute value inequality.** An absolute value inequality with the < symbol (Type 1) can be transformed into a conjunction of two inequalities or into a double inequality. And an absolute value inequality with the > symbol (Type 2) can be transformed into a disjunction of two inequalities. We begin with type 1 absolute value inequalities.

Solving a Type 1 Absolute Value Inequality

An absolute value inequality of the type $\left| ax - b \right| < c$ or $\left| ax - b \right| \le c$ is called **Type 1** inequality.

EXAMPLE 7   Solve $\left| 3x + 1 \right| < 4$.

Solution: **Algebraically**

- The inequality is already in the standard form.

- Transform the absolute value inequality into a double inequality . *

    $-4 < 3x + 1 < 4$

> * Use the rule $|A| < p$ if and only if $-p < A < p$. (section 1.2 C).

- Solve the double inequality.

$$-4 < 3x + 1 < 4 \longrightarrow -4 - 1 < 3x < 4 - 1$$
$$\longrightarrow -5 < 3x < 3$$
$$\longrightarrow -\frac{5}{3} < x < \frac{3}{3} \longrightarrow -\frac{5}{3} < x < 1$$

Thus, the solution of the inequality is

$$-\frac{5}{3} < x < 1 \quad \text{or} \quad \left(-\frac{5}{3}, 1\right) \text{ or}$$

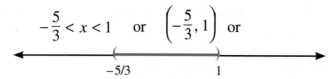

Graphically

Let $y1 = |3x+1| - 4$. Graph $y1$ on a suitable range. Use ZOOM-IN and TRACE to find interval(s) where the graph is below x-axis. The x-intercepts are approximately -1.67 and 1.

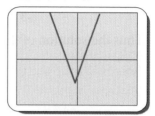

Figure 3.29

EXAMPLE 8   Solve $|2x - 1| - 5 \le 6$.

Solution: **Algebraically**

• Write the inequality in the standard form:

$$|2x - 1| \le 6 + 5 \quad \longrightarrow \quad |2x - 1| \le 11$$

• Transform the absolute value inequality into a double inequality. *

$$-11 \le 2x - 1 \le 11$$

> * Use the rule $|A| \le p$ if and only if $-p \le A \le p$. (section 1.2 C)

• Solve the double inequality.

$$-11 \le 2x - 1 \le 11 \quad \longrightarrow \quad -11 + 1 \le 2x \le 11 + 1$$
$$\longrightarrow \quad -10 \le 2x \le 12$$
$$\longrightarrow \quad -5 \le x \le 6$$

Thus, the solution of the inequality is $-5 \le x \le 6$ or

Graphically

Let $y1 = |2x - 1| - 11$. Graph $y1$ on a suitable range.

Find interval (s) where the graph is below the x-axis. The x-intercepts are -5 and 6.

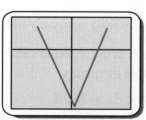

Figure 3.30

EXAMPLE 9   Solve $|x - 2| < \delta$ (delta).

Solution: **Algebraically**

• It is already in the standard form : $|x - 2| < \delta$

• Writing the inequality as a double inequality: $-\delta < x - 2 < \delta$

- Solving the double inequality gives :

$$2 - \delta < x - 2 + 2 < 2 + \delta \quad \longrightarrow \quad 2 - \delta < x < 2 + \delta$$

Thus, the solution of the inequality is $(2 - \delta, 2 + \delta)$

It is not possible to draw a graph because δ is not known.

EXAMPLE 10   Solve $\left| f(x) - L \right| < 0.01$ for $f(x)$.

Solution: **Algebraically**

- The inequality is in the standard form: $\left| f(x) - L \right| < 0.01$

- Writing as a double inequality gives: $-0.01 < f(x) - L < 0.01$

- Solving the double inequality for $f(x)$ gives:

$$L - 0.01 < f(x) - L + L < L + 0.01 \quad \text{or}$$
$$L - 0.01 < f(x) < L + 0.01$$

Thus, the solution of the inequality is $(L - 0.01, L + 0.01)$.

It is not possible to draw a graph because L is not known.

Solving Type 2 Absolute Value Inequality

An absolute value inequality of the type $\left| ax - b \right| > c$ or $\left| ax - b \right| \geq c$ is called **Type 2** inequality. We explain the strategy to solve this type of inequality in the following examples.

EXAMPLE 11   Solve the inequality $\left| 5 - 2x \right| > 3$.

Solution: **Algebraically**

- The inequality $\left| 5 - 2x \right| > 3$ is already in the standard form.

- Write the inequality as the union of two inequalities like *
$$5 - 2x > 3 \qquad \text{or} \qquad 5 - 2x < -3$$

> * Recall: $|A| > p$ if and only if
> $A > p$ or $A < -p$.
> (section 1.2 C).

- Solve the inequalities   or

$$
\begin{array}{l|l}
5 - 2x > 3 & 5 - 2x < -3 \\
-2x > 3 - 5 & -2x < -3 - 5 \\
-2x > -2 & -2x < -8 \\
2x < 2 & 2x > 8 \\
x < 1 & x > 4
\end{array}
$$

- Take the union of the two solutions.

Thus, the solution is $(-\infty, 1) \cup (4, \infty)$.

EXAMPLE 12   Solve $\left|5x-2\right|-1\geq 7$.

Solution: **Algebraically**

Step 1   Write the inequality in the standard form: $\left|K\right|\geq$ number.

$$\left|5x-2\right|-1\geq 7 \quad\longrightarrow\quad \left|5x-2\right|\geq 8$$

Step 2   Write the inequality as the union of two inequalities like

$$5x-2\geq 8 \qquad\text{or}\qquad 5x-2\leq -8$$

Step 3   Solve the inequalities

$$\begin{array}{c|c} & \text{or} \\ 5x-2\geq 8 & 5x-2\leq -8 \\[4pt] x\geq 2 & x\leq -\dfrac{6}{5} \end{array}$$

Step 4   Take the union of the two solutions.

-6/5   2

Thus, the solution of the inequality is $\left(-\infty,-\dfrac{6}{5}\right]\cup[2,\infty)$.

Graphically

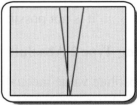

Let $y1=\text{abs}(5x-2)-8$. Graph $y1$ on a suitable range. Use ZOOM-IN and TRACE to locate the x-intercepts. Finally, estimate the interval where the graph is above the x-axis. The x-intercepts are -1.2 and 2.

Figure 3.31

EXAMPLE 13   Use a graphing calculator to estimate the

solution of $\left|2(x+1)^2-2x^2\right|-0.1<0$.

Solution:

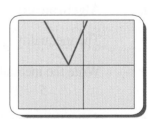

Let $y1=\left|2(x+1)^2-2x^2\right|-0.1$. Graph $y1$ on a suitable range. On the standard range the graph looks like Figure 3.32(a).

We are looking for the interval where the graph is below the x-axis. But the graph does not clearly show any part below the x-axis. To make sure that this is true, we ZOOM-IN near the corner of the graph. Try zooming in a couple of times. Now the graph has a portion that is below the x-axis.

Figure 3.32(a)

Now use ZOOM-IN and TRACE to locate the x-intercepts.

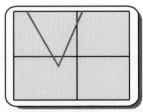

The interval on which the graph is below the x-axis is approximately $(-0.5233,-0.476)$.

Figure 3.32(b)

Thus, the solution of $\left|2(x+1)^2-2x^2\right|<0.1$ is the interval $(-0.5233,-0.476)$.

EXERCISE 3.5

In exercises (1-22), solve the inequality and give the answer using interval notation.

1. $5 - 4x \leq 25$ **2.** $3 - 2x < 7$ **3.** $2 - 3x \geq 11$ **4.** $4x + 5 > 13$

5. $3(x - 1) - 5(x + 1) > 2$ **6.** $2(x - 2) - 3(x + 1) \geq 5$ **7.** $2x - 7(3x + 2) < -7$ **8.** $5(2x + 1) - 4x \leq 17$

9. $2 < 3x - 4 < 5$ **10.** $-3 < 4x + 5 < 9$ **11.** $8 \leq 4x - 5 \leq 11$ **12.** $1 \leq 2x + 7 \leq 6$

13. $\dfrac{1}{3} \leq \dfrac{3x - 10}{2} \leq 2$ **14.** $-1 < \dfrac{3x + 5}{2} < 4$ **15.** $\dfrac{1}{3} \leq \dfrac{1 - 2x}{3} \leq \dfrac{1}{2}$ **16.** $\dfrac{1}{4} \leq \dfrac{3x - 1}{4} \leq \dfrac{1}{3}$

17. $\dfrac{3x - 1}{2} - \dfrac{x}{3} \leq 1$ **18.** $\dfrac{5x + 3}{5} - \dfrac{x}{2} < 2$ **19.** $\dfrac{x - 3}{2} - \dfrac{2x - 5}{3} > \dfrac{x}{3} + 2$ **20.** $\dfrac{x - 2}{3} - \dfrac{x + 2}{2} \geq \dfrac{2x + 3}{3} - 1$

21. $\dfrac{2 - 7x}{3} \leq \dfrac{x + 1}{2}$ **22.** $\dfrac{9 + 2x}{5} + 2 < \dfrac{2 - 5x}{2}$

In exercises (23-44), solve the inequality both algebraically and graphically and give the answer using interval notation.

23. $x^2 \geq 4$ **24.** $x^2 \geq 25$ **25.** $x^2 < 9$ **26.** $x^2 < 25$ **27.** $x^2 - x \leq 2$

28. $x^2 + 2x > 3$ **29.** $x^2 - x > 12$ **30.** $x^2 + 7x \leq -10$ **31.** $2x + x^2 \geq 24$

32. $-x^2 + 8x > 12$ **33.** $x^4 - 81 \leq 0$ **34.** $x^4 - 16 \geq 0$ **35.** $x(x + 1)(x - 1) \leq 0$

36. $x(x - 1)(x + 2) > 0$ **37.** $(x - 1)(x + 2)(x - 3) > 0$ **38.** $(x + 1)(x + 2)(x - 4) < 0$

39. $x^2 + 2x - 1 > 0$ **40.** $x^2 - x - 1 < 0$ **41.** $2x^2 + 8x - 1 > 0$ **42.** $2x^2 - 3x + 1 < 0$

43. $(x - 3)(x^2 - x - 2) \leq 0$ **44.** $(x + 2)(x^2 - x - 6) \geq 0$

In exercises (45-48), use a graphing calculator to solve the inequality approximately to the nearest two decimal places.

45. $x^3 + 3x^2 - 2x - 5 \geq 0$ **46.** $x^3 + 2x^2 - 3x + 4 > 0$

47. $4x^4 + x^3 - 10x - 5 < 0$ **48.** $3x^4 + 2x^3 + 5x^2 - 10 \leq 0$

49. A roll of 50 ft fence is to be used to enclose a rectangular garden of sides x and $25 - x$. For what values of x will the area of the garden exceed 100 ft^2?

50. A farmer wants to fence a rectangular patch of sides x and $30 - x$ with a roll of 60 ft wire. For what values of x will the area of the patch exceed 200 ft^2?

51. The profit (P) of a company after selling x units of an item is given in millions by

$$P(x) = 1.2x\left(5 - x^2\right).$$

For what level of sales (x) will the company make an excess of 4 millions in profit?

52. The profit (P) of a company after selling x units of an item is given by $P(x) = x(-2 + x)$. For what level of sales (x) will the company make in excess of 2 million in profit?

53. A page of print is supposed to contain at least 100 in^2 of printed region. If the dimensions of the page are 16×12 in, for what choices of equal margins (x) on four sides will the area for printing be at least 100 in^2?

54. The dimensions of a page are 12×10 in. For what choices of equal margins (x) on four sides, the area of printing on the page will be at least 80 in^2?

55. If 24 trees are planted per acre, then each tree produces 600 apples per year. Each additional tree planted per acre reduces the yield of each tree by 12 apples per year. Let x represent number of trees in excess of 24 trees per acre planted. For which x-values will the yield per acre be at least 650?

In exercises (56-75), solve the inequality and give answer using interval notation.

56. $\dfrac{x+2}{x-3} \geq 0$ **57.** $\dfrac{x-3}{x+5} > 0$ **58.** $\dfrac{x-1}{x-5} < 0$ **59.** $\dfrac{x+4}{x-6} \leq 0$ **60.** $\dfrac{2x}{x-1} \geq 1$

61. $\dfrac{-3x}{x+2} \leq 1$ **62.** $\dfrac{3x}{x+2} < 2$ **63.** $\dfrac{-4x}{x-3} > 3$ **64.** $\dfrac{x^2-5x+6}{x-1} < 0$ **65.** $\dfrac{x^2-3x+2}{x-4} > 0$

66. $\dfrac{x^2-x-2}{x} > 0$ **67.** $\dfrac{x^2-2x-8}{x} < 0$ **68.** $\dfrac{1}{x-4} - \dfrac{1}{x-2} \leq \dfrac{2}{5}$ **69.** $\dfrac{1}{x+3} - \dfrac{1}{x-1} \geq \dfrac{2}{3}$

70. $\dfrac{2}{x+1} - \dfrac{1}{x-2} < \dfrac{1}{3}$ **71.** $\dfrac{3}{x-4} - \dfrac{2}{x-3} > \dfrac{1}{2}$ **72.** $\dfrac{x-1}{x-2} > \dfrac{x-3}{x-4}$ **73.** $\dfrac{x+2}{x-1} \geq \dfrac{x+4}{x+1}$

74. $\dfrac{1}{x} < \dfrac{3-x}{x-1}$ **75.** $\dfrac{1}{x} > \dfrac{5+2x}{x+2}$

In exercises (76-79), use a graphing calculator to solve the inequality and give the answer using interval notation.

76. $\dfrac{x^3+5x^2-6}{x-3} > 4$ **77.** $\dfrac{x^3-3x^2-8}{x-2} > 5$ **78.** $\dfrac{x^3+2x^2-x-4}{x+1} < 5$ **79.** $\dfrac{x^3-x^2+2x-5}{x-1} > 10$

80. The cost of removing $x\%$ of the waste is given by $C(x) = \dfrac{500}{100-x}$ (million). If at most 20 million is funded for the purpose, up to what percent of the waste can be removed?

In exercises (81-104), solve the inequality and give answer in interval notation.

81. $\left|x-3\right| < 2$ **82.** $\left|x-5\right| < 3$ **83.** $\left|x+2\right| < 4$ **84.** $\left|x+4\right| < 5$ **85.** $\left|x-1\right| \leq 2$

86. $\left|x-3\right| \leq 5$ **87.** $\left|x-7\right| < 3$ **88.** $\left|x+7\right| \leq 2$ **89.** $\left|x-3\right| > 5$ **90.** $\left|x+4\right| > 3$

91. $\left|2x-1\right| \geq 1$ **92.** $\left|x-2\right| \geq 7$ **93.** $\left|3x-1\right| - 8 < 0$ **94.** $\left|2x+1\right| - 7 < 0$ **95.** $\left|\dfrac{3x}{2} - 1\right| \geq 2$

96. $\left|\dfrac{2x}{5} + 1\right| \leq 3$ **97.** $\left|x^2-4\right| \leq 5$ **98.** $\left|x^2-4\right| \geq 5$ **99.** $\left|x^2-x-1\right| \leq 1$ **100.** $\left|\dfrac{x-2}{x+1}\right| > 2$

101. Write $\left|f(x)-L\right| < 0.02$ as an interval.   **102.** Write $\left|f(x)-l\right| < 2$ as an interval.

103. If $\left|x-1\right| < \delta$, write $\left|x+4\right|$ in terms of δ.   **104.** If $\left|x-2\right| < \delta$, write $\left|x+7\right|$ in terms of δ.

Writing Exercises

105. Describe the possible change in sign of $f(x)$ for x near a zero of f.

106. Describe the unit interval around $x = 3$. Then describe a δ – interval around $x = a$.

3.6 DOMAIN OF A FUNCTION (REVISITED)

In this section we will use new tools, and terminology of this chapter to give a better form and more substance to the guiding principles for finding the domain of a function.

> **Objective** ▶▶
>
> In this section you will learn about:
>
> A. Finding the domain of a function.

A. FINDING THE DOMAIN OF A FUNCTION

The **first guiding principle** for finding the domain states that x-values that make the denominator of a function zero are not acceptable. For this, we solve the equation:

> Denominator $= 0$

The domain consists of all x's such that $x \neq$ root of the above equation.

For example, to find the domain of the function $f(x) = \dfrac{x-3}{x^2-16}$, we set the denominator to zero and solve the equation $x^2 - 16 = 0$.

$$x^2 - 16 = 0 \longrightarrow (x-4)(x+4) = 0 \longrightarrow x = 4, \ -4$$

Now, the domain is written as

Domain: All x's such that $x \neq \pm 4$

The **second guiding principle** for finding the domain states that the radicand of an even root must be non-negative. For this, we solve the inequality

Radicand ≥ 0

The domain consists of the solutions of the above inequality. We usually write the domain in the interval form.

For example, the domain of the function $f(x) = \sqrt{5x-3}$

is given by the solution of the inequality $5x - 3 \geq 0 \longrightarrow 5x \geq 3 \longrightarrow x \geq \dfrac{3}{5}$.

Thus, the domain of $f(x) = \sqrt{5x-3}$ is written as : $\left[\dfrac{3}{5}, \infty \right)$.

EXAMPLE 1   Find the domain of $f(x) = \dfrac{x+3}{2x^2 - 7x + 3}$.

Solution: The function does not contain any even root, so we use only the first guiding principle for the domain.

Solving the equation $2x^2 - 7x + 3 = 0$ gives

$$(2x-1)(x-3) = 0 \longrightarrow x = \dfrac{1}{2} \text{ and } x = 3$$

Thus, the domain of the function $f(x)$ does not contain $x = \dfrac{1}{2}$ and $x = 3$. In short,

Domain: $\left\{ x \,\middle|\, x \neq \dfrac{1}{2}, \text{ and } x \neq 3 \right\}$ or the set of all real numbers except $\dfrac{1}{2}$ or 3.

Remark: *We can also solve the equation graphically.*

EXAMPLE 2   Find the domain of $f(x) = \sqrt{x^2 - 2x - 3}$.

Solution: By the second guiding principle, we solve $x^2 - 2x - 3 \geq 0$ **(1)**

Step 1   The inequality is in the standard form: $x^2 - 2x - 3 \geq 0$.

Step 2   Solve the equation $x^2 - 2x - 3 = 0$ or $(x-3)(x+1) = 0$

$$\longrightarrow x = 3 \text{ or } x = -1$$

Step 3   By plotting these roots on the number line, we divide the line into three intervals A, B, and C.

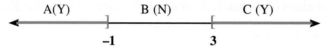

Interval A is $(-\infty, -1)$, interval B is $(-1, 3)$, and interval C is $(3, \infty)$

Step 4

Test number $x = -2$ gives	Test number $x = 0$ gives	Test number $x = 4$ gives
$(-2)^2 - 2(-2) - 3 \geq 0$	$(0)^2 - 2(0) - 3 \geq 0$	$(4)^2 - 2(4) - 3 \geq 0$
$4 + 4 - 3 \geq 0$	$-3 \geq 0$	$16 - 8 - 3 \geq 0$
$5 \geq 0$		$5 \geq 0$
This is a true statement. Therefore, we write "Y" above part A.	This is not a true statement. Therefore, we write "N" above part B.	This is a true statement. Therefore, we write "Y" above part C.

Step 5   Shading in the "Y" intervals and including the end points gives

$$A(Y) \qquad B(N) \qquad C(Y)$$
$$ -1 3$$

Thus, the domain of $f(x)$ is the same as the solution of the inequality (**1**) and we write it as

Domain: $(-\infty, -1] \cup [3, \infty)$.

Remark: *We can also solve inequality (**1**) graphically.*

EXAMPLE 3   Find the domain of $f(x) = \dfrac{3}{\sqrt{9x - 7}} + \dfrac{1}{x^2 - 4}$.

Solution: The domain of $f(x)$ is the intersection of the domains of

$$g(x) = \frac{3}{\sqrt{9x - 7}} \quad \text{and} \quad h(x) = \frac{1}{x^2 - 4}$$

For the domain of $g(x) = \dfrac{3}{\sqrt{9x - 7}}$ we solve

the inequality $9x - 7 > 0$ *

$$9x > 7 \quad \longrightarrow \quad x > \frac{7}{9}$$

> * Note that we are making use of both the principles: denominato$r \neq 0$ **and** radicand ≥ 0. So, we choose radicand > 0.

$$\xleftarrow{} \overset{(}{\underset{7/9}{}} \xrightarrow{}$$

For the domain of $h(x) = \dfrac{1}{x^2 - 4}$ we solve the equation $x^2 - 4 = 0$.

$$(x - 2)(x + 2) = 0 \quad \longrightarrow \quad x = 2 \text{ and } x = -2$$

Thus, the domain of f consists of all numbers x in the interval $\left(\dfrac{7}{9}, \infty\right)$ except -2 and 2. Since -2

does not belong to $\left(\dfrac{7}{9}, \infty\right)$, the domain of f actually consists of all real numbers in the interval

$\left(\dfrac{7}{9}, \infty\right)$ except $x = 2$. This can be written as $\left(\dfrac{7}{9}, 2\right) \cup (2, \infty)$.

EXAMPLE 4   Find the domain of $f(x) = \sqrt[3]{x^2 - 8x}$.

Solution: The "expression" part of the function $f(x)$ contains neither a denominator nor an even root. Therefore, by the guiding principles for the domain, we impose no restrictions on x-values. Consequently, the domain is $(-\infty, \infty)$.

> **Remark:** *You can check the answer graphically.*

EXAMPLE 5   Find the domain of $g(x) = 2x^3 - 3x^2 + 5$.

Solution: According to the guiding principles for finding the domain, there are no restrictions on the x-values.

Thus, the domain of $g(x) = 2x^3 - 3x^2 + 5$ is given by

Domain: $(-\infty, \infty)$.

> **Remark:** *The domain of a polynomial function is always $(-\infty, \infty)$, unless otherwise restricted.*

EXERCISE 3.6

In exercises (1-30), find the domain of the function.

1. $f(x) = \dfrac{x+1}{x-3}$
2. $f(x) = \dfrac{x-1}{x+9}$
3. $g(x) = \dfrac{x-1}{(x+2)(x-3)}$
4. $g(x) = \dfrac{x+5}{(x-8)(x+7)}$

5. $h(x) = \dfrac{3}{x^2 - x}$
6. $f(x) = \dfrac{5}{x^2 + 7x}$
7. $f(x) = \sqrt{3x-4}$
8. $f(x) = \sqrt{4x+7}$

9. $g(x) = \sqrt{2-7x}$
10. $h(x) = \sqrt{27-9x}$
11. $f(x) = \sqrt{x^2 - 4}$
12. $g(x) = \sqrt{x^2 - 25}$

13. $h(x) = \sqrt{x^2 - 2x}$
14. $g(x) = \sqrt{x^2 + 6x}$
15. $g(x) = \sqrt{(x-5)(x+2)}$

16. $f(x) = \sqrt{(x+1)(x+4)}$
17. $f(x) = \sqrt{9-x^2}$
18. $g(x) = \sqrt{25-x^2}$

19. $g(x) = \dfrac{x^2 - x - 12}{x-4}$
20. $f(x) = \dfrac{2x^2 + 3x - 6}{x+7}$
21. $f(x) = \dfrac{3-x}{\sqrt{2-x}}$

22. $f(x) = \dfrac{7+x}{\sqrt{5+x}}$
23. $g(x) = \sqrt[5]{x^3 - 3x^4 - 2x^3 + 7}$
24. $f(x) = \sqrt[3]{x^4 + 3x^3 - 2x + 9}$

25. $h(x) = x^5 - 7x^4 + 8x^3 + x^2 - 5x - 10$
26. $g(x) = 6x^4 - 3x^3 + 5x^2 + 7x - 11$
27. $f(x) = \dfrac{x+1}{\sqrt{x^2 - 3x}} + \dfrac{3}{x-5}$

28. $g(x) = \dfrac{x-5}{\sqrt{x^2 + 2x}} + \dfrac{6}{x-9}$
29. $g(x) = \sqrt{x^2 - 2x + 1} + \dfrac{1}{x-2}$
30. $f(x) = \sqrt{x^2 - x - 2} - \dfrac{5}{x+5}$

Writing Exercises

31. Explain why the domain of a polynomial function is the entire set of real numbers.

32. Identify a function whose domain is the entire set of real numbers.

33. Explain why the domain of $f(x) = \sqrt{p(x)}$, where $p(x)$ is a polynomial, is not the entire set of real numbers.

3.7 ROOTS OF POLYNOMIAL EQUATIONS (REVISITED)

Objectives ▶▶

In this section you will learn about:

A. Real Roots;

B. Complex Roots;

C. Descartes Rule of Signs; and

D. Relations between Roots and Coefficients.

In section 3.1, we learned that every polynomial equation has at least one root, real or complex. We also learned how to form a polynomial equation with desired roots. The main objective of this section is to discuss additional techniques for solving polynomial equations. To accomplish this objective we will consider roots of special types. We will also study the relation between roots and **coefficients** of the equations. The graphing calculator will be used in some cases. It should be noticed that graphing techniques do not provide enough information about complex roots. Descarte's Rule of Signs is an effective method for obtaining information about the number of real roots. In this section all equations will be assumed to have integer coefficients unless stated otherwise.

It may be observed that every polynomial equation with rational coefficients can always be reduced to an equivalent polynomial equation with integer coefficients. Recall that two equations are said to be equivalent if they have same roots. This is explained in the following equation.

$$2x^3 - \frac{5}{7}x^2 + \frac{4}{3}x - 8 = 0$$

$$\rightarrow \frac{42}{21}x^3 - \frac{15}{21}x^2 + \frac{28}{21}x - \frac{168}{21} = 0$$

Change each coefficient to a fraction with the same denominator.

$$\rightarrow \frac{1}{21}(42x^3 - 15x^2 + 28x - 168) = 0$$

$$\rightarrow 42x^3 - 15x^2 + 28x - 168 = 0$$

A. REAL ROOTS

We have seen that an equation may have real or complex roots. A repeated application of the **Fundamental Theorem of Algebra** assures that every equation of degree n has exactly n roots if all the roots, real and complex, are considered along with their multiplicities. Real roots may be integers, rational numbers or irrational numbers. Irrational roots of equations with rational coefficients occur in pairs.

Property of Irrational roots:

If an irrational number $a + b\sqrt{c}$ is a root of polynomial equation $f(x) = 0$ with rational coefficients, then $a - b\sqrt{c}$ is also a root of the equation. Here a and b are rational numbers.

Remarks:

1. For $a+b\sqrt{c}$ to be irrational $b \neq 0$ and c is not the square of a number.

2. $a+b\sqrt{c}$ and $a-b\sqrt{c}$ are said to be **conjugate** of each other.

3. The pair of roots $a+b\sqrt{c}$ and $a-b\sqrt{c}$ of an equation $f(x) = 0$ lead to the linear factors $\left(x-\left(a+b\sqrt{c}\right)\right)$ and $\left(x-\left(a-b\sqrt{c}\right)\right)$ of $f(x)$. These factors produce the following quadratic factor of $f(x)$:

$$\left(x-\left(a+b\sqrt{c}\right)\right)\ \left(x-\left(a-b\sqrt{c}\right)\right) = \left((x-a)-b\sqrt{c}\right)\ \left((x-a)+b\sqrt{c}\right)$$

$$= (x-a)^2 - b^2\,c$$

$$= x^2 - 2ax + a^2 - bc$$

The following property gives information about rational roots.

Property of rational roots:

Let $a_n x^n + a_{n-1} x^{n-1} + \ldots + a_1 x + a_0 = 0$ be a polynomial equation such that all coefficients are integers. If a rational number

$\dfrac{p}{q}$ (expressed in lowest terms) is a root of the equation then p is a

factor of a_0 and q is a factor of a_n.

Remark: *The above property of rational roots gives possible* **candidates** *for rational roots, but none of them may, infact, be a root. For example, consider the equation*

$$x^2 + x + 2 = 0$$

$$x^2 + x + 2 = a_2 x^2 + a_1 x + a_0$$

where $a_2 = 1$ and $a_0 = 2$

Possible factors of a_2 are ± 1 *and possible factors of a_0 are ± 1 and ± 2. So, the possible candidates for rational roots are ± 1 and ± 2. However, an application of quadratic formula or graphing of $y = x^2 + x + 2$ shows that the equation $x^2 + x + 2 = 0$ does not have real roots.*

Quadratic Formula

$$x = \frac{-1 \pm \sqrt{1 - 4(2)(1)}}{2}$$

$$= \frac{-1 \pm \sqrt{-7}}{2}$$

$$= -1 + i\frac{\sqrt{7}}{2}\ ,\ -1 - i\frac{\sqrt{7}}{2}$$

Graph of $y = x^2 + x + 2$

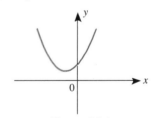

Figure 3.7.1

In general, real roots of odd multiplicity can be located by the following criterion.

Location property of real roots:

Let $f(x) = 0$ be a polynomial equation with real coefficients. Suppose a and b are two real numbers such that $f(a)$ and $f(b)$ have opposite signs (or equivalently, $f(a)\,f(b) < 0$), then $f(x) = 0$ has at least one real root that lies between a and b.

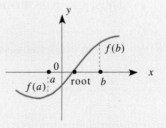

Figure 3.7.2

EXAMPLE 1   Find a rational root of the equation $2x^3 - 3x^2 - 4x + 6 = 0$. Use the factor theorem to determine the remaining roots.

Solution:

Step 1   If $2x^3 - 3x^2 - 4x + 6 = 0$ has a rational root, let it be written as $\dfrac{p}{q}$ so that p and q do not have a common factor other than 1 and -1.
Then $p = \pm 1, \pm 2, \pm 3$ and $q = \pm 1, \pm 2$

> $f(x) = a_n x^n + a_{n-1} x^{n-1} + \ldots + a_1 x + a_0$. p is a factor of a_0 and q is a factor of a_n.

Step 2   Possible candidates for rational root $\dfrac{p}{q}$ are:

$$\pm \frac{1}{2}, \pm 1, \pm 2, \pm \frac{3}{2}, \pm 3 .$$

Step 3   We substitute each of these values in $2x^3 - 3x^2 - 4x + 6$ to verify if it is a root.

$\dfrac{1}{2}$: $2\left(\dfrac{1}{2}\right)^3 - 3\left(\dfrac{1}{2}\right)^2 - 4\left(\dfrac{1}{2}\right) + 6 = \dfrac{7}{2}$

> a is a root of $f(x) = 0$ if $f(a) = 0$
>
> We may use graphing calculator to evaluate $f(x)$ for various values of x.

$-\dfrac{1}{2}$: $2\left(-\dfrac{1}{2}\right)^3 - 3\left(-\dfrac{1}{2}\right)^2 - 4\left(-\dfrac{1}{2}\right) + 6 = 7$

1 : $2(1)^3 - 3(1)^2 - 4(1) + 6 = 1$

−1 : $2(-1)^3 - 3(-1)^2 - 4(-1) + 6 = 5$

2 : $2(2)^3 - 3(2)^2 - 4(2) + 6 = 2$

−2 : $2(-2)^3 - 3(-2)^2 - 4(-2) + 6 = -14$

$\dfrac{3}{2}$: $2\left(\dfrac{3}{2}\right)^3 - 3\left(\dfrac{3}{2}\right)^2 - 4\left(\dfrac{3}{2}\right) + 6 = \mathbf{0}$

$-\dfrac{3}{2}$: $2\left(-\dfrac{3}{2}\right)^3 - 3\left(-\dfrac{3}{2}\right)^2 - 4\left(-\dfrac{3}{2}\right) + 6 = -\dfrac{3}{2} .$

3 : $2(3)^3 - 3(3)^2 - 4(3) + 6 = 21$

−3 : $2(-3)^3 - 3(-3)^2 - 4(-3) + 6 = -63$

Thus, $x = \dfrac{3}{2}$ is the only rational root of the equation.

Step 4   We use synthetic division to write $f(x) = \left(x - \dfrac{3}{2}\right) g(x)$

$\dfrac{3}{2}$	2	−3	−4	6
		3	0	−6
	2	0	−4	0

> Equivalently factor $f(x)$ by grouping.
>
> $(2x^3 - 3x^2) - 2(2x - 3)$
>
> $= x^2 (2x - 3) - 2(2x - 3)$
>
> $= (x^2 - 2)(2x - 3)$

Therefore,

$$f(x) = \left(x - \frac{3}{2}\right)(2x^2 - 4).$$

Step 5   The other roots of $2x^3 - 3x^2 - 4x + 6 = 0$ are given by $2x^2 - 4 = 0$.

$\longrightarrow \quad 2(x^2 - 2) = 0$

$\longrightarrow \quad x^2 - 2 = 0 \quad \longrightarrow \quad x = \pm\sqrt{2}$

Hence the roots of $2x^3 - 3x^2 - 4x + 6 = 0$ are $\frac{3}{2}, \sqrt{2}, -\sqrt{2}$.

⬤ Note   Later on we will learn a *test for the bounds* of the roots which will help us reduce the testing work.

Graphically,

- Enter $2x^3 - 3x^2 - 4x + 6$ as $y1$.
- Select a suitable window.
- Use TRACE to approximate the roots.

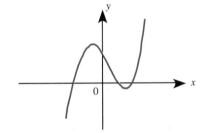

Figure 3.7.3

EXAMPLE 2 $f(x) = 0$ is a fourth degree equation which is known to have a rational root greater than 1. If the leading coefficient of $f(x)$ is 1 and its constant term is 3, then what is the rational root?

Solution: Suppose the rational root is written as $\frac{p}{q}$ such that p and q do not have a common factor other than 1 and -1. Then

(i)   possible values of p are $\pm1, \pm3$.

(ii)   possible values of q are ±1.

Therefore, possible candidates for the root are $\pm1, \pm3$. Since the root is greater than 1, the root is 3.

> If $\frac{p}{q}$ is a root of $a_n x^n + a_{n-1} x^{n-1} +$
> $\ldots + a_1 x + a_0 = 0$
> then
> p is a factor of a_0 and q is a factor of a_n.

EXAMPLE 3   The equation $x^3 - x - 1 = 0$ has exactly one real root. Estimate this root correctly to two decimal places.

Solution:

Let $f(x) = x^3 - x - 1$.

Step 1   We find two values a and b of x such that $f(a)$ **and $f(b)$ have different signs.** By inspection, we find that these numbers are 1 and 2, because

$$f(1) = 1^3 - 1 - 1 = -1 \quad \text{and} \quad f(2) = 2^3 - 2 - 1 = 5$$

Thus $x^3 - x - 1 = 0$ has a root between 1 and 2.

Step 2   We will successively narrow down these values so that the two bounds for the root differ only in the third place. Calculating the value of $f(x)$ for $x = 1.1, 1.2, 1.3, 1.4, \ldots$ we find that the root lies between 1.3 and 1.4, since $f(1.3) = (1.3)^3 - 1.3 - 1 = -.103,$ and

$$f(1.4) = (1.4)^3 - 1.4 - 1 = .344$$

Again calculation of $f(x)$ for $x = 1.31, 1.32, \ldots$ we find that the root lies between 1.32 and 1.33, since

$$f(1.32) = (1.32)^3 - 1.32 - 1 = -.020032 \text{ and}$$

$$f(1.33) = (1.33)^3 - 1.33 - 1 = .022637$$

Finally, the calculation of $f(x)$ for $x = 1.321, 1.322, \ldots$ shows that the root lies between 1.324 and 1.325, since $f(1.324) = (1.324)^3 - 1.324 - 1 = -.0030598$ and

$$f(1.325) = (1.325)^3 - 1.325 - 1 = .0012031$$

Hence the real root of $x^3 - x - 1 = 0$ correct to two places of decimal is 1.32.

Graphically,

- Enter $x^3 - x - 1$ as $y1$.
- Select a suitable window, say standard window.
- Graph the function.
- Move the cursor near the x-intercept.
- Successive Zoom-In at the intercept.
- Finally, press TRACE and estimate the root.

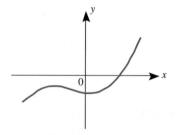

Figure 3.7.4

EXAMPLE 4   There may be many polynomial equations with integer coefficients which have $\sqrt{2} - 1$ and $\sqrt{2} + 1$ as its roots.

    a.   What is the minimum possible degree of such an equation?

    b.   Construct an equation of smallest degree with integer coefficients that has $\sqrt{2} - 1$ and $\sqrt{2} + 1$ as its roots.

Solution:

    a.   Let $f(x) = 0$ be an equation with integer coefficients that has $\sqrt{2} - 1$ and $\sqrt{2} + 1$ as two of its roots.

If $\sqrt{2} - 1$ is a root of $f(x) = 0$ then $-\sqrt{2} - 1$ is also a root of $f(x) = 0$.

If $\sqrt{2} + 1$ is a root of $f(x) = 0$ then $-\sqrt{2} + 1$ is also a root of $f(x) = 0$.

> If $a + b\sqrt{c}$ is a root of $f(x) = 0$,
> so is $a - b\sqrt{c}$.

It turns out that such an equation must have at least four roots $\sqrt{2} - 1$, $-\sqrt{2} - 1$, $\sqrt{2} + 1$, $-\sqrt{2} + 1$.

In other words,

$\left(x - \left(\sqrt{2} - 1\right)\right)\left(x - \left(-\sqrt{2} - 1\right)\right)\left(x - \left(\sqrt{2} + 1\right)\right)\left(x - \left(-\sqrt{2} + 1\right)\right)$ is a factor of $f(x)$.

Therefore, degree of $f(x) = 0$ is at least four.

b. From part (a), an equation of least degree with roots $\sqrt{2} - 1$ and $\sqrt{2} + 1$ is

$$\left(x - \left(\sqrt{2} - 1\right)\right)\left(x - \left(-\sqrt{2} - 1\right)\right)\left(x - \left(\sqrt{2} + 1\right)\right)\left(x - \left(-\sqrt{2} + 1\right)\right) = 0$$

or $\left(x + 1 - \sqrt{2}\right)\left(x + 1 + \sqrt{2}\right)\left(x - 1 - \sqrt{2}\right)\left(x - 1 + \sqrt{2}\right) = 0$

or $\left((x + 1)^2 - 2\right)\left((x - 1)^2 - 2\right) = 0$

or $x^4 - 6x^2 + 1 = 0$

B. COMPLEX ROOTS

Now we turn towards complex roots of an equation. As we have seen earlier that graphing technique does not help in determining complex roots. The following result is helpful in determining complex roots.

> **Property of Complex roots:**
>
> Let $f(x) = 0$ be an equation with real coefficients. If $a + bi$ is a complex root of $f(x) = 0$ then $a - bi$ is also a complex root of $f(x) = 0$.

Remark: *Complex roots of polynomial equations with real coefficients occur in pairs. Thus, an equation either does not have a complex root or has an even number of complex roots.*

EXAMPLE 5 An equation with rational coefficients has following roots:

$$-3, \frac{1 + \sqrt{2}}{3}, 3 - 5i$$

What other information about the roots can be drawn?

Solution:

$\dfrac{1 + \sqrt{2}}{3}$ is a root $\rightarrow$ $^{*}\dfrac{1 - \sqrt{2}}{3}$ is also a root

$3 - 5i$ is a root $\rightarrow$ * $3 + 5i$ is also a root

> * If $f(x) = 0$ has rational coefficients then roots $a + b\sqrt{c}$ and $a - b\sqrt{c}$ occur in pairs. Also complex roots occur in pairs.

Thus, it follows that the equation must have -3, $\dfrac{1 + \sqrt{2}}{3}$, $3 - 5i$, $\dfrac{1 - \sqrt{2}}{3}$, and $3 + 5i$ among its roots.

EXAMPLE 6   What is the minimum degree of an equation with rational coefficients one of whose roots is

$$2\sqrt{5} - 3i?$$

Solution:

$2\sqrt{5} - 3i$ is a root	$\longrightarrow$	$2\sqrt{5} + 3i$ is a root
$2\sqrt{5} - 3i$ is a root	$\longrightarrow$	$-2\sqrt{5} - 3i$ is a root
$2\sqrt{5} + 3i$ is a root	$\longrightarrow$	$-2\sqrt{5} + 3i$ is a root.

> Complex roots occur in pairs.

Therefore, the equation has at least four roots: $2\sqrt{5} - 3i$, $2\sqrt{5} + 3i$, $-2\sqrt{5} - 3i$, and $-2\sqrt{5} + 3i$.

Hence the degree of the equation is greater than or equal to four.

EXAMPLE 7   Construct an equation of lowest degree, with integer coefficients, that has roots

    a. $-3, -3, 2 - 5i$ **b.** $0, 4, 3 - i\sqrt{5}$ **c.** -1 (multiplicity 2), $\sqrt{5} - 3i$

Solutions:

    a.   Roots are: $-3, -3, 2 - 5i$

Step 1   Obtain additional information about the roots, if any.

        $2 - 5i$ is a root $\longrightarrow$ $2 + 5i$ is also a root

    Therefore, the equation must have at least four roots: $-3, -3, 2 - 5i$, and $2 + 5i$.

Step 2   Write the corresponding linear factors

    $x - (-3) = x + 3$,

    $x - (-3) = x + 3$,

    $x - (2 - 5i) = x - 2 + 5i$, and

    $x - (2 + 5i) = x - 2 - 5i$.

Remark: *The graph of*
$x^4 + 2x^3 + 14x^2 + 138x + 261 = 0$
does not show the complex roots.

Step 3   Multiply the linear factors and form the equation.

    $(x + 3)(x + 3)(x - 2 + 5i)(x - 2 - 5i) = 0$

    $(x^2 + 6x + 9)((x - 2)^2 + 25) = 0$

    $(x^2 + 6x + 9)(x^2 - 4x + 29) = 0$

    $x^4 + 2x^3 + 14x^2 + 138x + 261 = 0$

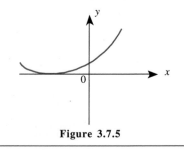

Figure 3.7.5

    b.

Step 1   Obtain additional information about the roots, if any.

    $3 - i\sqrt{5}$ is a root $\longrightarrow$ $3 + i\sqrt{5}$ is also a root.

    Therefore, the equation has at least four roots: $0, 4, 3 - i\sqrt{5}$, and $3 + i\sqrt{5}$.

Step 2   Write the corresponding linear factors.

$x - 0 = x,$

$x - 4,$

$x - \left(3 - i\sqrt{5}\right) = x - 3 + i\sqrt{5}$, and

$x - \left(3 + i\sqrt{5}\right) = x - 3 - i\sqrt{5}$.

Step 3   Multiply the linear factors and form the equation.

$x(x - 4)\left(x - 3 + i\sqrt{5}\right)\left(x - 3 - i\sqrt{5}\right) = 0$

$(x^2 - 4x)\left((x - 3)^2 + 5\right) = 0$

$x^4 - 10x^3 + 38x^2 - 56x = 0$

c.

Step 1 $\sqrt{5} - 3i$ is a root $\longrightarrow$ $\sqrt{5} + 3i$ is also a root.

Again, $\sqrt{5} - 3i$ is a root $\longrightarrow$ $-\sqrt{5} - 3i$ is also a root.

and $\sqrt{5} + 3i$ is a root $\longrightarrow$ $-\sqrt{5} + 3i$ is also a root.

The roots $-\sqrt{5} - 3i$ and $-\sqrt{5} + 3i$ have been taken to get the equation with integer coefficients.
The root -1 has multiplicity two $\longrightarrow$ -1 and -1 are also the roots.

Therefore, the equation has at least six roots.

$-1, -1, \sqrt{5} - 3i, \sqrt{5} + 3i, -\sqrt{5} - 3i,$ and $-\sqrt{5} + 3i$.

Step 2   Write the corresponding linear factors.

$x - (-1) = x + 1,$

$x - (-1) = x + 1,$

$x - \left(\sqrt{5} - 3i\right) = x - \sqrt{5} + 3i$,

$x - \left(\sqrt{5} + 3i\right) = x - \sqrt{5} - 3i$,

$x - \left(-\sqrt{5} - 3i\right) = x + \sqrt{5} + 3i$, and

$x - \left(-\sqrt{5} + 3i\right) = x + \sqrt{5} - 3i$.

Step 3   Multiply the linear factors and form the equation.

$(x + 1)(x + 1)\left(x - \sqrt{5} + 3i\right)\left(x - \sqrt{5} - 3i\right)\left(x + \sqrt{5} + 3i\right)\left(x + \sqrt{5} - 3i\right) = 0$

$(x + 1)^2 \left(\left(x - \sqrt{5}\right)^2 + 9\right)\left(\left(x + \sqrt{5}\right)^2 + 9\right) = 0$

$(x^2 + 2x + 1)\left(x^2 + 14 - 2\sqrt{5}\,x\right)\left(x^2 + 14 + 2\sqrt{5}\,x\right) = 0$

$(x^2 + 2x + 1)\left(\left(x^2 + 14\right)^2 - 20x^2\right) = 0$

$(x^2 + 2x + 1)\left(x^4 + 8x^2 + 196\right) = 0$

$x^6 + 2x^5 + 9x^4 + 16x^3 + 204x^2 + 392x + 196 = 0$

C. DESCARTES RULE OF SIGNS

Graphing $y = f(x)$ and then reading the x-intercepts of the graph is normally a good technique for solving an equation $f(x) = 0$. The advent of graphing software and graphing calculators has made solving an equation easy. However, this approach is fraught with some shortcomings.

1. Although, it is possible to figure out from a graph that a real root is a multiple root, the multiplicity may not be clear.

    The following are graphs of equations, each of which has 1 as its root.

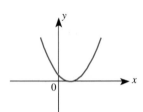

Figure 3.7.6

Multiplicity = 2

$y = (x - 1)^2$

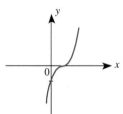

Figure 3.7.7

Multiplicity = 2

$y = (x - 1)^2 (2x - 3)$

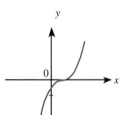

Figure 3.7.8

Multiplicity = 3

$y = (x - 1)^3$

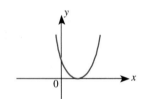

Figure 3.7.9

Multiplicity = 3

$y = (x - 1)^3 (2x - 3)$

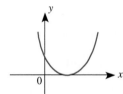

Figure 3.7.10

Multiplicity = 4

$y = (x - 1)^4$

2. The graph does not show complex roots. We cannot even know the number of complex roots for sure because the multiplicity of real roots may sometimes not be determined by looking at the graph.

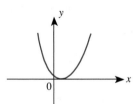

Figure 3.7.11

$y = (x - 1)^2 (x^2 + 1)$

Two complex roots

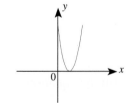

Figure 3.7.12

$y = (x - 1)^2 (x^2 + 1) (x^2 + 3)$

Four complex roots

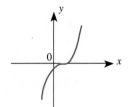

Figure 3.7.13

$y = (x - 1)^3 (x^2 + 1)$

Two complex roots

3. Sometimes the roots may be too large or too small and may not show on the screen. One may have to adjust the window manually with great care to find where the graph crosses the x-axis with a high degree of accuracy.

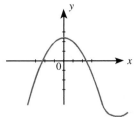

Figure 3.7.14

$y = .01(x^2 - 5)(2x - 47)$
Root at $x = 23.5$

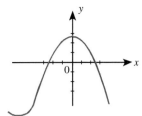

Figure 3.7.15

$y = -.01(x^2 - 5)(2x + 56)$
Root at $x = -28$

So far, we have gathered the following information:

1. The number of roots of a polynomial equation: The number of roots is equal to the degree of the equation. (See section 3.1.)

2. Irrational roots: Irrational roots of the form $a + b\sqrt{c}$ of an equation with rational coefficients occur in pairs.

3. Complex roots: Complex roots of an equation with real coefficients occur in pairs.

4. Rational Roots: Rational roots of an equation with integer coefficients can be obtained from the leading and the constant term of the equation.

We give two more results known as Descartes Rule of signs before formulating a strategy for solving a polynomial equation. These results not only give significant information about the roots but also take care of some of the problems mentioned earlier.

Descartes Rule of Signs	
Let $f(x) = 0$ be an equation with real coefficients.	* Consider $f(x) = 3x^3 - 5x^2 + 8$
* The number of positive roots is either equal to the number of changes in the signs of the coefficients of $f(x)$ or it is less than that by an even integer.	Number of changes in the signs for $f(x) = 2$ $[3x^3 - 5x^2 + 8]$ change change $f(-x) = 3(-x)^3 - 5(-x)^2 + 8$ $= -3x^3 - 5x^2 + 8$
* The number of negative roots is equal to the number of changes in the signs of the coefficients of $f(-x)$ or it is less than that by an even integer.	Number of changes in the signs for $f(-x) = 1$ $[-3x^3 - 5x^2 + 8]$ No change change

EXAMPLE 8   Given that all roots of $x^4 + x^3 - 2x^2 - x + 1 = 0$ are real, determine how many roots are positive and how many roots are negative.

Solution:

Step 1   Find the number of changes in the signs of the coefficients of $f(x)$.

$$f(x) = x^4 + x^3 - 2x^2 - x + 1$$
$$\quad\quad\quad \text{No} \quad \text{Yes} \quad \text{No} \quad \text{Yes}$$

There are two changes.

Step 2   Find the number of changes in the signs of the coefficients of $f(-x)$.

$$f(x) = x^4 + x^3 - 2x^2 - x + 1$$

$$f(-x) = (-x)^4 + (-x)^3 - 2(-x)^2 - (-x) + 1$$
$$= \underbrace{x^4 - x^3 - 2x^2 + x + 1}_{}$$
Yes   No   Yes   No

There are two changes.

Step 3   Apply Descartes Rule of Signs.

Two signs changes for $f(x)$ $\longrightarrow$ 0 or 2 positive roots of $f(x) = 0$.

Two signs changes for $f(-x)$ $\longrightarrow$ 0 or 2 negative roots of $f(x) = 0$.

Step 4   Draw conclusion.

There are 0, 2, or 4 real roots of $x^4 + x^3 - 2x^2 - x + 1 = 0$.

But it is given that $x^4 + x^3 - 2x^2 - x + 1 = 0$ has all its roots real, and the degree of equation is 4. Thus, $x^4 + x^3 - 2x^2 - x + 1 = 0$ has four real roots. So, two of the roots are positive and two are negative.

 Note   Descartes Rule does not give any information about a root that may be zero. For example

$$x^4 + 2x^3 = 0$$

has no positive root since $f(x) = x^4 + 2x^3$ has no change of sign. Also $f(-x) = x^4 - 2x^3$ shows one change of sign. Therefore, the equation $x^4 + 2x^3 = 0$ has exactly one negative root.

But the situation in which zero is a root is very simple. When an equation $f(x) = 0$ has zero as a root, we can factor out x^k, where k is the multiplicity of the root 'zero'. For example, in the above case $x^4 + 2x^3 = x^3(x + 2)$. So, for the equation $x^4 + 2x^3 = 0$, zero is a root of multiplicity three, and the equation has one negative root.

EXAMPLE 9   Use Descartes Rule of signs to obtain information regarding the roots of the equation $x^3 + 2x - 1 = 0$.

Solution: Let $f(x) = x^3 + 2x - 1$.

Step 1   Find the number of changes in the signs of the coefficients of $f(x)$.

$$f(x) = \underbrace{x^3 + 2x - 1}_{}$$
No   Yes

There is only one change.

Step 2   Find the number of changes in the signs of the coefficients of $f(-x)$.

$$f(-x) = (-x)^3 + 2(-x) - 1$$
$$= \underbrace{-x^3 - 2x - 1}_{}$$
No   No

There is no change.

Step 3   Apply Descartes Rule of Signs. The equation $x^3 + 2x - 1 = 0$ has one positive root and no negative root.

Step 4   Draw conclusion.

Since x cannot be factored out of $f(x)$, $x^3 + 2x - 1 = 0$ does not have $x = 0$ as a root.

Therefore, step 3 shows that $x^3 + 2x - 1 = 0$ has exactly one real root.

Hence $x^3 + 2x - 1 = 0$ has one real root (which is positive) and two complex roots.

EXAMPLE 10 Use Descartes Rule of signs to obtain information regarding the roots of the equation $x^4 + 2x^2 - 5x - 3 = 0$.

Solution: Let $f(x) = x^4 + 2x^2 - 5x - 3$.

Step 1 Find the number of changes in the signs of the coefficients of $f(x)$.

$$f(x) = x^4 + 2x^2 - 5x - 3$$
$$\underbrace{\quad}_{No} \underbrace{\quad}_{Yes} \underbrace{\quad}_{No}$$

There is only one change of sign.

Step 2 Find the number of changes in the signs of the coefficients of $f(-x)$.

$$f(-x) = (-x)^4 + 2(-x)^2 - 5(-x) - 3$$
$$= x^4 + 2x^2 + 5x - 3$$
$$\underbrace{\quad}_{No} \underbrace{\quad}_{No} \underbrace{\quad}_{Yes}$$

There is only one change of sign.

Step 3 Apply Descartes Rule of Signs.

By Descartes Rule of signs there is exactly one positive root and exactly one negative root.

Step 4 Draw conclusion.

Since x cannot be factored out of $x^4 + 2x^2 - 5x - 3$, zero is not a root of

$$x^4 + 2x^2 - 5x - 3 = 0$$

Step 3 shows that the equation has exactly one positive root and exactly one negative root. So, $x^4 + 2x^2 - 5x - 3 = 0$ has just two real roots.

Hence $x^4 + 2x^2 - 5x - 3 = 0$ has two real roots and two complex roots.

Remark: *When there is an odd number of changes of signs, Descartes Rule of Signs assures of at least one root of the kind under investigation.*

The following result gives information about upper and lower bounds for the real roots of a polynomial equation with real coefficients.

Bounds for Real Roots

Let $f(x) = 0$ be a polynomial equation with real coefficients. Assume that the coefficient of the highest degree term is positive.

* A positive number u is an upper bound for the real roots of $f(x) = 0$, if the third line (Coefficients of the quotient) obtained on dividing $f(x)$ by $x - u$ using synthetic division does not contain any negative number.

* A negative number l is a lower bound for the real roots of $f(x) = 0$, if the third line (coefficients of the quotient) obtained on dividing $f(x)$ by $x - l$ using synthetic division contains numbers that are alternately positive and negative. Zeros may be given + or – sign suitably.

⬤**Note** A number greater than an upper bound is also an upper bound, and a number less than a lower bound is also a lower bound.

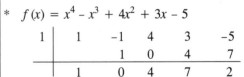

$$ * \quad f(x) = x^4 - x^3 + 4x^2 + 3x - 5$$

1	1	−1	4	3	−5
		1	0	4	7
	1	0	4	7	2

No real root of $x^4 - x^3 + 4x^2 + 3x - 5 = 0$ can be greater than 1.

−3	1	−1	4	3	−5
		−3	12	−48	135
	1	−4	16	−45	130

No real root of $x^4 - x^3 + 4x^2 + 3x - 5 = 0$ can be less than −3.

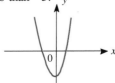

Figure 3.7.16

Actual roots $x \approx .81481928$; $x \approx -1.143195$

EXAMPLE 11   Determine the rational roots of the equation $x^4 + 4x^3 + 4x^2 - 16 = 0$, if any.

Solution:

Step 1   Apply the criterion for rational roots.

Here, $f(x) = x^4 + 4x^3 + 4x^2 - 16 = 0$

If the rational root is $\dfrac{p}{q}$ (written in lowest terms) then

p is a factor of -16, so, $p = \pm 1, \pm 2, \pm 4, \pm 8, \pm 16$.

and q is a factor of 1, so, $q = \pm 1$.

Therefore, $\dfrac{p}{q} = \pm 1, \pm 2, \pm 4, \pm 8, \pm 16$.

Step 2   Determine which of the candidates is a root.

Method 1:   Substitute each value for x in the expression and find the value $f(x)$. (See example 1 on Page 209.)

Method 2:   Divide $f(x)$ by $x - 1$, $x - 2$, $x - 4$, $x - 8$, $x - 16$, successively and see if one of these is a root or an upper bound. We will terminate the division once an upper bound is reached.

$x - 1$:

1	1	4	4	0	−16
		1	5	9	9
	1	5	9	9	−7

$x = 1$ is neither a root nor an upper bound.

$x - 2$:

2	1	4	4	0	−16
		2	12	32	64
	1	6	16	32	48

$x = 2$ is not a root **but it is an upper bound.**

Divide $f(x)$ by $x - (-1)$, $x - (-2)$, $x - (-4)$, $x - (-8)$, $x - (-16)$ to determine a root or a lower bound.

$x + 1$:

−1	1	4	4	0	−16
		−1	−3	−1	1
	1	3	1	−1	−15

$x = -1$ is neither a root nor a lower bound.

$x + 2$:

−2	1	4	4	0	−16
		−2	−4	0	0
	1	2	0	0	−16

Again, $x = -2$ is neither a root nor a lower bound.

x + 3:

$$\begin{array}{r|rrrrr} -3 & 1 & 4 & 4 & 0 & -16 \\ & & -3 & -3 & -3 & 9 \\ \hline & 1 & 1 & 1 & -3 & \boxed{-7} \end{array}$$

Once again, $x = -3$ is neither a root nor a lower bound.

x + 4:

$$\begin{array}{r|rrrrr} -4 & 1 & 4 & 4 & 0 & -16 \\ & & -4 & 0 & -16 & 64 \\ \hline & 1 & (-)0 & 4 & -16 & \boxed{48} \end{array}$$

This shows that -4 is not a root but **it certainly is a lower bound.**

Step 3   Draw conclusion.

Since $x = 2$ is an upper bound and $x = -4$ is a lower bound, it is no use to continue to check above $x = 2$ and no use to continue below $x = -4$. Hence $x^4 + 4x^3 + 4x^2 - 16 = 0$ has no rational root.

Strategy for finding real roots of a polynomial equation with integer coefficients:

Strategy

1. Use Descartes Rule of Signs to determine a possible number of real roots.

2. Use the criterion for rational roots.

    a. Find possible rational roots r. $f(r) = 0$.

    b. By direct substitution or synthetic division, simultaneously, check for this root to be a lower or upper bound.

    c. Use the synthetic division to write $f(x) = (x - r)\,g(x)$.

    d. Repeat steps 2(a), 2(b) for $g(x)$, until you check out all the candidates for roots or lower and upper bounds.

3. Gather the information from Step 2 to write $f(x) = (x - r_1)(x - r_2)\ldots (x - r_m)\,h(x)$.

4. **a.** If $h(x)$ is linear or quadratic, solve the equation for $h(x) = 0$ for additional roots, if any.

    b. If degree of $h(x) > 3$, use the test for 'Bounds', if necessary. Then approximate the remaining real roots by graphing $y = h(x)$ on a graphing calculator.

Remarks: *1.*   *The above strategy determines exactly or approximately the real roots of $f(x) = 0$. It fails to find complex roots, unless $h(x)$ is a quadratic, is reducible to a quadratic, or can be written as a product of these types.*

    2.   *The number of complex roots = degree of the equation – number of real roots.*

EXAMPLE 12   Find all the real roots and complex roots, if possible, of

a. $x^4 - 3x^3 + 5x^2 + 7x - 10 = 0$ b. $6x^4 + 5x^3 - 10x^2 - 16x - 15 = 0$

Find the number of complex roots.

Solutions:

a.   Here, $f(x) = x^4 - 3x^3 + 5x^2 + 7x - 10$

Step 1   Apply Descartes Rule of Signs.

$$f(x) = \underbrace{x^4 - 3x^3}_{\text{Yes}} \underbrace{+ 5x^2}_{\text{Yes}} \underbrace{+ 7x}_{\text{No}} \underbrace{- 10}_{\text{Yes}}$$

There are three changes. So, $f(x) = 0$ has 1 or 3 positive roots.

$$f(-x) = (-x)^4 - 3(-x)^3 + 5(-x)^2 + 7(-x) - 10$$

$$= \underbrace{x^4 + 3x^3}_{\text{No}} \underbrace{+ 5x^2}_{\text{No}} \underbrace{- 7x}_{\text{Yes}} \underbrace{- 10}_{\text{No}}$$

There is only one change. So, $f(x) = 0$ has exactly one negative root.

Step 2   Determine rational roots.

Here, $a_4 = 1$ and $a_0 = -10$. If $\dfrac{p}{q}$ (in lowest terms) is a rational root of $f(x) = 0$, then

$p = \pm 1, \pm 2, \pm 5$

$q = \pm 1$

Therefore, possible rational roots are:
$$\pm 1, \pm 2, \pm 5$$

Testing for rational roots:

x = 1

```
1 | 1   -3    5    7   -10
  |      1   -2    3    10
  --------------------------
    1   -2    3   10 |  0
```

1 **is a root** but not an upper bound.

$$f(x) = (x - 1)(x^3 - 2x^2 + 3x + 10)$$

Use reduced polynomial.

x = -1

```
-1 | 1   -2    3    10
   |     -1    3    -6
   -------------------------
     1   -3    6  |  4
```

−1 is neither a root nor a **lower bound.**

Use reduced polynomial.

x = 2

```
2 | 1   -2    3    10
  |      2    0     6
  -------------------------
    1    0    3 |  16
```

2 is not a root but it is an **upper bound.**

Use reduced polynomial.

x = -2

```
-2 | 1   -2    3    10
   |     -2    8   -22
   -------------------------
     1   -4   11 | -12
```

−2 is not a root but **it is a lower bound.**

Step 3   From step 2,

$$x^4 - 3x^3 + 5x^2 + 7x - 10 = (x - 1)(x^3 - 2x^2 + 3x + 10)$$

The other real roots of $x^4 - 3x^3 + 5x^2 + 7x - 10 = 0$

are the roots of $x^3 - 2x^2 + 3x + 10 = 0$

Step 4   Here $g(x) = x^3 - 2x^2 + 3x + 10$ is a cubic. So, we use graphing calculator.

- Enter $x^3 - 2x^2 + 3x + 10$ for $y1$.
- Select standard window to graph.

There is only one intercept.

- ZOOM in at (or close to) the x-intercept.

The other real root is approximately equal to -1.34.

Hence $x^4 - 3x^3 + 5x^2 + 7x - 10 = 0$ has two real roots: 1 and another approximately equal to -1.34.

The equation has $4 - 2 = 2$ complex roots.

Remark: *There may be a slight variation in approximating the second root depending upon the calculator settings, the point which is the focus or center of zooming-in, and the number of times you zoom-in.*

b.   Here, $f(x) = 6x^4 + 5x^3 - 10x^2 - 16x - 15$

Step 1   Apply Descartes Rule of Signs.

$$f(x) = 6x^4 + 5x^3 - 10x^2 - 16x - 15$$
$$\text{No} \quad \text{Yes} \quad \text{No} \quad \text{No}$$

There is only one change. So, $f(x) = 0$ has only one positive root.

$$f(-x) = 6(-x)^4 + 5(-x)^3 - 10(-x)^2 - 16(-x) - 15$$
$$= 6x^4 - 5x^3 - 10x^2 + 16x - 15$$
$$\text{Yes} \quad \text{No} \quad \text{Yes} \quad \text{Yes}$$

There are three changes. So, $f(x) = 0$ has one or three negative roots.

Step 2   Determine rational roots.

Here, $a_4 = 6$ and $a_0 = -15$. If $\dfrac{p}{q}$ (in lowest terms) is a rational root, then

$$p = \pm 1, \pm 3, \pm 5 \quad \text{and} \quad q = \pm 1, \pm 2, \pm 3$$

Therefore, the possible rational roots are:

$$\frac{p}{q} = \pm 1, \ \pm \frac{1}{2}, \ \pm \frac{1}{3}, \ \pm 3, \ \pm \frac{3}{2}, \ \pm 5, \ \pm \frac{5}{2}, \ \pm \frac{5}{3}.$$

Candidates for the positive roots are: $\dfrac{1}{3}, \dfrac{1}{2}, 1, \dfrac{3}{2}, \dfrac{5}{2}, \dfrac{5}{3}, 3,$ and 5

We will start with $\dfrac{5}{2}$ and hope that it is an upper bound.

$x = \dfrac{5}{2}:$

$$
\begin{array}{r|rrrrr}
\frac{5}{2} & 6 & 5 & -10 & -16 & -15 \\
 & & 15 & 50 & 100 & 210 \\
\hline
 & 6 & 20 & 40 & 84 & \boxed{195}
\end{array}
$$

$x = \dfrac{5}{2}$ is not a root, but it is an upper bound.

> **Note** We could have started with 5, and even 5, is an upper bound. In that case, we could have tested the next lower possible rational root $\left(\dfrac{5}{2}\right)$. Since the next lower possible rational root $\left(\dfrac{5}{3}\right)$ is actually a root as shown below, $x = \dfrac{5}{2}$ is the least upper bound.

$x = \dfrac{5}{3}:$

$$
\begin{array}{r|rrrrr}
\frac{5}{3} & 6 & 5 & -10 & -16 & -15 \\
 & & 10 & 25 & 25 & 15 \\
\hline
 & 6 & 15 & 15 & 9 & \boxed{0}
\end{array}
\qquad x = \frac{5}{3} \text{ is a root.}
$$

Also, the above division process gives

$$
\begin{aligned}
f(x) &= \left(x - \frac{5}{3}\right)(6x^3 + 15x^2 + 15x + 9) \\
&= (3x - 5)(2x^3 + 5x^2 + 5x + 3)
\end{aligned}
$$

Since the equation has only one positive root and we have found one, we now concentrate on negative roots.

Possible negative roots are

$$
-5,\ -3,\ -\frac{5}{2},\ -\frac{5}{3},\ -\frac{3}{2},\ -1,\ -\frac{1}{2},\ -\frac{1}{3}
$$

and the remaining roots of $6x^4 + 5x^3 - 10x^2 - 16x - 15 = 0$ are the roots of $2x^3 + 5x^2 + 5x + 3 = 0$

Let us try $x = -\dfrac{5}{2}$.

$x = -\dfrac{5}{2}:$

$$
\begin{array}{r|rrrr}
-\frac{5}{2} & 2 & 5 & 5 & 3 \\
 & & -5 & 0 & -\frac{25}{2} \\
\hline
 & 2 & (-)\,0 & 5 & \boxed{-\frac{19}{2}}
\end{array}
$$

$x = -\dfrac{5}{2}$ **is not a root, but it is a lower bound.**

$x = -\dfrac{5}{3}:$

$$
-\dfrac{5}{3} \bigg\vert \quad
\begin{array}{cccc}
2 & 5 & 5 & 3 \\
 & -\dfrac{10}{3} & -\dfrac{25}{9} & -\dfrac{100}{27} \\
\hline
2 & \dfrac{5}{3} & \dfrac{20}{9} & \boxed{-\dfrac{19}{27}}
\end{array}
$$

$x = -\dfrac{3}{2}:$

$$
-\dfrac{3}{2} \bigg\vert \quad
\begin{array}{cccc}
2 & 5 & 5 & 3 \\
 & -3 & -3 & -3 \\
\hline
2 & 2 & 2 & \boxed{0}
\end{array}
$$

$x = -\dfrac{5}{3}$ is not a root. $x = -\dfrac{3}{2}$ is a root.

Also, $2x^3 + 5x^2 + 5x + 3 = \left(x + \dfrac{3}{2}\right)(2x^2 + 2x + 2)$

$$= (2x + 3)(x^2 + x + 1)$$

Step 3   From step 2,

$$6x^4 + 5x^3 - 10x^2 - 16x - 15 = (3x - 5)(2x^3 + 5x^2 + 5x + 3)$$

$$= (3x - 5)(2x + 3)(x^2 + x + 1)$$

Step 4   We apply the quadratic formula to $x^2 + x + 1 = 0$ to obtain the remaining roots.

$$x^2 + x + 1 = 0 \;\rightarrow\; x = \frac{-1 \pm \sqrt{1^2 - 4(1)(1)}}{2(1)}$$

$$= \frac{-1 \pm \sqrt{-3}}{2} = \frac{-1 \pm i\sqrt{3}}{2}$$

Hence $6x^4 + 5x^3 - 10x^2 - 16x - 15 = 0$ has just two real roots. They are $x = \dfrac{5}{3}$ and $-\dfrac{3}{2}$.

The other two roots are complex, and they are $x = \dfrac{-1}{2} - \dfrac{i\sqrt{3}}{2}$ and $\dfrac{-1}{2} + \dfrac{i\sqrt{3}}{2}$.

⬤Note   The above strategy for solving higher degree equations works only if we can find enough rational roots. If an equation has no rational root, then this strategy fails. For example, the

equation $x^4 + x^3 - x^2 - 2x - 2 = 0$ has four roots: $-\sqrt{2}, \sqrt{2}, \dfrac{-1 + i\sqrt{3}}{2}, \dfrac{-1 - i\sqrt{3}}{2}$. The

graphing calculator can give only approximate values of the roots $-\sqrt{2}$ and $\sqrt{2}$, in which case the remaining quadratic factor $g(x)$ (step 4) can really not be found to write the equation in the form $(x - a)(x - b) = g(x)$. In such a case the old-trusted method of factoring comes to the rescue. Notice that

$$x^4 + x^3 - x^2 - 2x - 2 = x^4 - 2x^2 + x^3 - 2x + x^2 - 2$$

$$= x^2(x^2 - 2) + x(x^2 - 2) + 1(x^2 - 2)$$

$$= (x^2 - 2)(x^2 + x + 1)$$

Now each of the quadratic equations. $x^2 - 2 = 0$ and $x^2 + x + 1 = 0$ can be solved using quadratic formula.

Alternatively, if we know that sum of two of the roots is zero, we could find the roots as discussed in the next objective.

D. RELATIONS BETWEEN ROOTS AND COEFFICIENTS

Many times, when we know some relation(s) involving the roots of an equation, it becomes easier to solve the equation. In such a case we adopt an alternative approach which is facilitated by the fact that there are relations between roots of an equation and its coefficients. These relations follow significant patterns and have been used to develop important results in the theory of equations. Cardano's method and Euler's method use these relations to obtain formulas for solving cubic and biquadratic (fourth degree) equations respectively. It is not our intention to develop these formulas here, but only to use the results.

Quadratic equation

Let r_1 and r_2 be roots of a quadratic equation $ax^2 + bx + c = 0$. Then we know that
$$ax^2 + bx + c = a(x - r_1)(x - r_2)$$

Expanding the right hand side, we get
$$ax^2 + bx + c = a(x^2 - (r_1 + r_2)x + r_1 r_2)$$
$$= ax^2 - a(r_1 + r_2)x + ar_1 r_2$$

Comparing the coefficients on both sides we get

$$-a(r_1 + r_2) = b \longrightarrow r_1 + r_2 = -\frac{b}{a}$$

$$ar_1 r_2 = c \longrightarrow r_1 r_2 = \frac{c}{a}$$

$$2x^2 - 3x + 5 = 0$$
$$r_1 + r_2 = -\frac{(-3)}{2}$$
$$= \frac{3}{2}$$
$$r_1 r_2 = \frac{5}{2}$$

Remark: *In case of a quadratic equation,*

$$sum\ of\ the\ roots\ = -\frac{coefficient\ of\ x}{coefficient\ of\ x^2}$$

$$product\ of\ the\ roots\ = \frac{constant\ term}{coefficient\ of\ x^2}.$$

Cubic Equation: For cubic equation, relations between roots and coefficients are given below.

If r_1, r_2, and r_3 are roots of a cubic equation, then sum of the roots

$$= r_1 + r_2 + r_3 = -\frac{coefficient\ of\ x^2}{coefficients\ of\ x^3}.$$

The sum of the product of the roots taken two at a time

$$= r_1 r_2 + r_2 r_3 + r_1 r_3 = \frac{coefficient\ of\ x}{coefficient\ of\ x^3}.$$

The product of the roots $= r_1 r_2 r_3 = -\dfrac{constant\ term}{coefficient\ of\ x^3}.$

$$x^3 - 5x^2 + 7x + 8 = 0$$
$$r_1 + r_2 + r_3 = -\frac{(-5)}{1} = 5$$
$$r_1 r_2 + r_2 r_3 + r_1 r_3 = \frac{7}{1} = 7$$
$$r_1 r_2 r_3 = \frac{-8}{1} = -8$$

Biquadratic Equation: Similar to the cubic equations, we have following relations between roots and coefficients of a biquadratic equation.

If r_1, r_2, r_3 and r_4 are roots of a biquadratic equation, then

the sum of the roots $= r_1 + r_2 + r_3 + r_4 = -\dfrac{\text{coefficient of } x^3}{\text{coefficient of } x^4}$,

the sum of the product of the roots taken two at a time

$= r_1 r_2 + r_2 r_3 + r_3 r_4 + r_1 r_4 + r_1 r_3 + r_2 r_4$

$= \dfrac{\text{coefficient of } x^2}{\text{coefficient of } x^4}$,

the sum of the product of the roots taken three at a time

$= r_1 r_2 r_3 + r_2 r_3 r_4 + r_1 r_3 r_4 + r_1 r_2 r_4$

$= -\dfrac{\text{coefficient of } x}{\text{coefficient of } x^4}$, and

the product of the roots $= r_1 r_2 r_3 r_4 = \dfrac{\text{constant term}}{\text{coefficient of } x^4}$.

$3x^4 - 5x^2 + 8x + 9 = 0$
or
$3x^4 + 0 \cdot x^3 - 5x^2 + 8x + 9 = 0$

$r_1 + r_2 + r_3 + r_4 = -\dfrac{0}{3} = 0$

$r_1 r_2 + r_2 r_3 + r_3 r_4 + r_1 r_4 + r_2 r_4$
$= \dfrac{-5}{3} = -\dfrac{5}{3}$.

$r_1 r_2 r_3 + r_2 r_3 r_4 + r_1 r_3 r_4 + r_1 r_2 r_4$
$= -\dfrac{8}{3}$.

$r_1 r_2 r_3 r_4 = \dfrac{9}{3} = 3$.

EXAMPLE 13 Find the roots of the equation
$$25x^3 + 50x^2 - 4x - 8 = 0$$
given that the sum of two of its roots is zero.

Solution: Let a, b, c be the roots of the equation
$$25x^3 + 50x^2 - 4x - 8 = 0.$$

Step 1 Write down the relations between roots and coefficients

$a + b + c = -\dfrac{50}{25} = -2$

$ab + bc + ac = \dfrac{-4}{25} = -\dfrac{4}{25}$

$abc = -\dfrac{-8}{25} = \dfrac{8}{25}$

sum of roots $= -\dfrac{\text{coefficient of } x^2}{\text{coefficient of } x^3}$.

sum of the products taken two at a time
$= \dfrac{\text{coefficient of } x}{\text{coefficient of } x^3}$.

product of roots
$= -\dfrac{\text{constant coefficient}}{\text{coefficient of } x^3}$.

Step 2 By the given condition, assume $a + b = 0$.

Step 3 Solve the resulting system of equations.

$a + b + c = -2$ ...(1)

$(a + b)c + ab = \dfrac{-4}{25}$ ...(2)

$abc = \dfrac{8}{25}$ ...(3)

$a + b = 0$ ...(4)

Equations (1) and (4) $\longrightarrow$ $0 + c = -2$ $\longrightarrow$ $c = -2$

Substituting $a + b = 0$ in (2), we get $ab = -\dfrac{4}{25}$

Now $a + b = 0$ $\longrightarrow$ $a = -b$

Therefore, $ab = -\dfrac{4}{25}$ $\longrightarrow$ $(-b)(b) = -\dfrac{4}{25}$ $\longrightarrow$ $b^2 = \dfrac{4}{25}$ $\longrightarrow$ $b = \dfrac{2}{5}$ or $b = -\dfrac{2}{5}$

If $b = \dfrac{2}{5}$ then $a = -b = -\dfrac{2}{5}$

If $b = -\dfrac{2}{5}$ then $a = -b = -\left(-\dfrac{2}{5}\right) = \dfrac{2}{5}$.

Hence the three roots are $-\dfrac{2}{5}, \dfrac{2}{5}, -2$.

EXAMPLE 14   Find the roots of the equation

$$2x^3 - 11x^2 + 13x - 4 = 0,$$

given that the product of two of its roots is 2.

Solution: Let a, b, and c be the roots of the equation

$$2x^3 - 11x^2 + 13x - 4 = 0.$$

Step 1 $a + b + c = -\left(-\dfrac{11}{2}\right) = \dfrac{11}{2}$ ...(1)

$ab + bc + ac = \dfrac{13}{2}$ ...(2)

$abc = \dfrac{-4}{2} = 2$ ...(3)

Step 2   By the given condition, assume

$$ab = 2 \qquad \qquad ...(4)$$

Step 3   Equations (3) and (4) give

$2c = 2 \longrightarrow c = 1$ ...(5)

Equations (1) and (5) give

$a + b + 1 = \dfrac{11}{2} \longrightarrow a + b = \dfrac{9}{2}$ ...(6)

$a = \dfrac{9}{2} - b$ from (6).

Substituting into (4) gives $\left(\dfrac{9}{2} - b\right)b = 2$

or $b^2 - \dfrac{9}{2}b + 2 = 0 \longrightarrow 2b^2 - 9b + 4 = 0$

$\longrightarrow (2b - 1)(b - 4) = 0 \longrightarrow 2b - 1 = 0$ or $b - 4 = 0$

$\longrightarrow b = \dfrac{1}{2}$ or $b = 4$

Now if $b = 4$ then $ab = 2 \longrightarrow a = \dfrac{2}{b} = \dfrac{2}{4} = \dfrac{1}{2}$

and if $b = \dfrac{1}{2}$ then $ab = 2 \longrightarrow a = \dfrac{2}{b} = \dfrac{2}{\frac{1}{2}} = 4$

Hence the roots of the equation are 1, $\dfrac{1}{2}$, and 4.

EXAMPLE 15   Find the roots of the equation
$$20x^3 - 44x^2 - 3x + 36 = 0$$
given that it has a root of multiplicity 2.

Solution: Let a, b, and c be the roots of the equation
$$20x^3 - 44x^2 - 3x + 36 = 0.$$

Step 1 $a + b + c = -\left(-\dfrac{44}{20}\right) = \dfrac{44}{20} = \dfrac{11}{5}$ ...(1)

$ab + bc + ac = \dfrac{-3}{20} = -\dfrac{3}{20}$ ...(2)

$abc = -\dfrac{36}{20} = -\dfrac{9}{5}$ ...(3)

Step 2   By the given condition, assume
$$a = b$$ ...(4)

Step 3   We use (4) to rewrite (1), (2), and (3):

$2a + c = \dfrac{11}{5}$ ...(5)

$a^2 + 2ac = -\dfrac{3}{20}$ ...(6)

$a^2 c = -\dfrac{9}{5}$ ...(7)

From (5), $c = \dfrac{11}{5} - 2a$.

Substituting c into (7) gives $a^2\left(\dfrac{11}{5} - 2a\right) = -\dfrac{9}{5}$

or $-2a^3 + \dfrac{11}{5}a^2 + \dfrac{9}{5} = 0$

or $-10a^3 + 11a^2 + 9 = 0$ ...(8)

Since a is a root of the given equation, we get
$$20a^3 - 44a^2 - 3a + 36 = 0$$ ...(9)

By adding (9) and 2 times (8), we can eliminate the a^3 term :
$$-22a^2 - 3a + 54 = 0$$

Using the quadratic formula, we get

$$a = \frac{-(-3) \pm \sqrt{(-3)^2 - 4(-22)(54)}}{2(-22)}$$

$$= \frac{3 \pm \sqrt{4761}}{-44} = \frac{3 \pm 69}{-44} = \frac{3}{2} \text{ or } \frac{-18}{11}$$

We check to see if these values are roots of the equation.

$$a = \frac{3}{2}: \quad 20\left(\frac{3}{2}\right)^3 - 44\left(\frac{3}{2}\right)^2 - 3\left(\frac{3}{2}\right) + 36$$

$$= \frac{540}{8} - \frac{396}{4} - \frac{9}{2} + 36$$

$$= \frac{135}{2} - 99 - \frac{9}{2} + 36 = 0$$

So, $a = \frac{3}{2}$ is a root.

$$a = -\frac{18}{11}: \quad 20\left(\frac{-18}{11}\right)^3 - 44\left(\frac{-18}{11}\right)^2 - 3\left(\frac{-18}{11}\right) + 36 \neq 0$$

So, $\frac{-18}{11}$ is not a root.

Therefore, two of the roots are $a = \frac{3}{2}$, $b = \frac{3}{2}$.

$$c = \frac{11}{5} - 2a = \frac{11}{5} - 2\left(\frac{3}{2}\right) = -\frac{4}{5}$$

Hence the three roots are: $\frac{3}{2}, \frac{3}{2}, -\frac{4}{5}$.

EXAMPLE 16   Find the roots of the equation

$$x^4 - 10x^3 + 25x^2 - 36 = 0$$

given that the sum of two of the roots equals the sum of the other two. Assume that the roots are all distinct.

Solution: Let a, b, c, and d be the roots of the equation

$$x^4 - 10x^3 + 25x^2 - 36 = 0.$$

Step 1 $a + b + c + d = 10$ ...(1)

$ab + bc + cd + ad + ac + bd = 25$

or $(a + b)(c + d) + ab + cd = 25$ ...(2)

$abc + bcd + acd + abd = 0$

or $ab(c + d) + cd(a + b) = 0$ ...(3)

$abcd = -36$ ...(4)

Step 2   By the given condition, assume

$$a + b = c + d$$ ...(5)

Step 3   (1) and (5) give
$$a + b = c + d = 5 \qquad \qquad \ldots(6)$$

(2) and (6) give
$$25 + ab + cd = 25$$
or $\quad ab + cd = 0 \qquad$ or $\quad ab = -cd \qquad \ldots(7)$

(7) and (4) give
$$(ab)(-ab) = -36$$
$$(ab)^2 = (cd)^2 = 36$$

Therefore, $ab = \pm 6$ and $cd = \pm 6$.

Now $\quad a + b = 5$ and $ab = 6$ give
$$a = 2 \text{ and } b = 3$$
or $\quad a = 3$ and $b = 2$

Again, $a + b = 5$ and $ab = -6$ give
$$a = -1 \text{ and } b = 6$$
or $\quad a = 6$ and $b = -1$

$$
\begin{aligned}
&a + b = 5\\
&ab = 6 \;\rightarrow\; b = \frac{6}{a}.\\
&a + \frac{6}{a} = 5\\
&\text{or } a^2 - 5a + 6 = 0\\
&\rightarrow\; a = 2 \text{ or } 3\\
&\rightarrow\; a = 2 \;\rightarrow\; b = 3\\
&\qquad a = 3 \;\rightarrow\; b = 2
\end{aligned}
$$

Similarly, solving for c and d, we get
$$c = 2, d = 3 \text{ or } c = 3, d = 2$$
and $\quad c = -1, d = 6 \text{ or } c = 6, d = -1$

Summarizing our findings and the fact that the roots are all distinct, it follows that the four roots are: **2, 3, –1, and 6.**

You can verify that each of these satisfies the original equation.

EXAMPLE 17   Solve the equation $x^4 - 2x^3 + 6x^2 + 8x - 40 = 0$, given that sum of the two of the roots is zero and the sum of the other two roots is 2.

Solution: Let a, b, c, and d be the roots of the equation $x^4 - 2x^3 + 6x^2 + 8x - 40 = 0$.

Step 1
$$a + b + c + d = 2 \qquad \qquad \ldots(1)$$
$$(a + b)(c + d) + ab + cd = 6 \qquad \qquad \ldots(2)$$
$$ab(c + d) + cd(a + b) = -8 \qquad \qquad \ldots(3)$$
$$abcd = -40 \qquad \qquad \ldots(4)$$

Step 2   By the given conditions, assume
$$a + b = 0 \qquad \text{or} \qquad a = -b \qquad \ldots(5)$$
$$c + d = 2 \qquad \text{or} \qquad d = 2 - c \qquad \ldots(6)$$

Step 3   We solve for a, b, c, and d.

(2), (5), and (6) give
$$ab + cd = 6 \qquad \qquad \ldots(7)$$

(3), (5), and (6) give
$$2ab = -8 \text{ or } ab = -4 \qquad \qquad \ldots(8)$$

(4) and (8) give

$$-4\,cd = -40 \ \text{ or } cd = 10 \qquad\qquad\qquad \dots(9)$$

Now, (5) and (8) give

$$a = -2 \ \text{ or } 2$$

$$a = -2 \longrightarrow b = 2$$

$$a = 2 \longrightarrow b = -2$$

Therefore, two of the roots are -2 and 2.

(6) and (9) yield

$$c^2 - 2c + 10 = 0$$

Using quadratic formula

$$c = \frac{2 \pm \sqrt{4 - 4(10)(1)}}{2}$$

$$= \frac{2 \pm \sqrt{-36}}{2} \ = \ \frac{2 \pm 6i}{2} = \mathbf{1 \pm 3i}$$

$$c = 1 + 3i \longrightarrow d = \frac{10}{c} = \frac{10}{1 + 3i}$$

$$= \frac{10(1 - 3i)}{(1 + 3i)(1 - 3i)} = \frac{10(1 - 3i)}{10} = 1 - 3i$$

Similarly, $c = 1 - 3i \longrightarrow d = 1 + 3i$

Therefore, the other two roots are $1 - 3i$ and $1 + 3i$. Hence the roots are $\pm 2, 1 \pm 3i$.

Side box:

$$a + b = 0$$
$$ab = -4$$
$$\rightarrow a^2 = 4$$
$$\rightarrow a = \pm 2$$
$$\rightarrow b = \mp 2$$

$$c + d = 2$$
$$cd = 10$$
$$\rightarrow c + \frac{10}{c} = 2$$
$$\rightarrow c^2 - 2c + 10 = 0$$

EXERCISE 3.7

In exercises (1-6), find a rational root of the equation and use the factor theorem to determine the remaining roots.

1. $2x^3 - x^2 - 4x + 2 = 0$
2. $x^3 - 8x - 8 = 0$
3. $5x^3 + 17x^2 - 7x - 3 = 0$
4. $x^3 - 7x^2 + 17x - 15 = 0$
5. $x^3 - x^2 + x + 3 = 0$
6. $4x^3 - 10x^2 + 4x + 5 = 0$

In exercises (7-10), find rational roots of the equations. Use the factor theorem to determine the remaining roots.

7. $x^4 + x^3 - 9x^2 - 3x + 18 = 0$
8. $x^4 + 2x^3 - 2x^2 - 5x - 1 = 0$
9. $6x^4 - 7x^3 + 8x^2 - 7x + 2 = 0$
10. $4x^4 - 13x^3 + 20x^2 - 8x - 24 = 0$

In exercises (11-16), the equations have exactly one real root. Estimate this root correctly to two places of decimal. (You may need your calculator to set up tables).

11. $x^3 - 2x - 3 = 0$
12. $2x^3 + x - 1 = 0$
13. $x^3 - 2x^2 - x - 2 = 0$
14. $3x^3 - 4x^2 - 7 = 0$
15. $2x^3 + 4x^2 + 1 = 0$
16. $-2x^3 + x^2 - 3x - 1 = 0$

In exercises (17-20), the equations have exactly two real roots. Use the location property to locate the real roots and estimate the values of the roots correct to the hundredth place (You may need your calculator to set up tables.)

17. $x^4 - 6x^3 + 19x^2 - 18x - 26 = 0$
18. $3x^4 - 6x^3 + 8x^2 + 2x - 3 = 0$

19. $x^4 - 3x^2 - 5 = 0$ **20.** $3x^4 - 3x^2 - 5x + 2 = 0$

In questions (21-24), explain the reason for your answer.

21. $f(x) = 0$ is a fourth degree polynomial equation which is known to have a rational root greater than 2. If its leading coefficient is 1 and the constant term is -5, what is this root?

22. $f(x) = 0$ is a third degree polynomial equation with leading coefficient 2 and constant term 5. It is known that $f(x) = 0$ has one rational root which is positive but less than 1. Find the root.

23. $f(x) = 0$ is a fourth degree polynomial equation with leading coefficient 2 and the constant term -5. It is known that the equation has exactly two rational roots. If one of the rational roots is less than -4 and the other rational root is positive and close to 2, what are the two rational roots?

24. $g(x) = 0$ is a fourth degree polynomial equation with leading coefficient 100 and constant term 11. Two of the roots are rational. If the rational roots are both approximately zero, find their exact values.

In exercises (25-42), find an equation of lowest degree with the given roots.

25. $1, 2, 3$ **26.** $-1, 0, \dfrac{2}{3}$ **27.** $-\dfrac{1}{2}, \dfrac{1}{2}, \dfrac{1}{2}$ **28.** $2, -3, -3$ **29.** $\sqrt{5} - 1, -\sqrt{5}$

30. $\dfrac{2}{3}\sqrt{7}, 3\sqrt{2} + 1$ **31.** $\dfrac{2 + 3\sqrt{5}}{4}, \dfrac{-2 + 3\sqrt{5}}{4}$ **32.** $\dfrac{\sqrt{7} - 1}{2}, \dfrac{-\sqrt{3} + 5}{3}$ **33.** $i, -i + 1$

34. $2i - 3, 3 + 2i$ **35.** $\dfrac{3}{5} - \dfrac{2}{3}i, -2$ **36.** $0, 0, 1 + i$ **37.** $1 - i\sqrt{2}, 3$ **38.** $2 + i\sqrt{3}, -1$

39. $\sqrt{3} + 2i$ **40.** $\sqrt{2} - 5i$ **41.** $\sqrt{2} - \sqrt{3}, 1$ **42.** $0, 2\sqrt{5} + \sqrt{2}$

In exercises (43-52), use Descartes Rule of Signs to obtain information about the roots of the equation.

43. $x^2 + x + 1 = 0$ **44.** $x^2 + 5x - 7 = 0$ **45.** $x^3 + x^2 - 5x + 3 = 0$ **46.** $x^3 - 3x - 1 = 0$

47. $2x^3 + 5x^2 + x - 8 = 0$ **48.** $-x^3 + 3x^2 - 3x + 8 = 0$ **49.** $x^4 - 2 = 0$ **50.** $x^4 + 7 = 0$

51. $x^4 + x^3 - 2x^2 + 7x + 8 = 0$ **52.** $2x^4 + x^2 - 9 = 0$

In exercises (53-60), use Descartes Rule of Signs and the theorem about locating the real roots to find two integers which are upper and lower bounds for each real roots.

53. $15x^2 + 26x - 21 = 0$ **54.** $16x^2 - 40x + 25 = 0$ **55.** $x^3 - 2x^2 + x - 2 = 0$ **56.** $4x^3 - 2x^2 + 6x - 3 = 0$

57. $8x^3 + 9x + 1 = 0$ **58.** $7x^3 - 8x^2 - 3 = 0$ **59.** $x^4 - 8x^2 - 8 = 0$ **60.** $x^4 - x - 7 = 0$

In exercises (61-76), use the strategy to solve higher degree polynomial equations and find the roots of the equation.

61. $4x^3 - x^2 + 4x - 1 = 0$ **62.** $3x^3 + 8x^2 + 8x - 5 = 0$ **63.** $4x^3 - 4x^2 - 11x + 6 = 0$

64. $3x^3 - 5x^2 - 6x + 10 = 0$ **65.** $2x^3 + x^2 - 10x + 6 = 0$ **66.** $6x^3 + 14x^2 - 3x - 7 = 0$

67. $4x^3 + 4x^2 - 9x - 2 = 0$ **68.** $8x^3 - 12x^2 + 6x - 1 = 0$ **69.** $18x^3 - 33x^2 - 28x - 5 = 0$

70. $7x^3 - 25x^2 + 16x + 12 = 0$ **71.** $x^4 + x^3 - x^2 + 5x - 30 = 0$ **72.** $6x^4 + 11x^3 + 8x^2 - 6x - 4 = 0$

73. $6x^4 - 7x^3 - 40x^2 - 8x + 24 = 0$ **74.** $10x^4 - 6x^3 - 33x^2 + 3x + 14 = 0$

75. $6x^4 - 25x^3 + 39x^2 - 29x - 15 = 0$ **76.** $8x^4 + 12x^3 - 4x^2 + 12x + 8 = 0$

In exercises (77-86), solve the equation using rules about relations between roots and coefficients and using an additional condition on the roots given along with the equation.

77. $x^3 - 3x - 2 = 0$; there is a root of multiplicity 2.

78. $9x^3 + 18x^2 - 2x - 4 = 0$; the sum of two of the roots is zero.

79. $x^3 + x^2 - 4x + 6 = 0$; the sum of two of the roots is 2.

80. $9x^3 + 45x^2 - 4x - 20 = 0$; one root is the negative of the other.

81. $2x^3 + 7x^2 - 9 = 0$; the difference between two roots is 4.

82. $2x^3 + x^2 - 6x - 3 = 0$; the product of two of the roots equals 3.

83. $x^4 + 5x^3 + 5x^2 - 5x - 6 = 0$; the sum of two of the roots is zero and the product of the other two is 6.

84. $x^4 - 3x^3 - 3x^2 + 11x - 6 = 0$; two of the roots are equal and the sum of the other two roots is 1.

85. $x^4 - 3x^3 - 7x^2 + 27x - 18 = 0$; the difference between two of the roots is 1 and the sum of the other two is 0.

86. $x^4 - 5x^3 + 10x^2 - 10x + 4 = 0$; the product of each of the two pairs of roots equals 2 and the roots are not repeated.

Writing Exercises

87. Let $f(x) = 0$ be a polynomial equation with leading coefficient equal to 1. Explain why the rational roots of $f(x) = 0$, if any, are integers.

88. You have a graphing calculator which has the capability of producing tables of values of a function. Explain at least two methods (numerical and graphical) by which you can locate the roots correctly to two places of decimal.

89. Let $f(x) = 0$ be a polynomial equation with integer coefficients. Comment on the statement that "the equation must have rational roots".

90. Does the strategy formulated to find roots of a polynomial equation work for all polynomial equations. Explain your answer with examples.

3.8 CHAPTER SUMMARY

1. The **roots** of an equation $p(x) = q(x)$ are the same as the **zeros** of the function
$$f(x) = p(x) - q(x)$$

2. If a root of an equation is repeated k times, we call it a root of **multiplicity** k.

3. The **factor theorem** says that if $x = r$ is a zero of a polynomial function $f(x)$, then $x - r$ is a factor of the expression part of $f(x)$. Conversely, if $x - r$ is a factor of the expression part of $f(x)$, then $x = r$ is a zero of $f(x)$.

4. The roots of a quadratic equation $ax^2 + bx + c = 0$ are given by the formula
$$x = \frac{-b \pm \sqrt{b^2 - 4ac}}{2a}$$

5. To solve a **cubic equation** $f(x) = 0$ where the leading coefficient is 1, we find one root $x = k$ by inspection, then divide $f(x)$ by $x - k$ using synthetic division and find the other two roots by equating the quotient to zero.

6. The roots of a **rational equation** $\dfrac{p(x)}{q(x)} = 0$ are the same as the roots of $p(x) = 0$, provided they are different from the roots of $q(x) = 0$.

7. An **absolute value equation**, $\left| K \right|$ = number, can be split into two ordinary equations
    $$K = \text{number} \quad \text{or} \quad K = -\text{number}.$$

8. If $A = B$ is an equation, then the set of its roots is contained in the set of roots of the equation $A^n = B^n$, where n is a positive integer.

9. The roots of $A^n = B^n$ that are not the roots of $A = B$ are called **extraneous roots.**

10. To solve a polynomial inequality such as $f(x) > 0$ or $f(x) < 0$, find the roots of $f(x) = 0$. Plot these solutions on a number line and check each interval using a test number for the solution of the inequality.

11. A **Type 1 absolute value inequality**, $\left| K \right|$ **< number**, can be written as a double inequality (or a conjunction of inequalities) as
    $$-\text{number} < K < \text{number}.$$

12. A **Type 2 absolute value inequality**, $\left| K \right|$ **> number**, can be written as a disjunction of two inequalities as
    $$K > \text{number} \quad \text{or} \quad K < -\text{number}$$

13. The **domain** of a function $f(x) = \dfrac{p(x)}{q(x)}$ excludes the roots of the equation $q(x) = 0$.

14. The domain of an even root is the same as the solution of the inequality "radicand ≥ 0".

15. The domain of a polynomial function consists of all real numbers.

16. If $r_1, r_2, \ldots, r_n$ are roots of a polynomial equation $f(x) = a_n x^n + a_{n-1} x^{n-1} + \ldots + a_0 = 0$
    then $f(x) = a_n (x - r_1)(x - r_2) \ldots (x - r_n)\, g(x)$.

17. Every equation of degree n has exactly n roots, the roots may be real or complex, distinct or repeated.

18. Let $f(x) = 0$ be a polynomial equation with rational coefficients. Suppose $a + b\sqrt{c}$, where a, b, and c are rational and c is not a perfect square, is a root of $f(x) = 0$, then $a - b\sqrt{c}$ is also a root of $f(x) = 0$.

19. Let $f(x) = a_n x^n + a_{n-1} x^{n-1} + \ldots + a_0 = 0$ be a polynomial equation with integer coefficients. If a rational number $\dfrac{p}{q}$ (written in its lowest terms) is a root of $f(x) = 0$ then p is a factor of a_0 and q is a factor of a_n.

20. Let $f(x) = 0$ be a polynomial equation and a and b two real numbers such that $f(a)$ and $f(b)$ have opposite signs. Then there is at least one root of $f(x) = 0$ that lies between a and b.

21. Let $f(x) = 0$ be a polynomial equation with real coefficients, and suppose a complex number $a + bi$ is one of its roots. Then $a - bi$, the complex conjugate of $a + bi$, is also a root of $f(x) = 0$.

22. Descartes Rule of Signs: Let $f(x) = 0$ be an equation with real coefficients. Then

    a. The number of positive roots is either equal to the number of changes in the signs of the coefficients of $f(x)$ or it is less than that by an even number.

    b. The number of negative roots is either equal to the number of changes in the signs of the coefficients of $f(-x)$ or it is less than that by an even number.

22. Test for upper bound for real roots: Let $f(x) = 0$ be a polynomial equation with real coefficients. Assume that the coefficient of the highest degree term is positive. Then a positive number u is an upper bound for the real roots of $f(x) = 0$, if the third line (coefficient of the quotient) obtained on dividing $f(x)$ by $x - u$ using synthetic division does not contain any negative number.

23. Test for lower bound for real roots: Let $f(x) = 0$ be a polynomial equation with real coefficients. Assume that the coefficient of highest degree term is positive Then a negative number l is a lower bound for the real roots of $f(x) = 0$ if the third line (coefficients of the quotient) in the synthetic division of $f(x)$ by $x - l$ contains numbers that are alternatively positive and negative. The number zero may be given any sign, plus or minus.

24. If r, and r_2 are the roots of the equation

$$ax^2 + bx + c = 0 \text{ then}$$

$$r_1 + r_2 = -\frac{b}{a} \text{ and } r_1 r_2 = \frac{c}{a}$$

25. If $r_1, r_2,$ and r_3 are the roots of the cubic equation

$$ax^3 + bx^2 + cx + d = 0 \text{ then}$$

$$r_1 + r_2 + r_3 = -\frac{b}{a}, \quad r_1 r_2 + r_1 r_3 + r_2 r_3 = \frac{c}{a}, \quad \text{and} \quad r_1 r_2 r_3 = -\frac{d}{a}.$$

26. If r_1, r_2, r_3 and r_4 are roots of the biquadratic (fourth degree) equation

$$ax^4 + bx^3 + cx^2 + dx + e = 0 \text{ then}$$

$$r_1 + r_2 + r_3 + r_4 = -\frac{b}{a} \qquad r_1 r_2 + r_1 r_3 + r_1 r_4 + r_2 r_3 + r_2 r_4 + r_3 r_4 = \frac{c}{a}$$

$$r_1 r_2 r_3 + r_1 r_2 r_4 + r_1 r_3 r_4 + r_2 r_3 r_4 = -\frac{d}{a} \qquad r_1 r_2 r_3 r_4 = \frac{e}{a}.$$

3.9 CHAPTER REVIEW

In exercises (1-4), solve the equation for the indicated unknown.

1. $5x - 3y = 9$, for y **2.** $6x + 7y = 11$, for x **3.** $A = \frac{1}{2}(b + B)h$, for B **4.** $5x + 2y = 11xy - 9$, for y

In exercises (5-8), solve the equation.

5. $5x^2 = 6x + 8$ **6.** $3x^2 + 4x - 15 = 0$ **7.** $2x^2 = 3x + 7$ **8.** $3x^2 + x = 3$

In exercises (9-13), find the zeros of the function.

9. $f(x) = 2x^3 - x^2 - 7x + 6$ **10.** $f(x) = 2x^3 - 9x^2 - 23x + 66$ **11.** $g(x) = x^3 - x^2 - 3x - 1$

12. $g(x) = 2x^3 - 7x^2 + 5x - 6$ **13.** $f(x) = x^4 - x^3 - 10x^2 + 22x - 12$

14. The profit (P) of a company after selling x units of an item is given by $P(x) = -0.5x^2 + 2.3x + 10$ (millions)
   a. For what sales (x) will the profit become 5 million?
   b. For what sales (x) will the profit exceed 4 million?

15. The height (h) of an object thrown upwards from the ground level with an initial velocity v_0 is given by $h(t) = v_0 t - 16t^2$.
   a. If an object is thrown with an initial velocity (v_0) of 64 ft/sec, how long does it take to reach the ground?
   b. If the initial velocity is 96 ft/sec, find the time when the object is at a height of 100 ft.
   c. If the initial velocity is 96 ft/sec, find the time interval when the object is above 50 ft.

16. The distance s covered by a particle moving in a straight line, after time t seconds is given by
$$s = 20t + 10t^2$$
   a. Find the time when the particle has covered a distance of 10 ft.
   b. Find the time interval when the distance covered by the particle is less than 20 ft.

17. A piece of wire 16 in. long is cut into two pieces. The piece x in. long is bent into a circle and the remaining piece $16 - x$ is bent into a square. Find the value(s) of x that will make combined area less than 16 in^2.

In exercises (18-21), find the zeros of the function.

18. $f(x) = \dfrac{x^2 - 5x - 14}{2x - 5}$ **19.** $f(x) = \dfrac{x^2 + 14x + 45}{3x + 4}$ **20.** $g(x) = \dfrac{2x^2 - 8}{x - 3}$ **21.** $h(x) = \dfrac{3x^2 + 44x - 15}{x - 5}$

In exercises (22-25), solve the equation.

22. $\dfrac{9}{3x - 1} - \dfrac{5}{x + 1} = 2$ **23.** $\dfrac{6}{2x - 3} - \dfrac{4}{2x + 1} = 1$

24. $\dfrac{9}{x - 5} - \dfrac{5}{x + 2} = \dfrac{1}{x^2 - 3x - 10}$ **25.** $\dfrac{7}{2x - 7} - \dfrac{5}{3x + 5} = \dfrac{1}{6x^2 - 11x - 35}$

In exercises (26-31), solve the equation.

26. $\left|3x - 2\right| - 5 = 0$ **27.** $\left|7x + 5\right| - 12 = 0$ **28.** $\left|x^2 - 16\right| = 0$

29. $\left|x^2 - 36\right| = 0$ **30.** $\left|x - 2\right| = \left|3x - 1\right|$ **31.** $\left|3x + 11\right| = \left|2x - 9\right|$

In exercises (32-39), write the function without absolute value bars.

32. $f(x) = \left|x - 1\right| - x$ **33.** $f(x) = \left|2x + 11\right| + x$ **34.** $g(x) = \left|x + 5\right| - \left|x - 2\right|$

35. $f(x)=\left|3x-9\right|-\left|2x+7\right|$ **36.** $h(x)=\left|x-2\right|+2$ **37.** $g(x)=\left|5x-12\right|-7$

38. $f(x)=1-\left|x-3\right|$ **39.** $g(x)=-11-\left|x+20\right|$

In exercises (40-45), solve the equation.

40. $\sqrt{x-7}-2=0$ **41.** $\sqrt{x+12}-3=0$ **42.** $\sqrt{2x-3}+1-x=0$

43. $\sqrt{3x+22}+2=x$ **44.** $\sqrt{x+3}-\sqrt{2x-1}=1$ **45.** $\sqrt{2x-5}-\sqrt{3x-5}+1=0$

In exercises (46-49), solve the equation.

46. $x^{2/3}=25$ **47.** $(x+4)^{2/3}=9$ **48.** $(x-7)^{3/2}=27$ **49.** $(x-10)^{3/2}=8$

In exercises (50-65), solve the inequality and give answer using interval notation.

50. $\dfrac{x-1}{3}-\dfrac{2x-5}{2}\geq\dfrac{1}{3}-\dfrac{x}{2}$ **51.** $\dfrac{2x+3}{4}-\dfrac{3x+1}{3}<\dfrac{1}{2}+\dfrac{x}{3}$ **52.** $x^2\leq28+3x$

53. $x^2>5x+50$ **54.** $x^2-x-1\geq0$ **55.** $x^2+2x-6<0$

56. $\dfrac{2x-3}{x+1}>0$ **57.** $\dfrac{x+7}{3x+5}<0$ **58.** $\dfrac{x+8}{x-1}\geq2$ **59.** $\dfrac{2x+9}{x+7}\leq3$

60. $\left|2x-7\right|-5\leq0$ **61.** $\left|5+4x\right|-11<0$ **62.** $\left|5-2x\right|\geq7$ **63.** $\left|3x-2\right|>7$

64. $\left|x^2-2x-7\right|\geq1$ **65.** $\left|x^2-4x-5\right|\leq1$

In exercises (66-71), find the domain of the function.

66. $f(x)=\sqrt{x^2-x-30}$ **67.** $g(x)=\sqrt{x^2-2x-35}$ **68.** $g(x)=\dfrac{x-2}{x^3-2x^2-8x}$

69. $f(x)=\dfrac{x+10}{-x^3+2x^2+80x}$ **70.** $h(x)=3x^5+3x^3-8x-9+|2x-3|$ **71.** $g(x)=6x^4-3x^3+2x^2-\left|3x+7\right|$

In exercises (72-74), find a rational root of the equation and use factor theorem to determine the remaining roots.

72. $2x^3-5x^2-10x+3=0$ **73.** $3x^3-16x^2+37x-28=0$ **74.** $4x^4-4x^3+9x^2-12x-9=0$

In exercises (75-77), use the table feature of your graphing calculator to estimate the real roots rounded to one place of decimal.

75. $8x^3+12x^2-6x-9=0$ **76.** $3x^3-x^2-26x+28=0$ **77.** $2x^4-6x^3+3x^2-6x+1=0$

78. $g(x)=0$ is a polynomial equation with leading coeffcient 2 and constant term 3. If it is known that the equation has a positive rational root then, what are the possible values of this root?

79. $g(x)=0$ is a polynomial equation that is known to have two rational roots. There are no sign changes in the coefficients of $g(x)$. If the leading coefficient of $g(x)$ is 5 and its constant term is 1, then determine the rational roots.

In exercises (80-82), find the equation of lowest degree with the given roots.

80. $2+3i,-1$ **81.** $\sqrt{2}+1,3-i$ **82.** $2\sqrt{3}+i$

In exercises (83-87), use Descartes Rule of Signs to obtain information about the roots of the given equation.

83. $2x^3-x^2+8=0$ **84.** $3x^3+5x-1$ **85.** $x^4+x^3+7=0$

86. $2x^4-5x^3+7x^2+8x+1$ **87.** $3x^4+7x^2-8x-9=0$

In exercises (88-90), use the strategy for solving an equation to find all roots of the given equation.

88. $6x^4 - 11x^3 + 14x^2 + 7x - 6 = 0$ **89.** $3x^3 - 13x^2 + 7x - 1 = 0$ **90.** $8x^4 - 44x^3 + 76x^2 - 44x + 8 = 0$

91. Solve the equation $2x^3 - 5x^2 + 1 = 0$ if it is known that sum of two of its roots equals 2.

92. Solve the equation $6x^4 - 25x^3 + 35x^2 - 20x + 4 = 0$, given that one of the roots is the reciprocal of the other.

3.10 CHAPTER TEST

1. Solve: $2x^3 + 9x^2 - 8x - 15 = 0$.

2. Solve: $\sqrt{3x-5} + 1 = x$.

3. Solve: $|5x-7| - 8 \le 10$.

4. Solve: $\dfrac{2x-3}{5} - \dfrac{x}{2} \le 1 - \dfrac{x-2}{2}$.

5. Solve: $x^2 \ge 3x + 10$.

6. Solve: $\dfrac{x+11}{x-1} \ge 3$.

7. Find the zeros of the function

$$f(x) = \frac{x^2 - 2x - 4}{x - 1}$$

8. Find the zeros of the function

$$f(x) = \left| x^2 - 5x - 24 \right|$$

9. Find the domain of each function   **a.** $f(x) = \sqrt{x^2 - 49}$ **b.** $g(x) = \dfrac{x^2 + 1}{x^3 - x}$

10. If a farmer keeps 20 sheep per acre of grazing land, then the average weight of a sheep at the market is 100 lb. He estimates that the average market weight per sheep will be reduced by 2 lb for each additional sheep added per acre of grazing land. If he adds x sheep (above 20), the total market weight is given by $w(x) = (20 + x)(100 - 2x)$. How many sheep per acre should the farmer keep if he wants the total weight to be in excess of 2250 lb?

11. Use Descartes Rule of signs to obtain information about the roots of the equation $x^3 - 3x^2 + 7x - 21 = 0$

12. Use Descartes Rule of signs and the theorem to find two integers which are upper and lower bounds for the real roots of the equation $8x^3 - 12x^2 - 2x + 3 = 0$.

Graphing Techniques

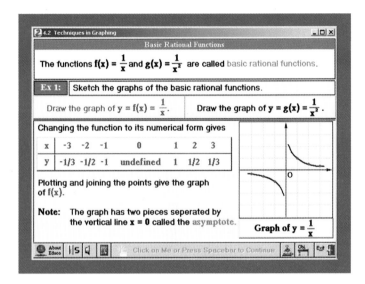

Graphing Techniques

GRAPHING TECHNIQUES

In this chapter you will learn how to find a linear relation that represents a given line. Since polynomial functions of degree two are frequently used in common applications, we will discuss their graphs in detail. Although calculus can be used to graph a variety of functions quickly and efficiently, we will discuss in this chapter several simple techniques for graphing that are better and faster than graphing by plotting points. For graphing a rational function we will use its vertical and horizontal asymptotes as important guiding lines.

The discussion in this chapter is divided into six sections.

4.1   EQUATIONS OF LINES

Recall that the graph of a first degree function is always a straight line. In this section we will find relations that describe the given line.

> **Objectives** ▶ ▶
>
> In this section you will learn about:
>
> A. Point-Slope equation representing a line;
>
> B. The Slope-Intercept form of an equation;
>
> C. Relations between slopes of two parallel or perpendicular lines; and
>
> D. Linear functions in table form.

A.   EQUATION OF A LINE IN POINT SLOPE FORM

Let us find a relation that describes the line through the point (x_1, y_1) and has slope m. Let l be the line that passes through (x_1, y_1) and has slope m (Figure 4.1). Let $Q(x, y)$ be any point on the line l. By using the fact that the slope of the line segment PQ is the same as the slope (m) of the line l, we get

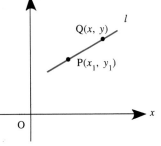

Figure 4.1

> * The slope of the line that joins two points (x_1, y_1) and (x_2, y_2) is $\dfrac{y_2 - y_1}{x_2 - x_1}$.

* $\dfrac{y - y_1}{x - x_1} = m$ or

   $$y - y_1 = m(x - x_1)$$

> **Point-Slope Form**
>
> An equation of the line that passes through the point (x_1, y_1) and has slope m is given by $y - y_1 = m(x - x_1)$.

B. THE SLOPE-INTERCEPT FORM OF AN EQUATION

Consider a straight line having slope m and y-intercept b. Then the line passes through the point $(0, b)$ and has slope m. Substitute $(0, b)$ into the point-slope form to get the equation of the line:

$$y - b = m(x - 0)$$
$$y - b = mx$$
$$y = mx + b \qquad (1)$$

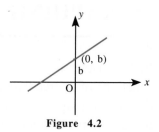

Figure 4.2

Equation (1) is called the **slope-intercept** form of the straight line.

> **Slope-Intercept Form**
> The equation of a line with slope m and the y-intercept b is $y = mx + b$.

EXAMPLES:

1. The slope-intercept form of the equation of the line whose slope and y-intercept are 3 and -5, respectively, is $y = 3x + (-5)$
$$= 3x - 5.$$

2. The slope intercept form of the equation of the line whose graph is shown in Figure 4.3 is:

$$y = \frac{2}{3}x + 2.$$

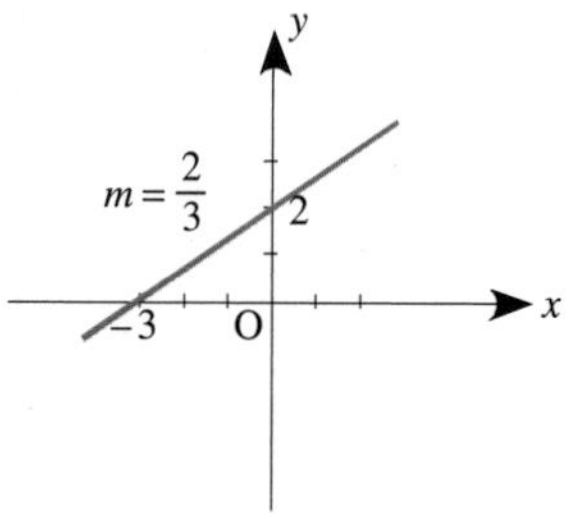

Figure 4.3

Remark: *Each of these equations is a special case of the more general form: $Ax + By + C = 0$ where A, B, and C are constants and A and B are not both 0.*

If $A = 0$, then $By + C = 0$ or $y = -\dfrac{C}{B}$ is

** a **horizontal line**.*

If $B = 0$, then $Ax + C = 0$ or $x = -\dfrac{C}{A}$ is

*** a **vertical line**.*

* The equation of a horizontal line is of the form $y = $ constant.

** The equation of a vertical line is of the form $x = $ constant.

EXAMPLE 1   Find the equation of the line whose graph passes through $(-2, 5)$ and has slope -3.

Solution: We are given a point on the line and its slope. Therefore, we use the point-slope form of the equation of a line. Labeling the point $(-2, 5)$ as $\left(x_1, y_1\right)$ gives $x_1 = -2$ and $y_1 = 5$. Therefore, by substituting $x_1 = -2$, $y_1 = 5$ and $m = -3$ in the equation

$$y - y_1 = m\left(x - x_1\right), \text{ we get}$$
$$y - 5 = -3(x - (-2))$$
$$y - 5 = -3x - 6$$
$$y = -3x - 6 + 5$$
$$y = -3x - 1$$

Thus, $y = -3x - 1$ is the equation of the line that passes through $(-2, 5)$ and has slope -3.

EXAMPLE 2   Find the equation of the line that passes through two points $(-1, 5)$ and $(2, -3)$.

Solution: If we label the two points as (x_1, y_1) and (x_2, y_2) we get $x_1 = -1$, $y_1 = 5$, $x_2 = 2$ and

$y_2 = -3$. First, we find the slope (m) of the line. $m = \dfrac{y_2 - y_1}{x_2 - x_1} = \dfrac{-3 - 5}{2 - (-1)} = \dfrac{-8}{3}$. Now

we replace x_1 with -1, y_1 with 5, and m with $\dfrac{-8}{3}$ in the formula,

$$y - y_1 = m\left(x - x_1\right) \quad \text{OR}$$

$$y - y_2 = m(x - x_2)$$

$$y - 5 = -\frac{8}{3}(x - (-1)) \qquad y - (-3) = -\frac{8}{3}(x - 2)$$

$$y - 5 = -\frac{8}{3}x - \frac{8}{3} \qquad y + 3 = -\frac{8}{3}x + \frac{16}{3}$$

$$y = -\frac{8}{3}x - \frac{8}{3} + 5 \qquad y = -\frac{8}{3}x + \frac{16}{3} - 3$$

$$y = \frac{-8}{3}x + \frac{7}{3} \qquad y = \frac{-8}{3}x + \frac{7}{3}$$

Thus the equation of the line that passes through $(-1, 5)$ and $(2, -3)$ is $y = -\dfrac{8}{3}x + \dfrac{7}{3}$.

EXAMPLE 3   Find an equation of the line that passes through the point $(5, -2)$ and
    a. is vertical   **b.** is horizontal

Solutions:

   a.   The equation of a vertical line is of the form $x = $ constant.

   The line passes through the point $(5, -2)$, so $x = 5$.

   Thus the equation of the vertical line that passes through the point $(5, -2)$ is $x = 5$.

   b.   Similarly the equation of a horizontal line is of the form $y = $ constant. The line contains the point $(5, -2)$. Hence, $y = -2$ is the equation of the horizontal line passing through $(5, -2)$.

EXAMPLE 4   Find the slope and y-intercept of the line whose equation is $5x + 2y = 7$.

Solution: If we can write the equation in the slope intercept form $y = mx + b$, then the slope m is given by the coefficient of x and the constant is the y-intercept b. Therefore, first we solve the equation for y.

$$5x + 2y = 7 \quad \longrightarrow \quad 2y = 7 - 5x \quad \longrightarrow \quad y = \frac{7}{2} - \frac{5}{2}x \quad \text{or} \quad y = -\frac{5}{2}x + \frac{7}{2}$$

Thus the slope $m = -\dfrac{5}{2}$ and the y-intercept $b = \dfrac{7}{2}$.

C. RELATIONS BETWEEN SLOPES OF TWO PARALLEL OR PERPENDICULAR LINES

Parallel and Perpendicular Lines

Since any transversal (line) form congruent angles with two parallel lines, the right triangles in Figure 4.4, namely $\Delta A_1 B_1 C_1$ and $\Delta A_2 B_2 C_2$ are similar.

Hence, the slope m_1 of line 1 and slope m_2 of line 2 are equal. Two parallel lines have the same slope.

For two perpendicular lines, the angle between the lines is a right angle (Figure 4.5). The relationship between the slopes of two perpendicular lines is not so obvious. It can be shown that if the lines are perpendicular, then the slope of one of the lines is the negative reciprocal of the slope of the other line, if the lines are non-vertical.

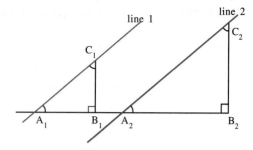

Figure 4.4

Parallel and Perpendicular Lines

Two lines with slopes m_1 and m_2 are **parallel** if and only if $m_1 = m_2$.

Two lines with slopes m_1 and m_2 are **perpendicular** if and only if $m_2 = -\dfrac{1}{m_1}$ or $m_1 m_2 = -1$.

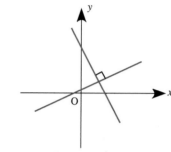

Figure 4.5

EXAMPLES:

1. The lines $y = 5x + 9$ and $y = 5x - 10$ are two **parallel** lines, because both have the same slope $(m_1 = m_2 = 5)$.

2. The lines $y = \dfrac{3}{2}x + 1$ and $y = -\dfrac{2}{3}x + 5$ are **perpendicular** lines, because the slope $\dfrac{3}{2}$ of one line is the negative reciprocal of the slope $\dfrac{-2}{3}$ of the other line.

EXAMPLE 5   Find the equations of the lines that pass through the point $(2, -3)$ and are
  a.   parallel to the line $2x + 3y = 6$ or
  b.   perpendicular to the line $3x - 5y = 10$

Solutions:

  a.   Since the line through $(2, -3)$ is parallel to the line $2x + 3y = 6$, its slope is obtained by writing the equation $2x + 3y = 6$ as

$$3y = 6 - 2x \quad \longrightarrow \quad y = 2 - \frac{2}{3}x \quad \longrightarrow \quad y = -\frac{2}{3}x + 2.$$

Therefore, the equation of the line through $(2, -3)$ with the slope $-\dfrac{2}{3}$ is

$$y - (-3) = -\frac{2}{3}(x - 2) \longrightarrow y + 3 = -\frac{2}{3}x + \frac{4}{3}$$

$$\longrightarrow \quad y = -\frac{2}{3}x + \frac{4}{3} - 3$$

$$\longrightarrow \quad y = -\frac{2}{3}x - \frac{5}{3}$$

4.4

b.   The slope of the required line is the negative reciprocal of the slope of the line $3x - 5y = 10$. First, we find the slope of $3x - 5y = 10$ by writing the equation as

$$3x - 10 = 5y \quad \longrightarrow \quad \tfrac{3}{5}x - 2 = y \quad \longrightarrow \quad y = \tfrac{3}{5}x - 2$$

Therefore, the slope of the line that passes through $(2, -3)$ and is perpendicular to the given line is the negative reciprocal of $\tfrac{3}{5}$. The equation of this line is

$$y - (-3) = \tfrac{-5}{3}(x - 2) \quad \longrightarrow \quad y + 3 = -\tfrac{5}{3}x + \tfrac{10}{3}$$

$$\longrightarrow \quad y = -\tfrac{5}{3}x + \tfrac{10}{3} - \tfrac{3}{1}$$

$$\longrightarrow \quad y = -\tfrac{5}{3}x + \tfrac{1}{3}.$$

EXAMPLE 6   Is the triangle with vertices A(2, 4), B(0, 4), and C(1, 3) a right triangle?

Solution: In section **2.5** we used the distance formula and Pythagorean theorem to show that the triangle ABC was a right triangle. Now we will use the fact that two lines (sides) are perpendicular if the slope of one side is the negative reciprocal of the slope of the other side. Let us check the slopes of sides AB, AC, and BC.

The slope of side AB $= \dfrac{4-4}{0-2} = \dfrac{0}{-2} = 0 = m_1$

The slope of side AC $= \dfrac{3-4}{1-2} = \dfrac{-1}{-1} = 1 = m_2$

The slope of side BC $= \dfrac{3-4}{1-0} = \dfrac{-1}{1} = -1 = m_3$

Since the slope of side BC is the negative reciprocal of the slope of side AC, the sides BC and AC are perpendicular. Consequently, the angle C is a right angle. Thus the triangle ABC is a right triangle.

D. LINEAR FUNCTIONS IN TABLE FORM

A function $f(x)$, in its formula form, is linear if $f(x) = ax + b$, where a and b are constants. A function $f(x)$, in its graphical form, is linear if the graph is a straight line. How do we recognize a linear function from its numerical (table) form? One way is to change the numerical form into the graphical form and check if the graph is a straight line. Another method that uses the fact that the slope of a straight line is always constant is stated as follows:

> **Linear Function In Numerical (Table) Form**
>
> A function in its numerical (table) form is a linear function if the ratios $\dfrac{y_2 - y_1}{x_2 - x_1}$
>
> for any two observation pairs (x_1, y_1) and (x_2, y_2) are the same.

Remarks: **1.**   *In a real life situation, if the ratios* $\dfrac{y_2 - y_1}{x_2 - x_1}$ *are **almost** the same, we call the*

function as linear.

2.   *If a table of values is that of a linear function, then its formula form is obtained by*

finding an equation of the line through any two pairs (x_1, y_1) *and* (x_2, y_2) .

EXAMPLE 7

On August 15, 2004, the daytime temperatures recorded at the airport from 8 a.m. to 3 p.m. were as follows:

t	8 AM	9	10	11	12	13	14	15
T(F°)	50	55	60	65	70	75	80	85

Determine if the relation between the time (t) and the temperature (T) is linear. If it is, then express the relationship as an equation.

Solution:

Let x be the number of hours after 8 a.m. and y be the temperature (T). The table is rewritten as

*

x	0	1	2	3	4	5	6	7
y	50	55	60	65	70	75	80	85

* $x = t - 8$, because x is the number of hours after 8 a.m.

Consider the ratio $\dfrac{y_2 - y_1}{x_2 - x_1}$ for different pairs.

For (0, 50) and (1, 55) : $\dfrac{y_2 - y_1}{x_2 - x_1} = \dfrac{55 - 50}{1 - 0}$

$$= \frac{5}{1} = 5$$

For (0, 50) and (2, 60) : $\dfrac{y_2 - y_1}{x_2 - x_1} = \dfrac{60 - 50}{2 - 0}$

$$= \frac{10}{2} = 5$$

Similarly, you can check the slope of other pairs of points.

Since each ratio $\dfrac{y_2 - y_1}{x_2 - x_1}$ for any two pairs is the same number 5, the relation between t

and T represents a linear function. In order to find its formula form, we find an equation of the line through any two pairs such as (0, 50) and (4, 70). We already know that the slope is 5. Therefore, an equation of the line that passes through (0, 50) and has slope = 5 is

$$y - 50 = 5(x - 0)$$

or $y = 5x + 50$ …(1)

Thus, the linear relation between time(t) and temperature (T) is

$$T = 5(t - 8) + 50$$ $x = t - 5$

$$= 5t + 10$$

EXAMPLE 8 A farmer wishes to plant a grove of apple trees. Suppose that from past experience he knows that when 100 trees are planted then each tree yields approximately 200 apples per year. Furthermore, he notices that for each additional tree planted in the grove, the yield per tree decreases by 20 apples.

    a. If y denotes the yield per tree when x trees are planted, then identify whether the relation between x and y is linear? If so, find it?

    b. Write an expression for the total yield when x trees are planted.

Solutions:

    a. Let y be the yield per tree when x trees are planted. Clearly, y depends on x, or y is a function of x. To find the function, first we write the given information about the yield per tree and the number of trees planted in a table form.

x	100	101	102	103	104	105 ...
y	200	180	160	140	120	100 ...

Use the fact that for each additional tree above 100 trees, the yield goes down by 20 apples per tree.

The numerical (table) form of the function is linear because the ratio $\dfrac{y_2 - y_1}{x_2 - x_1}$ for any pairs

like $(100, 200)$ and $(104, 120)$ is the same $= \dfrac{120 - 200}{104 - 100} = \dfrac{-80}{4} = -20.$

Therefore, an equation of the line with slope $= -20$ and containing $(100, 200)$ is given by

$$y - 200 \;=\; -20(x - 100)$$
$$y \;=\; -20x + 2000 + 200, \text{ or}$$
$$y \;=\; -20x + 2200.$$

Thus, $y = -20x + 2200$ is the linear relationship between the yield (y) per tree and the number (x) of trees planted.

    b. The total yield $=$ (number of trees planted) (yield per tree)
$$= \quad x \cdot (-20x + 2200)$$
$$= \quad -20x^2 + 2200x$$

EXERCISE 4.1

In exercises (1-30), find the slope intercept form $y = mx + b$ of the equation of the line that satisfies the given conditions.

1. Passes through the point $(-1, 2)$ and slope is 3.

2. Passes through the point $(2, 7)$ and has slope of -5.

3. Passes through $(2, -5)$ and slope is -3.

4. Passes through the point $(-1, -2)$ and has slope of $\dfrac{2}{3}$.

5. Passes through $(1, -3)$ and $(-2, 7)$.

6. Passes through $(2, 9)$ and $(-1, 6)$.

7. Passes through $(-1, 7)$ and $(-2, 9)$.

8. Passes through $(-1, -4)$ and $(-3, 5)$.

9. Has slope $\dfrac{2}{3}$ and y-intercept is 5.

10. Has slope 1 and y-intercept is -2.

11. Has slope $-\dfrac{5}{2}$ and y-intercept is 2.　　　　**12.** The slope is $-\dfrac{2}{3}$ and the y-intercept is $-\dfrac{1}{2}$.

13. Passes through $(-2, 5)$ and is parallel to the graph of the relation $2x - y - 5 = 0$.

14. Passes through $(1, 3)$ and is parallel to the graph of the relation $4x + y = 6$.

15. Passes through $(1, -7)$ and is parallel to the graph of the relation $3x - 2y - 8 = 0$.

16. Passes through $(-2, -5)$ and is parallel to the graph of the relation $x - 5y + 7 = 0$.

17. Passes through $(0, -1)$ and is perpendicular to the graph of the relation $5x - y = 7$.

18. Passes through $(-3, -7)$ and is perpendicular to the graph of the relation $2x + 2y - 3 = 0$.

19. Passes through $(2, -2)$ and is perpendicular to the graph of the relation $x + 2y - 10 = 0$.

20. Passes through $(2, 0)$ and is perpendicular to the graph of the relation $y - 6x + 9 = 0$.

21. Passes through $(1, 7)$ and is a vertical line.　　**22.** Passes through $(-2, -3)$ and is a vertical line.

23. Passes through $(2, -5)$ and is a horizontal line.　　**24.** Passes through $(-1, 9)$ and is a horizontal line.

25. Has x-intercept 5 and y-intercept is -2.　　**26.** Has x-intercept -4 and y-intercept is 3.

27. Has x-intercept $\dfrac{1}{2}$ and y-intercept is $\dfrac{1}{3}$.　　**28.** Has x-intercept -1 and y-intercept is -5.

29. Passes through the origin and is perpendicular to $2x + 3y = 6$.

30. Passes through the origin and is parallel to $3x + 4y - 7 = 0$.

In exercises (31-36), verify that the numerical (data or table) form represents a linear function and determine a possible formula form of the function.

31.

x	-3	-2	-1	0	1	2	3	4
y	7	5	3	1	-1	-3	-5	-7

32.

x	-2	-1	0	1	2	3	4
y	12	9	6	3	0	-3	-6

33.

x	-3	-2	-1	0	1	2	3
y	-14	-11	-8	-5	-2	1	4

34.

x	1	2	3	4	5	6
y	-8	-4	0	4	8	12

35.

year	1985	1986	1987	1988	1989	1990	1991	1992
x	0	1	2	3	4	5	6	7
Sales(y) million	7	8.5	10	11.5	13	14.5	16	17.5

36.

year	1991	1992	1993	1994	1995	1996
x	0	1	2	3	4	5
Sales(y) million	12	14	16	18	20	22

37.   A company buys a new machine for $50,000. After 10 years, the machine has a salvage value of $15,000. If the value of the machine depreciates in a linear manner (straight line depreciation), find a linear function that gives the value (*V*) of the machine after *x* years where $0 \leq x \leq 10$.

38.   A man buys a new car for $20,000. After six years, the car has a salvage value of $12,000. If the value of the car depreciates in a linear manner (straight line depreciation), find a linear function that gives the value (*V*) of the car after *x* years where $0 \leq x \leq 6$.

39.   A factory has a total cost (*C*) consisting of an overhead of $2500 and a manufacturing cost of $8 per unit. If *x* units are produced, express the total cost as a linear function of *x*. What is the rate of change of cost (marginal cost)?

4.2 TECHNIQUES IN GRAPHING

In this section, we will consider how a change in the "expression" part of the function can affect the graph. Some changes can move the graph up or down or right or left. Other changes can cause the stretch on shrink in the graph, or reflect the graph through the *x*-axis or *y*-axis. We will first explore the graphs of basic functions before we study how the changes affect the graphs.

Objectives ▶▶

In this section you will learn about:
A.   Basic Functions;
B.   Completing the Square;
C.   Vertical and Horizontal Translations;
D.   Reflection;
E.   Partial Reflection;
F.   Vertical Stretching and Shrinking;
G.   Symmetry; and
H.   Even and Odd Functions.

A. BASIC FUNCTIONS

There are several functions that occur frequently in pre-calculus and calculus and are known as **basic functions.** We will look at only basic **rational, power,** and **radical** functions in this objective.

Basic Rational Functions

The rational functions $f(x) = \dfrac{1}{x}$ and $g(x) = \dfrac{1}{x^2}$ are called **basic rational functions.**

EXAMPLE 1   Sketch the graphs of the basic rational functions.

Solutions:

a.   We draw the graph of $y = f(x) = \dfrac{1}{x}$.

Changing the function to its numerical form gives

x	−3	−2	−1	1	2	3
y	−1/3	−1/2	−1	1	1/2	1/3

Plotting and joining the points gives the graph of *f*(*x*) (Figure 4.6).

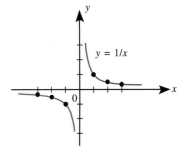

Figure 4.6

b. We draw the graph of $y = g(x) = \dfrac{1}{x^2}$.

Changing $g(x)$ to a numerical form gives:

x	–3	–2	–1	1	2	3
y	1/9	1/4	1	1	1/4	1/9

By plotting and joining the points we get the graph of $g(x)$ (Figure 4.7).

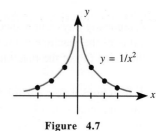

Figure 4.7

⬤ Note — These two graphs have two pieces. As x becomes numerically small, y becomes numerically large. In this case, we say the y-axis is a vertical asymptote. Similarly, as x becomes numerically large, y becomes numerically small and the point (x, y) gets closer to the x-axis. In this case, we say the x-axis is a horizontal asymptote.

Basic Power Functions

The power functions $f(x) = x^n$ when $n = 1, 2, 3,$ 4 or 5 are called basic **power functions.**

EXAMPLE 2 Sketch the graphs of the basic power functions.

Solutions: We consider the five basic power functions. We start with the first one.

a. Let $y = f(x) = x$. This is also known as the **identity function.** By changing to a numerical form, we get a set of points:

x	–1	0	1	2
y	–1	0	1	2

The graph (Figure 4.8) is obtained by plotting and joining the points.

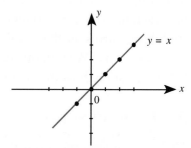

Figure 4.8

Remark: *The graph of the identity function is a straight line with an angle of inclination of 45°.*

b. We graph $y = f(x) = x^2$. Its table form is:

x	–2	–1	0	1	2
y	4	1	0	1	4

When we plot and join the points we get the graph (Figure 4.9) of $f(x) = x^2$.

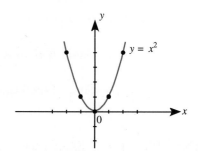

Figure 4.9

Remark: *The graph of $f(x) = x^2$ is a parabola.*

c. Graph $f(x) = x^3$. Let $y = x^3$.

Writing in a numerical form, we get:

x	–2	–1	0	1	2
y	–8	–1	0	1	8

The graphical form (Figure 4.10) is obtained by plotting and joining these points.

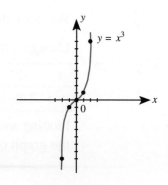

Figure 4.10

Similarly, we draw the graphs of $f(x) = x^4$ (Figure 4.11) and $f(x) = x^5$ (Figure 4.12).

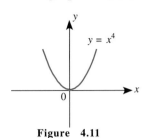

Figure 4.11

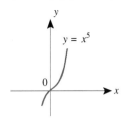

Figure 4.12

Important Observations

1. The graph of each basic power function contains $(0, 0)$.

2. For the graphs of $f(x) = x^{2m}$, the larger that m is, the flatter the bottom of the parabola-shaped graph becomes (Figure 4.13 (a)).

3. For the graphs of $f(x) = x^{2m+1}$, as m gets larger the graph between -1 and 1 becomes flatter. (Figure 4.13(b)).

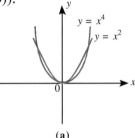

(a)

(b)

Figure 4.13

Basic Radical Functions

The radical function $y = \sqrt{x}$ is called the basic radical function.

The table of values for the basic radical function $y = \sqrt{x}$ is:

x	0	1	4	9
y	0	1	2	3

Its graph is a partial parabola (Figure 4.14).

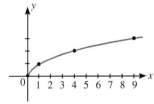

Figure 4.14

Important Observations

1. The graph of basic radical function passes through $(0, 0)$.

2. $x \geq 0$ and all values of y are positive. Therefore the graph lies only in the first quadrant.

3. As x increases, value of the function or of y also increases.

•   Before we begin studying shifting of graphs, we review an algebraic skill called **completing the square.**

B. COMPLETING THE SQUARE

The process of writing

$$* \quad x^2 + bx = \underbrace{\left(x + \frac{b}{2}\right)^2}_{\text{Square}} - \frac{b^2}{4}$$

$$\underbrace{\text{Half of } b}$$

is called the completing of squares in x.

$$* \quad \left(x + \frac{b}{2}\right)^2 - \frac{b^2}{4}$$

$$= x^2 + 2(x)\left(\frac{b}{2}\right) + \frac{b^2}{4} - \frac{b^2}{4}$$

$$= x^2 + bx$$

EXAMPLE 3 Complete the square in each of the following polynomials.

a. $x^2 + 4x$ **b.** $x^2 - 3x$ **c.** $x^2 + \dfrac{5}{2}x$ **d.** $2x^2 + 3x$

Solutions:

a. $x^2 + 4x = (x + 4x + 2^2) - 2^2$

$= (x + 2)^2 - 2^2 = (x + 2)^2 - 4$

$\hookrightarrow$ Half the coefficient of x

b. $x^2 - 3x = \left(x - \dfrac{3}{2}\right)^2 - \left(\dfrac{3}{2}\right)^2 = \left(x - \dfrac{3}{2}\right)^2 - \dfrac{9}{4}$

$\hookrightarrow$ Half the coefficient of x

c. $x^2 + \dfrac{5}{2}x = \left(x + \dfrac{5}{4}\right)^2 - \left(\dfrac{5}{4}\right)^2 = \left(x + \dfrac{5}{4}\right)^2 - \dfrac{25}{16}$

$\hookrightarrow$ Half the coefficient of x.

d. Before we can complete the square in x, we factor out the coefficient of x^2 so that the coefficient of x^2 becomes 1.

$* \; 2\left[x^2 + \dfrac{3}{2}x\right] = 2\left[\left(x + \dfrac{3}{4}\right)^2 - \dfrac{9}{16}\right]$

$\hookrightarrow$ Half the coefficient of x.

$= 2\left(x + \dfrac{3}{4}\right)^2 - \dfrac{9}{8}$

> * Before completing the square, factor out the coefficient of x^2:
>
> $ax^2 + bx = a\left[x^2 + \dfrac{b}{a}x\right]$

C. VERTICAL AND HORIZONTAL TRANSLATIONS

In the remainder of this section, we will give several methods for sketching graphs using the basic graphs as starting points. The first method involves functions whose graphs are obtained by moving known graphs horizontally or vertically.

> **Translation**
>
> A vertical or horizontal **translation** of a graph means a shift of the graph parallel to itself in either vertical or horizontal directions.

- Suppose we know the graph of $y = f(x)$ and we wish to draw the graph of $y = f(x) + c$, where $c > 0$.

  Obviously, every y-value on the new graph is obtained by adding c to the corresponding y-value on the old graph. In other words, if (x, y) is a point on the old graph, then $(x, y + c)$ is a point on the new graph. This amounts to lifting all points on the old graph c units upward. Similarly, the shift is downward if $c < 0$. We rephrase this rule as follows:

Vertical Translation

If the function $y = f(x)$ changes to $y = f(x) + c$, then the new graph (of $y = f(x) + c$) is obtained by vertically translating (shifting) the old graph (of $y = f(x)$) by $|c|$ units. The shift is upward for $c > 0$ and downward for $c < 0$.

EXAMPLE 4   Start with one of the basic graphs of power functions and sketch the graph of

    a. $f(x) = x^2 + 2$ **b.** $g(x) = x^3 - 1$

Solutions:

    a.   We start with the basic graph of $f(x) = x^2$ and by lifting the graph **2 units upward** we obtain the graph of $f(x) = x^2 + 2$ (Figure 4.15).

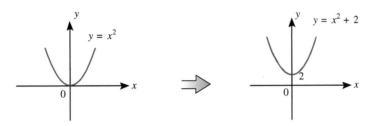

Figure   4.15

    b.   We start with the graph of $f(x) = x^3$ and lower the graph **1 unit vertically downward** to obtain the graph of $g(x) = x^3 - 1$ (Figure 4.16).

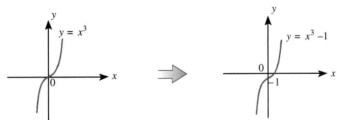

Figure   4.16

Suppose we know the graph of $y = f(x)$. The graph of $y = f(x - c)$ is obtained by moving all points (x, y) on the old graph to new location $(x + c, y)$. This amounts to moving the old graph horizontally. We state the rule of shifting the graph horizontally as follows:

Horizontal Translation

If the function $\boldsymbol{y = f(x)}$ changes to $\boldsymbol{y = f(x - c)}$, then the new graph (of $f(x - c)$) is obtained by horizontally translating (shifting) the old graph (of $f(x)$) by $|c|$ units. **The shift is to the right, if $c > 0$ and to the left if $c < 0$.**

EXAMPLE 5   Start with one of the basic graphs and sketch the graph of

    a. $f(x) = (x - 2)^2$ **b.** $g(x) = (x + 1)^3$

Solutions:

a.   We will start with the known graph of $f(x) = x^2$. By translating this graph horizontally **2 units to the right** we obtain the graph of $f(x) = (x - 2)^2$ (Figure 4.17).

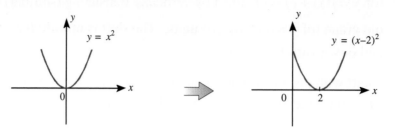

Figure   4.17

b.   In this case, we start with the basic graph of $y = x^3$ and move the graph horizontally **1 unit to the left** to obtain the graph of $g(x) = (x + 1)^3$ (Figure 4.18).

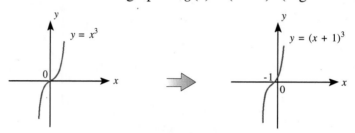

Figure   4.18

EXAMPLE 6   Sketch the graph of

     a. $f(x) = \sqrt{x-1} + 2$ **b.** $g(x) = \dfrac{1}{x+1} + 1$

Solutions:

a.   We start with the graph of $y = \sqrt{x}$. First, we move horizontally **1 unit to the right** to obtain the graph of $y = \sqrt{x-1}$. Then by lifting **2 units vertically upwards** we obtain the graph of $y = \sqrt{x-1} + 2$ (Figure 4.19).

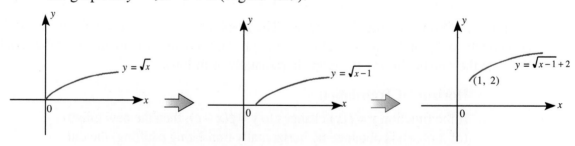

Figure   4.19

b.   Similarly, start with the graph of $y = \dfrac{1}{x}$, move the graph horizontally **1 unit to the left**, and then lift the graph **1 unit vertically upward** to obtain the graph of $y = \dfrac{1}{x+1} + 1$ (Figure 4.20).

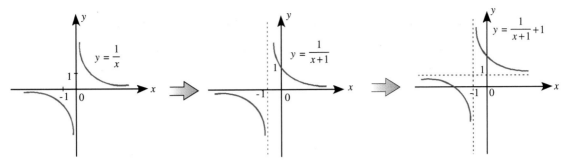

Figure   4.20

EXAMPLE 7   Sketch the graph of $y = f(x - 1) + 2$ if the graph of $y = f(x)$ is shown in Figure 4.21.

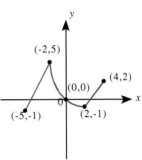

Figure   4.21

Solution: To obtain the graph of $y = f(x - 1)$, every point (x, y) on the old graph (of $y = f(x)$) moves to a new position $(x + 1, y)$. In particular, the point

$(-5, -1)$ becomes $(-5 + 1, -1) = (-4, -1)$,

$(-2, 5)$ becomes $(-2 + 1, 5) = (-1, 5)$,

$(0, 0)$ becomes $(0 + 1, 0) = (1, 0)$,

$(2, -1)$ becomes $(2 + 1, -1) = (3, -1)$, and

$(4, 2)$ becomes $(4 + 1, 2) = (5, 2)$.

Similarly, to obtain the graph of $y = f(x - 1) + 2$ from the graph of $y = f(x - 1)$, every point (x, y) on the intermediate graph (of $y = f(x - 1)$) changes to $(x, y + 2)$. In particular, the point

$(-4, -1)$ becomes $(-4, -1 + 2)$ or $(-4, 1)$,

$(-1, 5)$ becomes $(-1, 5 + 2)$ or $(-1, 7)$,

$(1, 0)$ becomes $(1, 0 + 2)$ or $(1, 2)$,

$(3, -1)$ becomes $(3, -1 + 2)$ or $(3, 1)$, and

$(5, 2)$ becomes $(5, 2 + 2)$ or $(5, 4)$.

By plotting the points in the new locations and joining them in the same shape as the original graph, we obtain the graph of $y = f(x - 1) + 2$ (Figure 4.22).

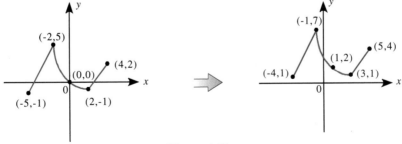

Figure 4.22

EXAMPLE 8   Sketch the graph of $f(x) = x^2 - 6x + 5$.

Solution: $f(x) = x^2 - 6x + 5$

$= (x^2 - 6x + 9) - 9 + 5$ For completing the square.

$= (x - 3)^2 - 4$

Now we sketch the graph of $f(x)$ by using the basic graph of $y = x^2$. We shift the basic graph 3 units horizontally to the right and 4 units vertically down (Figure 4.23).

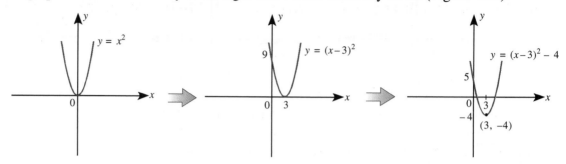

Figure 4.23

EXAMPLE 9   Verify that the point $P(2, 4)$ is on the graph of $f(x) = x^2$. What translation(s) of the graph will turn $x = 2$ into a zero of the new function?

Solution: For $x = 2$, $y = f(2) = 2^2 = 4$. Therefore, the point $P(2, 4)$ is on the graph of $f(x) = x^2$. By looking at the graph (Figure 4.24), it is clear that if we lower the graph of $f(x) = x^2$ vertically down 4 units, the point $P(2, 4)$ will fall on the x-axis. Consequently, $x = 2$ will become a zero of the translated function. Since the vertical lowering or lifting is achieved through a vertical translation, so $x = 2$ becomes a zero of $f(x) - 4$ or $x^2 - 4$.

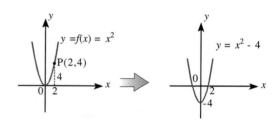

Figure 4.24

EXAMPLE 10   Start with the graph of $f(x) = x^2$ and sketch the graph of $f(x) = x^2 - 4x + 1$.

Solution: First, by completing the square we write

$$f(x) = x^2 - 4x + 1 = (x - 2)^2 - 4 + 1 = (x - 2)^2 - 3.$$

To obtain the graph of $y = (x - 2)^2 - 3$, we move the graph of $y = x^2$ horizontally 2 units to the right and then lower the resultant graph 3 units vertically downward (Figure 4.25).

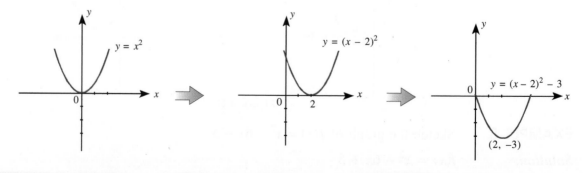

Figure 4.25

D. REFLECTION

A **reflection** of the graph of $y = f(x)$ with respect to a line is its **image** in that line.

Suppose we want to draw the graph of $y = -f(x)$, starting from the graph of $y = f(x)$. Clearly, every y-value on the new graph is the negative of the corresponding y-value on the old graph. That is, if (x, y) is a point on the old graph, then $(x, -y)$ will be a point on the new graph. By looking at the positions of points (x, y) and $(x, -y)$ (Figure 4.26 (a)), we see that one point is the reflection of the other through (or with respect to) the x-axis. We restate this fact as follows.

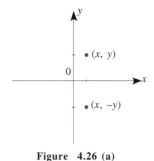

Figure   4.26 (a)

> **Reflection through the X-axis**
>
> If the function $y = f(x)$ changes to $y = -f(x)$, then the new graph (of $-f(x)$) is obtained by reflecting the old graph (of $f(x)$) through the x-axis.

Similarly, if (x, y) is a point on the graph of $y = f(x)$, then $(-x, y)$ is the corresponding point on the graph of $y = f(-x)$. Since the point (x, y) is the reflection of $(-x, y)$ through the y-axis (Figure 4.26(b)), so we have the following rule.

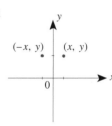

> **Reflection Through the Y-axis**
>
> If the function $y = f(x)$ changes to $y = f(-x)$, then the new graph (of $(f(-x))$ is obtained by reflecting the old graph (of $f(x)$) through the y-axis.

Figure   4.26(b)

EXAMPLE 11   Start with one of the basic graphs and sketch the graph of the following functions.

    a. $f(x) = -x^2 + 1$ **b.** $g(x) = -x^3 - 1$ **c.** $h(x) = -(x - 1)^4$

    d. $f(x) = -\dfrac{1}{x}$ **e.** $g(x) = -\dfrac{1}{x^2}$

Solutions:

    a. We start with the graph of $y = x^2$, reflect the graph in the x-axis, and then lift the resulting graph vertically up 1 unit (Figure 4.27)).

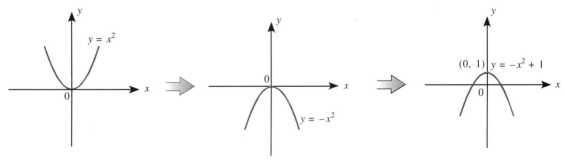

Figure   4.27

b.   The graph of $y = x^3$ is reflected in the x-axis to obtain the graph of $y = -x^3$. The resultant graph is lowered vertically down 1 unit to obtain the graph of $y = -x^3 - 1$ (Figure 4.28).

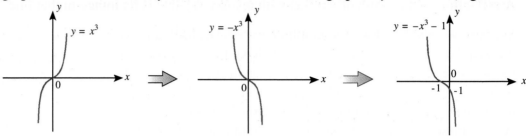

Figure   4.28

c.   First, we sketch the graph of $y = (x - 1)^4$ from the graph of $y = x^4$ by the horizontal translation of 1 unit to the right. Then we reflect the resulting graph in the x-axis (Figure 4.29).

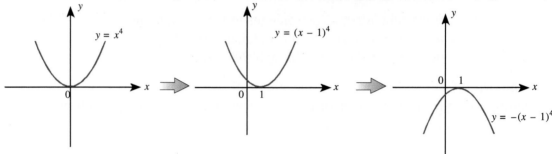

Figure   4.29

d.   The graph of $f(x) = -\dfrac{1}{x}$ is obtained by reflecting the graph of $y = \dfrac{1}{x}$ about the x-axis (Figure 4.30).

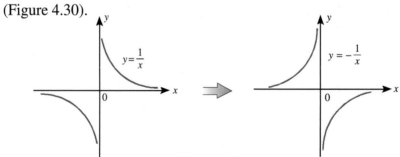

Figure   4.30

e.   By starting with the second basic rational function $y = \dfrac{1}{x^2}$ and reflecting its graph in the x-axis gives the graph of $f(x) = -\dfrac{1}{x^2}$ (Figure 4.31).

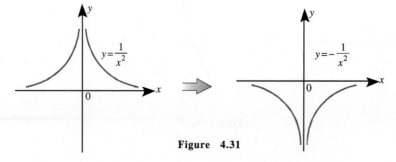

Figure   4.31

E. PARTIAL REFLECTION

Since the absolute value of a quantity is always non-negative, the graph of $y = |f(x)|$ should not go below the x-axis. In other words, if (x, y) is a point on the graph of $y = f(x)$, then $\left(x, |y|\right)$ is the corresponding point on the graph of $y = |f(x)|$. Consequently, the coordinates (therefore locations) of points above the x-axis will not change, whereas the coordinates (x, y) of the points below the x-axis will change to $(x, -y)$. This change occurs when we reflect a graph through the x-axis. This is called **partial reflection** because we reflect across the x-axis the part of the graph that is below the x-axis.

> **Reflection for Absolute Value Function**
>
> If the function $y = f(x)$ changes to $y = \left| f(x) \right|$, then the new graph (of $|f(x)|$) is obtained by redrawing the part of the old graph (of $f(x)$) that is above the x-axis and reflecting across the axis the part that is below the x-axis.

EXAMPLE 12   Start with a basic graph and sketch the graph of

  a. $f(x) = |x|$ b. $f(x) = |x^2 - 4|$

  c. $g(x) = |x - 2| + 1$ d. $h(x) = \left| -|x - 1| \right|$

Solutions:

  a.   The graph of $f(x) = |x|$ is easily obtained by partially reflecting the basic graph of $f(x) = x$ (Figure 4.32).

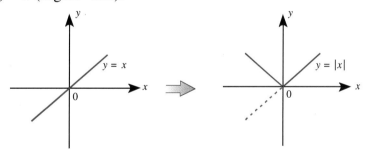

Figure   4.32

  b.   To draw the graph of $y = |x^2 - 4|$, we start with the basic graph of $y = x^2$. By the vertical translation of 4 units downwards we obtain the graph of $y = x^2 - 4$. Finally, the graph of $y = |x^2 - 4|$ is obtained by reflecting partly the portion of the graph that is below the x-axis (Figure 4.33).

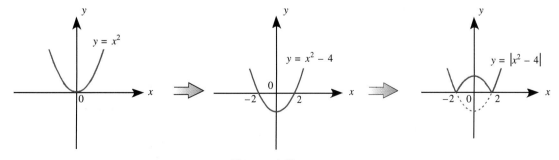

Figure   4.33

c. We can obtain the graph of $y = |x - 2|$ by translating the graph of $y = |x|$ (from part (a)) horizontally 2 units to the right. Then the graph of $y = |x - 2| + 1$ is obtained by the vertical translation of 1 unit upward (Figure 4.34).

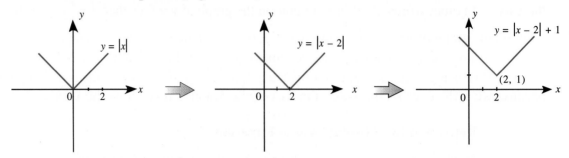

Figure   4.34

d. We start with the graph of $y = |x|$ (of part (a)). By the horizontal translation of 1 unit to the right we get the graph of $y = |x - 1|$. The reflection of $y = |x - 1|$ through the x-axis gives the graph of $y = -|x - 1|$. Finally, the reflection of negative part of $-|x - 1|$ through the x-axis gives the graph of $y = \left| -|x - 1| \right|$ (Figure 4.35). Note that the final graph is the same as of $y = |x - 1|$, since $y = \left| -|x - 1| \right| = |x - 1|$.

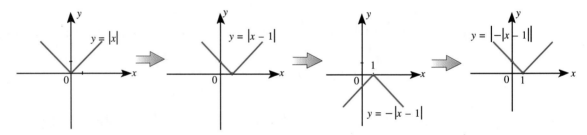

Figure   4.35

F. VERTICAL STRETCHING AND SHRINKING

We next consider how to draw the graph of $y = c\,f(x)$, $c > 0$ if the graph of $y = f(x)$ is known. We observe that a point (x, y) on the graph of $y = f(x)$ becomes (x, cy) on the graph of $y = c\,f(x)$. If $c > 1$, then each old y-value increases by a factor of c. If $c < 1$, then each old y-value decreases.

We call this process **vertical stretching** or **vertical shrinking.**

Stretching and Shrinking

If the function $y = f(x)$ changes to $y = c\,f(x)$, $c > 0$, then the new graph (of $cf(x)$) is obtained by

(i) a **vertical stretching** of the old graph (of $f(x)$) by a factor of c, if $c > 1$.

(ii) a **vertical shrinking** of the old graph (of $f(x)$) by a factor of c, if $c < 1$.

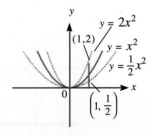

Figure   4.36

EXAMPLE 13 To obtain the graph of $y = 2x^2$, we stretch vertically the graph of $y = x^2$ by a factor of 2 (Figure 4.37).

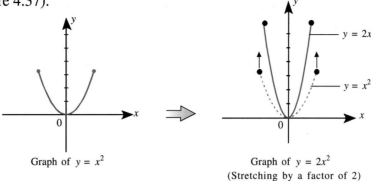

Graph of $y = x^2$

Graph of $y = 2x^2$
(Stretching by a factor of 2)

Figure   4.37

EXAMPLE 14 The graph of $y = \dfrac{1}{2}x^2$ is obtained by shrinking vertically the graph of $y = x^2$ by a factor of $\dfrac{1}{2}$ (Figure 4.38).

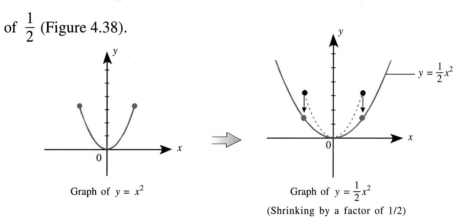

Graph of $y = x^2$

Graph of $y = \dfrac{1}{2}x^2$
(Shrinking by a factor of 1/2)

Figure   4.38

EXAMPLE 15 Starting with the graph of $y = x^3$, draw the graphs of the following functions.

a. $f(x) = 4x^3 - 1$ **b.** $g(x) = -\dfrac{1}{2}(x-2)^3 + 3$

Solutions:

a. Starting with the graph of $y = x^3$, stretch it vertically by a factor 4 (Figure 4.39(a)).

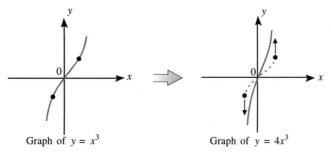

Graph of $y = x^3$

Graph of $y = 4x^3$

Figure   4.39a

4.21

Next, shift the graph of $y = 4x^3$ vertically down by one unit (Figure 4.39(b)).

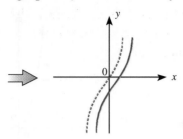

Graph of $y = 4x^3 - 1$

Figure   4.39b

b.   Start with the graph of $y = x^3$ (Figure 4.40(a)), shift 2 units to the right to obtain the graph of $y = (x - 2)^3$ (Figure 4.40b).

Next shrink the graph by $\dfrac{1}{2}$ to get the graph of $y = \dfrac{1}{2}(x - 2)^3$ (Figure 4.40(c)). Then

reflect this over the x-axis to get the graph of $y = -\dfrac{1}{2}(x - 2)^3$ (Figure 4.40(d)).

Finally move the graph up by 3 units to obtain the graph of $y = -\dfrac{1}{2}(x - 2)^3 + 3$ (Figure 4.40(e)).

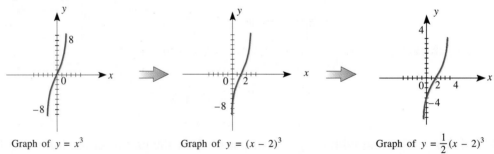

Graph of $y = x^3$

Figure   4.40 (a)

Graph of $y = (x - 2)^3$

Figure   4.40 (b)

Graph of $y = \dfrac{1}{2}(x - 2)^3$

Figure   4.40 (c)

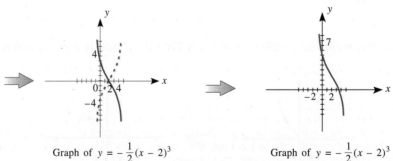

Graph of $y = -\dfrac{1}{2}(x - 2)^3$

Figure   4.40 (d)

Graph of $y = -\dfrac{1}{2}(x - 2)^3 + 3$

Figure   4.40 (e)

G. SYMMETRY

Symmetry is a geometrical concept. Symmetry tells whether one part of a graph is a reflection of another part. Here we introduce three types of symmetry:

1. **Symmetry about the x-axis**

    Algebraically: The graph of a relation is symmetrical about the x-axis if on replacing y **with** $-y$ the equation of the relation does not change.

    Graphically: The graph is symmetrical about the x-axis if one part of the graph is the reflection across the x-axis of the other part of the graph (Figure 4.41).

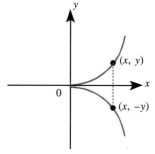

Figure 4.41

2. **Symmetrical about the y-axis**

    Algebraically: The graph of a relation is symmetrical about the y-axis if on replacing x **with** $-x$, the equation of the relation does not change.

    Graphically: The graph is symmetrical about the y-axis if one part of the graph is the reflection in the y-axis of the other part of the graph (Figure 4.42).

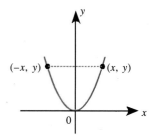

Figure 4.42

3. **Symmetrical about the origin**

    Algebraically: The graph of a relation is symmetrical about the origin if on replacing x **with** $-x$ **and** y **with** $-y$ the equation of the relation does not change.

    Graphically: A graph is symmetrical about the origin if one part of the graph is the reflection of the other part through the origin. (Figure 4.43).

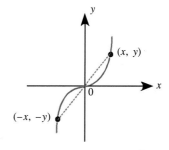

Figure 4.43

EXAMPLE 16   List basic power functions whose graphs are symmetrical about
        a.   the y-axis   **b.**   the origin

Solutions:

    a.   If we replace x with $-x$ in $y = x^2$ and $y = x^4$, the equations do not change. Therefore, the graphs of $f(x) = x^2$ and $f(x) = x^4$ are symmetrical about the y-axis.

    b.   Also, by replacing x with $-x$ and y with $-y$, the equations $y = x$, $y = x^3$, and $y = x^5$ do not change. So the graphs of $f(x) = x$, $f(x) = x^3$, and $f(x) = x^5$ are symmetrical about the origin.

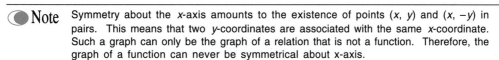 **Note**   Symmetry about the x-axis amounts to the existence of points (x, y) and $(x, -y)$ in pairs. This means that two y-coordinates are associated with the same x-coordinate. Such a graph can only be the graph of a relation that is not a function. Therefore, the graph of a function can never be symmetrical about x-axis.

H. EVEN AND ODD FUNCTIONS

A function $f(x)$ is said to be **even** if $f(-x) = f(x)$ for all x in the domain of f.
The graph of an even function is symmetrical about y-axis.

A function $f(x)$ is said to be **odd** if $f(-x) = -f(x)$ for all x in the domain of f.
The graph of an odd function is symmetrical about origin.

EXAMPLE 17   Determine whether the function is even or odd.

$$\textbf{a.} \quad f(x) = x^3 + 3x \qquad \textbf{b.} \quad f(x) = x^4 + 5x^2 \qquad \textbf{c.} \quad f(x) = x\left|x\right| \qquad \textbf{d.} \quad f(x) = \frac{3}{x + x^2}$$

Solutions:

a.   By replacing x with $-x$, we get

$$f(-x) = (-x)^3 + 3(-x) = -x^3 - 3x = -(x^3 + 3x) = -f(x).$$

Therefore, by definition, $f(x)$ is an **odd function.**

b.   By substituting $-x$ for x we get

$$f(-x) = (-x)^4 + 5(-x)^2 = x^4 + 5x^2 = f(x)$$

Therefore, $f(x) = x^4 + 5x^2$ is an **even function.**

c.   Writing $-x$ for x gives

$$f(-x) = (-x)\left|-x\right| = -\,x\left|x\right| = -f(x)$$

Thus, $f(x) = x\left|x\right|$ is an **odd function.**

d.   Replacing x with $-x$ gives

$$f(-x) = \frac{3}{-x + (-x)^2} = \frac{3}{-x + x^2}$$

$f(-x)$ is neither equal to $f(x)$ nor equal to $-f(x)$.

Therefore, $f(x) = \dfrac{3}{x + x^2}$ is **neither even nor odd.**

EXERCISE 4.2

In exercises (1-7), identify the shape of the graph of the function.

1. $f(x) = x^3$ **2.** $g(x) = x^2$ **3.** $h(x) = \dfrac{1}{x}$ **4.** $F(x) = \dfrac{1}{x^2}$ **5.** $G(x) = x$ **6.** $g(x) = x^4$ **7.** $h(x) = x^5$

In exercises (8-11), compare the graphs of the functions.

8. $f(x) = x^3$ and $g(x) = x^5$ **9.** $f(x) = x^2$ and $g(x) = x^4$

10. $f(x) = \dfrac{1}{x}$ and $g(x) = \dfrac{1}{x^2}$ **11.** $f(x) = x$ and $g(x) = x^3$

In exercises (12-13), determine if each of the basic functions is symmetrical about the (a) the y-axis   (b) the origin

12. $f(x) = \dfrac{1}{x}$ **13.** $g(x) = \dfrac{1}{x^2}$

In exercises (14-33), complete the square.

14. $x^2 + 6x$ **15.** $x^2 + 10x$ **16.** $x^2 - 8x$ **17.** $x^2 - 16x$ **18.** $x^2 + 3x$

19. $x^2 + x$ **20.** $y^2 - 5y$ **21.** $z^2 - \frac{1}{2}z$ **22.** $y^2 + \frac{3}{2}y$ **23.** $y^2 - \frac{5}{2}y$

24. $z^2 - z$ **25.** $y^2 + 9y$ **26.** $2x^2 + 16x$ **27.** $2x^2 - 8x$ **28.** $3y^2 + 5y$

29. $2z^2 - 7z$ **30.** $5t^2 - 2t$ **31.** $3t^2 + 10t$ **32.** $\frac{1}{2}t^2 + 5t$ **33.** $\frac{1}{4}y^2 - 3y$

In exercises (34-82), start with one of the basic graphs of a power function and draw the graph of the given function.

34. $g(x) = x^3 + 3$ **35.** $f(x) = x^3 + \frac{5}{2}$ **36.** $f(x) = x^3 - 2$ **37.** $g(x) = x^3 - \frac{9}{2}$

38. $h(x) = (x - 1)^2$ **39.** $g(x) = (x + 3)^2$ **40.** $f(x) = (x + 2)^3$ **41.** $g(x) = (x - 3)^3$

42. $g(x) = x - 2$ **43.** $f(x) = x + 5$ **44.** $f(x) = x^2 - 2x - 1$ **45.** $g(x) = x^2 + 2x - 2$

46. $h(x) = x^2 - 6x + 6$ **47.** $f(x) = x^2 + 4x + 5$ **48.** $g(x) = -x^2 + 2$ **49.** $f(x) = -x^2 + 3$

50. $h(x) = -x^3 - 2$ **51.** $f(x) = -x^3 + 3$ **52.** $f(x) = -(x + 1)^4$ **53.** $g(x) = -(x - 3)^4$

54. $g(x) = \left| x + 1 \right|$ **55.** $h(x) = \left| x - 3 \right|$ **56.** $h(x) = \left| x^2 - 1 \right|$ **57.** $f(x) = \left| x^2 - 2 \right|$

58. $f(x) = \left| x - 1 \right| - 1$ **59.** $g(x) = \left| x - 1 \right| + 4$ **60.** $f(x) = \left| x + 1 \right| - 1$ **61.** $f(x) = \left| x + 2 \right| - 2$

62. $f(x) = 2 - \left| x - 1 \right|$ **63.** $g(x) = -2 - \left| x - 1 \right|$ **64.** $g(x) = 1 - \left| x - 2 \right|$ **65.** $f(x) = 1 - \left| x + 1 \right|$

66. $g(x) = -2 - \left| x + 2 \right|$ **67.** $g(x) = 3x^2 + 1$ **68.** $f(x) = 4x^2 - 2$ **69.** $h(x) = 1 - 2x^2$

70. $g(x) = -2 - 3x^2$ **71.** $f(x) = \frac{1}{2}x^2 - 1$ **72.** $g(x) = \frac{1}{4}x^2 + 2$ **73.** $g(x) = 1 - \frac{1}{2}x^2$

74. $f(x) = -2 - \frac{1}{3}x^2$ **75.** $f(x) = 2x^2 - 4x - 1$ **76.** $g(x) = 2x^2 + 4x + 4$ **77.** $g(x) = 3x^2 - 6x + 1$

78. $f(x) = 4x^2 + 8x + 5$ **79.** $h(x) = 2(x - 1)^3 + 1$ **80.** $f(x) = 3(x + 1)^2 - 2$ **81.** $f(x) = -2(x + 1)^3 + 1$

82. $g(x) = -4(x - 1)^3 - 2$

In exercises (83-92), start from the given graph and sketch the graph of the given function.

83. Draw the graph of $y = \sqrt{x + 1}$ **84.** Draw the graph of $y = \sqrt{x - 2} + 1$ **85.** Draw the graph of $y = -\sqrt{x - 1}$

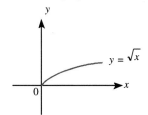   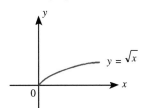   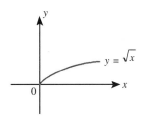

86. Draw the graph of

$y = -\sqrt{x + 1} + 1$

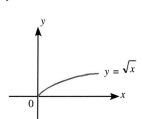

87. Draw the graph of

$y = -\sqrt{x + 2} - 1$

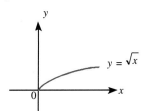

88. Draw the graph of

$y = \dfrac{1}{x - 1} + 1$

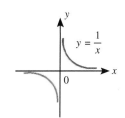

89. Draw the graph of $y = \dfrac{-1}{x-2} + 1$

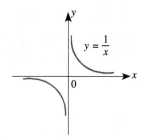

90. Draw the graph of $y = -\dfrac{1}{x+1} - 2$

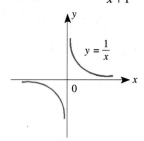

91. Draw the graph of $y = f(x+1) + 1$

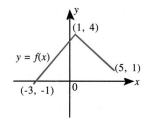

92. Draw the graph of $y = f(x-1) - 1$

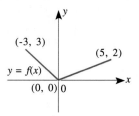

In exercises (93-102), verify that the indicated point P is on the graph of the function. Then give the translation of the function that will move the point to the x-axis (a zero of the new function).

93. $f(x) = \pi x^2,\ P(1, \pi)$

94. $f(x) = -4x^2,\ P(-2, -16)$

95. $f(x) = x^3,\ P(2, 8)$

96. $g(x) = \dfrac{x^3}{2},\ P(-2, -4)$

97. $g(x) = x^3 - 2x^2 + 3x + 8,\ P(1, 10)$

98. $f(x) = x^3 - 2x + 7,\ P(-1, 8)$

99. $h(x) = \dfrac{2x+3}{x-2},\ P(3, 9)$

100. $g(x) = \dfrac{x+5}{3x-1},\ P(1, 3)$

101. $f(x) = \sqrt{x+5}\ ,\ P(4, 3)$

102. $g(x) = \sqrt{x-8}\ , P(9, 1)$

In exercises (103-116), determine whether the function is even or odd function or neither.

103. $f(x) = x^5 + 2x$

104. $g(x) = x^6 + 4x^2$

105. $g(x) = -x^3 + 2x$

106. $f(x) = -3x^8 + 4x^6 - 4x^2 + 2$

107. $h(x) = 3x\left|x\right|$

108. $f(x) = -5x^2\left|x\right|$

109. $g(x) = x^2\left|x\right| + 1$

110. $g(x) = -2x|x| + 9x^3$

111. $f(x) = \dfrac{1}{2x + x^3}$

112. $g(x) = \dfrac{x^5 + 4x}{x^3 + 6x}$

113. $k(x) = \dfrac{2}{x^2 + 1}$

114. $h(x) = \dfrac{2x^2 + 7}{x^4 + 3x^2 + 1}$

115. $g(x) = \dfrac{x^3}{x\left|x\right| + x}$

116. $f(x) = \dfrac{x^3\left|x\right|}{x^2\left|x\right| + 5}$

Writing Exercises

117.   Describe the change in the graph of $y = f(x)$ if the the function changes to $y = \left|f(x)\right|$.

118.   Describe the change in the graph of $y = f(x)$ if the function changes to $y = f(x - c) + d$, where c and d are positive.

119.   Use the concept of symmetry to describe an **even** function.

4.3 GRAPHS OF QUADRATIC FUNCTIONS

In this section we will study polynomial functions of degree 2, the quadratic functions. The graph of a quadratic function is always bowl-shaped and is called a parabola. Many applications can be modeled by a quadratic function. Among these the optimization problems are very common.

Objectives ▶ ▶

In this section you will learn about:

A. Graphing A Quadratic Function; and

B. Maximum or Minimum Value of a Quadratic Function.

QUADRATIC FUNCTION

A function of the form $f(x) = ax^2 + bx + c$, where a, b and c are constants and $a \neq 0$, is called a **quadratic function.** We will see that the graph of a quadratic function is always a curve similar to the graph of $f(x) = x^2$ and is called a **parabola.** A parabola, which is a bowl-shaped graph, may **open up** (Figure 4.44(a)) **or down** (Figure 4.44(b)).

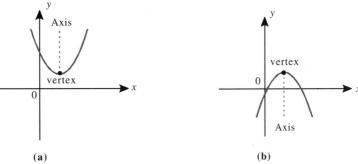

(a)   **(b)**

Figure   4.44

Important Features of a Parabola:

1. The lowest point (Figure 4.44(a)) or the highest point (Figure 4.44(b)) is called the **vertex.**

2. The vertical line through the vertex is called the **axis** of the parabola.

3. The graph is **symmetrical** about its axis.

A. GRAPHING A QUADRATIC FUNCTION

We will discuss two methods to graph a quadratic function $f(x) = ax^2 + bx + c$. The first method uses our previous skills such as **completing the square** and **techniques in graphing.** The second method uses the results of the first method. We start with the first method.

Method 1

EXAMPLE 1   Sketch the graph of $f(x) = 2x^2 - 4x + 5$

Procedure

Graph $f(x) = ax^2 + bx + c$

Step **1**   Write $y = f(x)$ $\longrightarrow$

Step **2**   Complete the square in x and $\longrightarrow$ write $y = f(x)$ in the form
$$y = a(x - h)^2 + k$$

Solution:

Let $y = f(x) = 2x^2 - 4x + 5$

$y = 2\left[x^2 - 2x\right] + 5$

$= 2\left[(x - 1)^2 - 1\right] + 5$

$= 2(x - 1)^2 - 2 + 5 = 2(x - 1)^2 + 3$

Step 3 If $a > 0$, start with the basic graph of $y = x^2$ and use translations and stretching or shrinking to draw the graph of the function in Step 2.

$\longrightarrow$ Since $a = 2 > 0$, so we start with the graph of $y = x^2$.

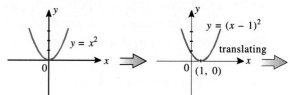

If $a < 0$, start with $y = -x^2$ the reflection of $y = x^2$ in the x-axis and then use the techniques in graphing to complete the graph.

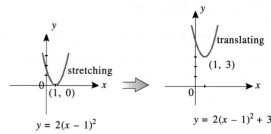

Figure 4.45

Step 4 Check to verify that the vertex of the parabola is the point (h, k).

$\longrightarrow$ The coordinates of the vertex $(1, 3)$ are given by $y = 2(x-1)^2 + 3$

$$\underset{(1 \quad , \quad 3)}{\uparrow \qquad \uparrow}$$

EXAMPLE 2 Sketch the graph of $f(x) = -x^2 + 4x - 3$.

Solution:

Step 1 We write $y = f(x) = -x^2 + 4x - 3$

Step 2 Completing the square in x gives

$$y = -\left[x^2 - 4x\right] - 3 = -\left[(x-2)^2 - 4\right] - 3 = -(x-2)^2 + 4 - 3.$$
Thus $y = -(x - 2)^2 + 1$.

Step 3 Since the coefficient of the perfect square is -1, so we start with the graph of $y = -x^2$.

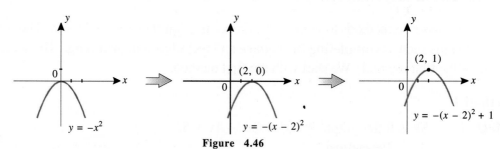

Figure 4.46

Step 4 The location of the vertex is at $(2, 1)$ and it is indicated by the equation

$$y = -(x - 2)^2 + 1$$

$$\underset{(2 \quad , \quad 1)}{\downarrow \qquad \downarrow}$$

Method 2   (*For quadratic functions*)

If we wanted to draw a parabola accurately, then we must know

1.   whether the parabola **opens upward** or **downward,**
2.   the **vertex** of the parabola, and
3.   how **wide** the opening of the parabola is.

For a quadratic function $f(x) = ax^2 + bx + c$, it is easy to know that the parabola opens up if $a > 0$ and opens down if $a < 0$. Let us find a formula that will give us the vertex. The vertex (h, k) is immediately known as soon as we write the function as $a(x - h)^2 + k$. To find formulas that give h and k, we go through process of completing the square in $y = f(x) = ax^2 + bx + c$.

Factoring out 'a' from the first two terms gives

$$ax^2 + bx + c = a\left[x^2 + \frac{b}{a}x\right] + c$$

$$= a\left[\left(x + \frac{b}{2a}\right)^2 - \frac{b^2}{4a^2}\right] + c \qquad \text{Completing the square}$$

$$= a\left(x + \frac{b}{2a}\right)^2 - \frac{b^2}{4a} + c$$

$$= a\left(x + \frac{b}{2a}\right)^2 + \frac{4ac - b^2}{4a}$$

$$= a\left(x - \left(-\frac{b}{2a}\right)\right)^2 + \frac{4ac - b^2}{4a}$$

$$\qquad\qquad\quad \underset{h}{\downarrow} \qquad\qquad \underset{k}{\downarrow}$$

Comparing with $y = a(x - h)^2 + k$, we get $h = -\dfrac{b}{2a}$ and $k = \dfrac{4ac - b^2}{4a}$.

Coordinates of the Vertex of a Parabola

The coordinates of the vertex of the parabola

$y = ax^2 + bx + c$ are $\left(-\dfrac{b}{2a}, \dfrac{4ac - b^2}{4a}\right)$

EXAMPLE 3   Find the vertex of the parabola

   a. $y = 2x^2 - 4x$ **b.** $y = -4x^2 + 16$

Solutions:

   a.   Comparing $y = 2x^2 - 4x$ with $y = ax^2 + bx + c$, we get $a = 2$, $b = -4$, and $c = 0$. Substituting a, b, and c in

$$\left(-\frac{b}{2a}, \frac{4ac - b^2}{4a}\right), \text{ we get } \left(-\frac{-4}{2(2)}, \frac{4(2)(0) - (-4)^2}{4(2)}\right) \text{ or } (1, -2).$$

b. Similarly, by comparing $y = -4x^2 + 16$ with $y = ax^2 + bx + c$, we get $a = -4$, $b = 0$, and $c = 16$. Substituting a, b and c in

$$\left(-\frac{b}{2a}, \frac{4ac-b^2}{4a}\right), \text{ we get } \left(-\frac{0}{2(-4)}, \frac{4(-4)(16)-(0)^2}{4(-4)}\right) \text{ or } (0, 16).$$

Now we are ready to give a method that is more accurate and faster than Method 1.

Method 2 (Graphing a Quadratic Function)

EXAMPLE 4   Sketch the graph of $f(x) = x^2 - x + 1$

Procedure

Graph $f(x) = ax^2 + bx + c$ *Solution:*

Step 1   Let $y = f(x)$ $\longrightarrow$ Let $y = x^2 - x + 1$

Step 2   If the coefficient a of x^2 is positive then the parabola opens upward. If $a < 0$, then it opens downward. $\longrightarrow$ Since the coefficient of x^2 is positive, so the parabola will open upward.

Step 3   Find the coordinates of the vertex by using the formula $\left(-\frac{b}{2a}, \frac{4ac-b^2}{4a}\right)$. $\longrightarrow$ The vertex is located at

$$\left(-\frac{-1}{2(1)}, \frac{4(1)(1)-(-1)^2}{4(1)}\right) \text{ or } \left(\frac{1}{2}, \frac{3}{4}\right)$$

Step 4   To determine the width of the opening of the parabola, find a point on each side of the vertex by completing the table. $\longrightarrow$ Let $x = 0$ and $x = 1$ be the x-coordinates of points on the left and right of the vertex, respectively.

x	y
A value less than $-\frac{b}{2a}$.	Find corresponding y-value by substituting in $y = ax^2 + bx + c$.
A value more than $-\frac{b}{2a}$.	Find corresponding y-value by substituting in $y = ax^2 + bx + c$

$\longrightarrow$

x	y	
0	1:	$y = (0)^2 - 0 + 1 = \mathbf{1}$
1	1:	$y = (1)^2 - 1 + 1 = \mathbf{1}$

Step 5   Plot the vertex and two points in Step 4 and complete the sketch of a parabola. (Use the fact that a parabola is symmetrical about the axis). $\longrightarrow$

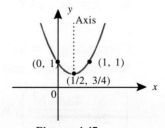

(0, 1)   (1, 1)
(1/2, 3/4)

Figure 4.47

With Graphing Calculator

Let $y_1 = x^2 - x + 1$. Graph y_1 on a suitable range. Use ZOOM-IN and TRACE to estimate the coordinates of the vertex.

EXAMPLE 5   Sketch the graph of $f(x) = -2x^2 + 6x + 1$.

Solution:

- Let $y = f(x) = -2x^2 + 6x + 1$.

- Since the coefficient of x^2 is negative, so the parabola opens downward.

- The vertex is located at $\left(-\dfrac{6}{2(-2)}, \dfrac{4(-2)(1)-36}{4(-2)}\right)$ or $\left(\dfrac{3}{2}, \dfrac{11}{2}\right)$.

- Let $x = 1$ and $x = 2$ be the x-coordinates of points to the left and the right of the vertex, respectively. Completing the table gives

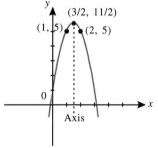

x	y	
1	5:	$y = -2(1)^2 + 6(1) + 1 = -2 + 6 + 1 = \mathbf{5}$
2	5:	$y = -2(2)^2 + 6(2) + 1 = -8 + 12 + 1 = \mathbf{5}$

- Plotting the vertex and the two points, we complete the graph (Figure 4.48).

Figure 4.48

Remark: *The y-intercept found by setting $x = 0$ in $y = ax^2 + bx + c$ gives an additional point to draw the graph. In the above example, the y-intercept is $y = -2(0)^2 + 6(0) + 1 = 1$.*

B. MAXIMUM OR MINIMUM VALUE OF A QUADRATIC FUNCTION

A quadratic function $f(x) = ax^2 + bx + c$ has either a maximum or a minimum value, but not both. It has a minimum value if $a > 0$ and the maximum value if $a < 0$. Moreover, these extreme values of the function occur at the vertex of the parabola (Figure 4.49).

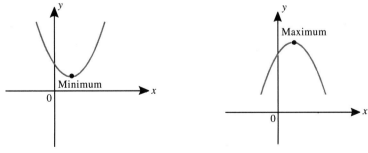

Figure 4.49

Using the results (formula) from Method 2 that gives the vertex of the parabola, we state the following.

Maximum or Minimum Value of a Quadratic Function

A quadratic function $f(x) = ax^2 + bx + c$, where $a \neq 0$ has

1. the **maximum** value if $a < 0$ and

2. the **minimum** value if $a > 0$.

The extreme value of $f(x)$ is $\dfrac{4ac - b^2}{4a}$ and it occurs when $x = -\dfrac{b}{2a}$.

EXAMPLES:

1. For the function $H(x) = -0.03x^2 + 2.3x - 10$, we can talk about its **maximum** value, because the coefficient of x^2 is negative. (*Its graph is a parabola that opens downward.*)

2. For the function $C(x) = 2.5x^2 - 3.7x + 100$, we can determine only the **minimum** value of C, because the coefficient of x^2 is positive. (*Its graph is a parabola that opens upward.*)

EXAMPLE 6

A farmer with 500 ft of fence wants to enclose a rectangular field next to a river. He decides not to use a fence along the river. Suppose he uses x ft on the sides perpendicular to the river bank (Figure 4.50). Find x that will give the maximum enclosed area. What is the maximum enclosed area?

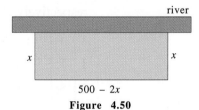

Figure 4.50

Solution:

From Figure 4.50, the area (A) of the rectangular field is a function of x and since the length of the fence is 500, the length of the side parallel to the river is $500 - 2x$. The area is given by

$$\begin{aligned} A(x) &= x(500 - 2x) \\ &= 500x - 2x^2 \\ &= -2x^2 + 500x. \end{aligned}$$

which is a quadratic function. By comparing with $ax^2 + bx + c$, we get $a = -2$, $b = 500$, and $c = 0$.

Since $a < 0$, so the area (A) will attain its maximum value at the vertex. The x-coordinate of the vertex is given by

$$x = -\frac{b}{2a} = -\frac{500}{2(-2)} = 125$$

Therefore, $500 - 2x = 250$ is the other side.

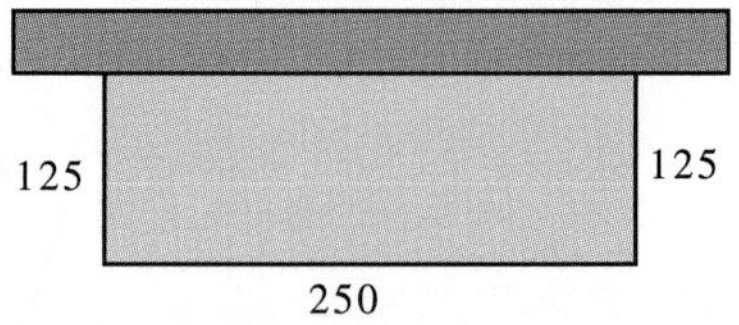

Thus, for the maximum enclosed area, the farmer should enclose a rectangular field of dimensions 125 ft and 250 ft.

Figure 4.51

The maximum enclosed area $(A) = 250(125) = 31250$ ft^2.

Remark: *The maximum enclosed area (A) is also given by the second coordinate of the vertex, namely,*

$$\frac{4ac - b^2}{4a} = \frac{4(-2)(0) - (500)^2}{4(-2)} = \frac{-250000}{-8}$$

$$= 31250 \text{ ft}^2.$$

With Graphing Calculator

Let $y_1 = -2x^2 + 500x$. Graph y_1 on any suitable range.

Use ZOOM-IN and TRACE to locate the vertex of the parabola.

EXAMPLE 7   A bullet is shot upwards with an initial velocity of 1000 ft/sec from a point 10 ft above the ground, and its height above the ground at time t is given by $h(t) = -16t^2 + 1000t + 10$.

    a.   How high will the bullet go?

    b.   How long will it take the bullet to reach the highest point?

Solutions: The height $h(t)$ of the bullet at any time t (Figure 4.52) is given by the quadratic function

$$h(t) = -16t^2 + 1000t + 10$$

    a.   The h-coordinate of the highest point (vertex) A is given by

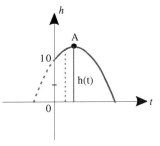

$$\frac{4ac - b^2}{4a} = \frac{4(-16)(10) - (1000)^2}{4(-16)}$$

$$= \frac{-640 - 10^6}{-64} = 15635 \text{ ft.}$$

Thus the bullet rises up to the height of 15,635 ft.

Figure 4.52

    b.   The t-coordinate of the highest point (vertex) A is given by

$$t = -\frac{b}{2a} = -\frac{1000}{2(-16)} = 31.25 \text{ sec.}$$

Therefore, the bullet reaches the highest point in 31.25 seconds.

With Graphing Calculator

Let $y_1 = -16x^2 + 1000x + 10$. Graph y_1 on x-min = 0, x-max = 70, y-min = 0, and y-max = 20,000.

Use ZOOM-IN and TRACE and estimate the coordinates of the highest point (vertex).

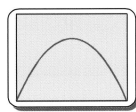

Figure 4.53

Exercise 4.3

In exercises (1-8), indicate which of the given graphs could not be the graph(s) of the given function.

1. $f(x) = 3x^2$,

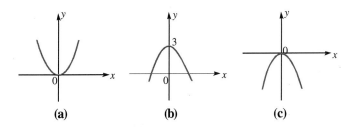

            (a)   **(b)**   **(c)**

2. $g(x) = 4x^2$,

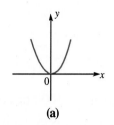
(a)

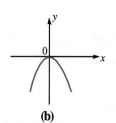
(b)

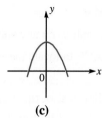
(c)

3. $f(x) = -2x^2$,

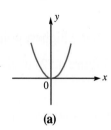
(a)

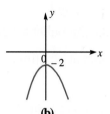
(b)

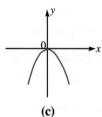
(c)

4. $g(x) = -3x^2$,

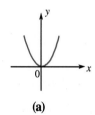
(a)

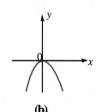
(b)

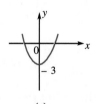
(c)

5. $h(x) = (x-1)^2$,

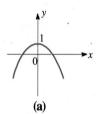
(a)

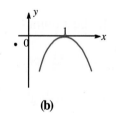
(b)

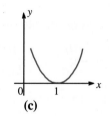
(c)

6. $f(x) = 1 - x^2$,

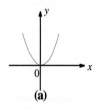
(a)

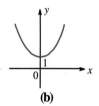
(b)

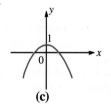
(c)

7. $g(x) = 2\left(1 - x^2\right)$,

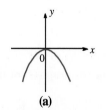
(a)

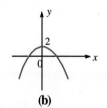
(b)

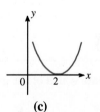
(c)

8. $h(x) = -(2 - x)^2$,

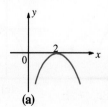
(a)

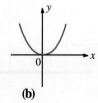
(b)

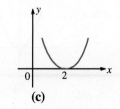
(c)

In exercises (9-42), find the vertex of the parabola.

9. $y = (x - 1)^2 + 5$ 10. $y = (x + 5)^2 - 7$ 11. $y = (x + 1)^2 + 3$ 12. $y = (x - 3)^2 - 5$

13. $y = (x - 2)^2$ 14. $y = (x + 7)^2$ 15. $y = -(x - 1)^2 + 2$ 16. $y = -(x + 3)^2 + 5$

17. $y = -(x + 2)^2 - 1$ 18. $y = -(x - 5)^2 + 3$ 19. $y = 2(x - 3)^2 + 1$ 20. $y = 4(x + 2)^2 - 2$

21. $y = 2(x + 5)^2 - 1$ 22. $y = 3(x - 4)^2 + 2$ 23. $y = -3\left(x - \dfrac{1}{2}\right)^2 + 1$ 24. $y = -12\left(x + \dfrac{5}{2}\right)^2 - 4$

25. $y = -4\left(x + \dfrac{3}{2}\right)^2 - \dfrac{1}{2}$ 26. $y = -8\left(x - \dfrac{7}{2}\right)^2 + \dfrac{1}{4}$ 27. $y = x^2 + 4x + 1$ 28. $y = x^2 + 8x - 5$

29. $y = x^2 + 6x - 1$ 30. $y = x^2 - 12x + 1$ 31. $y = x^2 + 3x + 1$ 32. $y = x^2 + 5x + 2$

33. $y = x^2 - 5x + 5$ 34. $y = x^2 - 3x - 10$ 35. $y = 2x^2 - 8$ 36. $y = 4x^2 + 12$

37. $y = 2x^2 - 4x$ 38. $y = 2x^2 + 12x$ 39. $y = 2x^2 + 3x + 1$ 40. $y = 2x^2 - 5x + 9$

41. $y = -3x^2 + 6x - 1$ 42. $y = -4x^2 - 8x + 5$

In exercises (43-62), sketch the graph of the function.

43. $f(x) = x^2 + 3x + 5$ 44. $f(x) = x^2 - 4x + 6$ 45. $f(x) = x^2 + 6x - 7$ 46. $f(x) = x^2 - 2x + 7$

47. $f(x) = -x^2 - 2x + 5$ 48. $f(x) = -x^2 + 6x - 3$ 49. $f(x) = -x^2 + 4x + 2$ 50. $f(x) = -x^2 - 4x + 4$

51. $f(x) = 2x^2 + 8x - 3$ 52. $f(x) = 4x^2 - 2x + 3$ 53. $g(x) = -3x^2 - 6x + 5$ 54. $f(x) = -4x^2 + 8x + 1$

55. $h(x) = 4x^2 - 12x + 3$ 56. $f(x) = 3x^2 + 12x - 1$ 57. $f(x) = -3x^2 + 4x - 2$ 58. $g(x) = -4x^2 - x + 5$

59. $h(x) = -4x^2 + 20x - 25$ 60. $f(x) = 2x^2 - 8x + 3$ 61. $f(x) = -2x^2 + 8x - 11$ 62. $g(x) = -6x^2 + 12x + 1$

63.   A farmer has 1200 feet of fence and wants to enclose a rectangular field of dimensions x by $600 - x$. For what x-value is the enclosed area (A) a maximum? What is the maximum area?

64.   A farmer wants to enclose a rectangular field of dimensions x by $500 - x$ with 1000 feet of fence. For what x-value is the enclosed area maximum?

65.   The profit (P) of a company after sales of x units is given by $P(x) = 3200x - x^2$. Find the volume of sales (x) that yields the maximum profit.

66.   The profit (P) of a company after sales of x units is given by $P(x) = 2000x - x^2$. For what x-value is the profit P maximum?

67.   A sheet of aluminum is 8 feet long and 16 inches wide. It is to be made into a gutter by bending up two sides so that they are perpendicular to the bottom. If x inches are turned up, find the x-value that will give the maximum capacity for the gutter.

68.   A stone is thrown upward from a platform that is 5 feet above the ground. If the stone is thrown with a velocity of 100 ft/sec, then the height (h) after t seconds is given by $h(t) = -16t^2 + 100t + 5$.

   a. How long will it take to reach the highest point ?   **b.** How high will it go?

69.   An object is thrown upward from the ground level with a velocity of 128 ft/sec. The height after t seconds is given by

$$h(t) = -16t^2 + 128t$$

   a. Find the maximum height reached by the object.   **b.** How long does it take to reach the highest point?

   c. When does the object hit the ground?

Writing Exercises

70.   Describe the two methods of graphing a quadratic function.

71.   Explain why the vertex of the parabola is called a **turning point.**

4.4 HOW TO GENERATE FUNCTIONS

Objective ▶ ▶

In this section you will learn about:

A. The Strategy for Generating a Function.

In the real world the formulas which represent functions do not come ready made. We need to translate the information in order to find the expression for the function. The task of formulating the "expression" part of the function may be somewhat involved. In this section we will give a set of guidelines that may help in this process

A. THE STRATEGY FOR GENERATING A FUNCTION

Step **1**   Draw a picture, if possible.

Step **2**   Label the dimensions of the picture with appropriate symbols, like x or y.

Step **3**   If two letters are used in Step 2, then find a relationship between x and y.

Step **4**   Write the expression part for the function.

Step **5**   Use Step 3 to express the function in terms of only one variable (say x), if possible.

Let us use the above procedure in the following examples.

EXAMPLE 1   A roll of 100 feet of chicken wire is used to enclose a rectangular vegetable garden. Express the area of the garden in terms of its length (x).

Solution:

Step 1   Let ABCD be the rectangular garden.

Figure 4.54

Step 2   A rectangle has two dimensions, namely, the length and width.
Let the length be x and y be the width.

Step 3   We have used the two letters in labeling the dimension, so we find a relationship between x and y. Since the total fence (perimeter) is 100 ft., we have

   * $2x + 2y = 100$

   → $x + y = 50$

   → $y = 50 - x$

> * The perimeter of a polygon is the sum of the sides. For a rectangle, the
>
>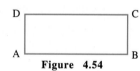
>
> sum of the sides is
> $$x + y + x + y$$
> $$= 2x + 2y$$

Step 4   The function is the area A of the rectangular garden and it depends upon x and y. Hence,

     $A = xy$ [Area = (length) (width)]

Step 5   To write A as a function of only x, we use Step 3 . (i.e., substitute $y = 50 - x$).

     $A(x) = x(50 - x) = 50x - x^2$

EXAMPLE 2   In Example 1, find the dimensions of a rectangle that give the largest area in the vegetable garden.

Solution: From Example 1, the area A of a rectangular garden is given by

$$A(x) = 50x - x^2$$

In order to draw its graph we write $A = 50x - x^2 = -x^2 + 50x$.   The second coordinate is represented by A.

Since the graph of this quadratic function is a parabola that opens downward (why?), so the area (A) is maximum at the vertex. We find the x-coordinate of the vertex:

* $x = -\dfrac{50}{2(-1)} = 25$

*   To graph $y = ax^2 + bx + c$

     Step 1   It opens upward if $a > 0$ and opens downward if $a < 0$

     Step 2 x-coordinate of the vertex

$$= -\frac{b}{2a}.$$

Thus, the dimensions of the rectangle that has the largest area are length $(x) = 25$ ft and width $y = 50 - x = 50 - \mathbf{25}$

$$= 25 \text{ ft.}$$

Therefore, among all rectangles with perimeter 100 ft, the one with the largest area is actually the square of side 25 ft.

With Graphing Calculator

Let $y_1 = 50x - x^2$. Graph y_1 under a suitable range like x-min $= 0$, x-max $= 100$, y-min $= 0$, and y-max $= 1000$. Use TRACE and ZOOM-IN to locate the coordinates of the top (OR use FMAX in TI-85). We obtain $x = 24.9999$ and $y = 625$ (area).

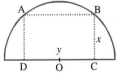

Figure 4.55

EXAMPLE 3   A rectangle is inscribed in a semicircle of radius 4 with its base along the diameter. Write the area of the rectangle in terms of its width.

Solution:

     Step 1   Let ABCD be the rectangle with base along the diameter where O is the center of the semicircle (Figure 4.56).

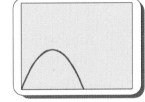

Figure 4.56

     Step 2   Let the width (BC) of the rectangle be x and the length CD $= y$ (Figure 4.56).

     Step 3   Since we have used two letters x and y we need to find a relationship between them. Consider the right triangle OBC, OC $= \dfrac{y}{2}$, and OB $=$ the radius $= 4$ (Figure 4.57).

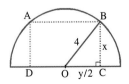

Figure 4.57

By the Pythagorean Theorem, we get $16 = x^2 + \dfrac{y^2}{4}$

Solving the equation for y^2, we get: $4(16 - x^2) = y^2$.

This gives $\pm\, 2\sqrt{16 - x^2} = y$.

Since we are measuring length y, it can not be negative. Therefore

$$2\sqrt{16 - x^2} = y$$

Step 4   The function is the area A of the rectangle. Obviously, it depends upon x and y, so
$$A = xy$$

Step 5   We substitute $y = 2\sqrt{16 - x^2}$ and obtain

$$A = x\left(2\sqrt{16 - x^2}\right) = 2x\sqrt{16 - x^2}\ .$$

Thus, the area of the inscribed rectangle is expressed as a function of its width.

EXAMPLE 4   A rectangular box, without top, is to be constructed from a 16 in. × 16 in. square piece of cardboard by cutting equal squares of side x from each corner and then bending up the sides. Write the volume of the box as a function of x.

Solution:

- Let ABCD be the square piece of cardboard with each side = 16 in. Let x be the side of each cut-out square (Figure 4.58).

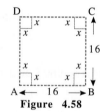

Figure 4.58

- After we bend up the sides, the box will have the dimensions given in Figure 4.59.

- The function is the volume (V) of the box and is given by
  $V(x) = \text{(length) (width) (height)}$

  $= (16 - 2x)\,(16 - 2x)x.$

  $= (16 - 2x)^2\, x$

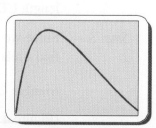

Figure 4.59

Thus, the volume of the box is given by $V(x) = x(16 - 2x)^2$.

EXAMPLE 5   In Example 4, use a graphing calculator to find the length of the side of the square to be cut out so that the box has the largest volume. What is the maximum volume?

Solution: Let $y_1 = x(16 - 2x)^2$. Graph y_1 on the range: $x\text{-min} = 0$, $x\text{-max} = 8$, $y\text{-min} = 0$, $y\text{-max} = 500$. We use ZOOM-IN and TRACE to locate the highest point in the graph (Figure 4.60). We obtain $x = 2.666$ and $y = 303.41$. Therefore, for the largest volume we should cut out each square of side 2.67 in. Then the largest volume will be 303.4 in^3.

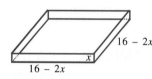

Figure 4.60

EXAMPLE 6   A water tank in the shape of a right circular cylinder has volume 10 ft³. If the material for the bottom and top of the tank costs $2 per square foot and for the curved surface $1 per square foot, then write a complete statement for the total cost function in terms of the radius of the tank.

Solution:

- We draw a picture of a cylindrical tank (Figure 4.61).

- The volume of a cylinder depends on two variables, the radius = x and the height = y.
  Then, $V = \pi x^2 y$.

Figure 4.61

- To find the relationship between x and y, we use the fact that the volume of the tank is 10 ft³.

  This gives $\pi x^2 y = 10$ or $y = \dfrac{10}{\pi x^2}$.

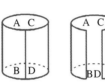

Figure 4.63

- The function is the total cost of constructing a cylindrical tank of radius x and height y. The top and bottom of the tank are two identical circular discs, each with area πx^2, so the cost of making this is

  $$C_1 = 2\left(2\pi x^2\right) = 4\pi x^2$$

  (dollars)

The side AC or BD
= circumference of the circular rim
= $2\pi x$. And
AB = CD = height = y

The curved surface is made by welding side AB with CD (Figure 4.62).

Figure 4.62

The cost C_2 for the material is given by

$$C_2 = 1(2\pi x \cdot y) = 2\pi xy \text{ (dollars)}$$ Refer to figure 4.63.

Therefore, the total cost (C) function is given by

$$C = C_1 + C_2 = 4\pi x^2 + 2\pi xy$$ Refer to figures 4.62 and 4.63.

- We express the above function in terms of the radius (x).

$$C(x) = 4\pi x^2 + 2\pi x \left(\frac{10}{\pi x^2}\right)$$

$$C(x) = 4\pi x^2 + \frac{20}{x} .$$

Remark: *By using a graphing calculator we can graph the function $y_1 = 4\pi x^2 + 20x^{-1}$ with range x-min = 0, x-max = 2, y-min = 30, y-max = 40. We can find the dimensions of the tank that will be the cheapest (lowest point of the graph) to make. Check the dimensions of such a tank. They should be x = .93 ft,*

$$y = \frac{10}{\pi (.93)^2} ft . \text{ The total cost is \$32.37.}$$

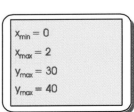

$X_{min} = 0$
$X_{max} = 2$
$Y_{max} = 30$
$Y_{max} = 40$

EXAMPLE 7   A person 5.5 ft. tall is walking away from a lamp post that is 20 ft high. Find a relationship between the length of the man's shadow (y) and the distance x between the lamp post and the man.

Solution:

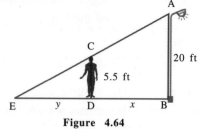

- Let AB be the lamp post, CD be the person, and ED be the person's shadow (Figure 4.64).

- Let the distance (BD) between the person and the lamp post be equal to x. And let y be the length of the person's shadow (DE).

Figure 4.64

- To find a relationship between x and y, we will use the fact that $\triangle$ABE is similar to $\triangle$CDE.

  Using the ratios of corresponding sides, we obtain $\dfrac{20}{5.5} = \dfrac{x+y}{y}$.

  Multiplying the equation by the lcd, $5.5y$, gives

  $$5.5y \cdot \frac{20}{5.5} = 5.5y \cdot \frac{x+y}{y} \longrightarrow 20y = 5.5x + 5.5y \longrightarrow 14.5y = 5.5x$$

  $$\longrightarrow \quad y = \frac{5.5x}{14.5} = \frac{11x}{29}$$

  Thus, the relationship between the person's shadow (y) and the distance (x) from the lamp post is given by $y = \dfrac{11}{29}x.$

EXAMPLE 8   A conical tank that is 10 ft. across its circular top and 15 ft. deep is partially filled with water. Find a relationship between the depth (x) and volume (y) of the water in the tank.

Solution:

Step 1   Let ABC be the conical tank and DEC be the water cone. (Figure 4.65).

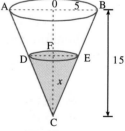

Step 2   Since AB = 10 ft, the radius OB = 5 ft. Also OC = 15 ft. Let FC = x, and the volume of the cone DEC = y.

Figure 4.65

Step 3   To find the volume of the water, we need the radius FE of the water cone. For this we use the fact that $\triangle$OBC and $\triangle$FEC are similar. Using ratios of corresponding sides we get:

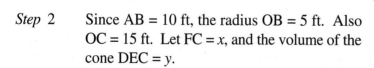

$$\frac{OB}{FE} = \frac{OC}{FC} \qquad \text{or} \qquad \frac{5}{FE} = \frac{15}{x}$$

We solve for FE and get FE $= \dfrac{x}{3}$.

Therefore, the volume (y) of the water cone is given by

$$y = \frac{1}{3}\pi(FE)^2 \, x \qquad\qquad V = \tfrac{1}{3}\pi r^2 h$$

$$= \frac{1}{3}\pi\left(\frac{x}{3}\right)^2 x = \frac{\pi x^3}{27}$$

EXERCISE 4.4

1. Express the area (A) of a rectangle of perimeter 20 in terms of its length (x).

2. Express the perimeter (P) of a rectangle of area 100 ft² in terms of its length (x).

3. Express the volume (V) of a rectangular box with a square base and of surface area 100 ft² in terms of the length (x) of the square base.

4. Express the surface area (S) of a rectangular box with a square base and of volume 100 ft³ in terms of the length (x) of the square base.

5. A farmer wishes to enclose a rectangular region adjacent to a lake. If she wants to enclose an area of 50,000 ft², express the amount (P) of fencing required in terms of the length (x) of fence parallel to the lake. (Assume that no fencing is required along the lake.)

6. 1200 feet of fencing is to be used to enclose a rectangular field and to divide it in half. Express the area (A) of the field in terms of the length (x) of fencing used to divide the pasture field in half.

7. A box with no top is to be made from a rectangular sheet of cardboard of dimensions 16 by 24 inches by cutting out equal squares from each corner and bending up the flaps. Express the volume (V) of the box in terms of the length (x) of the cut out squares.

8. An open gutter with perpendicular sides is to be constructed by bending up equal sides of a rectangular piece of vinyl sheet that is 12 inches wide. Express the area (A) of the cross-section of the gutter in terms of the length (x) turned up on each side.

9. A rectangular sheet of paper is to contain a print area of 66 in². If the margin on each side is $\frac{1}{2}$ in, express the area (A) of the page in terms of its length (x).

10. A 16 in length of wire is cut into two pieces. One piece that is x inches long is bent into a circle and the remaining piece is bent into a square. Express the combined area (A) in terms of x.

11. Suppose in Exercise 10, one piece that is x inches long is bent into circle and the remaining piece is bent into an equilateral triangle. Express the combined area (A) in terms of x.

12. A rectangle is inscribed in a right triangle with legs of lengths 6 and 8 inches, respectively. If the two adjacent sides of the rectangle lie along the legs of the triangle, express the area (A) of the rectangle in terms of the length (x) of its side that is along the larger leg of the triangle.

13. Express the distance (D) between a point (x, y) on the graph of $f(x) = x^2 + 2$ and the point (1, 2) in terms of x.

14. At noon time, a southbound ship A is 80 miles north of an eastbound ship B. If the ship A is traveling at the speed of 15 mph and the speed of the ship B is 12 mph, express the distance (d) between the ships at t hours in terms of t.

15. Suppose a father at point P on a straight road wishes to quickly reach his son who is located 3 miles from the road and 5 miles from P, in the field. Further suppose that the father travels x miles on the road before heading in a straight line toward his son. Express the total time (t) he took to reach his son in terms of x. (Assume that he walks 5 mph on the road and 2 mph across the field.)

16. A Norman window is constructed by adjoining a semicircle to the top of an ordinary rectangular window. Express the area (A) of the Norman window of perimeter 20 feet in terms of the width (x) of the window.

17. Express the area (A) of a rectangle that can be inscribed in a circle of radius 4 in terms of the half length (x) of the rectangle.

18. A rectangular beam is to be cut from a circular log of 22 in. diameter. If the strength (S) of the beam varies directly as its width (x) and the square of its depth (y), express the strength (S) in terms of its width (x).

19. A manufacturer receives an order to supply rectangular boxes with square bases each with volume of 9 ft^3. The cost of the material for the top and the sides is 50 cents per square foot and the material for the bottom of the box costs 75 cents per square foot. Express the total cost (C) of making one box in terms of the length (x) of the square base.

20. A cylindrical oil can is supposed to hold 200 in^3 of oil. Suppose it is made with a steel top and bottom and cardboard sides. The steel costs 4 cents per square inch, the cardboard costs 2 cents per square inch and rolling the crimp around the top and bottom circular edges costs 1 cent per linear inch. Express the total cost (C) of making such a can in terms of the radius (x) of the can.

21. A right circular cylinder is inscribed in a right circular cone of radius 6 in. and height 10 in. Express the volume (V) of the cylinder in terms of the radius (x).

22. A right circular cone is inscribed in a sphere of radius 10 in. Express the volume (V) of the cone in terms of its radius (x).

23. If the rent is $500 per month, then all 50 apartments in an apartment building will be rented out. The manager knows that one apartment will become vacant for every $15 increase in rent. Let x be the number of $15 increases in rent. Express the total amount (A) of rent collected if the manager raises the rent $15 per month for x months.

24. An orchard owner knows that if he plants 20 apple trees per acre, the average yield is 400 apples per tree. He also understands that for each additional tree per acre planted, the average yield per tree will be reduced by 15 apples due to crowding. If he plants $20 + x$ trees per acre, express the total average yield (Y) per acre, in terms of x.

25. In Exercise 24, how many trees per acre should he plant to get the maximum total yield ?

Writing Exercises

26. Write a procedure for setting up a function in a word problem.

27. Why can we answer the optimization question for a quadratic function only?

4.5 GRAPHS OF POLYNOMIAL FUNCTIONS

In Section 4.3 we learned how to sketch the graph of a polynomial function of degree two. In this section we will discuss the graph of a polynomial function of degree greater than 2, when x is finite and when $|x|$ is large.

The graphs of most polynomial functions of degree greater than two are not as easy to describe as are the graphs of first degree or second degree polynomial functions. In the case of a quadratic function, there was only one 'turning point' in the graph. At the turning point the graph changes from increasing to decreasing or from decreasing to increasing. The graph of a polynomial function of degree greater than 2 may have more than one turning point or no turning point at all (Figure 4.66).

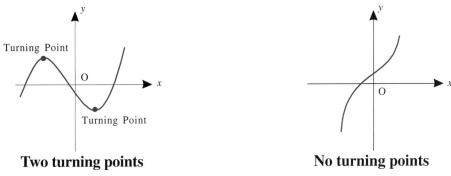

Two turning points   **No turning points**

Figure 4.66

As for other functions, we draw an approximate graph of a polynomial function by plotting points. However, we will describe a method that uses a minimum number of points for the graph. The following method, unlike the method for quadratic functions, may fail to give the turning points of the graphs. To determine the exact locations of turning points, we need calculus. We will discuss, here, how by finding zeros of a polynomial function and solving solutions of polynomial inequalities we can find approximate shapes of graphs of polynomial functions.

A. GRAPHING A POLYNOMIAL FUNCTION

EXAMPLE 1   Graph $f(x) = (x + 1)(x - 1)(x - 3)^2$

Procedure   *Solution:*

Consider $f(x) = p(x)$, where $p(x)$ is a polynomial. ⟶

Step 1   Find the zeros of the polynomial function or solve $p(x) = 0$.

The zeros of the function are given by

$(x + 1)(x - 1)(x - 3)^2 = 0$ or

$x + 1 = 0$	$x - 1 = 0$	$x - 3 = 0$
$x = -1$	$x = 1$	$x = 3$

Therefore, $x = 1, -1$ and 3 are the zeros of the function. (Recall, that the zeros of the function are the same as the x-intercepts of its graph.)

Step 2   Plot the zeros on the number line and solve the inequality

$$p(x) > 0$$

This will give intervals on the *x*-axis where the graph is above the *x*-axis.

⟶   We solve $(x + 1)\,(x - 1)\,(x - 3)^2 > 0$

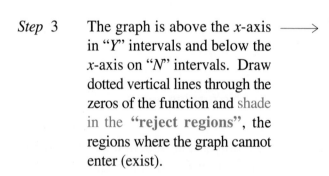

Plotting the points $x = -1$, 1, and 3 divides the number line into four intervals, A, B, C, and D.

Using $x = -2$ as the test number for interval A gives

$(-2 + 1)\,(-2 - 1)\,(-2 - 3)^2 > 0$ or $75 > 0$ which is true.

Therefore, write "*Y*" above interval A. Similarly, testing other intervals, we get:

Step 3   The graph is above the *x*-axis in "*Y*" intervals and below the *x*-axis on "*N*" intervals. Draw dotted vertical lines through the zeros of the function and shade in the **"reject regions"**, the regions where the graph cannot enter (exist).

⟶

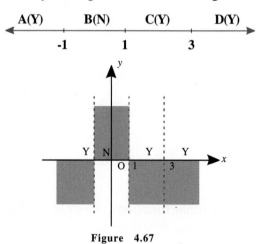

Figure 4.67

Step 4   Find zeros of the function, to get the *x*-coordinate where the graph meets *x*-axis.

⟶   1, –1 and 3 are the zeros of the function as found in step 1. So, the graph meets *x*-axis at the points (1, 0), (–1, 0), and (3, 0).

Step 5   Find a few points in each clear region by completing a table.

x	*y*

⟶   Let $y = (x + 1)\,(x - 1)\,(x - 3)^2$

x	*y*
–2	75
0	–9
2	3
4	15

Step 6   Plot the points and complete the graph. (Figure 4.68)

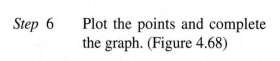

Remark: *This graph has three "turning points".*

Figure 4.68

With Graphing Calculator

Let $y_1 = (x + 1)(x - 1)(x - 3)^2$.

Graph y_1 on a suitable range (Figure 4.69).

From the graph it can be seen that the x-coordinates of the turning points are approximately $-.33$, 1.76, and 3.

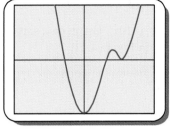

Figure   4.69

EXAMPLE 2   Graph $f(x) = x^3 - 3x^2 - 10x$.

Solution:

• To find the zeros of the function $f(x)$, we set $f(x) = 0$.

$x^3 - 3x^2 - 10x = 0$

Solving the equation gives

$x(x^2 - 3x - 10) = 0$

$x(x - 5)(x + 2) = 0$

Therefore, $x = 0$, $x = 5$ and $x = -2$ are the zeros of the function.

• We solve the inequality $f(x) > 0$.

$x(x - 5)(x + 2) > 0$

$\qquad \overset{A(N) \qquad\qquad B(Y) \qquad\qquad C(N) \qquad\qquad D(Y)}{\underset{\qquad\qquad -2 \qquad\qquad\qquad 0 \qquad\qquad\qquad 5}{\longleftarrow\!\!\!\!\longrightarrow}}$

Interval A	**Interval B**	**Interval C**	**Interval D**
Test number = -3	Test number = -1	Test number = 1	Test number = 6
$f(-3) = -3(-3 - 5)(-3 + 2) < 0$	$f(-1) = -1(-6)(1) > 0$	$f(1) = 1(-4)(3) < 0$	$f(6) = 6(1)(8) > 0$
Therefore, we write 'N' above interval A.	Therefore, we write 'Y' above interval B.	We write 'N' above interval C.	We write 'Y' above interval D.

• The graph is above the x-axis in the 'Y' intervals of x-axis and below the x-axis on the 'N' intervals. Draw vertical dotted lines through the zeros of the function and shade in the 'reject regions', that is, the regions where the graph cannot enter (Figure 4.70).

• Zeros of the function:

We observe from step 1 that $x = 0$, 5, and -2 are are the zeros of the function. So the graph meets x-axis at the points $(0, 0)$, $(5, 0)$ and $(-2, 0)$.

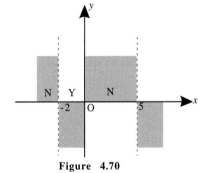

Figure   4.70

• For a few points in the clear regions, we complete the table

x	y
-3	-24
-1	6
2	-24
6	48

• Plotting these points and completing the graph give Figure 4.71.

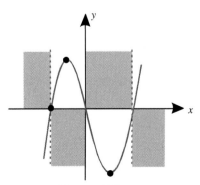

Figure   4.71

With Graphing Calculator

Let $y_1 = x^3 - 3x^2 - 10x$. Graph on a suitable range and check the graph in Figure 4.71.

The x-values of the turning points are approximately -1.15 and 3.1.

B. THE BEHAVIOR OF A POLYNOMIAL FUNCTION AT INFINITY

In Section 1.3, we observed that the value of a polynomial expression for a large $|x|$ value was dominated by the leading term of the polynomial expression. By the definition of a polynomial function, we state a similar result as follows:

> **Graph of a Polynomial Function at Infinity**
> The graph of a polynomial function
> $$f(x) = a_n x^n + a_{n-1} x^{n-1} + \ldots + a_1 x + a_0$$
> for large values of $|x|$ is approximately the same as the graph of $g(x) = a_n x^n$.

Remarks: *1.* *The rule says that a polynomial function at infinity behaves like a power function.*

2. *The rule is useful in approximating the value of a polynomial function for large x-values. For example, for $f(x) = x^3 - 3x^2 - 10x$, the value of the function when $x = 1250$ is approximated by evaluating the leading term of the polynomial. That is, $f(1250) \approx (1250)^3 = 1953125000$*

[The exact value is 1948425000].

EXAMPLE 3   Use a graphing calculator to check that the graphs of $f(x) = 3x^4 + 2x^3 - 8x^2 - 2x + 3$ and $g(x) = 3x^4$ resemble each other when $|x|$ is large.

Solution: Let $y_1 = 3x^4 + 2x^3 - 8x^2 - 2x + 3$ and $y_2 = 3x^4$. Graphing y_1 and y_2 on the standard range shows Figure 4.72.

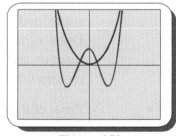

Figure 4.72

ZOOM-OUT to the left or right. We observe that both graphs are almost alike.

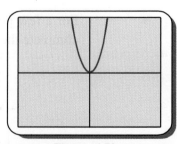

Figure 4.73

Thus, it shows that when $|x|$ is large, the graph of $f(x)$ is the same as that of $g(x)$.

EXERCISE 4.5

In exercises (1-20), sketch the graph of the polynomial function and verify your graph with a graphing calculator.

1. $f(x) = 2(x-1)(x-3)(x+2)$

2. $f(x) = 3(x+3)(x+4)(x-2)$

3. $g(x) = 3(x+1)(x-2)(x-5)$

4. $g(x) = 2(x+1)(x+2)(x-4)$

5. $h(x) = x^4 - 9x^2$

6. $f(x) = x^4 - 25x^2$

7. $f(x) = 2x^4 - 8x^2$

8. $h(x) = 3x^4 - 3x^2$

9. $k(x) = 2x^3 + 5x^2 - 2x - 5$

10. $g(x) = 2x^3 + 5x^2 - 3x$

11. $h(x) = (x-2)(x+1)^2$

12. $f(x) = (x+2)(x-4)^2$

13. $S(x) = (x-3)^2(x+1)$

14. $h(x) = (x-1)^2(x+5)$

15. $f(x) = x(x-3)(x+3)$

16. $g(x) = 2x(x-1)(x+3)$

17. $g(x) = -x(x-2)(x+2)$

18. $f(x) = -(x-1)(x+1)(x+3)$

19. $h(x) = x^3 - 4x$

20. $g(x) = x^3 - 9x$

In exercises (21-24), use the dominating term of the polynomial to approximate the value of the function at the indicated x-value.

21. $f(x) = 5x^6 + 5x^4 - 7x + 10,\ x = 1350$

22. $f(x) = 7x^5 - 4x^4 + 10x^2 - 9x + 3,\ x = 1270$

23. $g(x) = -8x^4 + 2x^2 + 11,\ x = 1120$

24. $g(x) = -9x^5 + 10x^3 - 6x^2 + 21x + 181, x = 1410$

25.   A rectangular box with an open top is to be made from an 8 in. by 12 in. rectangular piece of cardboard by cutting out equal squares from the four corners. If x denotes the length of the side of each cut-out square, the volume V of the box is given by

$$V(x) = x(12 - 2x)(8 - 2x)$$

Sketch the graph of $V(x)$. Use a graphing calculator to estimate the maximum possible volume of the box.

In exercises (26-39), give the function whose graph at infinity resembles the graph of the given polynomial function. Verify by graphing both functions.

26. $g(x) = 10x^5 + 7x^2 + 3$

27. $f(x) = 5x^4 - 8x^2$

28. $f(x) = -10x^4 + 6x^2 + 3x - 5$

29. $f(x) = -3x^3 + 5x^2 + 2x + 7$

30. $f(x) = -2(2x+1)(x-1)(x+5)$

31. $g(x) = 3(x-1)(x-3)(x+2)$

32. $g(x) = 4(x+1)(-2x+1)(x-4)$

33. $h(x) = 2(x+2)(x-3)(x-5)$

34. $g(x) = -4(x+5)(x-10)^2$

35. $f(x) = 3(x-1)^2(x+2)$

36. $f(x) = -20(x-11)(x+13)^2$

37. $g(x) = 5(x+1)(x-2)^2$

38. $g(x) = 120(x-20)^2(x+5)$

39. $h(x) = 3(x+1)^2(x-3)$

Writing Exercises

40.   Describe the procedure for graphing a polynomial function.

41.   Explain what is meant by a "turning point" in a graph.

42.   Is it true that there is always a turning point between two consecutive zeros of a polynomial function? Explain why or why not.

43.   Describe the behavior of a polynomial function at infinity.

4.6 GRAPHS OF RATIONAL FUNCTIONS

Objectives ▶ ▶

In this section you will learn about:

A. The Behavior of $f(x) = \dfrac{p(x)}{q(x)}$

   near $x = a$ where $p(a) \neq 0$, but $q(a) = 0$;

B. Vertical Asymptotes;

C. Horizontal Asymptotes; and

D. Graphing a Rational Function.

In this section we will describe techniques for graphing rational functions that reduce the plotting of points to a minimum and still enable us to draw a reasonably accurate sketch of the graph.

In a rational function $f(x) = \dfrac{p(x)}{q(x)}$, the zeros of the polynomial $p(x)$ are the zeros of the function $f(x)$, provided they are also not zeros of the denominator. At a zero of the function its graph meets the x-axis. Suppose for $x = a$, $q(a) = 0$ but $p(a) \neq 0$, then $f(a)$ is undefined. The obvious question arises, what is the behavior of the function (graph) for x near a zero of the denominator $q(x)$?

A. BEHAVIOR OF $f(x) = \dfrac{p(x)}{q(x)}$ NEAR $x = a$, WHEN $p(a) \neq 0$ BUT $q(a) = 0$.

Let us examine the behavior of $f(x) = \dfrac{3}{x-2}$ near $x = 2$.

Since the behavior of a function is determined by the function values, we observe the values of the function near $x = 2$. Let x get closer to 2 from both sides and compute corresponding function values. The following table shows function values for some choices of x-values:

x	1.9	1.99	1.999	2.001	2.01	2.1
$f(x)$	−30	−300	−3000	3000	300	30

We observe that the function value is numerically a large positive number when x is close to 2 on the right side of $x = 2$. For example, $f(2.001) = 3000$.

Also, the function value is numerically a large negative number when x is close to 2 on the left side of $x = 2$. For example, $f(1.999) = -3000$.

Therefore, the function values increase **without bound** as x gets closer to 2 from the right side. In common words, we say that the values 'blow up' as we get close to $x = 2$ from the right side.

In short, we write

$$f(x) \to \infty \quad \text{as} \quad x \to 2^{+} \quad \text{(for } x > 2)$$

Similarly, $\quad f(x) \to -\infty \quad \text{as} \quad x \to 2^{-} \quad \text{(for } x < 2).$

The graph of the function $f(x) = \dfrac{3}{x-2}$ gets closer and closer to the vertical line $x = 2$ as x gets closer and closer to 2. (Figure 4.74).

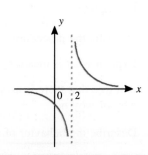

Figure 4.74

Therefore, the line $x = 2$ plays an important role in sketching the graph of the function. This line is called a **vertical asymptote.**

B. VERTICAL ASYMPTOTES

A line $x = a$ is a **vertical asymptote** of the graph of $f(x) = \dfrac{p(x)}{q(x)}$ if $\left| f(x) \right|$ increases without bound (blows up) as x gets close to a either from the left or from the right or both.

Remarks: *1.* *If $x = a$ is a vertical asymptote, then $f(a)$ is undefined.*

   2. *The graph of $f(x)$ has a break at $x = a$.*

   3. *The points on the graph get closer and closer to the asymptote $x = a$.*

Finding Vertical Asymptotes

Since the graph of a rational function resembles part of its vertical asymptote $x = a$ near a, it is important to know all asymptotes of the function.

To find vertical asymptotes of $f(x) = \dfrac{p(x)}{q(x)}$, we look for all a's such that $q(a) = 0$ but $p(a) \neq 0$. Note that a common zero $x = b$ of the numerator and denominator does not define a vertical asymptote. Consequently, before we find all vertical asymptotes of a rational function we first reduce the rational expression $\dfrac{p(x)}{q(x)}$ and then find the zeros of $q(x)$.

EXAMPLE 1   Find all vertical asymptotes of $f(x) = \dfrac{x^2 - 4x + 3}{x^2 - 9}$.

Procedure

Find all vertical asymptotes of $f(x) = \dfrac{p(x)}{q(x)}$

Solution:

Step 1   Reduce the rational expression $\dfrac{p(x)}{q(x)}$ $\longrightarrow$ $f(x) = \dfrac{(x - 3)(x - 1)}{(x - 3)(x + 3)}$

   by canceling (dividing) out common factor(s).

Step 2   For each common factor of the form $\longrightarrow$ $f(x) = \dfrac{x - 1}{x + 3}, \; x \neq 3$
   $cx - b$ in step 1, write the restriction on the domain in the form

   $cx - b \neq 0 \;$ or $\; x \neq \dfrac{b}{c}$.

Step 3   Set the denominator of the $\longrightarrow$ $x + 3 = 0$
resulting rational expression $x = -3$
equal to zero and write
solutions of the equation.

Step 4 $x = a$, $x = d$ ... are the vertical $\longrightarrow$ Thus, $x = -3$ is the only vertical asymptote
asymptotes of the function.   of $f(x) = \dfrac{x^2 - 4x + 3}{x^2 - 9}$.

EXAMPLE 2   Find all vertical asymptotes of the rational function $f(x) = \dfrac{2x + 3}{x^2 + 5x + 6}$.

Solution:

- We try to reduce the rational expression by factoring the numerator and the denominator.

$$f(x) = \frac{2x + 3}{(x - 2)(x - 3)}$$

There is no factor common to the numerator and the denominator.

- The vertical asymptotes are obtained from the solutions of the equation

$(x - 2)(x - 3) = 0$

$x - 2 = 0 \quad | \quad x - 3 = 0$

$x = 2 \quad\quad | \quad x = 3$

- Thus, the two vertical asymptotes are $x = 2$ and $x = 3$.

C. HORIZONTAL ASYMPTOTES

Behavior of $f(x) = \dfrac{p(x)}{q(x)}$ when $|x|$ is large.

The behavior of the function $f(x) = \dfrac{p(x)}{q(x)}$ when $|x|$ is large is given by the dominant part of the

rational expression $\dfrac{p(x)}{q(x)}$. As discussed in Section 1.4, the dominant part of

$$\frac{p(x)}{q(x)} = \begin{cases} \textbf{quotient of leading coefficients} \text{ of } p(x) \text{ and } q(x), \text{ if deg } p(x) = \text{deg } q(x) \\ \textbf{0}, \text{ if deg p(x)} < \text{deg q(x)} \\ \textbf{quotient in the division} \textbf{ of } p(x) \textbf{ by } q(x), \text{ if deg } p(x) > \text{deg } q(x) \end{cases}$$

In the first two cases, the function $y = f(x)$ will resemble a horizontal line when $|x|$ is large. This
horizontal line is called the **horizontal asymptote.**

A line $y = b$ is a **horizontal asymptote** of the graph of a function $y = f(x)$ if the values of $f(x)$ get closer to b as $\left| x \right|$ increases without bound.

Since the graph of a rational function $y = f(x) = \dfrac{p(x)}{q(x)}$ will resemble the graph of the horizontal asymptote, if it exists, when $\left| x \right|$ is large, so the graph of the horizontal asymptote will become an important information for completing the graph of the rational function.

Finding the Horizontal Asymptotes

The horizontal asymptote of $y = f(x) = \dfrac{p(x)}{q(x)}$ is

    $y =$ quotient of the leading coefficients of $p(x)$ and $q(x)$, if deg $p(x) =$ deg $q(x)$ and

    $y = 0$, if deg $p(x) <$ deg $q(x)$.

The horizontal asymptote does not exist if deg $p(x) >$ deg $q(x)$.

EXAMPLE 3   Find the horizontal asymptote of $f(x)$, if there exists any.

    a. $f(x) = \dfrac{8x^2 - 3x + 7}{2x^2 + 7x}$ **b.** $f(x) = \dfrac{8x - 3}{x^2 - 9}$ **c.** $f(x) = \dfrac{10x^2 - 8x - 1}{5x + 1}$

Solutions:

    a.   The degree of the numerator is the same as the degree of the denominator.

            Therefore, the horizontal asymptote is given by

            $y =$ quotient of leading coefficients

            $= \dfrac{8}{2} = 4$

            Therefore, $y = 4$ is the horizontal asymptote of $f(x)$.

    b.   In this case, the degree of the numerator is less than the degree of the denominator, so the horizontal asymptote of $f(x)$ is $y = 0$.

    c.   There is no horizontal asymptote, because the degree of the numerator is greater than the degree of the denominator.

    Remark: *In part (c), although there is no horizontal asymptote, the graph of the function for large values for x resembles the graph of "y = quotient" in the division of p(x) by q(x). In this case, it is y = 2x − 2 which is an oblique (slant) line, called the **oblique asymptote** (Appendix C).*

By using the horizontal and vertical asymptotes, we can minimize the plotting of points. We explain the procedure in examples of the next objective.

D. GRAPHING A RATIONAL FUNCTION

EXAMPLE 4   Sketch the graph of $f(x) = \dfrac{x^2 + x - 2}{x^2 + 2x - 3}$.

Procedure

Graph $f(x) = \dfrac{p(x)}{q(x)}$.

Solution:

Step 1   Let $y = f(x)$. $\longrightarrow$ $y = \dfrac{x^2 + x - 2}{x^2 + 2x - 3}$

Step 2   Reduce the rational expression $\longrightarrow$ By factoring the numerator and denominator we get

$\dfrac{p(x)}{q(x)}$ by canceling (dividing)

out common factor(s), which have the form $cx + b$.

$y = \dfrac{(x+2)\,\cancel{(x-1)}}{(x+3)\,\cancel{(x-1)}}$.

Step 3   Restrict the domain of the $\longrightarrow$ $y = \dfrac{x+2}{x+3}$, $x \ne 1$

function by writing $x \ne -\dfrac{b}{c}$ for

each canceled factor $cx + b$.

Step 4   Find zeros of the function $\longrightarrow$ For $x \ne 1$, $f(x) = \dfrac{x+2}{x+3} = 0 \Rightarrow x = -2$.
(Set the numerator equal to 0)   The graph intersects the x-axis at $x = -2$.

Step 5   Find all vertical asymptotes. $\longrightarrow$ The vertical asymptotes are given by
(Set the denominator equal to 0) $x + 3 = 0$ or $x = -3$.

Step 6   Find the horizontal asymptotes. $\longrightarrow$ The horizontal asymptote is $y = \dfrac{1}{1} = 1$.

Step 7   Find a few points on both sides of $\longrightarrow$ We select a few x-values on the left and right
each vertical asymptote.   of $x = -3$ and complete the table

x	-4	-5	-2	0
y	2	1.5	0	$.67$

Step 8   Draw the asymptotes as dotted $\longrightarrow$ Draw the lines $y = 1$ and $x = -3$, and plot
lines, plot the points, and   the points in Step 7, and complete the graph.
complete the graph.   In Step 3, we observe that the function is
indeterminate at $x = 1$. Therefore, we draw
a hole at $x = 1$ (Figure 4.75).

Step 9   Go back to Step 3 and note the $\longrightarrow$ The graph is as follows:
restricted domain. Show a hole

in the graph at each $x \ne -\dfrac{b}{c}$.

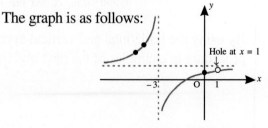

Figure 4.75

With Graphing Calculator

Check the answer by graphing $y_1 = \dfrac{x^2 + x - 2}{x^2 + 2x - 3}$ on a suitable range.

In general, the graph will not show a hole at $x = 1$. By a suitable choice of RANGE, it is possible to obtain a graph with a hole.

EXAMPLE 5   Sketch the graph of $f(x) = \dfrac{x^3 + 1}{x^2 - 1}$.

Solution:

Step 1   Let $y = f(x) = \dfrac{x^3 + 1}{x^2 - 1}$.

Step 2   By factoring the numerator and the denominator we reduce the rational expression to

$$* \quad y = \frac{(x+1)\left(x^2 - x + 1\right)}{(x+1)(x-1)}$$

$$= \frac{x^2 - x + 1}{x - 1}$$

> $*$ $x^3 + 1 = (x)^3 + (1)^3$
> $\qquad\qquad = (x + 1)(x^2 - x + 1),$
> because
> $(A)^3 + (B)^3$
> $\quad = (A + B)(A^2 - AB + B^2)$

Step 3   Since we cannot divide by zero, we say that $x + 1 \neq 0$ or $x \neq -1$. Next we draw the graph of

$$y = \frac{x^2 - x + 1}{x - 1} \ , \ x \neq -1.$$

Step 4   There is no zero of the function since $x^2 - x + 1 = 0$ has no real solutions.

Step 5   There is only one vertical asymptote, that is, $x - 1 = 0$ or $x = 1$.

Step 6   Since the degree of the numerator is greater than the degree of denominator, we conclude that there is no horizontal asymptote.

Step 7   By selecting a few x-values on both sides of the vertical asymptote $x = 1$, we complete a table :

x	-2	0	2	3	$.5$	1.5
y	-2.3	-1	3	3.5	-1.5	3.5

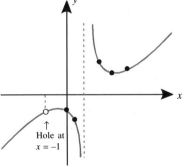

Step 8   By drawing the dotted line $x = 1$ and plotting the points in Step 7, we complete the graph.

Step 9   In Step 3, we have observed that $x \neq -1$. Therefore, we show a hole in the graph at $x = -1$ (Figure 4.76).

Figure 4.76

EXAMPLE 6   Graph $f(x) = \dfrac{x^2}{x^2 + 2x - 8}$.

Solution:

• Let $y = \dfrac{x^2}{x^2 + 2x - 8}$.

- We attempt to reduce the rational expression by factoring the numerator and the denominator.

$$y = \frac{x^2}{(x+4)(x-2)} \quad \text{It cannot be reduced.}$$

- The only zero of the function is $x = 0$.

- By setting the denominator to zero, we find all vertical asymptotes.
  $(x + 4)(x - 2) = 0$

  $x + 4 = 0 \quad \mid \quad x - 2 = 0$
  $x = -4 \quad \mid \quad x = 2$

  Thus, $x = -4$ and $x = 2$ are two vertical asymptotes of the graph.

- Since the degree of the numerator is the same as that of the denominator, the horizontal asymptote is $y = \frac{1}{1} = 1$.

- We select a few x-values on both sides of each vertical asymptote and complete the table:

x	−6	−5	−3	−2	0	1	3	4	8
y	2.25	3.57	−1.8	−.5	0	−.2	1.3	1	.9

- Draw the asymptotes, plot the points, and complete the graph (Figure 4.77).

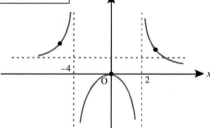

Remark: *Sometimes, the graph of a rational function may cross a horizontal asymptote. However, the graph never crosses a vertical asymptote.*

Figure 4.77

EXERCISE 4.6

In exercises (1-20), find the vertical and horizontal asymptotes of rational functions.

1. $f(x) = \dfrac{5}{3x+2}$ 2. $g(x) = \dfrac{-7}{x+8}$ 3. $g(x) = \dfrac{-3}{5x-3}$ 4. $f(x) = \dfrac{9}{3x+7}$

5. $h(x) = \dfrac{7x-3}{x+5}$ 6. $g(x) = \dfrac{x-5}{5x+9}$ 7. $f(x) = \dfrac{2x}{2x-3}$ 8. $f(x) = \dfrac{3x+4}{4x-5}$

9. $g(x) = \dfrac{3x^2-5}{x^2-x-2}$ 10. $f(x) = \dfrac{7x^2+3}{x^2+x-6}$ 11. $h(x) = \dfrac{5x^2+x-7}{x^2+9}$ 12. $g(x) = \dfrac{3x^2+5x-11}{x^2-9}$

13. $f(x) = \dfrac{7x-8}{x^2-3x-4}$ 14. $g(x) = \dfrac{5x+9}{x^2+x+1}$ 15. $h(x) = \dfrac{8x-3}{2x^2-7x+3}$ 16. $f(x) = \dfrac{3x+13}{3x^2+2x-5}$

17. $g(x) = \dfrac{9x^2-2x}{x-2}$ 18. $f(x) = \dfrac{5x^2-3x+4}{x+4}$ 19. $H(x) = \dfrac{x^2-5x+6}{x^2-4x+4}$ 20. $g(x) = \dfrac{2x^2+7x-4}{2x^2-5x+2}$

In exercises (21-36), sketch the graph of rational function.

21. $f(x) = \dfrac{x^2 - 9}{x - 3}$ **22.** $g(x) = \dfrac{x^2 - 16}{x - 4}$ **23.** $f(x) = \dfrac{x^2 - 9}{x + 3}$ **24.** $g(x) = \dfrac{x^2 - 16}{x + 4}$

25. $g(x) = \dfrac{x^3 - 1}{x^2 - 1}$ **26.** $f(x) = \dfrac{x^3 - 8}{x^2 - 4}$ **27.** $g(x) = \dfrac{x^2 - 1}{x^3 + 1}$ **28.** $f(x) = \dfrac{x^2 - 4}{x^3 + 8}$

29. $h(x) = \dfrac{x^2 - x - 12}{x^2 + 6x + 9}$ **30.** $g(x) = \dfrac{x^2 + 4x + 3}{x^2 + 2x - 3}$ **31.** $h(x) = \dfrac{x^2 - x - 12}{x^2 - 8x + 16}$ **32.** $f(x) = \dfrac{x^2 + 3x - 4}{x^2 - 3x + 2}$

33. $f(x) = \dfrac{2x - 6}{x^2 - 2x - 3}$ **34.** $g(x) = \dfrac{3x + 6}{x^2 + x - 2}$ **35.** $f(x) = \dfrac{3x - 6}{x^2 - x - 2}$ **36.** $f(x) = \dfrac{4x + 8}{x^2 + 7x + 10}$

In exercises (37-46), simplify the expression and then sketch the graph of the function.

37. $f(x) = \dfrac{2}{x - 2} - \dfrac{4}{(x - 2)^2}$ **38.** $g(x) = \dfrac{1}{x + 2} - \dfrac{2}{(x + 2)^2}$ **39.** $f(x) = \dfrac{1}{x - 3} + \dfrac{3}{(x - 3)^2}$

40. $f(x) = \dfrac{1}{x + 4} + \dfrac{1}{(x + 4)^2}$ **41.** $g(x) = \dfrac{1}{x - 1} - \dfrac{4}{(x - 1)^2}$ **42.** $f(x) = \dfrac{1}{x + 1} - \dfrac{2}{(x + 1)^2}$

43. $g(x) = \dfrac{3}{(x - 1)(x - 2)} - \dfrac{1}{(x - 1)(x + 3)}$ **44.** $f(x) = \dfrac{8}{x^2 + x - 6} - \dfrac{5}{x^2 - x - 2}$

45. $f(x) = \dfrac{\dfrac{2}{x - 1} - \dfrac{1}{x + 2}}{x + 5}$ **46.** $g(x) = \dfrac{1 - \dfrac{3}{x} - \dfrac{10}{x^2}}{1 - \dfrac{1}{x} - \dfrac{6}{x^2}}$

Writing Exercises

47. Explain what is meant by the asymptotic behavior of a graph.

48. What are the "dominant" terms in $\dfrac{p(x)}{q(x)}$ for the graph if $y = \dfrac{p(x)}{q(x)}$, $|x|$ is large?

4.7   Chapter Summary

1. The **equation of the line** that passes through the point (x_1, y_1) and has slope m is given by $y - y_1 = m(x, x_1)$.

2. The **slope intercept form** of the equation of a line is $y = mx + b$, where m is the slope and b is the y-intercept.

3. The **general form** of an equation of a line is
  $Ax + By + C = 0$, where A, B and C are constants where A, B are not both zeros.

4. The equation of a **horizontal line** is of the form $y = $ constant.

5. The equation of a **vertical line** is of the form $x = $ constant.

6. Two lines with slopes m_1 and m_2 are **parallel** if and only if $m_1 = m_2$.

7. Two lines with slopes m_1 and m_2 are **perpendicular** if and only if

$$m_2 = -\frac{1}{m_1} \quad \text{or} \quad m_1 m_2 = -1.$$

8. A function in its numerical form is a **linear function** if the ratio $\dfrac{y_2 - y_1}{x_2 - x_1}$ for any two pairs (x_1, y_1) and (x_2, y_2) is the same.

9. $f(x) = \dfrac{1}{x}$ and $g(x) = \dfrac{1}{x^2}$ are two **basic rational functions.**

10. $f(x) = x^n$ when $n = 1, 2, 3, 4,$ and 5 are called **basic power functions.**

11. $f(x) = \sqrt{x}$ is the basic radical function.

12. The graph of each power function contains $(0, 0)$.

13. For the graphs of $f(x) = x^{2m}$, the larger that m is, the flatter the graph between $x = -1$ and $x = 1$.

14. For the graphs of $f(x) = x^{2m+1}$, the flatter the graph between $x = -1$ and $x = 1$, the larger the value of m.

15. The process of writing $x^2 + bx$ as

$$x^2 + bx = \left(x + \frac{b}{2}\right)^2 - \frac{b^2}{4}$$

is called completing the square in x.

16. A **translation** of a graph means a movement (shift) in its location parallel to itself.

17. If the function $y = f(x)$ changes to $y = f(x) + c$, then the new graph is obtained by **vertically translating** the old graph by $|c|$ units. The shift is upward if $c > 0$ and downward for $c < 0$.

18. If the function $y = f(x)$ changes to $y = f(x - c)$, then the new graph is obtained by **horizontally translating** the old graph by $|c|$ units. The shift is to the right if $c > 0$ and to the left for $c < 0$.

19. If the function $y = f(x)$ changes to $y = -f(x)$, then the new graph is obtained by **reflecting** the old graph **across the x-axis.**

20. If the function $y = f(x)$ changes to $y = f(-x)$, then the new graph is obtained by **reflecting** the old graph **across the y-axis.**

21. If the function $y = f(x)$ changes to $y = |f(x)|$, then the new graph is obtained by redrawing the part of the old graph that is above the x-axis and reflecting across the x-axis the part that is below the x-axis. This is called **partial reflection.**

22.   If the function $y = f(x)$ changes to $y = c\,f(x)$, for $c > 0$, then the new graph is obtained by

    (i)   a **vertical stretching** of the old graph by a factor of c, if $c > 1$ and

    (ii) a **vertical shrinking** of the old graph by a factor of c, if $c < 1$.

23.   If by changing y to $-y$ the equation of a relation does not change, then the graph of $y = f(x)$ will be **symmetrical about the x-axis.**

24.   The graph of a relation will be **symmetrical about the y-axis** if replacing x with $-x$ the equation of the relation does not change.

25.   The graph of a relation is **symmetrical about the origin** if replacing x with $-x$ and y with $-y$ the equation of the relation does not change.

26.   A function is an **even** function if $f(-x) = f(x)$.

27.   A function is an **odd** function if $f(-x) = -f(x)$.

28.   The graph of a **quadratic function** $f(x) = ax^2 + bx + c$, $(a \neq 0)$ is always a **parabola.**

29.   The coordinates of the vertex of the parabola $y = ax^2 + bx + c$ are $\left(-\dfrac{b}{2a},\ \dfrac{4ac - b^2}{4a} \right)$.

30.   A quadratic function $f(x) = ax^2 + bx + c$ has

    (i)   a **maximum** value if $a < 0$ and   (ii) a **minimum** value if $a > 0$.

    The extreme value of f is equal to $\dfrac{4ac - b^2}{4a}$ and occurs when $x = -\dfrac{b}{2a}$.

31.   The graph of a polynomial function of degree two has only one **turning point**, whereas a polynomial function of degree greater than two may have more than one or no turning points.

32.   The graph of a polynomial function $f(x) = a_n x^n + a_{n-1} x^{n-1} + \ldots + a_1 x + a_0$ at infinity is approximately the same as the graph of $g(x) = a_n x^n$ given by the leading term of the polynomial.

33.   A line $x = a$ is a **vertical asymptote** of the graph of $f(x) = \dfrac{p(x)}{q(x)}$ if $\left| f(x) \right|$ increases without bound (blows up) as x gets closer to a.

34.   To find **vertical asymptotes** of a rational function, we first reduce the rational function, then find zeros of the denominator.

35.   A line $y = b$ is a **horizontal asymptote** of the graph of a function $y = f(x)$ if the values of $f(x)$ get closer to b as $\left| x \right|$ increases without bound.

36.   To find **horizontal asymptotes** of a rational function, we find the approximate value of the function when $\left| x \right|$ is large. If for large $\left| x \right|$, the function $f(x) = b$, then $y = b$ is the horizontal asymptote.

37. The horizontal asymptote of $y = f(x) = \dfrac{p(x)}{q(x)}$ is

$y = $ quotient of the leading coefficients of $p(x)$ and $q(x)$, if deg $p(x) = $ deg $q(x)$ and

$y = 0$, if deg $p(x) < $ deg $q(x)$.

The horizontal asymptote does not exist if deg $p(x) > $ deg $q(x)$.

4.8 CHAPTER REVIEW

In exercises (1-10), find the equation of the line whose graph satisfies the given conditions.

1. The line passes through points $(-1, 0)$ and $(3, -5)$.

2. The line passes through point $(2, 11)$ and $(3, 3)$.

3. The graph of the line passes through the point $(1, 5)$ and is parallel to the line $2x - 5y = 8$.

4. The line passes through the point $(-2, 3)$ and is parallel to the line $7x + y - 6 = 0$.

5. The line passes through the point $(2, -3)$ and is perpendicular to the line $x + 2y = 5$.

6. The line passes through the point $(-4, 0)$ and is perpendicular to the line $3x - 6y = 11$.

7. The lines passes through the point $(5, -3)$ and it is horizontal.

8. The line passes through the point $(-3, -7)$ and it is vertical.

9. The line has the x-intercept 3 and the y-intercept 2.

10. The line has the x-intercept -5 and the y-intercept 3.

11. Verify that the numerical form represents a linear function and determine a possible formula form of the function.

x	-2	-1	0	1	2	3
y	3	5/2	2	3/2	1	1/2

12. Verify that the numerical form represents a linear function and determine a possible formula form of the function.

x	-3	-2	-1	0	1	2	3
y	-2	$-3/2$	-1	$-1/2$	0	1/2	1

13. The sales of a company in 1998 and 2002 were 2.3 and 3.7 million dollars, respectively. Assuming that the growth was linear, find a relation between the sales (y) and the number of years (x) from 1998.

14. The sales of a company in 1997 and 2000 were 3.1 and 5.3 million dollars, respectively. Assuming that the growth was linear, find a relation between the sales (y) and the number of years (x) from 1997.

In exercises (15-22), complete the square.

15. $x^2 - 5x$ **16.** $t^2 + 11t$ **17.** $y^2 - 12y$ **18.** $x^2 + 18x$

19. $2t^2 - 7t$ **20.** $2y^2 + 5y$ **21.** $3z^2 - 5z$ **22.** $4z^2 + z$

In exercises (23-26), find the vertex of the parabola.

23. $y = x^2 - 6x + 5$ **24.** $y = x^2 + 12x + 19$ **25.** $y = 2x^2 - 5x + 1$ **26.** $y = 3x^2 + 7x + 6$

In exercises (27-34), draw the graph of the quadratic function. Find the coordinates of the vertex.

27. $f(x) = x^2 - 8x$ **28.** $f(x) = x^2 + 10x$ **29.** $g(x) = -x^2 + 6x + 1$ **30.** $f(x) = -x^2 + 5x - 3$

31. $f(x) = 3x^2 - 6x + 5$ **32.** $g(x) = x^2 + 12x - 1$ **33.** $g(x) = -2x^2 + 4x + 3$ **34.** $f(x) = 4x^2 + 2x - 3$

In exercises (35-50), start with one of the basic graphs and draw the graph of the function.

35. $f(x) = (x - 1)^2 + 3$ **36.** $g(x) = (x + 2)^2 - 1$ **37.** $g(x) = 2 - (x + 1)^2$ **38.** $f(x) = -3 - (x + 3)^2$

39. $f(x) = (x - 1)^3 + 1$ **40.** $g(x) = (x - 2)^3 - 2$ **41.** $g(x) = |x - 2| + 3$ **42.** $f(x) = |x - 3| + 2$

43. $f(x) = 2 - |x - 3|$ **44.** $g(x) = -3 - |x + 2|$ **45.** $g(x) = 2(x - 1)^2$ **46.** $f(x) = 4(x + 2)^2$

47. $h(x) = x^2 - 6x$ **48.** $f(x) = 2x^2 - 4x$ **49.** $f(x) = 2x^2 - 8x + 1$ **50.** $g(x) = 4x^2 - 8x + 5$

In exercises (51-52), use the graphs of $f(x) = \sqrt{x}$ and $g(x) = \dfrac{1}{x}$ and draw the graph of the function.

51. $f(x) = \sqrt{x - 2} + 1$ **52.** $g(x) = \dfrac{1}{x - 3} + 1$

In exercises (53-56), determine whether the function is even or odd.

53. $f(x) = -5x^3 - x$ **54.** $g(x) = -6x^4 + x^2 - 5$ **55.** $g(x) = x^2 |x| + x^4$ **56.** $h(x) = -x |x| + 5x^5$

In exercises (57-62), find all horizontal and vertical asymptotes of the rational function.

57. $f(x) = \dfrac{4x - 2}{x^2 - 5x + 6}$ **58.** $h(x) = \dfrac{5x + 17}{x^2 + 12x + 11}$ **59.** $g(x) = \dfrac{5x^2 - 3x + 7}{x^2 - 1}$

60. $g(x) = \dfrac{4x^2 - x + 3}{2x^2 + x - 3}$ **61.** $h(x) = \dfrac{x^4 - x^3 + x^2 + 2x - 2}{x^3 - x^2}$ **62.** $f(x) = \dfrac{x^4 + 2x^2 + 3}{x^3 + 2x^2}$

In exercises (63-79), sketch the graph of the function.

63. $f(x) = 5(x + 3)(x - 1)(x - 3)$ **64.** $g(x) = 2(x + 1)(x - 3)(x + 4)$ **65.** $g(x) = x^3 + 4x^2 + x - 6$

66. $f(x) = x^3 + x^2 - 10x + 8$ **67.** $h(x) = x^4 - 16x^2$ **68.** $f(x) = x^4 - 2x^2$

69. $f(x) = \dfrac{x - 2}{x + 3}$ **70.** $g(x) = \dfrac{x + 4}{x - 5}$ **71.** $g(x) = \dfrac{3}{x - 2}$ **72.** $f(x) = \dfrac{5}{x + 4}$

73. $h(x) = \dfrac{3x}{x^2 - 1}$ **74.** $g(x) = \dfrac{-4x}{x^2 - 4}$ **75.** $f(x) = \dfrac{x^2 - x - 6}{x^2 - 2x - 3}$ **76.** $f(x) = \dfrac{2x^2 - x - 1}{2x^2 - 3x - 2}$

77. $h(x) = \dfrac{6x^2 - 6x}{x^2 - 4}$ **78.** $f(x) = \dfrac{2x^2 + 6x}{x^2 - 1}$ **79.** $f(x) = \dfrac{x^2 - 8x + 7}{x + 2}$

80.   The total cost and revenue of x units of an item are given by

$$C(x) = 2x^2 + 5 \qquad \text{and} \qquad R(x) = -4x^2 + 36x.$$

Find a value of x that gives the maximum profit. What is the maximum profit?

81.   An object is thrown upward from a point 5 feet above the ground at a velocity of 100 ft./sec. at time 0. The height (h) above the ground at time t is given by

$$h(t) = -16t^2 + 100t + 5$$

a. How long will it take to reach the highest point?   **b.** How high will it go?

82. A farmer has a roll of 2500 ft. of fence. She wants to fence off a rectangular field with one side along the river. Assuming that she does not need fence along the river, express the area (A) in terms of the length (x) that is parallel to the river.

83. An oil can is to hold one liter (1000 cm^3) of oil. Its sides are made of cardboard which cost one cent/cm^2 and its top and bottom lids are made of steel that costs 3 cents/cm^2. Express the total cost (C) of manufacturing the can in terms of the radius (x) of the can.

84. A man 6 ft tall is standing near a lamp post that is 16 ft. high. Write the length (S) of his shadow in terms of his distance (x) from the lamp post.

85. Refer to Exercise 84 and write the distance (D) of the tip of his shadow from the base of the lamp post in terms of his distance (x) from the base of the lamp post.

86. An isosceles triangle is inscribed in a circle of radius 10 in. Express the area (A) of the triangle in terms of its base (x).

Writing Exercises

87. Describe the role of "dominant terms" in a polynomial and a rational function when $|x|$ is large.

88. Describe the procedure to set up a function in a word problem.

4.9 CHAPTER TEST

1. Find the equation of the line that passes through (1, 5) and (2, 1).

2. Find an equation of the line that passes through the point $(-3, 7)$ and is perpendicular to the line $3x + 5y = 7$.

3. Start from one of the basic graphs and draw the graph of the function.

    a. $f(x) = x^2 - 8x$ **b.** $g(x) = (x + 1)^3 + 2$ **c.** $h(x) = 3 - |x - 1|$

4. Sketch the graph of each function.

    a. $f(x) = -2x^2 + 4x$ **b.** $g(x) = x^4 - x^2$ **c.** $h(x) = \dfrac{9x^2 - 27x}{3x^2 - 12}$

5. The height $f(t)$, in feet, of an object thrown upward after t seconds is given by $f(t) = 256t - 16t^2$.
    a. Find the time when it reaches the highest point.   **b.** How high does it go?

6. A 5-gallon (0.668 ft^3) can is to be filled with a lubricating compound. The sides of the can are made of cardboard which costs 10 cents/ft^2 and the top and bottom lids are made of steel that costs 15 cents /ft^2. Express the total cost (C) of manufacturing a can in terms of its radius (x).

7. Graph $y = \dfrac{2x^2 - x - 1}{2x^2 - 3x - 2}$. Find the equations of the horizontal asymptote and the vertical asymptote. Give the (x, y) coordinates of any "holes".

Exponential and Logarithmic Functions

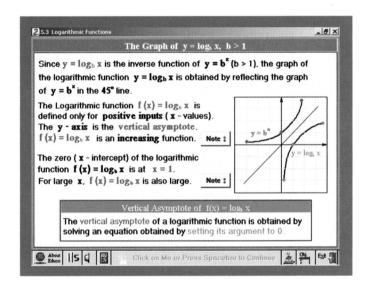

The Graph of $y = \log_b x, \ b > 1$

Since $y = \log_b x$ is the inverse function of $y = b^x$ ($b > 1$), the graph of the logarithmic function $y = \log_b x$ is obtained by reflecting the graph of $y = b^x$ in the $45°$ line.

The Logarithmic function $f(x) = \log_b x$ is defined only for **positive inputs** (x - values). The y - **axis** is the vertical asymptote. $f(x) = \log_b x$ is an **increasing** function.   **Note ‡**

The zero (x - intercept) of the logarithmic function $f(x) = \log_b x$ is at $x = 1$. For large x, $f(x) = \log_b x$ is also large.   **Note ‡**

$y = b^x$

$y = \log_b x$

Vertical Asymptote of $f(x) = \log_b x$

The vertical asymptote of a logarithmic function is obtained by solving an equation obtained by setting its argument to 0.

Click on Me or Press Spacebar to Continue

5

EXPONENTIAL AND LOGARITHMIC FUNCTIONS

Until now we have studied only algebraic functions, that is, functions that can be obtained from polynomial functions by any finite combination of the operations; addition, subtraction, multiplication, ratio, raising to an integral power, or taking roots. But these functions are not sufficient for the applications of mathematics in many disciplines and real world applications. In this chapter, after we study **inverse functions,** we will study two important non-algebraic functions (transcendental functions) called **exponential** and **logarithmic** functions. We will investigate their properties, solve their equations, and sketch their graphs. Finally, we will show some of their applications.

The discussion in this chapter is divided into six sections:

5.1   INVERSE FUNCTIONS

The notation $y = f(x)$ for a function says that "for every x in the domain a unique y is associated in the range". In this section we will investigate whether the reverse correspondence g of associating y (input) to x (output) defines a function or not. If it does, then the function g is called the inverse of f and is denoted by f^{-1}.

Objectives ▶ ▶

In this section you will learn about:

A . One to One Functions; and

B . Inverse Functions.

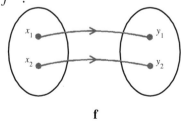

f

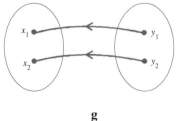

g

A. ONE TO ONE FUNCTIONS

Let the cost (C) of producing x items be

$$C(x) = 2x + 100$$

or $$y = C(x) = 2x + 100$$

$$y - 100 = 2x$$

$$\frac{y-100}{2} = x$$

In this case x is a **function** of cost (y), because for every y we get one and only one x. We label this function as $x = g(y) = \dfrac{y-100}{2}$.

Let us investigate the composite functions

$$
(C \circ g)(x) = C\big(g(x)\big) = C\left(\frac{x-100}{2}\right) = 2\left(\frac{x-100}{2}\right) + 100
$$

$$= x - 100 + 100 = x$$

$$
(g \circ C)(x) = g\big(C(x)\big) = g(2x + 100) = \frac{(2x+100) - 100}{2}
$$

$$= \frac{2x}{2} = x$$

> Function C
>
> Domain : x-values
> Range : y-values
>
> Function C^{-1}
>
> Domain : y-values
> Range : x-values
>
> By reversing the correspondence, we interchange the domain and range.

This shows that machine (function) g reverses what machine (function) C does, and machine C reverses what machine g does. Consequently, C and g are called **inverse functions**.

Unfortunately, this procedure of reversing the correspondence does not always produce a function. Consider the following example :

$$f(x) = x^2$$

$$y = f(x) = x^2 \qquad \text{\small y depends on x}$$

$$\pm\sqrt{y} = x \qquad \text{\small x depends upon y}$$

In this case, we get more than one x value for every y value. Here the procedure of reversing the correspondence does not produce a function. Therefore, before we start looking for the inverse of a given function, we must make sure whether the inverse function exists or not. For this, we introduce another family of functions called one-to-one functions.

> **One-to-One Function**
>
> A function f is said to be **one-to-one**, provided f has different outputs for different inputs.

For a one-to-one function $f(x)$,

$$f(x_1) \neq f(x_2) \quad \textbf{when} \quad x_1 \neq x_2$$

or equivalently if $\quad f(x_1) = f(x_2) \quad \textbf{then} \quad x_1 = x_2.$

> **One-to-One Function**
>
> A one-to-one function $f(x)$ satisfies the property that if $f\,|x_1| = |x_2|$, then $x_1 = x_2.$

This means that for each *y*-value we get one and only one *x*-value. We can translate this fact into a more convenient graphical form as follows:

Horizontal Line Test for Functions

A function *f*(*x*) is one-to-one if and only if each horizontal line intersects the graph of *y* = *f*(*x*) in at most one point.

Remark: *A one-one function must pass the vertical line test as well as the horizontal line test.*

EXAMPLE 1   Determine whether or not the graph represents a one-to-one function. (Figure 5.1).

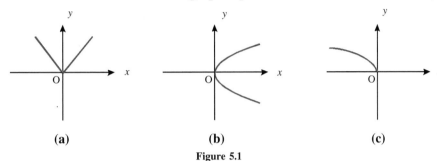

(a)   (b)   (c)

Figure 5.1

Solutions: **a.**   We apply the vertical line test to the graph in Figure 5.1(a). The graph passes the vertical line test, therefore, it is the graph of a function. The horizontal line test fails, because at least one horizontal line meets the graph in two points. Therefore, the graph in Figure 5.2(a) does not represent a one-to-one function.

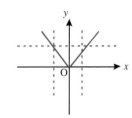

Figure 5.2 (a)

b.   The graph is **not that of a function** because it does not pass the vertical line test (See Figure 5.2 b). Therefore, the graph **does not** represent a one-to-one function.

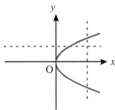

Figure 5.2 (b)

c.   The graph in Figure 5.2(c) passes the horizontal and vertical line tests. Therefore the graph represents a one-to-one function.

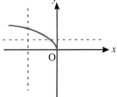

Remark: *Observe that the graph passes the horizontal line test in Example 1(b) even though the graph is not that of a function.*

Figure 5.2 (c)

EXAMPLE 2   Determine whether or not the function is one to one.

   a. $f(x) = \sqrt{x-2}$ **b.** $g(x) = 1 + |x-2|$

Solutions: **a.**   Suppose $f(x_1) = f(x_2)$.

$$\sqrt{x_1 - 2} = \sqrt{x_2 - 2} \quad \text{(square both sides)}$$

$$x_1 - 2 = x_2 - 2 \quad \longrightarrow \quad x_1 = x_2$$

Therefore, $f(x) = \sqrt{x-2}$ is a one-to-one function.

   b.   Suppose $g(x_1) = g(x_2)$.

$$1 + |x_1 - 2| = 1 + |x_2 - 2|$$

$$* \quad |x_1 - 2| = |x_2 - 2|$$

OR

$x_1 - 2 = x_2 - 2$	$x_1 - 2 = -x_2 + 2$
$x_1 = x_2$	$x_1 = -x_2 + 4$

* $|x_1 - 2| = |x_2 - 2|$

Divide by $|x_2 - 2|$, we get $\dfrac{|x_1 - 2|}{|x_2 - 2|} = 1$

$\dfrac{x_1 - 2}{x_2 - 2} = 1$	$\dfrac{x_1 - 2}{x_2 - 2} = -1$
cross multiply	cross multiply
$x_1 - 2 = 1(x_2 - 2)$	$x_1 - 2 = -(x_2 - 2)$
$x_1 - 2 = x_2 - 2$	$x_1 - 2 = -x_2 + 2$

For a one-to-one function, if $g(x_1) = g(x_2)$, then we expect $x_1 = x_2$ not $x_1 = -x_2 + 4$. Therefore, $g(x)$ is not a one-to-one function.

With Graphing Calculator

We sketch the graphs of $y1 = \sqrt{x-2}$ and $y2 = 1 + abs(x - 2)$
and use the horizontal line test on each.

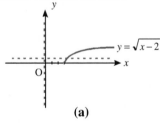

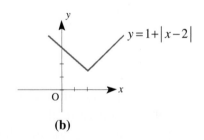

(a)   (b)

Figure 5.3

We see that in Figure 5.3(a), the test passes, but it fails in Figure 5.3 (b). Therefore, we have graphical verification that $f(x) = \sqrt{x-2}$ is one-to-one function, whereas $g(x) = 1 + |x-2|$ is not a one-to-one function.

EXAMPLE 3   Determine whether each function, in its numerical (table) form, is a one-to-one function.

a.

x	−2	−1	0	1	2	3
$f(x)$	5	7	5	2	1	0

b.

x	−2	−1	0	1	2	3
$g(x)$	3	1	−1	2	5	7

Solutions: **a.**   By definition, $f(x)$ is one-to-one only if it has different outputs for different inputs. But $f(x)$ has the same output 5 for two different inputs, namely -2 and 0. Thus, $f(x)$ is not a one-to-one function.

   b.   Since all the outputs are distinct, $g(x)$ is a one-to-one function.

B. Inverse Functions

We observe that for a one-to-one function reversing the correspondence of inputs and outputs and interchanging domain and range will always produce a function. The function so obtained is called the **inverse** function of the original function.

> **Inverse Function**
>
> If f is a one-to-one function with domain D and range R and $y = f(x)$, then the inverse function f^{-1} of f is given by $x = f^{-1}(y)$ with domain R and range D.

Remarks: 1.   *If f is a one-to-one function, then its inverse exists.*

2. $(f \circ f^{-1})(y) = y$ *and* $(f^{-1} \circ f)(x) = x$

3.   *If f^{-1} is the inverse of f, then f is inverse of f^{-1}, that is* $(f^{-1})^{-1} = f$.

To find the inverse of f.

Strategy

Step 1   Start with $f(x_1) = f(x_2)$ and solve. If $x_1 = x_2$, then the inverse exists. If the graph is known, apply the horizontal line test.

Step 2   Let $y = f(x) =$ expression.

Step 3   Solve the equation for x in terms of y.

Step 4   The inverse function f^{-1} is given by $x = f^{-1}(y)$.

We can write this in the standard form of a function where the inputs are denoted by x and the outputs by y by interchanging x and y.

Step 5   Interchange x and y.

EXAMPLE 4   Find the inverse of $f(x) = 5x + 3$.

Solutions:

Step 1   Obviously, the function $f(x)$ is one-to-one because the graph $y = 5x + 3$ is an oblique straight line; therefore it will pass the horizontal line test.

Step 2   Let $y = 5x + 3$.

Step 3   By solving the equation $y = 5x + 3$ for x, we get

$$y - 3 = 5x \quad \longrightarrow \quad \frac{y-3}{5} = x$$

Step 4   The inverse function f^{-1} is given by $x = f^{-1}(y) = \dfrac{y-3}{5}$

Step 5   We write this in the standard form as $y = f^{-1}(x) = \dfrac{x-3}{5}$

EXAMPLE 5   Find the inverse of the function $f(x) = \dfrac{3x+1}{2x+3}$ and state its domain and range.

Solution:

- With graphing calculator. Let $y1 = \dfrac{3x+1}{2x+3}$.

  Graph $y1$ (Figure 5.4) on the standard (or any suitable) range. Apply the horizontal line test. The graph passes the test; therefore, the function f is one-to-one. Alternatively, set $f(x_1) = f(x_2)$ and solve to see if $x_1 = x_2$.

  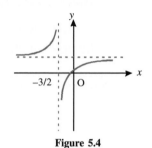

  Figure 5.4

- Let $y = \dfrac{3x+1}{2x+3}$.

- Solving the equation $y = \dfrac{3x+1}{2x+3}$ for x, we get

$$
\begin{aligned}
y(2x+3) &= 3x+1 \\
2xy + 3y &= 3x + 1 \\
2xy - 3x &= 1 - 3y \qquad \text{\small Get all } x\text{-terms on one side.} \\
x(2y-3) &= 1 - 3y \\
x &= \frac{1-3y}{2y-3}
\end{aligned}
$$

- $x = f^{-1}(y) = \dfrac{1-3y}{2y-3}$ *Step 5* $y = f^{-1}(x) = \dfrac{1-3x}{2x-3}$

* **The domain** of $f^{-1} = \left\{ x : x \neq \dfrac{3}{2} \right\}$

The range of $f^{-1} = $ domain of $f = \left\{ x : x \neq -\dfrac{3}{2} \right\}$

> * For the domain, we use our guiding principles to exclude zeros of the denominator.
>
> $2x - 3 = 0$ or $x = \dfrac{3}{2}$

EXAMPLE 6   Find the inverse of function $f(x) = \sqrt{x-2}$ on the domain $[2, \infty)$.

Solutions:

- We apply the horizontal line test to the graph of $y = \sqrt{x-2}$ (Figure 5.5). We can use the graphing calculator or a horizontal translation of the basic graph of $y = \sqrt{x}$ to find the graph of $y = \sqrt{x-2}$.

  The graph passes the test, so $f(x)$ is a one-to-one function and f^{-1} exists.

  Alternatively, set $f(x_1) = f(x_2)$ and solve to see that $x_1 = x_2$. Note $x \geq 2$.

  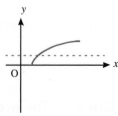

  Figure 5.5

$$\sqrt{x_1-2} = \sqrt{x_2-2} \;\Rightarrow\; x_1 - 2 = x_2 - 2 \;\Rightarrow\; x_1 = x_2$$

- Let $y = \sqrt{x-2}$. Note $y \geq 0$ and $x \geq 2$ (Given).

- To solve $y = \sqrt{x-2}$ for x, we square both sides :

$$y^2 = x - 2 \longrightarrow x = y^2 + 2.$$

- $x = f^{-1}(y) = y^2 + 2$

- $y = f^{-1}(x) = \mathbf{x^2 + 2}$

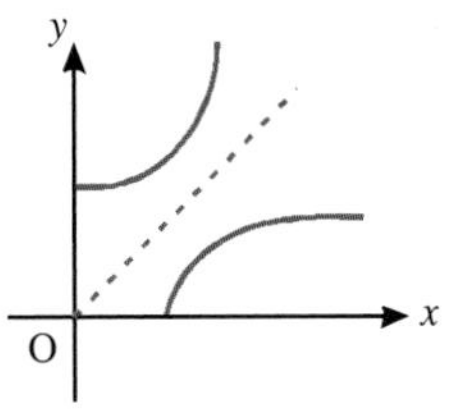

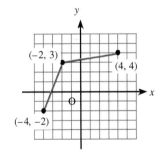

Figure 5.6

Remark: *With the graphing calculator, graph the three*

functions $y1 = \sqrt{x-2}$, $y2 = x^2 + 2$ *and* $y3 = x$ *on*

the range $x-min = -2$, $x-max = 10$, $y-min = -2$

and $y-max = 10$, $y2 = f^{-1}(x)$.

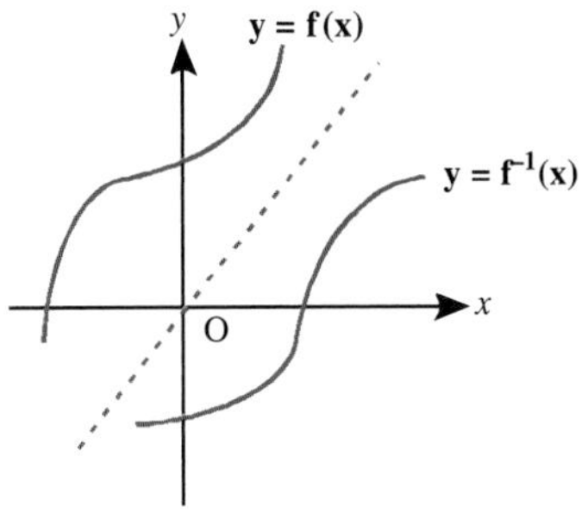

We observe that the graphs of f and f^{-1} are reflections of each other through the 45° line $y = x$ (Figure 5.6). This observation is useful in finding the inverse of a function in its graphical form.

Observation

The graph of f^{-1} is obtained by reflecting the graph of $y = f(x)$ through the line $y = x$ (Figure 5.7).

⬤**Note** The reflection of a point (x_1, y_1) through the line $y = x$ is (y_1, x_1).

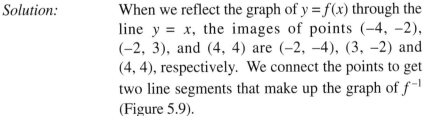

Figure 5.7

EXAMPLE 7   The graph of a function f consists of two line segments, shown in Figure 5.8. Draw the graph of f^{-1}.

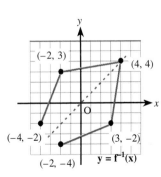

Figure 5.8

Solution: When we reflect the graph of $y = f(x)$ through the line $y = x$, the images of points $(-4, -2)$, $(-2, 3)$, and $(4, 4)$ are $(-2, -4)$, $(3, -2)$ and $(4, 4)$, respectively. We connect the points to get two line segments that make up the graph of f^{-1} (Figure 5.9).

Figure 5.9

EXAMPLE 8   Find the inverse of the function f whose numerical (table) form is given as follows :

x	-2	-1	0	1	2	3	4
$f(x)$	5	9	7	2	1	0	8

Solution: By changing the domain to range and the range to domain, we get the numerical (table) form of f^{-1}. Thus the inverse function f^{-1} is given as

x	5	9	7	2	1	0	8
$f^{-1}(x)$	-2	-1	0	1	2	3	4

or

x	0	1	2	5	7	8	9
$f^{-1}(x)$	3	2	1	-2	0	4	-1

EXERCISE 5.1

In exercises (1-20), determine whether the function is one to one.

1. $f(x) = 2 - 5x$ 2. $f(x) = 3 + 4x$ 3. $f(x) = x^2 + 1$ 4. $f(x) = -x^2 + 2$

5. $g(x) = x^4 + 1$ 6. $f(x) = -x^4 + 1$ 7. $g(x) = x^3 - 2$ 8. $g(x) = x^3 + 2$

9. $h(x) = \sqrt{x-2}$ 10. $g(x) = \sqrt{x+3}$ 11. $k(x) = |x-3|$ 12. $h(x) = |x+2|$

13. $f(x) = \dfrac{3}{x-2}$ 14. $g(x) = \dfrac{5}{x+1}$ 15. $f(x) = (x-1)^3 + 3$ 16. $f(x) = (x-2)^3 + 2$

17. $f(x) = \begin{cases} x^2, & -2 \le x \le 0 \\ x+1, & x > 0 \end{cases}$ 18. $f(x) = \begin{cases} x, & -1 \le x \le 0 \\ -x^2, & x > 0 \end{cases}$

19. $g(x) = \begin{cases} x^2, & -1 \le x < 1 \\ x, & x \ge 1 \end{cases}$ 20. $g(x) = \begin{cases} -x^2, & -1 \le x \le 1 \\ x+2, & x > 1 \end{cases}$

In exercises (21-24), verify that f and g are inverse functions by showing that $(f \circ g)(x) = x$ and $(g \circ f)(x) = x$.

21. $f(x) = \dfrac{2x-1}{x+5}$, $g(x) = \dfrac{5x+1}{2-x}$ 22. $f(x) = \dfrac{3x+7}{5x-9}$, $g(x) = \dfrac{9x+7}{5x-3}$

23. $f(x) = \sqrt{x-1}$, $g(x) = x^2 + 1$ 24. $f(x) = \sqrt{x+4}$, $g(x) = x^2 - 4$, $x \ge 0$

In exercises (25-42), find the inverse of the given function. State the domain and range of f^{-1}.

25. $f(x) = 7x - 11$ 26. $f(x) = 3x + 13$ 27. $f(x) = 5 - 8x$ 28. $f(x) = -2 - 7x$

29. $f(x) = 1 - x^3$ 30. $f(x) = x^3 - 8$ 31. $f(x) = x^3 + 2$ 32. $f(x) = 4 - x^3$

33. $f(x) = \sqrt{x-1}$ 34. $f(x) = \sqrt{x-4}$ 35. $f(x) = \sqrt[3]{x-1}$ 36. $f(x) = \sqrt[3]{x+8}$

37. $f(x) = \dfrac{2x-1}{x-3}$ 38. $f(x) = \dfrac{x+7}{-3x+5}$ 39. $f(x) = \dfrac{x}{x-2}$ 40. $f(x) = \dfrac{x+10}{2x}$

41. $f(x) = x^2 + 1, x \ge 0$ 42. $f(x) = -x^2 + 4, x \ge 0$

In exercises (43-46), sketch the graph of f^{-1} if f is the function defined by the graph.

43.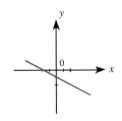

44.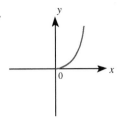

45.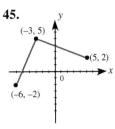

46.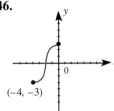

In exercises (47-50), find the inverse of the function f whose numerical (table) form is given.

47.

x	−1	0	1	2	3	4
$f(x)$	5	2	3	1	0	7

48.

x	−2	−1	0	1	2	3	4
$f(x)$	−1	4	2	3	11	0	5

49.

x	−1	0	1	2	4	9
$f(x)$	0.6	0.5	1	0.75	0.7	.68

50.

x	−2	0	2	4	5	6
$f(x)$	$\frac{1}{2}$	1	$-\frac{1}{2}$	0	−2	4

Writing Exercises

51. Describe the comparison between the correspondence of inputs and outputs of a function and the correspondences of its inverse function.

52. Explain the procedure for finding the inverse function of a given one-to-one function.

53. If a graph passes the horizontal line test, does it guarantee the existence of the inverse? Explain with examples.

5.2 EXPONENTIAL FUNCTIONS

If a quantity, such as the number of bacteria in a dish, begins with a small amount but quickly increases to a very large number, we say informally that the growth is **exponential.** Formally such a growth is represented by an exponential function like $f(x) = 2^x$ or 10^x or e^x. In the physical world, exponential growth is represented by e^x where e is called the **natural base** and $e \approx 2.71828182846$. This section deals with the properties and behavior of exponential functions.

Objectives ▶▶

In this section you will learn about:

A. The Exponential Function;

B. The Behavior of the Exponential Function; and

C. The Properties of the Exponential Function.

The number e was discovered by the Swiss mathematician Euler, one of the most profilic writer of mathematics.

A. THE EXPONENTIAL FUNCTION

If $b > 0$ and $^*\, b \neq 1$ then the exponential function with the base b is given by $f(x) = b^x$.

* When $b = 1$, the function is $f(x) = 1^x = 1$, which is not a one-to-one function.

To investigate the properties and behavior of the exponential function, we sketch the graphs of $f(x) = b^x$ when $b > 1$ and when $b < 1$. See Figure 5.10 and Figure 5.11.

EXAMPLE 1 Sketch the graph of $f(x) = 2^x$.

Solution: The first two guiding principles for the domain of a function do not cover exponential functions. For $b > 0$ and $b \neq 1$, there is no difficulty in computing b^x for any real number x. Hence, the domain of $f(x) = b^x$ is the set of all real numbers.

To find a few points on the graph, we select negative and positive values for x and find the corresponding values of the function.

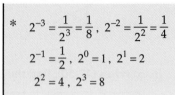

* $2^{-3} = \dfrac{1}{2^3} = \dfrac{1}{8}$, $2^{-2} = \dfrac{1}{2^2} = \dfrac{1}{4}$

$2^{-1} = \dfrac{1}{2}$, $2^0 = 1$, $2^1 = 2$

$2^2 = 4$, $2^3 = 8$

x	−3	−2	−1	0	1	2	3
$y = {}^* f(x)$	$\dfrac{1}{8}$	$\dfrac{1}{4}$	$\dfrac{1}{2}$	1	2	4	8

We plot the points. By connecting the points with a curve we get the graph as shown in Figure 5.10.

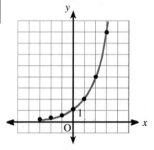

Figure 5.10

With Graphing Calculator

Let $y1 = 2 \wedge x = 2^x$. Graph $y1$ on the standard range.

EXAMPLE 2 Sketch the graph of $f(x) = \left(\dfrac{1}{2}\right)^x$.

Solutions: Clearly, the domain of the function consists of all real numbers. To graph $f(x) = \left(\dfrac{1}{2}\right)^x$, we find y-values for some x-values.

x	−3	−2	−1	0	1	2	3
$^*y$	8	4	2	1	$\dfrac{1}{2}$	$\dfrac{1}{4}$	$\dfrac{1}{8}$

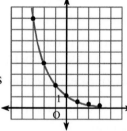

Figure 5.11

We plot the points. By connecting the points with a curve we get the graph as shown in Figure 5.11.

* $\left(\dfrac{1}{2}\right)^{-3} = 2^3 = 8$

$\left(\dfrac{1}{2}\right)^{-2} = 2^2 = 4, \left(\dfrac{1}{2}\right)^{-1} = 2^1 = 2,$

$\left(\dfrac{1}{2}\right)^2 = \dfrac{1}{2^2} = \dfrac{1}{4}, \left(\dfrac{1}{2}\right)^0 = 1$

$\left(\dfrac{1}{2}\right)^3 = \dfrac{1}{2^3} = \dfrac{1}{8}$

With Graphing Calculator

Let $y1 = (1/2) \wedge x$. Graph $y1$ on the standard (or any suitable) range.

Remark: *The real number 'e' mentioned in the introduction of this section is an irrational number with an approximate value of 2.71828182845. However, the algorithm built into the calculator uses a much better approximation of 'e'. Therefore, when working with the calculations involving 'e', we will use the built in constant 'e' in the calculator and not the number 2.71828182845.*

EXAMPLE 3   Sketch the graph of $f(x) = e^x$.

Solutions: As we did in Examples 1 and 2, we choose a few values for x and find the corresponding function values by using a calculator.

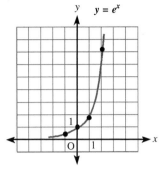

$y = e^x$

Figure 5.12

x	-2	-1	0	1	2	2.5
$y = e^x$	.14	.37	1	2.72	7.40	12.18

To sketch the graph of $y = e^x$, we plot these points and connect the points with a smooth curve. The graph is shown in Figure 5.12.

With Graphing Calculator

Let $y1 = e^x$. Graph $y1$ on the standard range.

B. THE BEHAVIOR OF THE EXPONENTIAL FUNCTION

Recall, to examine the behavior of an algebraic function, we find

(i)   the zeros of the function (x-intercepts),

(ii)   the y-intercept,

(iii)   the intervals on which it is increasing or decreasing, and

(iv)   the approximate shape of the graph when $\left| x \right|$ is very large.

Let us use the same procedure to analyze the behavior of the exponential function $y = f(x) = b^x$. We consider two cases :

Case (i): When b > 1

In this case the graph of $y = b^x$ will look like the graph of $y = 2^x$ (Figure 5.10) of Example 1. Thus, we conclude that for $b > 1$.

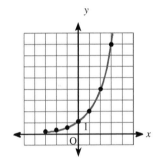

Figure 5.10 (repeated)

(i)   The function $y = b^x$ has no zeros (or x - intercepts).*

(ii)   The y-intercept of $y = b^x$ is 1. ($b^0 = 1$)

(iii)   The function $y = b^x$ is an increasing function (Figure 5.13(a)) for all real numbers.**

(iv)   When $x > 0$ and large, then $y = b^x$ is large, because b^x gets bigger and bigger as x gets bigger as seen below for 2^x.

x	10	15	20
$y = 2^x$	1024	32768	1048576

*   If $b > 0$ then $b^x > 0$ for all real numbers x.

** If $b > 1$ then $b^x > 1$ for all $x > 0$. Now $x_2 > x_1$

$\rightarrow$ $x_2 - x_1 > 0$

$\rightarrow$ $b^{x_2 - x_1} > 1$

$\rightarrow$ $\dfrac{b^{x_2}}{b^{x_1}} > 1$

$\rightarrow$ $b^{x_2} > b^{x_1}$

For $x < 0$ and large $\left| x \right|$, $y = b^{-x} = \dfrac{1}{b^x} \approx 0$, because b^x **is very large.**

Thus, we conclude that the graph of $y = b^x$ approaches the graph of $y = 0$ when $x < 0$ and $|x|$ is large. In other words, $y = 0$ is **asymptote** to the graph of $y = b^x$.

Case (ii) : when b < 1

In this case, the graph of $y = b^x$ will look like the graph of

$y = \left(\dfrac{1}{2}\right)^x$ (Figure 5.11) of Example 2. By looking at the

graph in Example 2, we conclude that for $b < 1$:

(i)   The function $y = b^x$ has no zeros.

(ii)   The y-intercept of $y = b^x$ is 1.

(iii) $y = b^x$ is a decreasing function (Figure 5.13(b)) for all real numbers.*

(iv)   When $x > 0$ and large, then $y = b^x$ will behave like $y = \left(\dfrac{1}{2}\right)^x = \dfrac{1}{2^x}$.

Since 2^x gets bigger as x gets bigger, so $\dfrac{1}{2^x}$ gets smaller as x gets

bigger.

Consequently, $y = b^x \approx 0$ as x gets bigger. This means that $y = 0$ is an **asymptote**. Similarly, we can show that y gets bigger as $|x|$ gets bigger for $x < 0$.**

We summarize the behavior of the exponential function $y = f(x) = b^x$ in the following graphs (Figure 5.13).

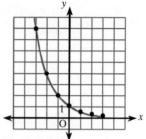

Figure 5.11   (repeated)

* If $0 < b < 1$ then $b^x < 1$ whenever $x > 0$.

$$x_2 > x_1 \quad \rightarrow \quad x_2 - x_1 > 0$$

$$\rightarrow \quad b^{x_2 - x_1} < 1$$

$$\rightarrow \quad \dfrac{b^{x_2}}{b^{x_1}} < 1$$

$$\rightarrow \quad b^{x_2} < b^{x_1}$$

** *If $x < 0$ and $|x|$ is large,*

then $b^x = b^{-|x|} = \dfrac{1}{b^{|x|}}$

$$b^{|x|} < 1 = \dfrac{1}{b^{|x|}} > 1$$

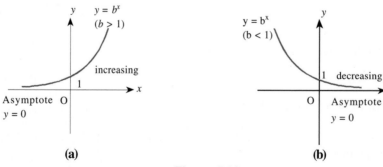

Figure 5.13

C. THE PROPERTIES OF THE EXPONENTIAL FUNCTION

The exponential function $f(x) = b^x$ ($b > 0$, and $b \ne 1$) has the following properties.

1.   The domain of $f(x) = b^x$ consists of all real numbers.

2.   The range of $f(x) = b^x$ consists of all **positive** real numbers.

3.   The graph of $y = b^x$ is an **increasing** graph if $b > 1$.

4. The graph of $y = b^x$ is a **decreasing** graph if $b < 1$.

5. The y-intercept of the graph of $y = b^x$ is 1.

6. The x-axis is the **asymptote** of $y = b^x$.

7. The exponential function $y = b^x$ has no zeros.

8. The exponential function $y = b^x$ is one-to-one function (why?).

   Hence $b^{x_1} = b^{x_2} \longrightarrow x_1 = x_2$

Remarks: 1. *Many exponential **growth** situations fit into the model*

$$A(t) = A_o e^{kt}, \text{ where } k > 0.$$

A_o = *initial amount*
k = *growth rate* > 0
t = *time*
$A(t)$ = *the amount after t units of time.*

*Similarly, many exponential **decay** situations fit into the model*

$$A(t) = A_o e^{-kt}, \text{ where } k > 0$$

We will use these models to solve growth or decay type application problems at the end of this chapter.

2. *You should know the ***basic exponential graphs** of*

   $f(x) = 2^x$, $f(x) = \left(\dfrac{1}{2}\right)^x$, *and* $f(x) = e^x$ *and their properties.*

   Sometimes it is faster to sketch the graph of a given exponential function by using translations and reflections on some basic graph.

3. *You should remember the important property that the equation* $b^x = 0$ *has no solution.*

* Basic exponential graphs

$y = 2^x :$

$y = \left(\dfrac{1}{2}\right)^x :$

$y = e^x :$

EXAMPLE 4 Start with one of the basic graphs to sketch the graph of the following functions.

   a. $f(x) = 2^{x-2}$ **b.** $f(x) = e^x + 2$ **c.** $f(x) = e^{-x} + 1$

Solutions: We will use translation and reflections on basic graphs to graph the given functions.

   a. We use the translation of 2 units to the right on the basic graph of $f(x) = 2^x$.

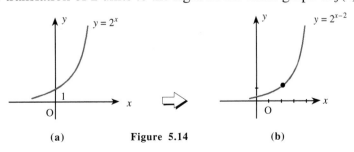

(a)   **Figure 5.14**   (b)

Thus, the graph of $f(x) = 2^{x-2}$ is shown in Figure 5.14(b)

b. Using the vertical translation of 2 units up on the basic graph of $f(x) = e^x$ gives the graph in Figure 5.15 (b).

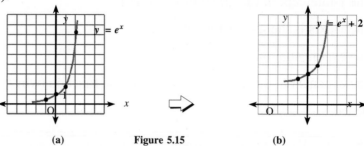

(a)   Figure 5.15   (b)

c. Using the reflection through the y-axis and then the vertical translation up one unit on the basic graph of $f(x) = e^x$ gives the graph of $f(x) = e^{-x} + 1$, as shown in Figure 5.16 (c).

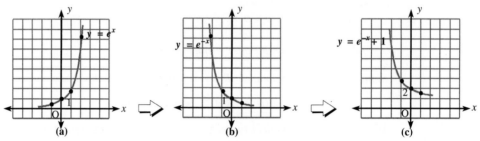

(a)   (b)   (c)

Figure 5.16

EXAMPLE 5 Find all the zeros of the function $f(x) = x^2 e^x - 4 e^x$.

Solution: The zeros of the function are given by the roots of the equation $x^2 e^x - 4 e^x = 0$.

Since e^x is a common factor, we get : $e^x \left(x^2 - 4 \right) = 0$.

We can factor $x^2 - 4$ as $(x - 2)(x + 2)$. This changes the above equation to

$$e^x (x - 2)(x + 2) = 0$$

Since the product of factors is zero, so

$e^x = 0$	**or**	$x - 2 = 0$	**or**	$x + 2 = 0$
No solution		$x = 2$	**or**	$x = -2$
(why?)				

Thus, $x = \mathbf{2, -2}$ are the only zeros of the function.

EXAMPLE 6 If $f(x) = e^x$, then simplify the expression $\dfrac{f(x+h) - f(x)}{h}$.

Solution: $f(x + h) = e^{x+h}$ and $f(x) = e^x$

Therefore, $\dfrac{f(x+h) - f(x)}{h} = \dfrac{e^{x+h} - e^x}{h}$

$$= \dfrac{e^x \cdot e^h - e^x}{h} = \dfrac{e^x \left(e^h - 1 \right)}{h}$$

EXAMPLE 7   Examine the behavior of the exponential function

$$f(x) = \left(1 + \frac{1}{x}\right)^x \text{ when } x \text{ is large.}$$

Solution: We compute the function values when x is large. The following table shows such values.

x	100	1000	10,000	100,000	1,000,000
$f(x)$	2.7	2.717	2.718145	2.71827	2.71828047

We observe that the function values get closer and closer to the number e as x gets larger.

Therefore, we conclude that the behavior of the function $\left(1 + \frac{1}{x}\right)^x$ resembles the behavior of the line $y = e$ when x is large.

EXERCISE 5.2

In exercises (1-28), sketch the graph of the function.

1. $f(x) = 3^x$ **2.** $f(x) = 3^{-x}$ **3.** $f(x) = 4^x$ **4.** $g(x) = 4^{-x}$ **5.** $f(x) = 6^x$

6. $g(x) = 6^{-x}$ **7.** $f(x) = \left(\frac{2}{3}\right)^x$ **8.** $g(x) = \left(\frac{3}{5}\right)^x$ **9.** $g(x) = \left(\frac{3}{4}\right)^x$ **10.** $f(x) = \left(\frac{1}{8}\right)^x$

11. $f(x) = (2.3)^x$ **12.** $g(x) = (3.5)^x$ **13.** $g(x) = e^{-x}$ **14.** $f(x) = e^{-2x}$ **15.** $f(x) = e^{2x}$

16. $g(x) = e^{3x}$ **17.** $g(x) = -e^x$ **18.** $f(x) = -e^{2x}$ **19.** $f(x) = e^{x+1}$ **20.** $f(x) = e^{x+3}$

21. $g(x) = 2^{x+3}$ **22.** $g(x) = 3^{x+1}$ **23.** $h(x) = e^{x-1} - 1$ **24.** $g(x) = e^{x+1} + 1$ **25.** $f(x) = e^x + e$

26. $f(x) = e^x - e$ **27.** $g(x) = 2^{|x|}$ **28.** $g(x) = 3^{|x|}$

In exercises (29-34), simplify the expression for $\dfrac{f(x+h) - f(x)}{h}$ **.**

29. $f(x) = e^{-x}$ **30.** $f(x) = -e^{-2x}$ **31.** $f(x) = e^{2x}$ **32.** $f(x) = e^{3x}$ **33.** $f(x) = e^{x+2}$ **34.** $f(x) = e^{x-4}$

In exercises (35-44), find all the zeros of the function.

35. $f(x) = x^2 e^x - 9e^x$ **36.** $g(x) = x^2 e^x - 16e^x$ **37.** $g(x) = x^2 e^{-x} - 5xe^{-x} + 6e^{-x}$

38. $f(x) = x^2 e^{-x} + 5xe^{-2x} + 4e^{-2x}$ **39.** $h(x) = \dfrac{x^2 e^x - e^x}{e^{-x}}$ **40.** $g(x) = \dfrac{x^3 e^{2x} + 4xe^{2x}}{e^{-x}}$

41. $f(x) = 3x^2 e^{-x} - x^3 e^{-x}$ **42.** $g(x) = 3x^3 e^{-3x} + 4x^2 e^{-3x}$ **43.** $g(x) = \dfrac{e^x}{\left(1 - e^x\right)^2}$ **44.** $f(x) = \dfrac{x e^x + 2e^x}{\left(1 + e^{2x}\right)^3}$

In exercises (45-46), examine the behavior of the function near $x = 0$.

45. $f(x) = (1 + x)^{\frac{1}{x}}$ **46.** $g(x) = (1 + x)^{\frac{2}{x}}$

47. The **hyperbolic sine** and **cosine** functions are defined as

$$\sin h(x) = \frac{e^x - e^{-x}}{2} \quad \text{and} \quad \cos h(x) = \frac{e^x + e^{-x}}{2}. \quad \text{Show that } \left(\cos h(x)\right)^2 - \left(\sin h(x)\right)^2 = 1.$$

48. Show that the functions $\sin h(x)$ and $\cos h(x)$ defined in #47 statisfy the equation $(\cos h(x))^2 + (\sin h(x))^2 = \cos h(2x)$

49. Show that $\sin h(x) = \dfrac{e^x - e^{-x}}{2}$ is an odd function. **50.** Show that $\cos h(x) = \dfrac{e^x + e^{-x}}{2}$ is an even function.

51. The number (N) of bacteria after time t hours is given by $N(t) = 50{,}000\ e^{5t}$. Find the number of bacteria present when

(a) $t = 0$ (b) $t = 1$ hour (c) $t = 4$ hours

In exercises (52-53), describe the behavior of the function when $|x|$ is large.

52. $f(x) = \left(1 + \dfrac{2}{x}\right)^x$ **53.** $f(x) = 5000\left(1 + e^{-x}\right)$

54. A radioactive substance decays according to the formula $A(t) = 50\left(\dfrac{5}{2}\right)^{-t}$, where $A(t)$ is the amount of substance present after t years. Find the amount present after 4 years.

55. According to the Newton's law of cooling, the temperature (T) after time t of an object whose initial temperature was T_2 and was placed in the surroundings of temperature T_1 is given by :

$$T(t) = T_1 + (T_2 - T_1)\,e^{kt}.$$

Suppose a container with liquid at temperature 110° is placed in a room at 72°, find the temperature of the liquid after time $t = 5$ if $k = -.08$.

56. The area under the curve $y = e^x$ from $x = 0$ to $x = 4$ can be approximated by the sum of the areas of the shaded rectangles. Estimate the area under the curve.

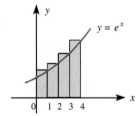

57. Find   **a.** the vertical distance PQ and

           b. the coordinates of the midpoint (M) of the segment PQ.

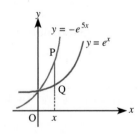

Writing Exercises

58. Describe the important features of exponential growth.

59. Describe the important features of exponential decay.

5.3 LOGARITHMIC FUNCTIONS

In Section 5.1 we observed that every one-to-one function has an inverse function. Since the exponential function $f(x) = b^x$ is one-to-one for $b > 0$ and $b \neq 1$, its inverse exists and is called **logarithmic** function. In this section we discuss the basic properties of the logarithmic function.

Objectives ▶▶

In this section you will learn about:

A. Logarithms;

B. Special Logarithmic Functions; and

C. Graphing Logarithmic Functions.

A. LOGARITHMS

Before we use the strategy for finding the inverse of a function $f(x) = b^x$ (Section 5.1), we learn how to solve an exponential equation in which the exponent contains an unknown. We start with a few concrete examples.

In the equation $10^2 = 100$, 2 is the exponent of 10 that gives 100. Similarly, in the equation $10^3 = 1000$, 3 is the exponent of 10 that gives 1000. In general, in the equation $b^x = y$, x is the exponent of b that gives y.

There is a shorthand for the long statement of the type

"the exponent of b that gives y"

Notation

* The exponent of b that gives y is called $\log_b y$, where

** $\log_b y$ is read as **logarithm with base b of y.**

The exponential function $y = b^x$ is one-to-one function.

> *   Logarithm is the exponent.
>
> **   log is short for 'logarithm'

Hence $b^{x_1} = b^{x_2} \longrightarrow x_1 = x_2$

$y = b^x$ is one-to-one, so the inverse function exists.

$y = f(x) = b^x$ if and only if $x = f^{-1}(y) = \log_b y$

i.e. $y = b^x$ if $x = \log_b y$

In the notation $\log_b y$, b is called the **base** and y is called the **argument** of the logarithm.

The statements $y = b^x$ and $x = \log_b y$ are equivalent. $y = b^x$ is called the **exponential form** and $x = \log_b y$ is its **logarithm form**.

EXAMPLE 1   Write each exponential form in logarithmic form (i.e., solve each for the exponent).

a. $125 = 5^3$ **b.** $2^{-5} = \dfrac{1}{32}$ **c.** $8^{2\backslash 3} = 4$ **d.** $10^{-3} = .001$ **e.** $x^r = s$

Solutions: **a.**   **3** is the exponent of 5 that gives 125 $\Rightarrow$ **3 = log$_5$125**.

b. $-\textbf{5}$ is the exponent of 2 that gives $\dfrac{1}{32}$ $\Rightarrow$ $-5 = \log_2 \dfrac{1}{32}$.

c. $\frac{2}{3}$ is the exponent of 8 that gives 4 $\longrightarrow$ $\frac{2}{3} = \log_8 4$.

d. -3 is the exponent of 10 that gives .001 $\longrightarrow$ $-3 = \log_{10}(.001)$.

e. r is the exponent of x that gives s $\longrightarrow$ $r = \log_x s$.

EXAMPLE 2   Write each logarithmic form in exponential form.

a. $\log_2 64 = 6$ b. $\log_3 \frac{1}{27} = -3$ c. $\log_{10}(0.1) = -1$

d. $\log_4 8 = \frac{3}{2}$ e. $\log_a a = 1$

Solutions: a.   Since logarithms are exponents (powers), so

$$\log_2 64 = 6 \longrightarrow 2^6 = 64$$

b. $\log_3 \frac{1}{27} = -3 \longrightarrow 3^{-3} = \frac{1}{27}$

c. $\log_{10} 0.1 = -1 \longrightarrow 10^{-1} = 0.1$

d. $\log_4 8 = \frac{3}{2} \longrightarrow 4^{3/2} = 8$

e. $\log_a a = 1 \longrightarrow a^1 = a$

EXAMPLE 3   Evaluate each log, if it exists.

a. $\log_2 8$ b. $\log_{10}.01$ c. $\log_5 1$ d. $\log_2(-4)$

Solutions: There are two ways to evaluate a log.

Method 1   (Inspection Method)

We write the complete statement for the log - notation and answer the question by inspection.

Method 2

We set the given log equal to x, change the log - form to the exponential form, express both sides with the **same** base, and then set the exponents equal and solve.

We demonstrate both methods for each part.

Method 1	*Method 2*
a. $\log_2 8$ = the exponent of 2 that gives 8 = 3 $2^3 = 8$	Let $\log_2 8 = x$. Writing this in exponential form, we get $2^x = 8$ $2^x = 8$ $2^x = 2^3 \longrightarrow x = 3$. Since exponential functions are one-to-one, therefore $\log_2 8 = \mathbf{3}$.

b. $\log_{10}0.01$ = the exponent of
10 that gives 0.01
= **-2** $10^{-2} = .01$

Let $\log_{10}0.01 = x$
$$10^x = 0.01 \quad \text{Exponential Form}$$
$$10^x = \frac{1}{100} = \frac{1}{10^2} = 10^{-2}$$
$$\Rightarrow \quad x = -2$$
Thus, $\log_{10}0.01 = -\mathbf{2}$.

c. $\log_5 1$ = the exponent of 5
that gives 1.
= 0 $5^0 = 1$

Let $\log_5 1 = x$.
$$5^x = 1 \quad \text{Exponential Form}$$
$$5^x = 5^0 \Rightarrow x = 0$$
Thus, $\log_5 1 = \mathbf{0}$.

Remark: *Verify that $\log_b 1 = 0$, for any base b.*

d. $\log_2(-4)$ = the exponent of
2 that gives -4

Since there is no such exponent,
$\log_2(-4)$ does not exist.

Let $\log_2(-4) = x$.
$$2^x = -4 \quad \text{Exponential Form}$$
Since -4 cannot be obtained as a power
of 2, there is no solution to the equation.
Thus, $\log_2(-4)$ does not exist.

Remark: *log b, where b is a negative argument, does not exist in real numbers. This fact will become more obvious when we define logarithmic functions and draw their graphs.*

B. Special Logarithmic Functions

1.   **The Common Logarithmic Function.**   The logarithm with base 10 is called the common logarithm and is written as:
$$f(x) = \log_{10}x \quad \text{or} \quad \text{simply } \log x$$

2.   **The Natural Logarithmic Function.** The logarithm with base e is called natural logarithm and is written as:
$$f(x) = \log_e x \quad \text{or} \quad \text{simply } \ln x$$

EXAMPLE 4   Find the inverse function of $f(x) = e^{x+1}$.

Solutions: We use the steps given in Section 5.1

Step 1 $f(x) = e^{x+1}$ is one-to-one because it is an exponential function.

Step 2   Let $y = e^{x+1}$.

Step 3   Solving for x, gives
$$e^{x+1} = y$$
$$x + 1 = \ln y$$
$$x = \ln y - 1$$

Step 4 $x = f^{-1}(y) = \ln y - 1$

Step 5   Interchanging x and y gives $y = \ln x - 1$
Thus, the inverse function is given by $f^{-1}(x) = \ln x - 1$.

EXAMPLE 5   Find the inverse function of $g(x) = 10^{x-2} + 1$.

Solution:

- $g(x) = 10^{x-2} + 1$ is one-to-one because it is an exponential function.

- Let $y = 10^{x-2} + 1$.

- Solving for x, gives

$$
\begin{aligned}
10^{x-2} + 1 &= y \\
10^{x-2} &= y - 1 \\
x - 2 &= \log_{10}(y-1) = \log(y-1) \\
x &= \log(y-1) + 2
\end{aligned}
$$

- $x = g^{-1}(y) = \quad \log(y-1) + 2$

- Interchanging x and y gives $y = \log(x-1) + 2$

Thus, the inverse function is given by $g^{-1}(x) = \log(x-1) + 2$.

EXAMPLE 6   Find the inverse function of $f(x) = e^{3x-5} - 2$

Solution: We use the steps given in Section 5.1

- $f(x) = e^{3x-5} - 2$ is an exponential function, so it is one-to-one.

- Let $y = e^{3x-5} - 2$

- Solving for x, gives

$$
\begin{aligned}
e^{3x-5} &= y + 2 \\
\mathbf{3x - 5} &= \log_e(y+2) = \mathbf{\ln{(y+2)}} \\
3x &= \ln(y+2) + 5 \\
x &= \frac{\ln(y+2) + 5}{3}
\end{aligned}
$$

- $x = f^{-1}(y) = \dfrac{\ln(y+2) + 5}{3}$

- Interchanging x, y, gives $y = \dfrac{\ln(x+2) + 5}{3}$

Thus, the inverse function is given by $f^{-1}(x) = \dfrac{\mathbf{\ln(x+2) + 5}}{\mathbf{3}}$

C. GRAPHING LOGARITHMIC FUNCTIONS

Since $y = \log_b x$ is the inverse function of $y = b^x \ (b > 1)$, so the graph of the logarithmic function $y = \log_b x$ is obtained by reflecting the graph of $y = b^x$ over the line which makes a 45° angle with the x-axis, namely $y = x$ (Figure 5.18(a)).

The Graph of $y = \log_b x, b > 1$

1. The logarithmic function $f(x) = \log_b x$ is defined only for **positive inputs** (x-values).

2. The y-axis is the **vertical asymptote.**

3. $f(x) = \log_b x$ is an **increasing** function.

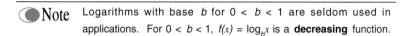

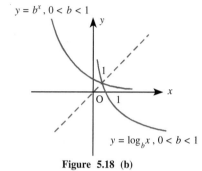

Figure 5.18 (a)

> ● **Note** Logarithms with base b for $0 < b < 1$ are seldom used in applications. For $0 < b < 1$, $f(x) = \log_b x$ is a **decreasing** function.

4. The zero (x-intercept) of the logarithmic function $f(x) = \log_b x$ is at $x = 1$.

5. For large x, $f(x) = \log_b x$ is also large.

> ● **Note** For $0 < b < 1$, $\log_b x$ becomes negative and $\left|\log_b x\right|$ is large for large x. Think, why ? Examine the graph in Figure 5.18(b).

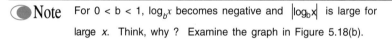

Figure 5.18 (b)

> ### Vertical Asymptote of $f(x) = \log_b[g(x)]$
>
> The vertical asymptote of a logarithmic function is obtained by solving $g(x) = 0$.

EXAMPLE 7   Sketch the graph of $f(x) = \ln x$.

Solution: Since $f(x) = \ln x$ is the inverse function of $g(x) = e^x$, we reflect the graph of $y = e^x$ across the line $y = x$ and obtain the graph of $y = \ln x$ (Figure 5.19(b)).

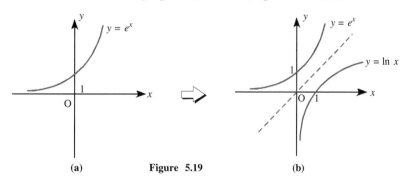

(a)   Figure 5.19   (b)

Remarks: *1.   The zero (x-intercept) of the logarithmic function $f(x) = \ln x$ is at $x = 1$.*

*2.   The y-axis is the **vertical asymptote**.*

*3. $f(x) = \ln x$ is an **increasing function**.*

4.   For large x, $f(x) = \ln x$ also becomes large.

5. $f(x) = \ln x$ is defined only for positive inputs ($x > 0$).

The **guiding principle** for finding the domain of a logarithmic function is that its **argument must be positive**.

EXAMPLE 8   Find the domain of the function

$$f(x) = \log_5 (9 - 2x)$$

Solution: For the domain, $9 - 2x > 0 \longrightarrow -2x > -9$

$$\longrightarrow x < \frac{9}{2}$$

Thus, the domain of the function $f(x) = \log_5 (9 - 2x)$

is $x < \frac{9}{2}$ **or** $\left(-\infty, \frac{9}{2}\right)$

Graphically :

Graph of $y = \log_5 (9 - 2x)$ is

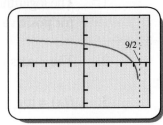

Figure 5.20

EXAMPLE 9   Find the zero(s) and vertical asymptote of the function $f(x) = \log_2(3x - 5)$. Also, sketch the graph of the function.

Solution :   To find the zeros of the function, we solve the equation

$$\log_2 (3x - 5) = 0$$

$$3x - 5 = 2^0 \qquad \text{Exponential Form}$$

$$3x - 5 = 1 \quad \textbf{or} \quad 3x = 6 \quad \textbf{or} \quad x = 2$$

Thus, **$x = 2$** is the zero of the function.

For the vertical asymptote, we set the argument of the logarithm to zero. We get:

$$3x - 5 = 0 \longrightarrow 3x = 5 \longrightarrow x = \frac{5}{3}$$

Therefore, $x = \dfrac{5}{3}$ is the vertical asymptote of the function.

Domain: $3x - 5 > 0 \longrightarrow x > \dfrac{5}{3}$.

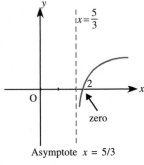

Figure 5.21 (a)

By using the basic shape of a logarithmic function, its zero, the vertical asymptote and its domain, we obtain the shape of the graph of the function as in Figure (5.21(a)).

We close the section by listing some important properties of the logarithmic function.

IMPORTANT OBSERVATIONS OF LOGARITHMIC FUNCTIONS

1.   The **domain** of function $f(x) = \log_b x$ consists of **all positive real numbers**. We recall that the domain of $f(x) = \log_b x$ is same as the range of $g(x) = b^x$.

2.   The **range** of $f(x) = \log_b x$ consists of **all real numbers**. We recall that the range of $f(x) = \log_b x$ is same as the domain of $g(x) = b^x$.

3.   The logarithmic function $f(x) = \log_b x$ is an **increasing** function for $b > 1$ and **decreasing** for $0 < b < 1$ (Figure 5.21(b)).

4.   There is no **y-intercept** for the graph of $y = \log_b x$.

5.   The y-axis ($x = 0$) is the only **vertical asymptote**.

6. $x = 1$ is the only **zero** of the function $f(x) = \log_b x$.

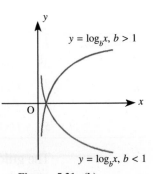

Figure 5.21 (b)

EXERCISE 5.3

In exercises (1-16), convert the expression to its logarithmic form.

1. $2^3 = 8$ **2.** $4^2 = 16$ **3.** $3^{-2} = \dfrac{1}{9}$ **4.** $5^{-3} = \dfrac{1}{125}$

5. $10^{-1} = .1$ **6.** $10^{-4} = .0001$ **7.** $5^x = 8$ **8.** $2^x = \dfrac{1}{5}$

9. $r^x = s$ **10.** $a^b = c$ **11.** $e^x = y$ **12.** $b^x = y$

13. $e^0 = 1$ **14.** $a^0 = 1$ **15.** $\sqrt{3} = 3^{1/2}$ **16.** $\dfrac{1}{\sqrt[3]{5}} = 5^{-\frac{1}{3}}$

In exercises (17-26), convert the expression to its exponential form.

17. $\log_3 27 = 3$ **18.** $\log_2 32 = 5$ **19.** $\log_{10} 100 = 2$ **20.** $\log_4 \dfrac{1}{16} = -2$ **21.** $\ln e^2 = 2$

22. $\ln \dfrac{1}{e^3} = -3$ **23.** $\log_4 64 = 3$ **24.** $\log_{10} .01 = -2$ **25.** $\log_a b = c$ **26.** $\log_y x = -z$

In exercises (27-50), find the value of the logarithm, if it exists, without using a calculator.

27. $\log_5 5$ **28.** $\log_2 16$ **29.** $\log_{10} 10$ **30.** $\log_2 \dfrac{1}{8}$

31. $\ln e$ **32.** $\log_a a$ **33.** $\ln 1$ **34.** $\log_x 1$

35. $\log_3 81$ **36.** $\log_4 64$ **37.** $\log_{10} .01$ **38.** $\log_{10} .001$

39. $\log_3 (-9)$ **40.** $\log_2 \left(-\dfrac{1}{8}\right)$ **41.** $\log (\ln e)$ **42.** $\ln (\log 10)$

43. $\log_3 3\sqrt{3}$ **44.** $\log_5 5\sqrt[3]{5}$ **45.** $\log_3 \dfrac{1}{27}$ **46.** $\log_7 \dfrac{1}{49}$

47. $\log_4 8$ **48.** $\log_9 27$ **49.** $\log_{16} 64$ **50.** $\log_4 32$

In exercises (51-55), find the inverse function of the given function.

51. $f(x) = e^{x+5}$ **52.** $g(x) = e^{2x-7}$ **53.** $f(x) = 10^{2x+3}$

54. $f(x) = e^{4x+9} + 8$ **55.** $f(x) = 10^{3x-4} - 5$

In exercises (56-69), find the domain of the logarithmic function.

56. $f(x) = \log_5 (x-2)$ **57.** $f(x) = \log_4 (x+8)$ **58.** $f(x) = \log_2 (x+3)$

59. $g(x) = \log_5 (2x-1)$ **60.** $f(x) = \log_3 |x|$ **61.** $h(x) = \log_2 |x-1|$

62. $g(x) = \log_2 x^3$ **63.** $f(x) = \log_5 x^4$ **64.** $h(x) = \log_7 (x^2 - 9)$

65. $g(x) = \log_4 (x^2 - 16)$ **66.** $f(x) = \log_5 (x^2 - 5x - 6)$ **67.** $f(x) = \log_3 (x^2 + 5x + 4)$

68. $g(x) = \log_{10} \sqrt{x-1}$ **69.** $g(x) = \log_e \sqrt{x+2}$

In exercises (70-81), find the zeros and asymptotes of the logarithmic function, if any.

70. $f(x) = \log_3(2x - 6)$

71. $g(x) = \log_2(4x + 5)$

72. $g(x) = \log_5(x^2 - 4)$

73. $f(x) = \log_3(x^2 - 9)$

74. $h(x) = \log_2(5x + 7)$

75. $g(x) = \log_7(3x - 1)$

76. $f(x) = \log_{10}(x^2 + 1)$

77. $g(x) = \log_e(x^2 + 4)$

78. $g(x) = \log \dfrac{5x + 2}{x - 3}$

79. $h(x) = \ln \dfrac{x + 5}{3x + 7}$

80. $f(x) = \ln(x^2 - 2x - 3)$

81. $g(x) = \log(x^2 + 2x - 8)$

In exercises (82-97), sketch the graph of the logarithmic function.

82. $f(x) = \log_3 x$

83. $g(x) = \log_4 x$

84. $g(x) = \log_{\frac{1}{2}} x$

85. $f(x) = \log_{\frac{1}{4}} x$

86. $h(x) = \log_{\frac{1}{3}} x$

87. $f(x) = \log_5 x$

88. $f(x) = \log_2(x - 1)$

89. $g(x) = \log_3(x + 2)$

90. $g(x) = \ln(x + 1)$

91. $f(x) = \log(x + 3)$

92. $f(x) = \log_2(x - 1) + 1$

93. $g(x) = \log_3(x - 2) - 1$

94. $g(x) = 1 - \log_3(x - 1)$

95. $f(x) = 2 - \log_2(x + 1)$

96. $f(x) = 1 + \ln(-x)$

97. $g(x) = \ln(-x) - 2$

98. If $[H^+]$ is the hydrogen ion concentration in gram - ions per liter, then the ***pH* of a solution** is defined as

$$pH = -\log[H^+]$$

Find the *pH* of well water, which has a hydrogen ion concentration of 10^{-6} grams - ions per liter.

99. The intensity R on the Richter scale of an earthquake is given by

$$R = \log \dfrac{A}{P}, \quad \text{where } A \text{ is the amplitude}$$

of the earthquake and P is the period in seconds. Find the measure on the Richter scale of an earthquake whose amplitude was 8000 micrometers and had a period of 0.2 second.

100. The loudness (L) of a sound with intensity (I) is given by

$$L = k \ln I, \text{ for some constant } k.$$

Find the loudness if the intensity (I) of a sound is 10^4.

101. The decibel voltage gain (*db* - gain) is given by

$$db - \text{gain} = 20 \log \dfrac{V_o}{V_i},$$

where V_o and V_i are the output voltage and input voltage of the device. Find the decibel voltage gain of an amplifier if its input is 0.7 volt and the output is 50 volts.

102. The decibel voltage gain (*db* - gain) is also given by

$$db - \text{gain} = 10 \log \dfrac{P_o}{P_i},$$

where P_o and P_i are the power out and power input of the device. Find the decibel voltage gain of an amplifier that has 80 watt output with 0.04 Watt input.

103. According to the double balance method an equipment costing $C that has a useful life of N years will depreciate to a book value of $B in n number of years, where n is given by

$$n = \frac{\log B - \log C}{\log\left(1 - \frac{2}{N}\right)}.$$

A truck that costs $50,000 has a useful life of 10 years. How old is the truck when its book value is $20,000?

In exercises (104-105), find (a) the vertical distance PQ and (b) the coordinates of the midpoint (M) of the segment PQ.

104.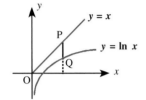

105.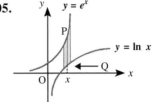

Writing Exercises

106. Distinguish between 'logarithm' and 'logarithmic function'.

107. Explain the behavior of $f(x) = \ln(x - a)$ near $x = a$.

108. Give the guiding principle for finding the domain of $f(x) = \ln g(x)$.

5.4   PROPERTIES OF LOGARITHMS

In elementary algebra we studied the laws of exponents. Since logarithms are obtained from exponents, those laws should translate naturally into the laws of logarithms. These laws along with a few other rules of its own become the **properties of logarithms**. These properties will show how applying a logarithm turns multiplication into addition, division into subtraction, and exponentiation into multiplication.

Objectives ▶ ▶

In this section you will learn about:

A . Properties of Logarithms;

B . Simplifying Logarithms;

C . Combining Logarithms into a Single Logarithm;

D . Changing the base of a Logarithm; and

E . Composition of Logarithmic and Exponential Functions

A. PROPERTIES OF LOGARITHMS

First, we translate each law of exponent into a corresponding law of logarithms.

1. We know from the law of exponents that $b^1 = b$.

Writing this in logarithmic form gives $\log_b b = 1$.

Property 1 of Logarithms: $\log_b b = 1$

The property says that when the base is same as the argument, the value of the logarithm is 1.

EXAMPLE 1   **1.** $\log_2 2 = 1$ **2.** $\ln e = \log_e e = 1$

2. We know from the law of exponents that $b^0 = 1$

Writing this in logarithmic form, we get $\log_b 1 = 0$

> **Property 2 of Logarithms:** $\log_b 1 = 0$

The property says that the logarithm of 1 is zero irrespective of the base.

EXAMPLE 2   **a.** $\log_5 1 = 0$ **b.** $\log_{10} 1 = 0$ **c.** $\ln 1 = 0$

3. We know from the law of exponents that $b^x \cdot b^y = b^{x+y}$

Let $b^x = M$ and $b^y = N \longrightarrow x = \log_b M,$ and $y = \log_b N$

We start with the product $MN = b^x \cdot b^y = b^{x+y}.$

By changing to logarithmic form, we get: $\log_b MN = x + y$
$$= \log_b M + \log_b N$$

> **Property 3 of Logarithms (Product Property)**
> $$\log_b MN = \log_b M + \log_b N$$

The property says that the logarithm of a product is a sum of logarithms.

EXAMPLE 3   **a.** $\log_2 2x = \log_2 2 + \log_2 x = 1 + \log_2 x$ $\qquad \log_2 2 = 1$

  b. $\log_{12} 4 + \log_{12} 36 = \log_{12}(4 \times 36) = \log_{12} 144 = 2$ $\qquad 12^2 = 144$
$$= \log_{12}(12 \times 12) = \log_{12} 12 + \log_{12} 12 = 1 + 1 = 2$$

  c. $\ln(a\,e) = \ln a + \ln e = \ln a + 1$ $\qquad \ln e = 1$

4. We know from the law of exponents that $\dfrac{b^x}{b^y} = b^{x-y}$

Let $b^x = M$ and $b^y = N \longrightarrow x = \log_b M$ and $y = \log_b N.$

We start with the quotient $\dfrac{M}{N} = \dfrac{b^x}{b^y} = b^{x-y} \longrightarrow \log_b \dfrac{M}{N} = x - y$
$$= \log_b M - \log_b N$$

> **Property 4 of Logarithms (Quotient Property)**
> $$\log_b \frac{M}{N} = \log_b M - \log_b N$$

The property says that the logarithm of a quotient will give the logarithm of the numerator minus the logarithm of the denominator. (Taking a logarithm changes division into subtraction.)

EXAMPLE 4   **1.** $\ln \dfrac{e}{x} = \ln e - \ln x = 1 - \ln x$ $\qquad \ln e = \log_e e = 1$

  2. $\log_5 75 - \log_5 3 = \log_5 \dfrac{75}{3} = \log_5 25$ $\qquad 5^2 = 25$
$$= \log_5(5 \times 5) = \log_5 5 + \log_5 5 = 2$$

5. We know from the laws of exponents that $\left(b^x\right)^n = b^{nx}$

Let $b^x = M \longrightarrow x = \log_b M.$

If we raise M to the power n, we get $M^n = \left(b^x\right)^n = b^{nx}$

Writing this in the logarithmic form, we get $\log_b M^n = nx$

$$= n \log_b M \qquad {\scriptstyle x\,=\,\log_b M}$$

Property 5 of Logarithms (Power Property)

$$\log_b M^n = n \log_b M$$

The power property says that the power of the argument of a logarithm can be written as the coefficient of the logarithm.

EXAMPLE 5   **a.** $\log_2 x^7 = 7 \log_2 x$ **b.** $3\log_{27} 3 = \log_{27} 3^3 = \log_{27} 27 = 1$

(When the coefficient of logarithm goes inside the logarithm, it becomes the exponent of its argument.)

c. $\ln(e^2 x^3) = \ln e^2 + \ln x^3 = 2 \ln e + 3 \ln x = 2(1) + 3 \ln x = 2 + 3 \ln x$

d. $\ln\left(\dfrac{3x^2}{e}\right) = \ln 3x^2 - \ln e = \ln 3 + \ln x^2 - \ln e = \ln 3 + 2 \ln x - 1$

6. By using the fact that the logarithmic function $f(x) = \log_b x$ and the exponential function $g(x) = b^x$ are inverse functions, we have

$$(g \circ f)(x) = x \longrightarrow g(f(x)) = x \longrightarrow b^{f(x)} = x \longrightarrow b^{\log_b x} = x$$

Thus we have the next property of logarithms.

Property 6 of Logarithms (Inverse Property)

$$b^{\log_b x} = x$$

The property says that a number raised to a log - power, which has the same base as the number, equals the argument of the log - power.

As a particular case $e^{\ln a} = a.$

EXAMPLE 6   **a.** $2^{\log_2 10} = 10$ **b.** $e^{\ln 5} = 5$ **c.** $e^{2\ln 3} = e^{\ln 3^2}$

$$= 3^2 = 9$$

7. Now let $b^x = M$ so that $x = \log_b M.$

We take the logarithm with base a of both sides of the original equation to obtain

$$\log_a b^x = \log_a M$$
$$x \log_a b = \log_a M \qquad \text{Power Property}$$

Divide by $\log_a b$: $x = \dfrac{\log_a M}{\log_a b}$

Since $x = \log_b M$, we get $\log_b M = \dfrac{\log_a M}{\log_a b}$.

Property 7 of Logarithms (Change of Base Property)

$$\log_b M = \frac{\log_a M}{\log_a b}.$$

The property says that a logarithm with the given base is equal to the quotient of logarithms, each with the new base. The argument of the logarithm in the numerator is the given argument and the argument of the logarithm in the denominator is the same as the given base.

EXAMPLE 7

1. $\log_2 5 = \dfrac{\log_{10} 5}{\log_{10} 2} = \dfrac{.69897}{.30103} = 2.32193$ Answers rounded to 5 decimal places.

2. $\log_2 5 = \dfrac{\ln 5}{\ln 2} = \dfrac{1.60944}{.69315} = 2.32193$ Answers rounded to 5 decimal places.

Important Note

Since most calculators compute only common or natural logarithms, property 7 must be used to calculate logarithms of any other base b. Likewise, property 7 allows the graphing of a function such as $f(x) = \log_2 (3x - 5)$. (see example 9, section 5.3) with a graphing calculator. We write $y_1 = \ln(3x - 5)/\ln 2$.

Alternative Form of Property 7

Writing $\log_b M = \dfrac{\log_a M}{\log_a b}$ as $\log_a b \cdot \log_b M = \log_a M$, we observe the following pattern:

$$\log_a b \cdot \log_b M = \log_a M \qquad \text{as if } b \text{ can be canceled}$$

In general, we have the following

CHAIN RULE OF LOGARITHMS

$$\log_a b \cdot \log_b c \cdot \log_c d \cdot \log_d x = \log_a x$$

EXAMPLE 8

a. $\log_3 5 \cdot \log_5 27 = \log_3 27 = 3$ $27 = 3^3$

b. $\log_9 5 \cdot \log_5 10 \cdot \log_{10} 3 = \log_9 3 = \dfrac{1}{2}$ $3 = 9^{\frac{1}{2}}$

EXAMPLE 9

Given that $\log 2 = 0.301$ and $\log 3 = 0.477$, evaluate each of the following.

a. $\log 12$ **b.** $\log 54$ **c.** $\log 5$ **d.** $\log 1.5$

Solutions: We express each argument in terms of the basic arguments 2 and 3, and the base 10.

a.

$$\log 12 = \log(2^2 \cdot 3) \qquad 12 = 2^2 \cdot 3$$
$$= \log 2^2 + \log 3 \qquad \text{Product property.}$$
$$= 2\log 2 + \log 3 \qquad \text{Power property.}$$
$$= 2(0.301) + 0.477 = 1.079$$

Therefore, $\log 12 = 1.079$.

b. $\log 54 \;=\; \log(2 \cdot 3^3)$ $54 = 2 \cdot 3^3$

$=\; \log 2 + \log 3^3$ Product property.

$=\; \log 2 + 3\log 3$ Power property.

$=\; 0.301 + 3(0.477) = 1.732$

Therefore,   **log 54 = 1.732**

c. $\log 5 = \log_{10} \dfrac{10}{2} \;=\; \log_{10} 10 - \log_{10} 2$ Quotient property.

$=\; \mathbf{1 - 0.301 = 0.699}$ $\log_{10} 10 = 1.$

d. $\log 1.5 \;=\; \log \dfrac{15}{10} \;=\; \log \dfrac{3}{2} \;=\; \log 3 - \log 2$ Quotient property

$=\; \mathbf{0.477 - 0.301 = 0.176}$

B. SIMPLIFYING LOGARITHMS

We use properties of logarithms to write a single logarithm as a sum or difference of simpler logarithms.

EXAMPLE 10   Re-write each logarithm in terms of logarithms of simpler arguments.

  a. $\log_2 \dfrac{x^2 \sqrt{y}}{4}$ **b.** $\log \sqrt{\dfrac{5x^2 + 1}{2x + 3}}$ **c.** $\ln \dfrac{(x+1)(x-2)^2}{x^3 \sqrt{2x+5}}$

Solutions:

a. $\log_2 \dfrac{x^2 y^{1/2}}{4} \;=\; \log_2 x^2 y^{1/2} \;-\; \log_2 4$ Quotient property.

$=\; \log_2 x^2 \;+\; \log_2 y^{1/2} - \log_2 2^2$ Product property.

$=\; 2\log_2 x + \dfrac{1}{2}\log_2 y - 2\log_2 2$ Power property.

$=\; \mathbf{2\log_2 x + \dfrac{1}{2}\log_2 y - 2}$ $\log_2 2 = 1.$

b. $\log\left(\dfrac{5x^2 + 1}{2x + 3}\right)^{1/2} \;=\; \dfrac{1}{2}\log \dfrac{5x^2 + 1}{2x + 3}$ Power property.

$=\; \dfrac{1}{2}\left[\log\left(5x^2 + 1\right) - \log(2x + 3)\right]$ Quotient property.

c. $\ln \dfrac{(x+1)\,(x-2)^2}{x^3\,(2x+5)^{1/2}} \;=\; \ln(x+1)\,(x-2)^2 - \ln x^3 (2x+5)^{1/2}$ Quotient property.

$=\; \ln(x+1) + \ln(x-2)^2 - (\ln x^3 + \ln(2x+5)^{1/2})$ Product property.

$=\; \ln(x+1) + 2\ln(x-2) - 3\ln x - \dfrac{1}{2}\ln(2x+5)$

C. COMBINING LOGARITHMS INTO A SINGLE LOGARITHM

Properties 3, 4, and 5 can be used to combine logarithms into a single logarithm. The following example demonstrates the process.

EXAMPLE 11   Write each of the following expressions as a single logarithm with a coefficient of 1.

   a. $\log_2 x - 3\log_2 y$

   b. $2\log a - 3\log b + \log c - 4\log d$

   c. $\dfrac{1}{2}\ln(x+1) - 2\ln(x+2) + 3\ln(x-1)$

   d. $3\ln x + \dfrac{1}{2}\ln y - 2$

Solutions:

a. $\log_2 x - 3\log_2 y = \log_2 x - \log_2 y^3$ Power property.

$\qquad\qquad = \log_2 \dfrac{x}{y^3}$ Quotient property.

b. $2\log a - 3\log b + \log c - 4\log d$

$= \log a^2 - \log b^3 + \log c - \log d^4$ Power property.

$= \log \dfrac{a^2}{b^3} + \log \dfrac{c}{d^4}$ Quotient property.

$= \log \dfrac{a^2}{b^3} \cdot \dfrac{c}{d^4}$ or $\log \dfrac{a^2 c}{b^3 d^4}$ Product property.

Remark: *The arguments of positive logarithms become part of the numerator of the single logarithm and the arguments of negative logarithms become part of the denominator.*

With this observation, we could write $\log a^2 - \log b^3 + \log c - \log d^4 = \log \dfrac{a^2 c}{b^3 d^4}$.

---

c. $\dfrac{1}{2}\ln(x+1) - 2\ln(x+2) + 3\ln(x-1)$

$= \ln(x+1)^{1/2} - \ln(x+2)^2 + \ln(x-1)^3$ Power property.

$= \ln \dfrac{(x+1)^{1/2}\,(x-1)^3}{(x+2)^2} = \ln \dfrac{(x-1)^3\sqrt{x+1}}{(x+2)^2}$

d. $3\ln x + \dfrac{1}{2}\ln y - 2$

$= 3\ln x + \dfrac{1}{2}\ln y - 2\ln e$ ln $e = 1$

$= \ln x^3 + \ln y^{1/2} - \ln e^2$

$= \ln \dfrac{x^3 y^{1/2}}{e^2} = \ln \dfrac{x^3 \sqrt{y}}{e^2}$ Power property.

D. CHANGING THE BASE OF A LOGARITHM

In order to use a calculator for evaluating logarithms to any base, we use property #7 to change the base of the logarithm to 10 or e.

EXAMPLE 12   Write each of the following expressions in terms of ln.

   a. $\log 10x$ **b.** $\log_2(x^2 + 4)$ **c.** $\log_b(5x + 2)$

Solutions: **a.** $\log_{10} x = \dfrac{\ln x}{\ln 10}$ Change of the base property.

   b. $\log_2(x^2 + 4) = \dfrac{\ln(x^2 + 4)}{\ln 2}$ Change of base.

   c. $\log_b(5x + 2) = \dfrac{\ln(5x + 2)}{\ln b}$ Change of base.

EXAMPLE 13   Use a calculator to approximate the value of each logarithm.

   a. $\log_2 5$ **b.** $\log_5 2$

Solutions: First we express each logarithm in terms of ln (or common log), then use the calculator to evaluate each.

   a. $\log_2 5 = \dfrac{\ln 5}{\ln 2}$ Change of base.

   $\approx \dfrac{1.6094}{.6931} = \mathbf{2.322}$ Use of calculator.

(Check with a calculator to confirm that $2^{2.322} \approx 5$.)

   b. $\log_5 2 = \dfrac{\ln 2}{\ln 5}$ Change of base.

   $\approx \dfrac{.6931}{1.6094} = \mathbf{.4307}$ Use a calculator.

(Check to confirm that $5^{.4307} \approx 2$.)

E. COMPOSITION OF LOGARITHMIC AND EXPONENTIAL FUNCTIONS

Since functions $f(x) = b^x$ and $g(x) = \log_b x$ are inverses of each other, their composition equals the identity function.

(1) $b^{\log_b x} = x$ **(2)** $\log_b b^x = x$

EXAMPLE 14   Evaluate   **a.** $2^{3\log_2 3+1}$ **b.** $e^{2\ln x-1}$

Solutions:

a. $2^{3\log_2 3+1}$ = $2^{3\log_2 3} \cdot 2^1$ $b^x \cdot b^y = b^{x+y}$

= $2^{\log_2 3^3} \cdot 2$ Power property.

= $3^3 \cdot 2$ Inverse property.

= $(27)2 =$ **54**

b. $e^{2\ln x-1}$ = $e^{2\ln x} \cdot e^{-1}$ $b^x \cdot b^y = b^{x+y}$

= $e^{\ln x^2} \cdot e^{-1}$ Power property.

= $x^2 \cdot e^{-1} = \dfrac{x^2}{e}$ Inverse property.

EXERCISE **5.4**

In exercises (1-12), use $\log 2 = a$ and $\log 3 = b$ to evaluate each logarithm.

1. $\log 24$ **2.** $\log 36$ **3.** $\log 50$ **4.** $\log 150$ **5.** $\log 75$ **6.** $\log 125$

7. $\log 60$ **8.** $\log 180$ **9.** $\log 36$ **10.** $\log 240$ **11.** $\log 0.3$ **12.** $\log 1.2$

In exercises (13-36), simplify the logarithm so that no argument contains a product, quotient, or a power.

13. $\log_3 9x^2$ **14.** $\log_2 16x^5$ **15.** $\log_5 5y^3$ **16.** $\log_4 4y^7$ **17.** $\ln e^3 x^2$

18. $\ln e^5 x^7$ **19.** $\log_3 \dfrac{27x}{y^2}$ **20.** $\log_2 \dfrac{16y^5}{x^7}$ **21.** $\log_2 \dfrac{4x^2}{y}$ **22.** $\log_5 \dfrac{y^2}{5x^3}$

23. $\ln \dfrac{e\sqrt{x}}{y}$ **24.** $\ln \dfrac{e^4 \sqrt[3]{x}}{y}$ **25.** $\ln \dfrac{e^2 \sqrt{x}}{\sqrt[3]{y}}$ **26.** $\ln \dfrac{e^3 \sqrt[4]{y}}{\sqrt[3]{x}}$ **27.** $\log \sqrt{\dfrac{2x+1}{3x+7}}$

28. $\log_{10} \sqrt{\dfrac{x+5}{2x+9}}$ **29.** $\ln \dfrac{\sqrt{(5x+9)}}{\sqrt[3]{2x-5}}$ **30.** $\ln \dfrac{\sqrt[3]{6x-7}}{\sqrt[4]{2x+11}}$

31. $\log_2 \dfrac{(x+2)^2 y^3}{\sqrt{x+3}}$ **32.** $\log_3 \dfrac{(y+1)^4 x^4}{\sqrt[3]{y+7}}$ **33.** $\ln \dfrac{(x+5)\sqrt{x+2}}{x^2(x+3)}$

34. $\ln \dfrac{(x-2)(7x+3)}{y^2 \sqrt{y+3}}$ **35.** $\ln \dfrac{(x-1)^3 (x+2)^2}{(x+5)^2 \sqrt{x+7}}$ **36.** $\ln \dfrac{\sqrt{x+4} \sqrt[3]{2y+7}}{(2x+3)^2 (y-9)^4}$

In exercises (37-56), write each as a single logarithm with a coefficient of 1.

37. $\log 15 + \log 2$ **38.** $\log 20 + \log 4$ **39.** $\log 20 - \log 3$

40. $\log 22 - \log 7$ **41.** $2\log_2 x + \log_2 5$ **42.** $\log_2 3 - 3\log_2 y$

43. $4\log_3 x + \log_3 11$ **44.** $3\log_3 x - \log_3 15$ **45.** $2\log(x+1) + 3\log(x+2)$

46. $5\log(y+2) - 2\log(3y-1)$ **47.** $2\log x - 3\log(x+7) + \log y - 2\log 5$

48. $3 \log x + \frac{1}{3} \log (y+1) - \frac{1}{4} \log y$ **49.** $3 \ln x - 2 \ln (x+1) + \frac{1}{2} \ln (x+2)$

50. $4 \ln (3x+5) - 2 \ln x - \frac{1}{3} \ln (2x+3)$ **51.** $\ln x + \frac{1}{2} \ln (x-1) - \frac{1}{3} \ln (x+7) - 5 \ln (2x+5)$

52. $2 \ln (x+1) + \frac{1}{3} \ln (2y-1) - 4 \ln (3x+4) - \frac{1}{2} \ln (4y+5)$ **53.** $2 + 3 \log_2 x$

54. $5 \log_3 x - 3$ **55.** $3 \ln x - 2 \ln y + 1$ **56.** $9 \ln (y+1) - 2 \ln (x+2) - 4$

In exercises (57-66), write in terms of ln.

57. $\log_5 x$ **58.** $\log_2 y$ **59.** $\log_3 (x+1)$ **60.** $\log_4 (y+11)$ **61.** $\log_2 (x^2 + 9)$

62. $\log_3 (8 - y^2)$ **63.** $\log (5x+9)$ **64.** $\log (7x^2 - 2)$ **65.** $\log_a (3x-7)$ **66.** $\log_b (5+2x)$

In exercises (67-70), use a calculator to approximate the value of the logarithm.

67. $\log_3 7$ **68.** $\log_7 3$ **69.** $\log_3 5$ **70.** $\log_5 3$

In exercises (71-86), evaluate using the properties of logarithms.

71. $5^{\log_5 7}$ **72.** $10^{\log 4}$ **73.** $3^{\log_3 5}$ **74.** $e^{\ln 7}$ **75.** $2^{\left(\log_2 5 + 1\right)}$ **76.** $5^{\left(\log_5 3 + 3\right)}$

77. $3^{\left(\log_3 7 - 1\right)}$ **78.** $2^{\left(\log_2 5 - 2\right)}$ **79.** $4^{2 \log_4 3}$ **80.** $3^{3 \log_3 2}$ **81.** $e^{3 \ln 2}$ **82.** $e^{-3 \ln 3}$

83. $e^{(2 \ln 3 + 1)}$ **84.** $e^{(3 \ln 2 + 3)}$ **85.** $e^{(2 \ln a + 3 \ln b)}$ **86.** $e^{(5 \ln x + 4 \ln y)}$

In exercises (87-90) , solve the equation for x.

87. $2^x - 1 = a$ **88.** $3^x + 4 = b$ **89.** $3^{-x} + 1 = b$ **90.** $5^{-x} - 2 = a$

91.   The loudness (L) of sound in terms of intensity (I) is given by $L = k \ln I$. What increase in intensity (I) will triple the loudness of the sound ?

92.   The decibel voltage gain (db - gain) is given by $\mathbf{db - gain = 30 \log} \dfrac{v_o}{v_i}$, where v_o and v_i are the output voltage and input voltage of the device. What increase in the rate $\dfrac{v_o}{v_i}$ will double the **db – gain** ?

93.   The intensity R on the Richter scale of an earthquake is given by $R = \log \dfrac{A}{P}$, where A is the amplitude of the earthquake and P is the period. Find the change in the intensity (R) if the amplitude doubles but the period stays the same. Does it increase or decrease ?

94.   Refer to Exercise 93. Find the change in the intensity (R) if the period doubles but the amplitude stays the same.

95.   Refer to Exercise 93. Find the change in the $\dfrac{A}{P}$ if the intensity (R) doubles.

In exercises (96 - 99), write the slope of the line PQ in terms of a single logarithm.

96.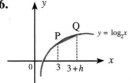
97.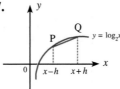
98.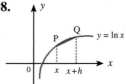
99.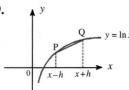

Writing Exercises

100. Write all seven properties of logarithms in words.

101. Describe the situations where logarithms can be or cannot be combined into a single logarithm.

5.5 EXPONENTIAL AND LOGARITHMIC EQUATIONS

Objectives ▶ ▶

In this section you will be able to solve:

A. Exponential Equations; and

B. Logarithmic Equations.

In Chapter 3 we solved various types of algebraic equations, using graphical and algebraic methods. We also discussed the connection between the roots of an equation and the zeros of a function. In this section we will study the roots of exponential and logarithmic equations. As in Chapter 3, the roots of an equation will be found graphically by locating the zeros (x-intercepts) of the corresponding function. We begin with exponential equations.

A. EXPONENTIAL EQUATIONS

Exponential equations are used in solving growth and decay problems. Before we learn how to solve an exponential equation, let us learn to identify an exponential equation.

> **Exponential Equation**
>
> An equation involving exponential terms with variables in the exponents is called an **exponential equation.**

EXAMPLES: **a.** $2^{3x-1} = 8$ **b.** $3^{x+1} = 5 \cdot 2^x$ **c.** $e^{x-1} - 2^{x+1} = 0$

Solving Exponential Equations

Like an algebraic equation, we can solve an exponential equation both algebraically and graphically. An algebraic method gives the **exact** roots of the equation, whereas a graphical method sometimes gives only estimated roots.

EXAMPLE 1   Solve $2^{3x-1} = 5$.

Solution:

Algebraically   **Procedure**

Step 1   Take ln (or log) of both sides $\longrightarrow$ $\ln 2^{3x-1} = \ln 5$
of the equation.

Step **2**   Use properties of logarithms to $\longrightarrow$
simplify each side.

$$(3x-1)\ln 2 \ = \ \ln 5 \qquad \text{Power property}$$

Step **3**   Solve the resulting equation. $\longrightarrow$

In this case, the resulting equation is a linear equation.

$$3x\ln 2 - \ln 2 \ = \ \ln 5$$
$$3x\ln 2 \ = \ \ln 5 + \ln 2$$
$$x \ = \ \frac{\ln 5 + \ln 2}{3\ln 2}$$

Thus, $x = \dfrac{\ln 5 + \ln 2}{3\ln 2} = \dfrac{\ln 10}{3\ln 2}$ is the **exact**

root of the equation.

With Graphing Calculator (Graphically)

The root of the equation $2^{3x-1} = 5$ is the same as the zero
of the function $f(x) = 2^{3x-1} - 5$.

Let $y1 = 2^{3x-1} - 5$. Graph $y1$ on the standard range.

By using ZOOM- IN and TRACE, we estimate the zero

(x-intercept) of the graph at $x \approx 1.1073$.

Check that $x = \dfrac{\ln 10}{3\ln 2} \approx 1.1073$.

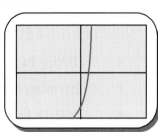

Figure 5.22

EXAMPLE 2   Solve $7^{x-1} \ = \ 3(2^{x-2})$.

Solution: **(Algebraically)**

Step **1**   By taking ln of both sides of the equation, we get $\ln 7^{x-1} = \ln 3(2^{x-2})$

Step **2**   By using the power and product properties, we get
$$(x-1)\ln 7 \ = \ \ln 3 + \ln 2^{x-2} \quad \textbf{or} \quad (x-1)\ln 7 \ = \ \ln 3 + (x-2)\ln 2$$

Step **3**   Solving the equation for x gives
$$x\ln 7 - \textbf{ln 7} \ = \ \ln 3 + x\ln 2 - 2\ln 2$$
$$\boldsymbol{x}\ln 7 - \boldsymbol{x}\ln 2 \ = \ \ln 3 - 2\ln 2 + \ln 7$$
$$x(\ln 7 - \ln 2) \ = \ \ln 3 - 2\ln 2 + \ln 7$$

$$x \ = \ \frac{\ln 3 - 2\ln 2 + \ln 7}{\ln 7 - \ln 2} \ = \ \frac{\ln 3 - \ln 4 + \ln 7}{\ln 7 - \ln 2}$$

$$= \ \frac{\ln\left(\dfrac{21}{4}\right)}{\ln\left(\dfrac{7}{2}\right)} \ = \ \frac{\ln 5.25}{\ln 3.5}$$

Thus, the **exact** zero of the function is given by

$$x \ = \ \frac{\ln 5.25}{\ln 3.5}$$

5.35

With Graphing Calculator (Graphically)

The roots of the equation $7^{x-1} = 3(2^{x-2})$ are the same as the zeros of the function $f(x) = 7^{x-1} - 3(2^{x-2})$. To estimate the zero of the function we let $y1 = 7^{x-1} - 3(2^{x-2})$.

Graph $y1$ on the standard (or any suitable) range. By using ZOOM-IN and TRACE we estimate the zero (x-intercept) as $x \approx 1.32365$

Check that $x = \dfrac{\ln(5.25)}{\ln(3.5)} \approx 1.32366$.

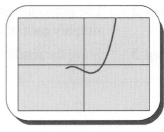

Figure 5.23

EXAMPLE 3   Find the zeros of the function $f(x) = e^{7x-3} - 5^{x-1}$

Solution: **(Algebraically)**

We solve the exponential equation

$$e^{7x-3} - 5^{x-1} = 0 \quad \textbf{or} \quad e^{7x-3} = 5^{x-1}$$

- Taking **ln** of both sides gives $\ln e^{7x-3} = \ln 5^{x-1}$.

- By using the power property, we get $(7x - 3)\ln e = (x - 1)\ln 5$.

- Solving the equation for x gives

$$(7x - 3) \cdot 1 = (x - 1)\ln 5 \qquad {\scriptstyle \ln e = 1}$$
$$7x - 3 = x\ln 5 - \ln 5$$
$$7x - x\ln 5 = 3 - \ln 5$$
$$x(7 - \ln 5) = 3 - \ln 5$$
$$x = \frac{3 - \ln 5}{7 - \ln 5}$$

Thus, $x = \dfrac{3 - \ln 5}{7 - \ln 5}$ is the **exact** zero of the function.

With Graphing Calculator (Graphically)

To find the zeros of the function $f(x) = e^{7x-3} - 5^{x-1}$.
We let $y1 = e^{7x-3} - 5^{x-1}$ Graph $y1$ on the range
x-min $= -2$, x-max $= 2$, y-min $= -2$, and y-max $= 2$.

By using ZOOM-In and TRACE, we estimate the zero of the function at $x = .25796$.

Check that $x = \dfrac{3 - \ln 5}{7 - \ln 5} \approx .25796$.

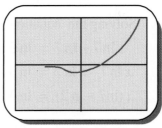

Figure 5.24

- Sometimes the exponential equation may not be in a form where the log - properties can simplify both sides of the equation. In such a situation we first split the equation in two convenient equations and then use the above strategy of three steps. We explain this procedure in the following example.

EXAMPLE 4   Solve $2e^x + 6e^{-x} = 7$

Solution: **(Algebraically)**

Step 1   If we take **ln** of both sides, we get $\ln(2e^x + 6e^{-x}) = \ln 7$

Step 2   Since there is no addition property of logarithms, we cannot simplify. Let us go back to the original equation and try to split it into two equations. This can be achieved if we can factor and set each factor to zero.

First, we multiply the equation $2e^x + 6e^{-x} = 7$ by e^x, we get

$$2e^{2x} + 6 = 7e^x \quad \text{or} \qquad e^x \cdot e^x = e^{2x} \text{ and } \ e^x \cdot e^{-x} = e^0 = 1$$

$$2e^{2x} - 7e^x + 6 = 0 \qquad\qquad \text{This is quadratic in } e^x.$$

$$(2e^x - 3)(e^x - 2) = 0 \qquad\qquad \text{Factor the quadratic.}$$

$$2e^x - 3 = 0 \quad \textbf{or} \quad e^x - 2 = 0$$

Now we use the 3-step procedure on each equation.

$$
\begin{array}{c|c}
\textbf{2}e^x \ = \ \textbf{3} & e^x \ = \ \textbf{2} \\[2mm]
e^x \ = \ \dfrac{3}{2} \ = \ 1.5 & \Rightarrow \quad x \ = \ \textbf{ln 2} \\[2mm]
\Rightarrow \quad x \ = \ \textbf{ln 1.5} &
\end{array}
$$

Thus, we get two **exact** roots of the equation. The approximate values are

$$x \approx 0.41 \quad \text{and} \quad x \approx 0.69$$

With Graphing Calculator

The root of the equation $2e^x + 6e^{-x} = 7$ are the same as the zeros of the function $f(x) = 2e^x + 6e^{-x} - 7$.

Let $y1 = 2e^x + 6e^{-x} - 7$. Graph $y1$ on the range x-min $= 0$, x-max $= 1$, y-min $= -.5$ and y-max $= 1$.

By using ZOOM - IN and TRACE, we estimate the zeros (x-intercepts) at $x = .4054$ and $x = .6931$.

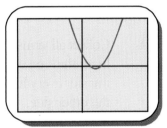

Figure 5.25

Remark: *It may not be possible to solve every equation algebraically. However, it is certainly possible to approximate the roots of such equations graphically.*

EXAMPLE 5   Solve $e^{x^2} - 2e^x - 1 = 0$

Solution: Notice that $e^{x^2} \neq \left(e^x\right)^2$. So, $e^{x^2} - 2e^x - 1 = 0$ is not a quadratic equation in e^x. It is not possible to factor $e^{x^2} - 2e^x - 1$. However, we can estimate the solution of this equation graphically.

The roots of $e^{x^2} - 2e^x - 1 = 0$ are the same as zeros of the function $f(x) = e^{x^2} - 2e^x - 1$. Let $y1 = e^{x^2} - 2e^x - 1$. Graph $y1$ on the standard range. By using ZOOM-IN and TRACE, we estimate the zeros (x-intercepts) at $\boldsymbol{x = -.7979}$ and $x = 1.5160$

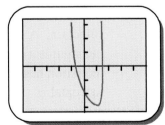

Figure 5.26

B. Logarithmic Equations

Before we give a method to solve a logarithmic equation, we explain its identifying features

> **Logarithmic Equation**
>
> An equation involving logarithmic functions is called a logarithmic equation.

$\log_2 x - \log_2(x - 1) = 3$ and $\ln x + \ln(x + 1) = \ln(x + 5)$ are examples of logarithmic equations.

Solving Logarithmic Equations

As in the case of an exponential equation, the algebraic method will produce the **exact** roots of the logarithmic equation, whereas the graphical method will give only approximate values of the roots.

EXAMPLE 6   Solve $\log_2 x = 1 - \log_2(x - 1)$

Algebraically   Procedure

Solution:

Step 1   Collect all terms involving logarithms on one side and transfer everything else to the other side. $\longrightarrow$ $\log_2 x + \log_2(x - 1) = 1$

Step 2   Combine all logarithmic terms into a single logarithm. $\longrightarrow$ $\log_2 x(x - 1) = 1$

Step 3   Write an equivalent exponential equation. $\longrightarrow$ $x(x - 1) = 2^1$

Step 4   Solve the resulting equation. $\longrightarrow$
$x^2 - x = 2 \longrightarrow x^2 - x - 2 = 0$
$(x - 2)(x + 1) = 0$
$x - 2 = 0$ **or** $x + 1 = 0$
$x = 2$ **or** $x = -1$

Step 5   Check each solution in Step 4 to see whether it belongs to the domain of each logarithm function. A solution that makes an argument of a logarithm in the equation negative or zero is not acceptable. $\longrightarrow$

Check $x = 2$. Try replacing x with 2 in the original equation. Both arguments (x and $x - 1$) stay positive, so $x = 2$ is an acceptable solution or root of the equation.

Check $x = -1$. When we replace x with -1, both arguments of the logs in the original equation become negative. Therefore, $x = -1$ is not an acceptable solution or root of the equation.

Thus, $x = 2$ is the only root of the equation.

With Graphing Calculator

The roots of the equation $\log_2 x = 1 - \log_2(x - 1)$ are the zeros
of the function

$$f(x) = \log_2 x + \log_2(x - 1) - 1 = \frac{\ln x}{\ln 2} + \frac{\ln(x - 1)}{\ln 2} - 1$$

$$= \frac{\ln x + \ln(x - 1)}{\ln 2} - 1$$

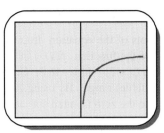

Figure 5.27

Since the graphing calculator accepts either common or natural logarithms, we let $y1 = \frac{\ln x + \ln(x - 1)}{\ln 2} - 1$.   Graph

$y1$ on the standard (or any suitable) range. By using ZOOM-IN and TRACE, we estimate the zero (x-intercept) of the
graph to be $x = 2$.

EXAMPLE 7   Solve $\ln(x + 3) = \ln x + \ln 3$

Solution: **(Algebraically)**

Step 1   By collecting all logs on one side, we obtain $\ln(x + 3) - \ln x - \ln 3 = 0$

Step 2   Combining all logarithmic terms into a single
logarithm gives

* $\ln \dfrac{x + 3}{3x} = 0$ Quotient property.

> * The arguments of positive logs become part of the numerator and the arguments of negative logs become parts of the denominator of the combined argument.

Step 3   Changing this into an exponential form gives

$$\frac{x + 3}{3x} = e^0 \quad \text{or} \quad \frac{x + 3}{3x} = 1 .$$

Step 4   We solve the equation for x.

$$\frac{x + 3}{3x} = 1$$

$$x + 3 = 3x \quad \text{or} \quad 3 = 2x \quad \text{or} \quad \frac{3}{2} = x.$$

Step 5   Test $x = \dfrac{3}{2}$.

Since $x = \dfrac{3}{2}$ does not make any of the arguments negative or zero, it is an acceptable

solution.

Thus $x = \dfrac{\mathbf{3}}{\mathbf{2}}$ is the only root of the equation.

Check: $\ln\left(\dfrac{\mathbf{3}}{\mathbf{2}} + 3\right) = \ln \dfrac{\mathbf{3}}{\mathbf{2}} + \ln 3$ becomes $\ln\left(\dfrac{\mathbf{9}}{\mathbf{2}}\right) = \ln\left(\dfrac{\mathbf{3}}{\mathbf{2}} \cdot 3\right)$, which is a true statement.

With Graphing Calculator

The roots of the equation $\ln(x + 3) = \ln x + \ln 3$ are the zeros of the function $f(x) = \ln(x + 3) - \ln x - \ln 3$. Let $y1 = \ln(x + 3) - \ln x - \ln 3$. Graph $y1$ on the standard (or any suitable) range. By using ZOOM-IN and TRACE we estimate the zero (x-intercept) at $x = 1.5$.

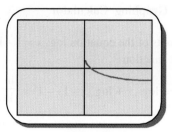

Figure 5.28

- The following example shows a situation when step 3 involves division by x, so we need to verify that x can't be 0.

EXAMPLE 8   Solve $2x \ln x + x = 0$

Solution: **(Algebraically)**

- Transferring the term x over to the right side gives
  $$2x \ln x = -x.$$

- We divide by $2x$, because $x \neq 0$ (the domain of $\ln x$ is $x > 0$).

  $$\ln x = -\frac{1}{2} \longrightarrow x = e^{-1/2} \qquad \text{Exponential Form}$$

- Test $x = e^{-1/2} = \dfrac{1}{\sqrt{e}}$.

  Since $x = \dfrac{1}{\sqrt{e}} > 0$, it is an acceptable solution of the equation.

  Thus, $x = \dfrac{1}{\sqrt{e}}$ is the only root of the equation.

  $$x \approx .60653$$

With Graphing Calculator

Let $y1 = 2x \ln x + x$. Graph $y1$ and estimate the zero (x-intercept) of the graph as $x \approx .6065$

Remark: *As mentioned for exponential equations, not every equation involving logarithms can be solved using the algebraic method described above. However, we can use the graphing technique to estimate the roots, if there exist any.*

EXAMPLE 9   Solve $2x \ln x = 1$

Solution: $2x \ln x$ cannot be written as $\ln$ of a polynomial. So, we use the graphical method.

The roots of $2x \ln x = 1$ are the zeros of the function $2x \ln x - 1$. Let $y1 = 2x \ln x - 1$. Graph $y1 = 2x \ln x - 1$ on the standard window. Use ZOOM-IN and TRACE to estimate the zeros (x-intercepts) of the graph. Estimated root is 1.44.

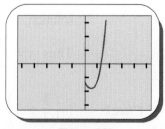

Figure 5.29

EXAMPLE 10 The subjective impression of loudness (L) is not a linear function of the physical intensity (I) of sound; it is a logarithmic function of the physical intensity (I), defined as

$$L = 10 \log \frac{I}{I_o},$$

where I_o is the lowest intensity at which the subjective pitch corresponding to the physical frequency of 1,000 hertz (cycles per second) can be experienced by an average person ($I_o = 10^{-12}$).

Find the physical intensity for a quiet automobile whose loudness is 40 decibels.

Solution: Using $I_o = 10^{-12}$ and $L = 40$, the above formula reduces to

$$40 = 10 \log \left(\frac{I}{10^{-12}} \right) = 10 \log (10^{12}\, I)$$

We solve this logarithmic equation for I.

- Dividing by 10 gives $\mathbf{4 = \log(10^{12}I)}$

- Changing to the exponential form gives $10^4 = 10^{12}\, I$ $\log x = \log_{10} x$

- Solving the equation for I gives
$$10^{-8} = I$$

Thus we conclude that for a quiet automobile the physical intensity equals 10^{-8}.

- Since $I = 10^{-8} = \dfrac{1}{10^8}$ keeps the argument of the logarithm positive,

$I = 10^{-8}$ is an acceptable solution of the equation.

EXERCISE 5.5

In exercises (1 - 26), solve the exponential equation.

1.	$8^{x-1} = 16$	**2.**	$9^{2x+1} = 27$	**3.**	$9^{2x-3} = 27^{1-x}$	**4.**	$4^{x+2} = 16^{3x-1}$
5.	$2^{x-1} = 7$	**6.**	$3^{x+1} = 5$	**7.**	$3^{2x-3} = 5$	**8.**	$3^{4x-1} = 7$
9.	$e^{2x-5} = 13$	**10.**	$e^{5x+2} = 11$	**11.**	$2^{x^2} = 15$	**12.**	$3^{x^2} = 12$
13.	$5^{x-2} = 2(3^{x-1})$	**14.**	$3^{x+1} = 5(7^{x-1})$	**15.**	$3^{2x+3} = 5 \cdot 2^{x-1}$	**16.**	$2^{3x+2} = 3 \cdot 11^{2x-1}$
17.	$e^{4x-5} = 3^{x-2}$	**18.**	$e^{x+4} = 2 \cdot 7^{3x-4}$	**19.**	$e^{3x-7} = 5^{2x}$	**20.**	$e^{2x} = 7 \cdot 3^{5x-1}$
21.	$9e^{-.5x} = 25$	**22.**	$5e^{-4x} = 16$	**23.**	$30e^{10x} = 70$	**24.**	$15e^{6x} = 25$
25.	$2^x = 15 \cdot 2^{-x} + 2$	**26.**	$3^x + 4 \cdot 3^{-x} = 5$				

In exercises (27-56), solve the logarithmic equation.

27.	$\log_2(3x - 7) = 0$	**28.**	$\log_4(4x + 5) = 0$	**29.**	$\log_3(2x - 3) - 1 = 0$
30.	$\log_2(3x - 1) = 1$	**31.**	$\log_5(5x + 6) = 2$	**32.**	$\log_3(4x + 7) = 2$

33. $3 \log_8 (2x - 7) = 2$ **34.** $2 \log_{16} (3x + 1) = 3$ **35.** $2 \log_4 (x - 1) = 3$

36. $3 \log_{27} (6x + 7) = 1$ **37.** $\ln (x^2 - 2x) = 0$ **38.** $\ln (x^2 + 4x) = 0$

39. $\ln (x^2 + 3x) = 0$ **40.** $\ln (x^2 - x) = 0$ **41.** $\log x + \log (x - 3) = 1$

42. $\log x + \log (x - 9) = 1$ **43.** $\log_8 (x - 2) + \log_8 x = 1$ **44.** $\log_6 x + \log_6 (x + 5) = 1$

45. $\ln (3x - 5) - \ln (x + 2) = \ln 2$ **46.** $\ln (5x + 3) - \ln (3x - 5) = \ln 3$

47. $\log_5 (x - 2) + \log_5 (x + 2) = 1$ **48.** $\log_6 (x - 3) + \log_6 (x - 4) = 1$

49. $\log_2 x + \log_2 (x - 2) = 3$ **50.** $\log_3 x + \log_3 (x - 8) = 2$

51. $2 (\log_4 x)^2 - 7 (\log_4 x) + 3 = 0$ **52.** $3 (\log_8 x)^2 - 4 (\log_8 x) + 1 = 0$

53. $\log_3 \left(\dfrac{x + 7}{x - 2} \right)^2 - 4 = 0$ **54.** $\log_4 \left(\dfrac{2x - 1}{x + 4} \right)^2 - 2 = 0$

55. $\log_2 \sqrt[3]{x} + \log_2 \sqrt[3]{x - 2} - 1 = 0$ **56.** $\log_3 \sqrt{x} + \log_3 \sqrt{x + 8} - 1 = 0$

57. Recall that pH of a solution is given by pH $= - \log [H^+]$. Find the hydrogen ion concentration of well water if its pH is 6.5.

58. The intensity R on the Richter Scale of an earthquake is given by $R = \log \dfrac{A}{P}$, where A is amplitude and P is the period. Find the period of an earthquake having an amplitude of 90,000 and which measured 5 on the Richter Scale.

59. Refer to Exercise 58. Find the amplitude of an earthquake whose period was .06 second and measured 5 on the Richter Scale.

60. According to the double declining - balance method, equipment costing C dollars with a useful life of N years will depreciate to a book value of B dollars in n years, where n is given by

$$n = \frac{\log B - \log C}{\log \left(1 - \dfrac{2}{N}\right)} = \frac{\log \dfrac{B}{C}}{\log \left(1 - \dfrac{2}{N}\right)}.$$

If equipment that cost $\$ 30{,}000$ has a useful life of 7 years, find its book value (B) after 3 years of use.

61. According to the Newton's law of cooling, the temperature (T) after time t of an object whose initial temperature was T_2 and was placed in the surroundings of temperature T_1 is given by

$$T(t) = T_1 + (T_2 - T_1) e^{kt}, \text{ for some constant } k.$$

Suppose for an object $k = - 0.1$, $T_1 = 70°$, and $T_2 = 120°$. Find the time it takes for the object's temperature to reach $90°$.

Writing Exercises

62. Explain the procedure for solving an exponential equation.

63. Explain the procedure for solving a logarithmic equation.

64. Explain the need for testing for extraneous roots of a logarithmic equation.

5.6 GROWTH AND DECAY FUNCTIONS (APPLICATIONS)

In the real world, things are continuously changing. For some situations the change is recorded as growth and for others as decay. For example, if the population A of bacteria is **growing continuously**, it depends upon time t and we write the growth expression as a function $A(t)$. We need to know the pattern of growth, because it helps us to write the expression for the function $A(t)$.

> **Objective ▶ ▶**
>
> In this section you will learn about:
>
> A. Solving Applied Problems (Growth and Decay).

In this section, we discuss functions that have an exponential pattern of growth (decay). For an exponential growth, the expression for the function fits into the model

* $A(t) = A_o e^{kt}, \qquad k > 0$

Similarly, the exponential decay model is

* $A(t) = A_o e^{-kt}, \quad k > 0$

$A_o =$ initial amount or value
$k =$ growth (decay) rate constant
$t =$ time

What if the growth (decay) is **not continuous** but **periodic**? For example, an amount is invested in an account that earns interest compounded every month? In such cases the above models change to

** $A(n) = A_o(1 + i)^n$, where

$i =$ growth (decay) rate per period
$n =$ number of periods

> * For a specific base b, the growth and decay models become
>
> $A = A_o b^{kt}, \ A = A_o b^{-kt}$ respectively.
>
> ** Initial Amount $= A_o$
>
> Amount at the end of the first period:
>
> $A_o +$ interest
> $A_o + iA_o = A_o(1 + i)$
>
> Amount at the end of the second period:
>
> $A_o(1 + i) +$ interest
> $A_o(1 + i) + iA_o(1 + i)$
> $A_o(1 + i)(1 + i) = A_o(1 + i)^2$ and so on.
>
> The amount at the end of n periods is
> $A_o(1 + i)^n$

This section deals with applied problems that fit into the above models. Once the right model is identified the rest is done by solving the exponential equation. We demonstrate **the procedure** in the following examples.

A. SOLVING APPLIED PROBLEMS (GROWTH OR DECAY)

EXAMPLE 1   A pathologist observes that the bacteria in the dish have been growing exponentially. Between the hours from 1 p.m to 4 p.m., the number of bacteria increases from 1000 to 1800.

   a.   How many bacteria should the pathologist expect at the time she leaves at 6 p.m?

   b.   At what time can she expect to have 4000 bacteria?

Solution:

   Step 1   Identify the model by determining whether the quantity is growing or decaying and whether the growth (decay) is continuous or periodic.

   In this example it is given that the growth is exponential and continuous.

Step 2   Write the expression for the growth (decay) function.

In this case $A(t) = A_o e^{kt}$

At   1 p.m., $t = 0$ and $A_0 = 1000$

$A(0) = 1000 = A_o e^o = A_o$

Therefore, $A(t) = 1000 e^{kt}$

Step 3   Exponential expressions have a second unknown k, called a **parameter.** Use the given information to find its value. Parameters do not vary for a specific problem, while variables such as t do vary. If the expression of the function has an extra unknown (other than the input t), then use the given information to find its value.

In this case we find the parameter k by using the fact that at 4 p.m. ($t = 3$) the number of bacteria $A(3)$ is 1800. This gives

$$1800 = 1000e^{k(3)}$$

Dividing by 1000 gives $1.8 = e^{3k}$

To solve this exponential equation, we take **ln** of both sides.

$$\textbf{ln 1.8} = \ln e^{3k} = 3k \ln e = \textbf{3}\textbf{\textit{k}}$$

This gives $k = \dfrac{\ln 1.8}{3} = 0.196$.

Step 4   Go back to Step 2 and substitute the value of the parameter k. Now we have determined the growth (decay) function.

In this example, the complete statement for the growth function is

$A(t) = 1000 e^{0.196t}$, where k is rounded to 3 decimal places.

Step 5   Now substitute the output or input, whichever is given, and solve the resulting equation. In this case,

a. $t = 5$, at 6 p.m. and we find $A(5)$ by substituting $t = 5$.
$A(5) = 1000e^{0.196(5)} = 1000e^{0.98} = 1000(2.664456) \approx \textbf{2664.}$

b. $A(t) = 4000$ and find t from the equation
$4000 = 1000e^{0.196t} \longrightarrow \textbf{4} = \textbf{\textit{e}}^{\,\textbf{0.196}\textbf{\textit{t}}}$.

To solve this exponential equation, we take ln of both sides.

$$\ln 4 = \ln e^{0.196t} = \textbf{0.196}\textbf{\textit{t}} \qquad\qquad \ln 4 = .196t$$

Therefore, $t = \dfrac{\ln 4}{0.196} = 7.073$ hours   .073 hours = .073 × 60 = 4.36 ≈ 5 min

≈ 7 hours and 5 min

Thus, she should wait until 8.05 p.m. when she will have 4000 bacteria.

EXAMPLE 2   The concentration of a drug in the body fluids depends on the time (t) elapsed after administration. Suppose the amount of the drug decreases exponentially, and 60% of the drug remains after 4 hours.

> **a.** Find the amount of drug remaining after 6 hours.
>
> **b.** How much time elapses until only half the drug remains?
>
> **c.** How much time elapses until 10% of the drug remains?

Solution:

- The amount of drug decreases exponentially, so it fits in the **exponential decay** model.

- The exponential decay function is given by $A(t) = A_o e^{-kt}$

- To find k we use the fact that when $t = 4$, $A(4) = 0.6A_o$. *

  This gives $0.6\,A_o = A_o e^{-k(4)}$

  Dividing by A_o we get: $0.6 = e^{-4k}$

  Taking **ln** of both sides gives

  $$\ln(0.6) = \ln(e^{-4k}) = (-4k)\ln e = -4k$$
  $$-0.511 = -4k$$
  $$0.13 = k \qquad \text{(round to two decimal places)}.$$

  > * 60% of initial amount
  >   = 60% of *Ao*
  >   = .6 *Ao*

- We go back to Step 2 and substitute $k = 0.13$ to obtain a complete statement of the function.

  $$A(t) = A_o e^{-kt} = A_o e^{-0.13\,t}$$

- **a.** After 6 hrs ($t = 6$), the amount of drug remaining is

  $$A(6) = A_o e^{-0.13(6)} = A_o(0.46)$$

  $e^{-.13(6)} \approx .46$

  Therefore, after 6 hours only 46% of the drug remains.

  b. We need to find t when $A(t) = 50\%$ of $A_o = 0.50\,A_o$.

  Thus, we replace $A(t)$ with. $0.5A_o$ and solve the equation for t.

  $0.5A_o = A_o e^{-0.13t}$. Dividing by A_o gives $0.5 = e^{-0.13t}$.

  Taking **ln** of both sides gives

  $\ln 0.5 = \ln e^{-0.13t} = -0.13t\,\ln e = \mathbf{-0.13\,t}$

  $\longrightarrow \quad -0.693 = -0.13\,t \longrightarrow t = \dfrac{0.693}{0.13} \approx 5.3 \text{ hours}$

  This gives $t = 5.3$ hours $\approx$ 5 hrs and 18 min.

  * Half-life = 5 hrs and 18 min.

  > * Half-life is the time it takes for the original amount to become half of itself.

  c. We replace $A(t)$ with $0.1\,A_o$ and solve for t.

  $0.1\,A_o = A_o e^{-0.13t}$

  Dividing by A_o gives $0.1 = e^{-0.13t}$

  Taking **ln** of both side gives

$$\ln (0.1) \;=\; \ln e^{-0.13t} \;=\; -0.13\,t \;\; \ln e \;=\; -0.13t$$

$$-2.3 \;=\; -0.13\,t \;\longrightarrow\; t = \frac{-2.3}{-1.3} \approx 17.7$$

This gives $t \approx 17.7$ hrs   **or**   17 hours and 42 min.

⬤**Note**   In the computation above, the value of k was rounded off to the nearest two decimal places.

This value was used to find t $\left(t = \dfrac{\ln 0.5}{0.13}\right)$ and the result was 5.3. Using a rounded value of k

for subsequent calculations can produce considerable error. With a calculator it is easy to store a much more exact value for k (to 10 decimal places or more). Hence a much accurate result for t can be obtained. From equation **(1)**, we have

$$\ln(0.6) \;=\; -4k \;\longrightarrow\; k = \frac{\ln (0.6)}{-4} \approx 0.1277064059$$

Store this in your calculator without writing all the digits on paper.

In part **(b)**

$$A(t) = A_o e^{-kt} \;\longrightarrow\; 0.5 A_o = A_o e^{-kt} \;\longrightarrow\; 0.5 = e^{-kt} \;\longrightarrow\; \ln (0.5) = -kt \;\longrightarrow\; t = \frac{\ln 0.5}{-k}$$

When computing this value, we use the RCL button on the calculator for k.

$\qquad t = 5.42766$ or $t \approx$ 5 hours 26 minutes.

Compare the result with the previous answer of 5 hours and 18 minutes.

In part **(c)**,

$$\ln (0.1) = -kt \;\rightarrow\; t = \frac{\ln (0.1)}{-k} = 18.0303 \text{ hours.}$$

Compare the result with the previous result of 17 hours and 42 min. Here $t \approx$ 18 hours and 2 min.

EXAMPLE 3   The half life of potassium K-42 is 12.5 hours.
   a.   How much of 10g sample is remaining after 7 hours?
   b.   How long will it be until 4 g remains?

Solutions:

   •   Clearly it is a decay model.

   •   The exponential decay function is described by $A(t) = A_o e^{-kt}$.

   •   To find k we use the fact that when $t = 12.5$,

$A(12.5) = 0.5 A_o$.

This gives $0.5 A_o = A_o e^{-k(12.5)}$

Dividing by A_o gives $0.5 = e^{-12.5k}$

Taking **ln** of both sides gives

$$\ln (0.5) \;=\; \ln e^{-12.5k} \;=\; -12.5\,k \cdot \ln e = -12.5\,k$$

$$k = \frac{\ln (0.5)}{-12.5} \approx 0.05545 \qquad\qquad \text{Store } k \text{ in the calculator.}$$

Short cut

$$k = \frac{-\ln(0.5)}{\text{Half-life}} = \frac{\ln 2}{\text{Half-life}}$$

$$\text{Half-life} = \frac{\ln 2}{k}.$$

$$-\ln .5 = -\ln \frac{1}{2}$$
$$= -(\ln 1 - \ln 2)$$
$$= \ln 2$$

- We substitute k in decay function. We get

$$A(t) = A_o e^{-kt}, \quad k = 0.05545$$

- **a.** We replace t with 7 and A_o with 10. We get

$$A(7) = 10\, e^{-7k} \approx 6.783 \qquad \text{Use the RCL button on your calculator for } k.$$

Therefore after 7 hours, only $6.783g$ of the sample remains.

b. We find t when $A(t) = 4$ and $A_o = 10$.

$$4 = 10\, e^{-kt}$$

$$0.4 = e^{-kt}$$

$$\ln(0.4) = \ln(e^{-kt}) = -kt$$

$$t = \frac{\ln(0.4)}{-k} \approx 16.524 \approx 16 \text{ hours } 31 \text{ minutes} \qquad \text{Use the RCL on calculator for } k.$$

Therefore, 4g of the sample will remain after 16 hours 31 minutes.

EXAMPLE 4 In Kenya the birth and death rates are 0.05 and 0.02 respectively. Find how long it takes the population of Kenya to double.

Solutions:

- Since the birth rate is larger than the death rate, it is a continuous growth model.

- The exponential growth of the population is given by the function

$$A(t) = A_o e^{kt}$$

- $k = \text{growth rate} = \text{birth rate} - \text{death rate}$
$$= 0.05 - 0.02 = 0.03$$

- $A(t) = A_o e^{0.03t}$

- We find t when $A(t) = 2A_o$ (double of the initial population A_o).

$$2 A_o = A_o e^{0.03t} \qquad \text{Divide by } A_o.$$

$$2 = e^{0.03t} \qquad \text{Take } \ln \text{ of both sides.}$$

$$\mathbf{\ln 2} = \ln e^{0.03t} = 0.03\, t \ln e = \mathbf{0.03t} \longrightarrow t = \frac{\ln 2}{0.03} \approx 23 \text{ years.}$$

In an exponential growth model, the **doubling time is** $\dfrac{\ln 2}{k}$.

EXAMPLE 5   Population of Escherichia coli bacteria doubles in every 20 minutes. What will a population of 2000 become in 10 hours?

Solutions:

- This represents a continuous growth model.

- The function that represents the continuous growth is $A(t) = A_0 e^{kt}$.

- To find **k** we use the fact that bacteria doubles in every 20 minutes.

$$A(t) = 2A_0 \text{ when } t = 20$$

$$2A_0 = A_0 e^{20k} \longrightarrow 2 = e^{20k}$$

$$\longrightarrow k = \frac{1}{20} \ln 2$$

- By substituting $A_0 = 2000$, we get:

$$A(t) = A_0 e^{\left(\frac{1}{20}\ln 2\right)t}$$

$$= 2000 \, e^{\left(\frac{1}{20}\ln 2\right)t}$$

- When $t = 600$ minutes
$\qquad 10 \text{ hr} \times \dfrac{60 \text{ minutes}}{1\text{hr}} = 600 \text{ minutes.}$

$$A(600) = 2000 \, e^{\left(\frac{1}{20}\ln 2\right)600}$$

$$= 2000 \, e^{30 \ln 2}$$

$$= 2000 \, e^{\ln (2^{30})} = \mathbf{2000 \times 2^{30}}$$

EXAMPLE 6   Suppose \$15,000 are invested in an account that pays

    a.   5% compounded monthly   **b.** 5% compounded continuously

    (i)   Find the value of the account at the end of the 10th year.

    (ii)   In how many years will the value of the account become \$75,000?

Solution :

a. •   The growth of the account is periodic.

- The periodic growth function is represented by

$$A(n) = A_o (1 + i)^n$$

$$= 15000 \,(1 + i)^n$$

- i = rate of growth per period

$$= \frac{5}{12}\% \approx 0.42\% \qquad \text{12 periods per year}$$

$$= 0.0042 \, *$$

> * The round off error for I will produce subsequent error. For greater accuracy store
>
> $$1 + i = 1 + \frac{5}{12}\%$$
>
> $$\approx 1.0041666667 \approx 1.0042$$
>
> in the calculator. Then use RCL, for $1 + i$ to compute.
>
> $$1500 \,(1 + i)^{120} \approx 24705.14$$

- We substitute $i = 0.0042$ in growth function; it gives

$$A(n) = 15000(1 + 0.0042)^n$$
$$= 15000(1.0042)^n$$

- (i) n = number of periods in 10 years

$$= 10(12) = 120$$

By substituting $n = 120$, we get

$$A(120) = 15000(1 + .0042)^{120} = 15000(1.0042)^{120}$$
$$= \$\,24{,}803.75$$

Thus, the value of the account at the end of the 10th year = \$ 24,803.75

(ii) We substitute $A(n) = 75000$ and solve for n.

$$75{,}000 = 15{,}000(1.0042)^n.$$
$$5 = (1.0042)^n$$

Taking **ln** of both sides gives

$\ln 5 = \ln(1.0042)^n = $ ***n (ln 1.0042)***

$$1.61 = 0.0042\,n \longrightarrow 383.3 = n$$

or $T = \dfrac{n}{12} = \dfrac{383.3}{12} \approx 32$ years. $**$

Thus, in approximately 32 years \$15,000 will become \$75,000.

b.
- The growth of the amount is continuous.

- The exponential growth function is
$$A(t) = A_o e^{kt} = 15000\, e^{kt}$$

- k = rate of growth = $5\% = 0.05$

- We substitute $k = 0.05$. $A(t) = 15000\, e^{0.05\,t}$

- (i) When $t = 10$, we have

$$A(10) = 15{,}000\, e^{0.05(10)} = 15{,}000\, e^{0.5}$$
$$\approx 15{,}000(1.65) \qquad e^{.5} \approx 1.6487$$
$$\approx 24{,}731$$

(ii) When $A(t) = 75{,}000$, we have

$$75{,}000 = 15{,}000\, e^{0.05t} \qquad \text{Dividing by 15,000}$$
$$5 = e^{0.05t} \qquad \text{Taking \textbf{ln} of both sides gives}$$
$$\mathbf{ln\,5} = \ln e^{0.05t} = 0.05t \cdot \ln e = \mathbf{0.05t}$$

$$t = \frac{\ln 5}{0.05} \approx 32.189 \text{ years or 32 years 2 months.}$$

> $**$ If $1 + i$ is stored in the calculator, we get
>
> $\ln 5 = \ln(1 + i)^n = n\ln(1 + i)$
>
> $n = \dfrac{\ln 5}{\ln(1+i)} \approx 387.07$
>
> $T = \dfrac{387.07}{12}$
>
> $= 32$ years, 3 months

EXERCISE 5.6

1. A bacteria culture starts with 120 bacteria and after three hours the population consists of 200 bacteria. Assuming that the culture grows exponentially, find the population after 5 hours.

2. A pathologist observes that a culture of cells triples in two days. Suppose the growth of the cells is exponential, find the number of cells in 6 days.

3. Assume that a population of ticks is growing exponentially. Find the number of ticks after 25 days if an initial population of 100 ticks triples in 10 days.

4. According to the last two censuses, the population of a country in 1980 was 4 million and in 1992 it was 9 million. Assuming the population grows at the same rate, what will the population of the country be in 1995?

5. Assuming that the world population increases exponentially from 2 billion in 1930 to 3 billion in 1960, estimate the population in the year 2010.

6. At the beginning of 1975 the population of a country was 40 million and growing at a rate of 3% per year. Assume that the growth is exponential. Estimate the population of the country at the beginning of the year 2010.

7. If the population of a bacteria doubles in 4 hours, how long will it take for it to triple its original size? (Assume that the growth of the bacteria is exponential).

8. Suppose the number of bacteria in a dish grows exponentially at the rate of 2% per hour. If 500 bacteria are present initially, find
   a. the number of bacteria present after 6 hours and
   b. the time required for the number of bacteria to become 2500.

9. If the sales of a company increased exponentially by 50% from 1985 to 1990, how much will the sales increase from 1990 to 1996?

10. Fifty grams of uranium decays exponentially and become 40 grams in 4 days. Find the half-life of uranium.

11. Thirty percent of a radioactive substance decays in four years. Assuming the decay is exponential, find half life of the substance.

12. The radioactive isotope strontium - 90 has a half-life of 25 years. Assume that 30 mg of the isotope decays exponentially, find
    a. how much of the isotope will remain in 10 years.
    b. in how many years will only 6 mg remain.

13. The radioactive element polonium has a half-life of 140 days. If 15 mg of this substance decays exponentially, find:
    a. how much of the substance would remain after 60 days.
    b. how long would it take before it becomes 4 mg.

14. A radioactive substance decays exponentially with a half-life 30 days. If 100 mg of the substance remains after 18 days,
    a. how much of the substance was present initially
    b. how much will remain after 20 days?
    c. how long will it take for 80% of the initial amount to disintegrate?

15. Almost all living things take up carbon as they grow. The carbon comes in two forms, normal carbon C^{12} and radioactive carbon C^{14}. While living, C^{14} is continually replenished. After the organism dies, C^{14} decays exponentially. It is known that the half-life of C^{14} is 5730 years. Find the age of a bone with only 30% of the original carbon C^{14} present.

16. A pathologist observes that there were 150 bacteria after the second day of the experiment and 280 bacteria after the fourth day of the experiment. If we assume that the population of bacteria increases exponentially, find the original number of bacteria in the dish.

17. Assume that a car costing $25,000 depreciates exponentially and loses 20% of its value during the fifth year of its life. Find its book value after the third year of its use.

18. If $6000 is invested at 5% interest, find the value (amount) of the account at the end of 5 years if the interest is compounded
    a. annually   **b.** semiannually   **c.** monthly   **d.** weekly   **e.** daily   **f.** continuously

19. If $10,000 is invested at 6% interest rate, find the amount (A) of the account at the end of 8 years if the interest is compounded
    a. annually   **b.** monthly   **c.** daily   **d.** continuously

20. Find the investment amount that becomes $30,000 if it is invested at 10% interest for 12 years. Assume that the interest is compounded
    a. semiannually   **b.** continuously

21. How long will it take for an account to double in value if the interest rate is 5.25% compounded continuously?

22. How long does it take for a deposit of $P to double at 10% interest compounded continuously?

23. In India .06 and .02 are the birth and death rates, respectively. Find how long it takes the population of India to double.

24. A fast growing bacteria doubles every 30 minutes. Find the number of bacteria after 8 hours if the initial count was 100.

25. There is a 10% increase in the sales every 3 months. If the present sales are 1.5 million, find the sales after 2 years.

Writing Exercises

26. Suppose you picked up some bacterial infection. What mathematical model describes its growth?

27. Suppose you have fever due to bacterial infection and you start taking antibiotics. What mathematical model describes the effect of the drug on the amount of bacteria in the body.

28. What is the importance of constant k in $A = A_o e^{kt}$ and $A = A_o e^{-kt}$?

5.7 CHAPTER SUMMARY

1. A function f is said to be **one-to-one** provided the function has different outputs for different inputs. This means that if $f(x_1) = f(x_2)$, then $x_1 = x_2$.

2. The **horizontal line test** says that a function is one-to-one if and only if each horizontal line intersects the graph of the function in at most one-point.

3. If f is a one-to-one function with domain D and range R, then the **inverse function** f^{-1} exists and has domain R and range D.

4. The graph of f^{-1} is obtained by reflecting the graph of $y = f(x)$ in the $45°$ line $y = x$.

5. A point $P(x, y)$ on $y = f(x)$, changes to (y, x) on the inverse function.

6. If $b > 0$ and $b \neq 1$, then the **exponential function** with base b is given by $f(x) = b^x$.

7. Important **properties of exponential function** $f(x) = b^x$ are :

    (i)   The domain of $f(x)$ consists of all real numbers.

    (ii) The range of $f(x)$ consists of all positive numbers.

    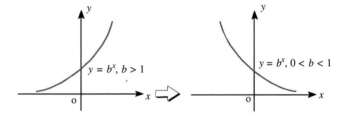

    (iii) For $b > 1$, the graph of $y = b^x$ is an **increasing** graph.

    (iv) For $0 < b < 1$, the graph of $y = b^x$ is a **decreasing** graph.

    (v)   The y-intercept of the graph of $f(x)$ is 1.

    (vi) The x-axis is the **asymptote** of $y = f(x)$.

    (vii) The function $y = b^x$ is one-to-one.

    (viii) The function $y = b^x$ has no zero.

8. $\log_a x$ is the **exponent** of "a" that gives x, i.e. $a^{\log_a x} = x$.

9. $y = b^x$ is called the **exponential form**, whereas $x = \log_b y$ is called its **logarithmic form**.

10. The **logarithmic function** $f(x) = \log_b x$, $b > 0$, and $b \neq 1$ is the inverse function of the exponential function $y = b^x$.

11. The logarithm with base 10 is called the **common logarithm** and is written as $\log_{10} x$ or simply $\log x$.

12. The logarithm with base e is called the **natural logarithm** and is written as $\log_e x$ or simply $\ln x$.

13. The **guiding principle** for finding the domain of the logarithmic function is that its argument must be positive.

14. The vertical asymptotes of a logarithmic function are obtained by equating its argument to zero.

15. Important **observations of the logarithmic function** $f(x) = \log_b x$ for $b > 0$ and $b \neq 1$:

(i) $x = 1$ is the only **zero** of the function.

(ii)   The graph of $f(x) = \log_b x$ has no y-intercept.

(iii) $x = 0$ is the **asymptote** of $y = f(x)$.

(iv)   For large x, $|f(x)|$ is also large.

(v)   The graph of $y = f(x)$ is an **increasing** graph for $b > 1$ and **decreasing** for $0 < b < 1$.

(vi)   The domain of $f(x)$ consists of all positive real numbers.

(vii) The range of $f(x)$ consists of all real numbers.

16. Important **properties of logarithms**

(i) $\log_b b = 1$

(ii) $\log_b 1 = 0$ $0 < b < 1$.

(iii) $\log_b MN = \log_b M + \log_b N$ Product Rule.

(iv) $\log_b \dfrac{M}{N} = \log_b M - \log_b N$ Quotient Rule.

(v) $\log_b M^n = n \log_b M$ Power Rule.

(vi) $b^{\log_b x} = x$ Inverse Rule.

(vii) $\log_b M = \dfrac{\log_a M}{\log_a b}$ Change of Base Rule.

(viii) $\log_a b \cdot \log_b c \cdot \log_c d \cdot \log_d x = \log_a x$ Chain Rule.

17. An **exponential equation** is an equation involving exponential functions.

18. The **zeros** of an exponential function $f(x)$ are the same as the **roots** of the exponential equation $f(x) = 0$.

19. An equation involving logarithmic functions is called a **logarithmic equation.**

20. The **zeros** of a logarithmic function $f(x)$ are the same as the roots of the logarithmic equation $f(x) = 0$.

21. A quantity A that **grows** exponentially has the equation.

$$A(t) = A_0 e^{kt} \qquad \begin{cases} A_0 = \text{initial value of } A \, ; \\ \quad k = \text{growth rate constant} \\ \quad t = \text{time} \end{cases}$$

22.   A quantity A that **decays** exponentially has the equation $A(t) = A_o e^{-kt}$.

23.   The half -life $= \dfrac{\ln 2}{k}$ for exponential decay.

24.   The doubling time $= \dfrac{\ln 2}{k}$ for exponential growth.

25.   If a quantity A is **growing periodically**, then the quantity after n **periods** is given by
$$A(n) = A_o (1 + i)^n,$$
where i is the growth rate per period and A_o is the initial value of A.

26.   If a quantity is **decaying periodically**, then the quantity remaning after n periods is given by
$$A(n) = A_o (1 - i)^n,$$

27.   The **Newton's Law of Cooling** is stated as
$$T(t) \;=\; T_1 + (T_2 - T_1)e^{kt}, \text{ where}$$

$T(t)$ is the temprature of the body after time t,

T_2 is the body's initial temprature,

T_1 is the temprature of the surroundings, and

k is some constant.

28.   The intensity R on the **Richter scale** of an earthquake is given by $R = \log \dfrac{A}{P}$, where A is the **amplitude** and P is the **period** in seconds.

29.   The **loudness** (L) of a sound with intensity (I) is given by $L = k \ln I$ for some constant k.

30.   The **double voltage gain** (db-gain) is given by
db-gain $= 20 \log \dfrac{V_o}{V_i}$, where $V_o = $ output voltage and $V_i = $ input voltage.

31.   The **decibel voltage gain** is also given by db-gain $= 10 \log \dfrac{P_o}{P_i}$, where

P_o = power output and

P_i = power input

32.   According to the double declining-balance method an equipment costing C dollars that has a useful life of N years will depreciate to a book value of B dollars in n years, where n is given by
$$n = \frac{\log \dfrac{B}{C}}{\log \left(1 - \dfrac{2}{N}\right)}.$$

5.8 CHAPTER REVIEW

In exercises (1-10), determine whether or not the function is one-to-one.

1. $f(x) = 2 - x^2$ **2.** $f(x) = 7 - 11x$ **3.** $g(x) = x^3 + 1$ **4.** $g(x) = x^4 - 10$

5. $h(x) = \sqrt{x+1}$ **6.** $h(x) = \sqrt{x-5}$ **7.** $F(x) = |x-1| + 2$

8. $f(x) = 5 - |x+3|$ **9.** $G(x) = \dfrac{|x|}{x}, \ x \neq 0$ **10.** $g(x) = |x| - x$

In exercises (11-18), find the inverse function and find its domain and range.

11. $f(x) = 9x - 2$ **12.** $f(x) = -5x + 12$ **13.** $f(x) = \sqrt{x-2}$ **14.** $f(x) = \sqrt{2x+3}$

15. $f(x) = \dfrac{5x-9}{x-3}$ **16.** $f(x) = \dfrac{x+5}{2x-11}$ **17.** $f(x) = x^2 - 1, \ x \geq 0$ **18.** $f(x) = x^3 + 5$

In exercises (19-22), sketch the graph of f^{-1} if f is the function defined by the graph.

19. 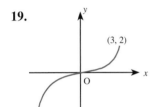   **20.** 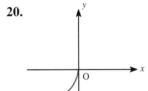   **21.** 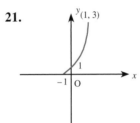   **22.**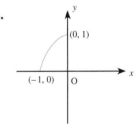

In exercises (23-30), sketch the graph of the function.

23. $f(x) = \left(\dfrac{2}{5}\right)^x$ **24.** $f(x) = \left(\dfrac{1}{12}\right)^x$ **25.** $g(x) = e^{3x}$ **26.** $g(x) = (7.5)^x$

27. $h(x) = \ln(x-3) + 1$ **28.** $g(x) = \ln(x-2) - 1$ **29.** $f(x) = \log_2(x-1) - 1$ **30.** $f(x) = \log_3(x+3) + 1$

In exercises (31-40), find the domain of the function.

31. $f(x) = e^{x-1} + 2$ **32.** $g(x) = e^{x+10} - 11$ **33.** $g(x) = \ln(x-1) + 1$ **34.** $h(x) = \log_3(4x+7) - 10$

35. $h(x) = \log_4(x^2 - 25)$ **36.** $g(x) = \ln(x^2 - 16)$ **37.** $f(x) = \log_2\sqrt{x-2}$ **38.** $h(x) = \log_7\sqrt{x+12}$

39. $g(x) = \ln(x^2 - 3x - 4)$ **40.** $f(x) = \log_3(2x^2 - 3x - 9)$

In exercises (41-68), solve the equation.

41. $x^2 e^x - 2xe^x = 3e^x$ **42.** $2e^{2x} \cdot x^2 = e^{2x}x + 3e^{2x}$ **43.** $x^3 e^{-x} - 4x^2 e^{-x} = 0$ **44.** $x^3 e^{-3x} + 12x^2 e^{-3x} = 0$

45. $\log_3(9x-2) = 0$ **46.** $\log_7(3x+17) = 0$ **47.** $\log_2\dfrac{3x-2}{1-x} = 0$ **48.** $\log_{11}\dfrac{5x+7}{3x-11} = 0$

49. $16^{3x-2} = 8^{x+1}$ **50.** $3^{3x-7} = 11$ **51.** $4^{2x-3} = 6$ **52.** $27^{2x-9} = 3^{5x+1}$

53. $e^{7x-3} = 12$ **54.** $e^{11x+5} = 13$ **55.** $7 \cdot 3^{x-1} = 2^{3x+2}$ **56.** $3 \cdot 2^{2x+7} = 5^{5x-1}$

57. $3\log_8(3x-5) = 2$ **58.** $2\log_4(2x+7) = 5$ **59.** $\log x + \log(x+9) = 1$ **60.** $\log_7 x + \log_7(x+6) = 1$

61. $2 \log_3 x - \log_3 (x-4) - \log_3 2 = 2$ **62.** $\log_5 (14x+3) - 2 \log_5 x = 1$ **63.** $\ln (5x-7) - \ln (x-1) = \ln 3$

64. $\ln (7x-9) + \ln 2 = \ln (4x-5)$ **65.** $\log x^2 - (\log x)^2 = 0$ **66.** $(\log x)^2 - \log x^3 + 2 = 0$

67. $\log_2 (x-2) - 2 \log_2 x + 3 = 0$ **68.** $\log_3 (x+4) - 2 \log_3 x + 2 = 0$

In exercises (69-72), simplify the logarithm so that no argument contains a product, quotient or a power.

69. $\log \dfrac{100 \, x^2 \, y^3}{(x+2)^4}$ **70.** $\log_7 \dfrac{49 \, (x+y)^3}{x^{11} \, y^7}$ **71.** $\ln \dfrac{e^3 \, (x+1)^2 \, (x-2)^5}{\sqrt{2x+1}}$ **72.** $\ln \dfrac{(x+7)^7 \, \sqrt[3]{x-y}}{e^2 \, \sqrt{2x+3y}}$

In exercises (73-76), write each expression as a single logarithm with coefficient 1.

73. $\log_2 x + \log_2 (x+3) + 2$ **74.** $\log_3 (x+11) - \log_3 (2x+7) - 2$

75. $2 \ln (x+1) - \dfrac{1}{2} \ln (x+2) - 3 \ln (x-1)$ **76.** $\ln (3x-5) + 7 - \dfrac{1}{3} \ln (x+4) - 2 \ln (2x+3)$

In exercises (77-82), find the value of the expression.

77. $\log_8 4$ **78.** $\log_{27} \left(\dfrac{1}{3} \right)$ **79.** $\ln e^4$ **80.** $\ln e^{-7}$ **81.** $e^{2 \ln 2 + 1}$ **82.** $e^{3 \ln 2 - 2}$

In exercises (83-86), convert the given log in terms of *ln*.

83. $\log_7 5$ **84.** $\log_{11} 19$ **85.** $\log_a x$ **86.** $\log_7 y$

87. The half-life of carbon - 14 (C^{14}) is 5730 years. If you discover that 80 % of the original amount of carbon - 14 is still in the bones, find the age of the bones.

88. The population of a city is growing exponentially. In 1980 the population was 2.3 million and 1990 the population was 3.8 million. Estimate

  a. the population in the year 2010. **b.** the year when the population is 5 million.

89. What amount should be deposited now in an account that pays 5 % per annum compounded every month, so that in 12 years it becomes $60,000?

Writing Exercises

90. How are the properties of exponents related to the properties of logarithms.

91. Explain the logarithm notation.

5.9 CHAPTER TEST

1. Find the inverse function of $f(x) = \dfrac{2-7x}{x-1}$ and state the domain and range of f^{-1}.

2. Sketch the graph:

  a. $f(x) = e^{x-2} + 1$ **b.** $g(x) = \ln (x+3) - 1$

3. Find the domain:

  a. $f(x) = e^{x+1} - 2$ **b.** $g(x) = \ln (x^2 - 4x - 5)$

4. Solve the equation for *x*.

    a. $x^4 e^{2x} = 4x^2 e^{2x}$ **b.** $5^{3x-1} = 8$ **c.** $2 \log_4 (5x - 9) = 3$

    d. $\log_2 x + \log_2 (x - 2) = 3$ **e.** $\ln (9x + 5) = \ln (2x - 3) + \ln 2$

5. Simplify: $\ln \dfrac{e^2 (x+3)^2 \sqrt{x+9}}{(x-2)^3}$.

6. Write $2 \log x - 3 \log (x + 7) - \dfrac{1}{2} \log (x + 3) + 1$ as a single log with coefficient 1.

7. Find the value of the following expressions:

    a. $\log_9 27$ **b.** $\ln e^2 + 3 \ln 1$ **c.** $e^{(3 \ln 2 + 2)}$

8. Express in terms of ln.

    a. $\log_3 8$ **b.** $\log_b 3x$

9. Assume that the population of fruit flies grows exponentially. A population of 200 fruit flies become 500 in 8 days. Estimate

    a. the number of fruit flies after 15 days.

    b. how long will it take for the number of fruit flies to reach 800.

10. If 50 grams of a radioactive substance decays to 40 grams in 6 days, find the half-life of this substance assuming that the substance is decaying exponentially.

11. Find the initial deposit that became $5000 in 5 years in an account paying 7% annual interest compounded daily.

Variation and Conic Sections

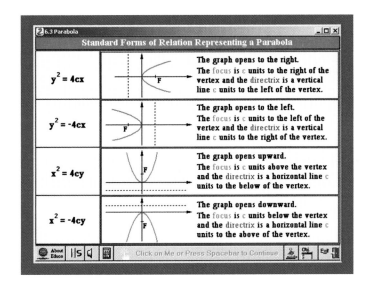

VARIATION AND CONIC SECTIONS

6

Recall that a complete statement of a function is written as

$$f(x) = \text{expression in } x$$

We start this chapter with functions for which the 'expression' part can be written very easily. The statements of such functions are **variation** type statements. We will next consider expressions in two letters, x and y, which may not represent functions. The graphs of these special second degree relations have the shapes of the cross sections of a cone. These graphs are called **conic sections.**

The discussion in this chapter is divided into five sections.

6.1 VARIATION

In this section we will discuss different types of variation statements that can be translated into mathematical expressions. We shall discuss three types of such statements:

- Direct Variation
- Inverse Variation
- Joint Variation

Objectives ▶ ▶

In this section you will learn about:

A. Direct Variation;

B. Inverse Variation; and

C. Joint Variation.

A. DIRECT VARIATION

A statement like "weight W varies directly as the height h" is equivalent to the statement that weight W depends upon height h and is equal to a constant times height h.

In function notation, $W(h) = k\,h$, where k is called a constant of variation, and which can be found by using the given information. In general, we state the direct variation as follows.

> **Direct Variation**
>
> If y varies directly as x (or if y is directly proportional to x), then $y(x) = k\,x$, for some constant k.
>
> The constant k is called the **constant of variation** or **constant of proportionality.**

EXAMPLE 1   Suppose Z varies **directly** as x and $Z(x)$ is 50 when $x = 3$
Write a complete statement for the function Z.

Solution: Since Z varies directly as x, so $Z(x) = k\,x$.
We find k by using the fact that when $x = 3$, $Z(3) = 50$. This gives

$$50 = 3k \quad \longrightarrow \quad k = \frac{50}{3}$$

Thus, a complete statement for the function Z is

$$Z(x) = \frac{50}{3}x \; .$$

EXAMPLE 2   Hooke's law states that the force $\boldsymbol{F}$ exerted on a spring varies directly as the amount of the stretch $\boldsymbol{x}$ of the spring. If a force of 90 lb stretches the spring 9 in, then write a complete expression for the force as a function of length of the stretch.

Solution: Because the force F varies directly as the amount x of stretch, we have

$$F(x) = k\ x.$$

To find k, we use the fact that when $x = 9$ in or $\frac{9}{12}$ ft $= \frac{3}{4}$ ft, then $F\left(\frac{3}{4}\right) = 90$.

Also $F\left(\frac{3}{4}\right) = \frac{3}{4}k$. This gives $\quad 90 = \left(\frac{3}{4}\right)k \quad \longrightarrow \quad k = 120$

Therefore, $\boldsymbol{F(x) = 120x.}$

B. Inverse Variation

The statement "the intensity $\boldsymbol{I}$ of light **varies inversely** as the square of the distance $\boldsymbol{d}$ from the source of light" says that the intensity $\boldsymbol{I}$ depends upon the distance $\boldsymbol{d}$ and is given by a constant $\boldsymbol{k}$ divided by the square of $\boldsymbol{d}$. Another way to say this is that I equals a constant k times **the inverse of d squared.**

In short,

$$I(d) = k \cdot \frac{1}{d^2} = \frac{k}{d^2}$$

> **Inverse Variation**
>
> If a quantity y **varies inversely** as x (or if y is inversely proportional to x), then $y(x) = \dfrac{k}{x}$, for some constant k.

EXAMPLE 3   Suppose the mass density ρ at a point $P(x, y)$ varies inversely as the square of the distance from the x-axis. Suppose the density at $(2, 4)$ is 10 lb/ft^3. Write a complete statement for the density function.

Solution: Since the density ρ at $P(x, y)$ varies inversely as the square of the distance from the x-axis, so

$$\rho(y) = \frac{k}{y^2}$$

At (2, 4), the density is $\rho(4) = 10$. Substituting $y = 4$ and $\rho(y) = 10$, we get:

$$10 = \frac{k}{4^2} \quad \longrightarrow \quad k = 160$$

Thus, a complete statement for the density function is

$$\rho(y) = \frac{160}{y^2}.$$

C. JOINT VARIATION

> **Joint Variation**
>
> If Z **varies jointly** as x and y then $Z(x, y) = k\,x\,y$, for some constant k.

⬤Note   Here Z is a function of two variables.

EXAMPLE 4   Suppose that for a fish tank with a square base of side x, the force F on the base **varies jointly as the square of the side x and the depth y** of water. If it is known that a force of 50 lb is exerted on the square base of a tank whose base side is 1 ft and the water level is 1 ft above the base, then write a general expression for the force function.

Solution: Since the force F varies jointly as the square of side x and depth y, so

$F(x, y) = k\,x^2\,y$

We use the fact that the force is 50 lb when $x = 1$ ft and $y = 1$ ft.

We get $50 = k(1)^2\,(1) \quad \longrightarrow \quad k = 50$.

Thus, a general expression for the force function is $F(x, y) = 50\,x^2 y$.

EXAMPLE 5   Determine whether the function represents a **direct, inverse,** or **joint** variation, or none of these.

a. $f(x) = \dfrac{3}{2x}$

b. $g(x) = 100\,x + 3$

c. $h(x) = 6x^2$

d. $f(x, y) = 2xy^2$

e.

x	−2	−1	8	1	2	3
y	−2	−4	$\frac{1}{2}$	4	2	$\frac{4}{3}$

f.

x	1	2	3	4	5	6
y	3	6	9	12	15	18

Solutions: **a.** $f(x) = \dfrac{3}{2}\left(\dfrac{1}{x}\right)$, therefore, it represents an **inverse** variation of x.

Here $k = \dfrac{3}{2}$.

b. $g(x) = 100\,x + 3$ does not represent any of these variations. Had it been $g(x) = 100\,x$, then it would have been a direct variation.

c. $h(x) = 6x^2$ implies that the quantity h **varies directly** as the square of x.

d. $f(x, y) = 2xy^2$ says that the quantity f **varies jointly** as x and the square of y.

e.   From the table, $xy = 4$ for all pairs x, y. This gives $y = \dfrac{4}{x}$. So the function represents an **inverse variation.**

f.   For a **direct variation** $y = kx$ or $\dfrac{y}{x} = k$, a constant. We check that for each pair, $\dfrac{y}{x} = 3$, a constant. Thus the function represents a **direct variation.**

EXERCISE 6.1

In exercises (1-20), write a complete statement of the function.

1.   The quantity m varies directly as the square of t.

2.   The quantity y varies directly as the cube of x.

3.   The quantity p varies directly as the square root of q.

4.   The quantity I varies directly as the cube root of s.

5.   The quantity d is inversely proportional to t.

6.   The quantity C is inversely proportional to square root of p.

7.   The quantity I is inversely proportional to the square of m.

8.   The quantity z varies inversely as the cube of x.

9.   The quantity m varies jointly as n and p.

10.   The quantity p varies jointly as x and square of y.

11.   The quantity s varies directly as d and inversely as the square of r.

12.   The quantity p varies directly as square of q and inversely as the cube of r.

13.   The quantity F varies directly as the product of M_1 and M_2 and inversely as the square of r.

14.   The quantity V varies directly as cube of m and inversely as the square root of r.

15.   The mass (m) at the point $P(x, y)$ varies as the square root of the distance of P from the x-axis.

16.   The quantity R is directly proportional to the product of the squares of x and y.

17.   The mass (m) at the point $P(x, y)$ varies inversely as the square of the distance of P from the y-axis.

18.   The density (ρ) at the point $P(x, y)$ varies directly as the distance of P from the origin.

19.   The density (ρ) at the point $P(x, y)$ varies directly as the product of the distances from the coordinate axes.

20.   The quantity p at the point $P(x, y)$ varies inversely as the product of the distances of P from the coordinate axes.

In exercises (21-28), write a complete statement of the function and then use the given information to find the constant of variation.

21. m varies directly as x, and $m = 50$ when $x = 5$.

22. p varies directly as square of t, and $p = 10$ when $t = 2$.

23. **Z** varies inversely as the square of *t*, and *Z* = 5 when *t* = 2.

24. **I** varies inversely as the square root of *x*, and *I* = 20 when *x* = 16.

25. **F** varies directly as *x*, and *F* = 90 when *x* = 14.

26. **s** varies inversely as the square of *r*, and *s* = 14 when *r* = 3.

27. **V** varies directly as **x** and inversely as the square root of *y*, and *V* = 50 when *x* = 2 and *y* = 9.

28. **V** varies jointly as square of *x* and cube of *y*, and *V* = 12 when *x* = 2 and *y* = 3.

In exercises (29-42), determine whether the function represents a direct, inverse, joint variation, or none of these.

29. $S(x) = Kx^2$ 30. $Z(x) = \dfrac{K}{x^3}$ 31. $A(x,y) = K\,y\,x^2$ 32. $p(t) = K\,t^4$

33. $V(x) = \dfrac{5}{3x}$ 34. $I(x) = 4x + 3$ 35. $M(x) = 5x - 3$ 36. $L(x, y) = K\,x^3\sqrt{y}$

37. $N(y) = \dfrac{7}{\sqrt{y}}$ 38. $M(x, y) = 2x^2 y^2 - 7$

39.

x	-3	-2	-1	1	2	3
y	$\dfrac{-7}{3}$	$\dfrac{-7}{2}$	-7	7	$\dfrac{7}{2}$	$\dfrac{7}{3}$

40.

x	1	4	9	16	25	36
y	5	10	15	20	25	30

41.

x	-8	-6	-4	4	8	10
y	-16	-12	-8	8	16	20

42.

x	-3	-2	-1	1	2	3
y	$\dfrac{4}{9}$	1	4	4	1	$\dfrac{4}{9}$

43. The distance (*d*) that a spring stretches varies directly as the weight on the spring. A weight of 100 lb stretches the spring by six inches. How far will a weight of 80 lb stretch a spring?

44. According to Hooke's law, the force F exerted on a spring is directly proportional to the amount of stretch *x* of the spring. If a force of 100 lb stretches the spring by 8 in, how far will a force of 75 lb stretch it?

45. Under a constant pressure, the volume (*V*) of a gas is directly proportional to the temperature (*T*). If the gas occupies 60 in³ when the temperature is 70°, find the volume of the gas at 100° temperature.

46. Hooke's law states that the force F exerted on a spring varies directly as the amount of stretch *x* of the spring. A force of 80 lb stretches the spring by 8 inches. How much force is needed to stretch the spring by 10 inches?

47. Under a constant temperature, the pressure (*P*) of a gas is inversely proportional to the volume (*V*). If a volume of 25ft³ of the gas exerts a pressure of 4 lb, find the pressure when the volume increases to 40ft³.

48. Under a constant pressure, the volume (*V*) of a gas is directly proportional to the temperature (*T*). If the gas occupies 80 in³ when the temperature is 90°, at what temperature will the volume of the gas be 96 in³?

49. The distance (*d*) covered by a falling object varies directly as the square of the time *t*. If the object falls 100 feet in 5 seconds, how far will it fall in 8 seconds?

50. Under a constant temperature, the pressure (*P*) of a gas is inversely proportional to the volume (*V*). A volume of 30ft³ of the gas exerts a pressure of 6 lb. Find the volume of the gas when the pressure is 9 lb.

51. The time (*T*) for one complete oscillation of a simple pendulum is directly proportional to the square root of the length of the pendulum. If a pendulum of length 3 feet takes 1 second to complete one oscillation, find the time for one oscillation of pendulum of length 4 feet.

52. The distance (*d*) covered by a falling object varies directly as the square of the time *t*. If the object falls 80 feet in 4 seconds, in how much time it will fall 125 feet?

53. The electric resistance (R) in a cable is inversely proportional to the radius (r) of the cable. If a cable with radius 0.25 in exerts an electrical resistance of 0.2 ohm, find the resistance of cable with a radius of 0.7 in.

54. The time (T) for one complete oscillation of a simple pendulum varies directly as the square root of the length of the pendulum. If a pendulum of length 5 feet takes 2 seconds to complete one oscillation, find the length of a pendulum which takes 3 seconds to complete one oscillation.

55. The strength (S) of a rectangular wooden beam of given length varies jointly as the width (x) and the square of depth (y). If a beam of width 2 inches and depth 4 inches (a 2 × 4 stud) has the strength of 200 pounds, find the strength of a beam (of the same length and wood) of width 4 inches and depth 6 inches.

56. The electric resistance (R) in a cable is inversely proportional to the radius (r) of the cable. If a cable with radius 0.5 inches exerts an electrical resistance of 0.3 ohm, find the radius of a cable with electric resistance of 0.4 ohm.

57. The strength (S) of a rectangular wooden beam varies jointly as the width (x) and square of the depth (y) and inversely as the length (z) of the beam. If a 2" × 4" beam of length 12 feet has a strength of 200 pounds, find the strength of the beam of the same wood that has cross section with width of 6 inches, depth of 6 inches, and length of 16 feet.

58. The strength (S) of a rectangular wooden beam of given length varies jointly as the square of width (x) and the depth (y). If a beam of width 3 inches and depth 5 inches has the strength of 250 pounds, find the strength of a beam (of the same length and wood) of width 4 inches and depth 6 inches.

Writing Exercises

59. Describe what is meant by a "direct variation".

60. Describe what is meant by an "inverse variation".

6.2 CIRCLE

Objectives ▶ ▶

In this section you will learn about:

A. Finding an Equation of a Circle;

B. Graphing a Circle; and

C. Graphing Half Circles.

The cross section of a right circular cone by a plane perpendicular to its axis is a circle.

Figure 6.1

A circle is the first member of the family of conic sections that we will discuss in this section. We will find a relation that describes a circle.

> **Circle**
> A circle consist of points in a plane equidistance from a fixed point, called the **center.** The distance from the center to a point on the circle is called the **radius.**

A. FINDING AN EQUATION OF A CIRCLE

Let us find a relation in x and y that describes a circle with center at (h, k) and radius r. Whenever we need to find any such relation, we use the three steps described below.

Step **1**   We draw a circle with center at (h, k) and radius r (Figure 6.2).

Step 2   The circle consists of points and the location of each point is given by its coordinates. Therefore, we take any point $Q(x, y)$ on the circle.

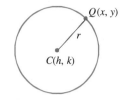

Figure 6.2

Step 3   To find a relationship between x and y, we use the fact that the distance between $Q(x, y)$ and the center $C(h, k)$ is the radius r.

The distance $CQ = r$.

By using the distance formula, we get:

$$* \quad \sqrt{(x - h)^2 + (y - k)^2} = r$$

> *   The distance (d) between two points (x_1, y_1) and (x_2, y_2) is given by
> $$d = \sqrt{(x_2 - x_1)^2 + (y_2 - y_1)^2}$$

By squaring both sides we get: $(x - h)^2 + (y - k)^2 = r^2$

> **Relation (Equation) of a circle**
>
> An equation or relation that describes a circle of radius r and center at (h, k) is
> $$(x - h)^2 + (y - k)^2 = r^2$$
> This is the standard form of the circle.

Remarks: *1.*   *If we expand each square, we obtain*

$x^2 - 2xh + h^2 + y^2 - 2yk + k^2 = r^2$ *or*

$x^2 + y^2 - 2xh - 2yk = r^2 - h^2 - k^2$

From this we notice three important observations.

(i)   The coefficient of x^2 = coefficient of y^2.

(ii)   There is no xy term.

(iii) $r^2 - h^2 - k^2$ is a constant.

2.   *In general, any equation of the form $Ax^2 + Ay^2 + Bx + Cy = D$ will represent a circle, or a point, or the empty set (why?).*

3.   *According to the vertical line test, it is a relation and not a function.*

EXAMPLE 1   Find a relation that describes the circle with end points of its diameter at $(-1, 2)$ and $(3, 4)$.

Solution: We need to find the center (h, k) and the radius (r) before we use the relation $(x - h)^2 + (y - k)^2 = r^2$

The coordinates of the center are the coordinates of the midpoint of the line segment joining $(-1, 2)$ and $(3, 4)$. Therefore,

$$h = \frac{-1 + 3}{2} = \frac{2}{2} = \mathbf{1} \quad \text{and} \quad k = \frac{2 + 4}{2} = \frac{6}{2} = \mathbf{3}.$$

Thus, the center is at **(1, 3)**.

By definition, the radius (r) is the distance from the center to a point on the circle. We know two such points, namely $(-1, 2)$ and $(3, 4)$.

Let us find the distance between $(3, 4)$ and the center $(1, 3)$.

This gives: $r = \sqrt{(1-3)^2 + (3-4)^2} = \sqrt{(-2)^2 + (-1)^2} = \sqrt{4+1} = \sqrt{5}$

Now we substitute $h = 1$, $k = 3$ and $r = \sqrt{5}$ in the equation $(x - h)^2 + (y - k)^2 = r^2$

$$(x - 1)^2 + (y - 3)^2 = \left(\sqrt{5}\right)^2$$

$$(x - 1)^2 + (y - 3)^2 = 5$$

$$x^2 - 2x + 1 + y^2 - 6y + 9 = 5$$

$$x^2 + y^2 - 2x - 6y + 5 = 0$$

⬤ **Note**   Alternatively, we can find the radius by using the fact that radius is equal to half the diameter.

B. GRAPHING A CIRCLE

To graph a circle we need its center and the radius. The following example shows how to find the center and radius.

EXAMPLE 2   Sketch the graph of each relation.

   a. $(x + 1)^2 + (y - 2)^2 = 4$ **b.** $x^2 + y^2 = 9$ **c.** $x^2 + y^2 - 2x + 6y = 6$

Solutions: In order to draw the graph of a circle, we need two pieces of information:
(1) its center and (2) its radius.

a.   Since the equation

$(x + 1)^2 + (y - 2)^2 = 4$

can easily be written in the standard form
as $(x - (-1))^2 + (y - 2)^2 = (2)^2$,
therefore the center is at **(–1, 2)** and the
radius is **2.**

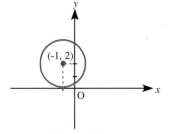

Figure 6.3

Thus, the graph of $(x + 1)^2 + (y - 2)^2 = 4$ is
the circle of radius 2 and center at
$(-1, 2)$ (Figure 6.3).

b.   By writing the equation $x^2 + y^2 = 9$ as
$(x - 0)^2 + (y - 0)^2 = (3)^2$, we conclude that
the center of the circle is at $(0, 0)$ and the
radius is 3 (Figure 6.4).

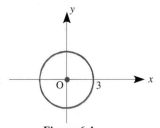

Figure 6.4

c.   We write the equation in the standard form
by completing the squares in x and y.

$$x^2 - 2x + y^2 + 6y = 6$$

$$(x^2 - 2x) + (y^2 + 6y) = 6$$

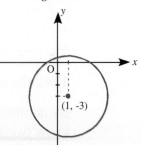

Figure 6.5

* $(x - 1)^2 - 1 + (y + 3)^2 - 9 = 6$

         $(x - 1)^2 + (y + 3)^2 = 6 + 1 + 9 = 16$

         $(x - 1)^2 + (y + 3)^2 = 4^2$

         $(x - 1)^2 + (y - (-3))^2 = 4^2$

> * $x^2 - 2x = (x - 1)^2 - 1$
>
> $y^2 + 6y = (y + 3)^2 - 9$

From this equation it follows that the center is located at $(1, -3)$ and radius is **4** (Figure 6.5).

C. GRAPHING HALF CIRCLES

The following examples explain the method of graphing upper and lower half circles.

EXAMPLE 3   Graph the following functions.

     a. $y = \sqrt{16 - x^2}$ **b.** $y = 1 - \sqrt{4 - x^2}$

Solutions:

     a.   *   By squaring both sides we get:

$$y^2 = 16 - x^2$$
$$x^2 + y^2 = 16$$
$$(x - 0)^2 + (y - 0)^2 = 4^2$$

> *   When we square an equation, there is a possibility of adding a branch of the graph. We call this an **extraneous branch** of the graph. (Recall the concept of an **extraneous root** of an equation.)

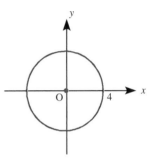

Figure 6.6

From the equation, the center of the circle is at $(0, 0)$ and the radius is 4 (Figure 6.6). However, the original equation says that y is non-negative (because a square root is always a non negative number). The part of the circle for which y is non negative is the upper half circle. Thus, the graph of $y = \sqrt{16 - x^2}$ is the upper semicircle of radius 4 and center at the origin as shown in Figure 6.7.

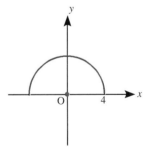

Figure 6.7

     b.   Similarly, we write the equation

$y = 1 - \sqrt{4 - x^2}$ as $y - 1 = -\sqrt{4 - x^2}$. By squaring both sides, we get

$$(y - 1)^2 = 4 - x^2 \text{ or } x^2 + (y - 1)^2 = 4$$
$$\text{or} \quad (x - 0)^2 + (y - 1)^2 = 2^2$$

The center of the circle is at $(0, 1)$ and the radius is 2 (Figure 6.8).

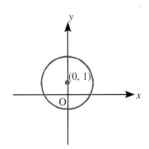

Figure 6.8

The original equation is $y - 1 = -\sqrt{4 - x^2}$, which means $y - 1 < 0$ or $y < 1$. But this is true only for the circle below the horizontal line $y = 1$. Thus, the graph of $y = 1 - \sqrt{4 - x^2}$ is the lower half of the circle as shown in Figure 6.9.

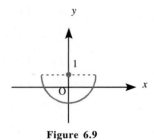

Figure 6.9

With Graphing Calculator

Graph $y1 = \sqrt{16 - x^2}$ and $y2 = 1 - \sqrt{4 - x^2}$ on a suitable range.

EXAMPLE 4

Solution:

Find the equation of the line touching the circle $x^2 - 6x + y^2 + 8y = 15$ at $(1, 2)$. The line touching the circle only at a single point $(1, 2)$ is called the **tangent line** at $(1, 2)$. To find the equation of this line, we need a point on its graph (line) and the slope of the line. We proceed to find the slope of the tangent line. By geometry, the line tangent to the circle at the point $P(1, 2)$ is perpendicular to the radial line that joins the point P to the center C of the circle (Figure 6.10).

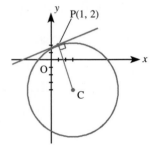

Figure 6.10

Therefore, we find the slope of CP. Then the slope of the tangent line will be its negative reciprocal.

To find the slope of the radial line CP, we proceed to find the center of the circle by completing the square.

$$(x^2 - 6x) + (y^2 + 8y) = 15 \qquad x^2 - 6x = (x - 3)^2 - 9$$

or $\quad (x - 3)^2 - 9 + (y + 4)^2 - 16 = 15 \qquad y^2 + 8y = (y + 4)^2 - 16$

$$(x - 3)^2 + (y + 4)^2 = 40$$

From the equation, the center of the circle is at $(3, -4)$.

- The slope of the radial line $CP = \dfrac{-4 - 2}{3 - 1} = \dfrac{-6}{2} = -3$.

> • The slope of a line passing through two points (x_1, y_1) and (x_2, y_2) is $\dfrac{y_2 - y_1}{x_2 - x_1}$.

This means that the slope of the tangent line is $-\dfrac{1}{-3}$ or $\dfrac{1}{3}$.

Now we substitute $x_1 = 1$, $y_1 = 2$, and $m = \dfrac{1}{3}$ in $y - y_1 = m(x - x_1)$, and we get

$$y - 2 = \frac{1}{3}(x - 1)$$

$$y = \frac{1}{3}x - \frac{1}{3} + 2$$

$$y = \frac{1}{3}x + \frac{5}{3}$$

Thus, equation of the line touching the circle at $(1, 2)$ is $y = \dfrac{1}{3}x + \dfrac{5}{3}$.

EXERCISE 6.2

In exercises (1-16), find a relation that describes the circle satisfying the given conditions.

1. The center is at $(2, -1)$ and radius is 5.

2. The center is at $(1, 2)$ and radius is 6.

3. The center is at $(-3, 2)$ and radius is 2.

4. The center is at $(-1, 8)$ and radius is 7.

5. The center is at $(-1, -7)$ and radius is 1.

6. The center is at $\left(\sqrt{2}, -1\right)$ and radius is 4.

7. The center is at $(-2, 0)$ and radius is 4.

8. The center is at $(-4, -3)$ and radius is $\sqrt{3}$.

9. The center is at $(1, 2)$ and passes through $(-3, -1)$.

10. The center is at $(-2, 3)$ and passes through $(5, 0)$.

11. The center is at $(5, -7)$ and passes through $(2, -3)$.

12. The center is at $(-3, 0)$ and passes through $(-1, -4)$.

13. The diameter has end points at $(3, -5)$ and $(5, 3)$.

14. The diameter has end points at $(7, -3)$ and $(-3, 5)$.

15. The diameter has end points at $(-5, 2)$ and $(1, 4)$.

16. The diameter has end points at $(1, 4)$ and $(-1, -2)$.

In exercises (17-38), verify that the relation describes a circle and then find the center (C) and radius (r) of the circle.

17. $(x-1)^2 + (y-3)^2 = 5$

18. $x^2 + y^2 = 5$

19. $(x+2)^2 + (y-5)^2 = 9$

20. $(x+4)^2 + (y-3)^2 = 7$

21. $(x+1)^2 + y^2 = 3$

22. $(x-9)^2 + (y+6)^2 = 16$

23. $x^2 + (y-2)^2 = 16$

24. $x^2 + (y+7)^2 = 9$

25. $x^2 + y^2 = 1$

26. $(x+4)^2 + (y-7)^2 = 5$

27. $x^2 + 2x + y^2 = 3$

28. $x^2 - 4x + y^2 = 7$

29. $x^2 + y^2 - 6y = 7$

30. $x^2 + y^2 - 8y = 1$

31. $x^2 + y^2 - 4x + 6y = 3$

32. $x^2 + y^2 - 2x - 4y = 11$

33. $x^2 + y^2 + x - 2y = 1$

34. $x^2 + y^2 - x + y = 10$

35. $2x^2 + 2y^2 - 4x + 8y = 22$

36. $4x^2 + 4y^2 + 4x - 8y = 2$

37. $3x^2 + 3y^2 + 6x + 9y = 1$

38. $2x^2 + 2y^2 - x - y = 11$

In exercises (39-46), sketch the graph of the function.

39. $y = \sqrt{4 - x^2}$

40. $y = \sqrt{3 - x^2}$

41. $y = -\sqrt{9 - x^2}$

42. $y = -\sqrt{16 - x^2}$

43. $y = 3 + \sqrt{4 - x^2}$

44. $y = 1 + \sqrt{9 - x^2}$

45. $y = 3 - \sqrt{4 - x^2}$

46. $y = -2 - \sqrt{16 - x^2}$

47. Find a linear equation whose graph (line) is tangent to the circle $x^2 + y^2 = 5$ at $(1, 2)$.

48. Find a linear equation whose graph (line) is tangent to the circle $x^2 + y^2 = 4$ at $(0, 2)$.

49. The figure shows the outer end of a storm water pipe for a large community. The central trap rod (PQ) is 8 feet across and the other vertical trap rods are equally spaced. To give extra strength to the vertical trap rods, the supervisor advised the workers to connect the point A to point B via the midpoints of the upper half of the vertical trap rods and repeat the same for the lower half of the trap rods. The workers are supposed to cut out the pieces of lengths BC, CD, DE and EF ... from a long rod and then weld those pieces to connect the midpoints. Are the pieces (BC, CD, etc.) of the same length? If not, then what different lengths of rod pieces will they need?

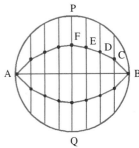

50. Find an equation of the line touching the circle

$$x^2 + y^2 - 4x + 6y = 45 \text{ at } (-1, 4)$$

Writing Exercises

51. Give a method of finding the center and radius of a circle whose equation is given.

52. State the relationship between the slopes of the radial line and tangent line at a point on the circle.

6.3 PARABOLA

Objectives ▶ ▶

In this section you will learn about:

A. Finding an Equation of a Parabola;

B. Graphing a Parabola; and

C. Graphing Half Parabolas.

A parabola is the second member of the family of conic sections.

A. FINDING AN EQUATION OF A PARABOLA

Parabola

A parabola consists of all points in the plane that are equidistant from a given line called the **directrix** and a fixed point, not on the line, called the **focus.**

The cross section of a right circular cone by an inclined plane, on either side of the axis of the cone, is a parabola.

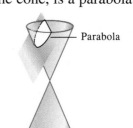

Parabola

Figure 6.11

Let us find a relation that describes the parabola with focus at $(c, 0)$ and the directrix $x = -c$. For a relationship we use the first three steps of the general method used in the last section on circles.

Step **1** Figure 6.12 shows the focus $F(c, 0)$ and the directrix $x = -c$.

Step **2** Let $Q(x, y)$ be any point on the parabola.

Step **3** To find a relationship between x and y, we use the fact that the point Q is equidistant from the focus F and the directrix. This means

$$QF = QN \qquad \text{(Figure 6.12)}$$

* $$\sqrt{(x-c)^2 + (y-0)^2} = QK + NK = x + c$$

By squaring both sides, we obtain

$$(x - c)^2 + y^2 = (x + c)^2$$
$$x^2 - 2xc + c^2 + y^2 = x^2 + 2xc + c^2$$
$$y^2 = 4cx \qquad (c > 0)$$

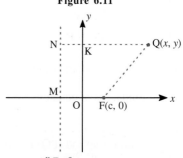

Figure 6.12

* Distance Formula:
$$\sqrt{(x_2 - x_1)^2 + (y_2 - y_1)^2}$$
$QK = x\text{-coordinate of } Q = x$
$NK = QM = c$, and
$QN = QK + NK$
$\quad\ = x + c.$

To examine the shape of $y^2 = 4cx$, we express this relation in terms of two functions as

$$y = \pm 2\sqrt{c}\sqrt{x}$$

Obviously, one function $\left(y = 2\sqrt{c}\sqrt{x}\right)$ is the reflection through the x-axis of the other function $\left(y = -2\sqrt{c}\sqrt{x}\right)$. Also the graph of $y = 2\sqrt{c}\sqrt{x}$ will resemble the graph of the * root function $y = \sqrt{x}$.

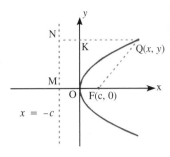

Figure 6.14

We combine these observations to draw the graph of $y^2 = 4cx$ in Figure 6.14.

Similarly, a relation that describes the parabola with focus at $(0, c)$ and the directrix $y = -c$ will be $x^2 = 4cy$, $(c > 0)$.

When we solve for y, we get

$$y = \frac{x^2}{4c} = \left(\frac{1}{4c}\right)x^2 ,$$

whose graph will look like the graph of the * power function $y = ax^2$ (a is a positive constant).

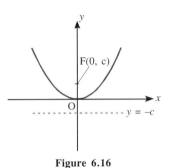

Figure 6.16

*   The graph of the root function $y = \sqrt{x}$ is

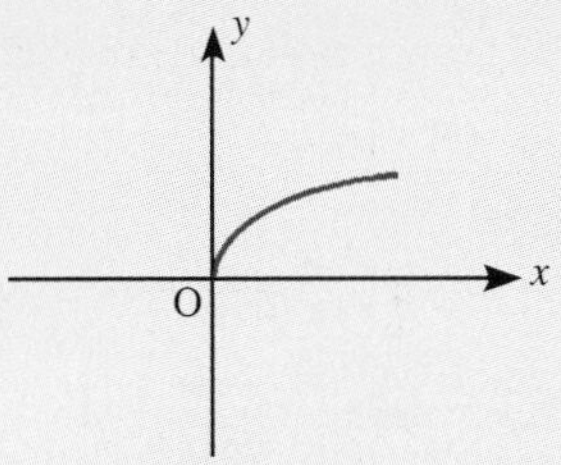

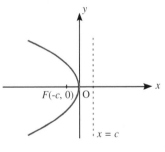

Figure 6.13

*   The graph of the power function $y = ax^2$, $(a > 0)$ is a parabola.

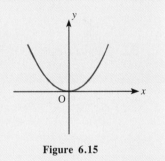

Figure 6.15

Thus, the graph of $x^2 = 4cy$ will look like the graph in Figure 6.16.

If we take the reflection of the first parabola ($y^2 = 4cx$) through the y-axis, we obtain the graph of

$$y^2 = -4cx, \qquad (c > 0) \qquad \text{(Figure 6.17)}$$

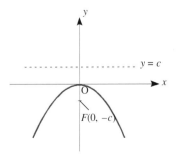

Figure 6.17

Also the reflection of the second parabola ($x^2 = 4cy$) through the x-axis gives the graph of

$$x^2 = -4cy, \qquad (c > 0) \qquad \text{(Figure 6.18)}$$

We summarize our discussion as follows:

Figure 6.18

Standard Forms of Relation Representing a Parabola

For $c > 0$, we have

1. $y^2 = 4cx$

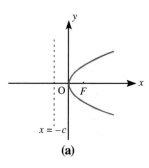

(a)

The graph opens to the right. The focus is c units to the right of the vertex and the directrix is a vertical line c units to the left of the vertex.

2. $y^2 = -4cx$

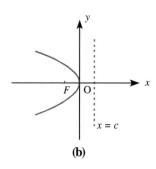

(b)

The graph opens to the left. The focus is c units to the left of the vertex and the directrix is a vertical line c units to the right of the vertex.

3. $x^2 = 4cy$

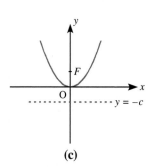

(c)

The graph opens upward. The focus is c units above the vertex and the directrix is a horizontal line c units below the vertex.

4. $x^2 = -4cy$

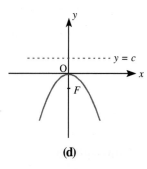

(d)

The graph opens downward. The focus is c units below the vertex and the directrix is a horizontal line c units above the vertex.

Figure 6.19

Remarks:

1. *According to the vertical line test, the first two represent relations and the last two are functions.*

2. *The line joining the vertex and focus is called the axis of the parabola.*

3. ***The graph is symmetrical about the axis of the parabola.***

4. *The vertex is midway between the focus and the directrix.*

5. *The equation representing a parabola is second degree in one variable and first degree in the other variable.*

EXAMPLE 1   Find an equation of the parabola whose vertex is at the origin and the focus at (0, 2).

Solution: From the location of the focus we determine the shape of the parabola (Figure 6.20). The standard equation that fits this shape of the parabola is $x^2 = 4cy$. To find c, we use the fact that the distance between the vertex and focus is c units. This gives $c = 2$. Thus, an equation of the parabola is $x^2 = 4(2)y$ or $x^2 = 8y$.

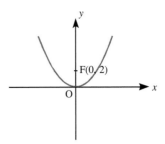

Figure 6.20

EXAMPLE 2   Find an equation of the parabola whose focus is on the *x*-axis, whose vertex is at the origin, and which passes through the point (2, 5).

Solution: From the location of the focus and the point (2, 5), we infer that the parabola opens to the right (Figure 6.21). The standard form that fits this shape is $y^2 = 4cx$. To find c, we use the fact that the graph passes through the point (2, 5). This means that the coordinates of the point must satisfy the equation of the graph.

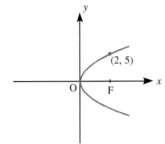

Figure 6.21

$$(5)^2 = 4c(2) \;\rightarrow\; 25 = 8c \;\rightarrow\; c = \frac{25}{8}$$

Thus, an equation of the parabola is $y^2 = 4\left(\dfrac{25}{8}\right)x$ or $y^2 = \dfrac{25}{2}x$.

B. GRAPHING A PARABOLA

The following examples will show that by comparing the equation of a parabola with one of the standard forms we can draw its graph.

EXAMPLE 3   Find the focus and the directrix of the parabola $y^2 = -8x$. Sketch the graph of the parabola.

Solution:

Step 1   Compare the equation with an appropriate standard form. In this case, we compare it with $y^2 = -4cx$. Comparing the right hand sides gives $4c = 8$.

Step 2   Hence, $c = 2$.

Step 3   Plot the coordinates of the vertex and draw a new set of (dotted) coordinate axes through the vertex. In this case, the vertex is the origin. Therefore, the two sets of axes coincide.

Step 4   Draw the standard graph (Figure 6.22).

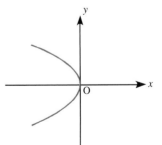

Figure 6.22

Step 5   To find the focus and the directrix, go c units from the vertex inside the parabola and c units outside the parabola along the axis. Thus, the focus is at $(-2, 0)$ and the directrix is $x = 2$ (Figure 6.23).

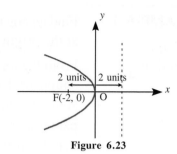

Figure 6.23

⬤ Note $y^2 = -8x$ is a relation and not a function.

Recall that:

If x is replaced by $x - h$,   then the graph is moved h units to the right. Consequently, the vertex is moved h **units to the right.**

If x is replaced by $x + h$,   then the vertex moves h **units to the left.**

If y is replaced by $y - k$,   then the vertex moves k **units up.**

If y is replaced by $y + k$,   then the vertex moves k **units down.**

Note: In $(y - k)^2 = 4c(x - h)$, the vertex is at (h, k).

EXAMPLE 4   Determine the vertex, focus, and directrix of $(y - 1)^2 = 16(x + 2)$.

Sketch the graph of the parabola.

Solution:

Step 1   Comparing the equation with $y^2 = 4cx$, we see that x has been replaced with $x + 2$, y has been replaced with $y - 1$, and $4c = 16$.

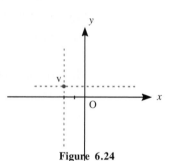

Figure 6.24

Step 2   We solve $4c = 16$ for c, and get $c = 4$.

Step 3   Because x is replaced with $x + 2$ and y with $y - 1$, the vertex (V) moves 2 units left and 1 unit above the origin (Figure 6.24).

Step 4   The parabola for $y^2 = 4cx$ opens to the right (Figure 6.25).

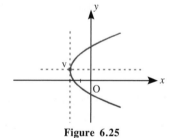

Figure 6.25

Step 5   From the vertex (V) we go $c = 4$ units inside the parabola along the axis and $c = 4$ units outside the parabola, and label the focus (F) and the directrix (Figure 6.26). Thus, the vertex of the parabola is at $(-2, 1)$, the focus is at $(2, 1)$ and the equation of the directrix is $x = -6$. The graph of the parabola is shown in Figure 6.26.

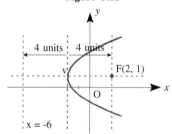

Figure 6.26

With Graphing Calculator

First, we can express the relation in terms of two functions. Then we use graphing calculator to draw both functions simultaneously.

$(y - 1)^2 = 16(x + 2) \rightarrow y - 1 = \pm 4\sqrt{x + 2} \rightarrow y = 1 \pm 4\sqrt{x + 2}$. Now let

$y1 = 1 + 4\sqrt{x + 2}$ and $y2 = 1 - 4\sqrt{x + 2}$.

Graph $y1$ and $y2$ together on a suitable range.

Use ZOOM-IN and TRACE to locate the vertex of the parabola.

EXAMPLE 5   Find the vertex, focus, and directrix of the parabola $x^2 + 6y + 12 = 0$.

Solution: Before we compare the equation we write it as:

$$x^2 = -6y - 12$$
$$= -6(y + 2).$$

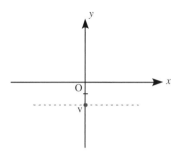

Figure 6.27

Step 1   Now by comparing the equation with $x^2 = -4cy$, we see that y has been replaced by $y + 2$ and $4c = 6$.

Step 2   Solving $4c = 6$ for c gives $c = \dfrac{3}{2}$.

Step 3   Because y is replaced with $y + 2$, the vertex moves down 2 units from the origin (Figure 6.27). The vertex is $V(0, -2)$.

Step 4   The parabola $x^2 = -4cy$ opens downward (Figure 6.28).

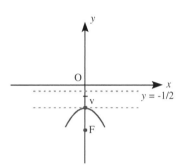

Figure 6.28

Step 5   To find the focus and directrix, we go $\dfrac{3}{2}$ units from the vertex inside, and $\dfrac{3}{2}$ units outside the parabola along the axis.

Therefore, the focus (F) is $\left(0, -\dfrac{7}{2}\right)$ and the directrix is $y = -\dfrac{1}{2}$.

Thus, the vertex of the parabola is $(0, -2)$, focus is $\left(0, -\dfrac{7}{2}\right)$, and the directrix is $y = -\dfrac{1}{2}$.

EXAMPLE 6   Find the vertex, focus, and directrix of the parabola $y^2 + 4y = -x - 3$.

Solution: Before we compare the equation with one of the standard forms, we complete the square.

$$y^2 + 4y = -x - 3$$
$$(y + 2)^2 - 4 = -x - 3$$
$$(y + 2)^2 = -x - 3 + 4$$
$$(y + 2)^2 = -x + 1 = -1(x - 1)$$

Step 1   By comparing this equation with $y^2 = -4cx$, we observe that x has been replaced with $x - 1$ and y has been replaced with $y + 2$, and $4c = 1$.

Step 2   Solving $4c = 1$ for c gives $c = \dfrac{1}{4}$.

Step 3   Because x is replaced with $x - 1$, and y with $y + 2$, the vertex moves 1 unit to the right and 2 units down the origin (Figure 6.29). The vertex is $V(1, -2)$.

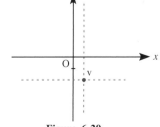

Figure 6.29

Step 4   The parabola $y^2 = -4cx$ opens to the left (Figure 6.30).

Step 5   To locate the focus and directrix we go $\dfrac{1}{4}$ units

from the vertex inside along the axis and $\dfrac{1}{4}$ unit outside along the axis of the parabola, respectively.

This gives the focus $F\left(\dfrac{3}{4}, -2\right)$ and the directrix $x = \dfrac{5}{4}$.

Thus, $(1, -2)$ is the vertex, $\left(\dfrac{3}{4}, -2\right)$ is the focus, and $x = \dfrac{5}{4}$ is the directrix of the parabola.

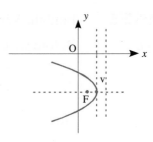

Figure 6.30

With Graphing Calculator

We can verify the coordinates of the vertex from the graph of relation. First, we write the relation as two functions by solving the equation for y. We will get two values of y in terms of x, say $y1$ and $y2$.

Graph $y1$ and $y2$ on the standard or any suitable range. By using ZOOM-IN and TRACE successively, we can locate the vertex of the parabola.

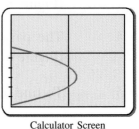

Calculator Screen

Figure 6.31

C. GRAPHING HALF PARABOLAS

The following example shows how to graph half parabolas.

EXAMPLE 7   Graph the following half parabolas.

    a. $y = 2\sqrt{x-1}$ **b.** $x = 2 + \sqrt{1-y}$

Solutions:

    a.   Before we compare the equation with one of the standard forms, we square both sides and get $y^2 = 4(x - 1)$.

- Now by comparing this equation with $y^2 = 4cx$, we see that x has been replaced by $x - 1$ and $4c = 4$.

- Because x is replaced with $x - 1$, the vertex moves 1 unit to the right of the origin (Figure 6.32). The vertex is $V(1, 0)$

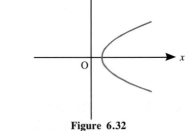

Figure 6.32

    * Finally, to test for any extraneous branch of the graph, we observe that $y = 2\sqrt{x-1}$ is non-negative. Therefore, we accept only the upper half of the parabola. Thus, the graph of

$y = 2\sqrt{x-1}$

is shown in Figure 6.33.

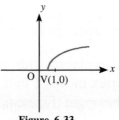

Figure 6.33

> * When we square an equation and graph the new relation, there is a possibility of extra branch of the graph of the original equation. This extra branch is what we call an **extraneous branch**.

With Graphing Calculator

Let $y1 = 2\sqrt{x-1}$. Graph $y1$ on the standard or any other suitable range.

b.   First, we re-write the equation as $x - 2 = \sqrt{1-y}$.

By squaring both sides, we get $(x-2)^2 = 1 - y$
$$= -(y-1).$$

- By comparing this equation with $x^2 = -4cy$, we see that x has been replaced with $x - 2$, and y has been replaced with $y - 1$, and $4c = 1$.

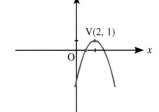

- Because x is replaced with $x - 2$ and y with $y - 1$, the vertex is moved 2 units to the right and 1 unit up the origin. We draw the graph of $x^2 = -4cy$

  with the vertex $V(2, 1)$ (Figure 6.34).

Figure 6.34

- To look for the extraneous branch, we observe that $x - 2 = \sqrt{1-y}$ is non-negative. This means $x \geq 2$. Therefore, we accept only the right half of the parabola. Thus, the graph of $x = 2 + \sqrt{1-y}$ is shown in Figure 6.35.

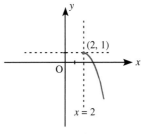

Figure 6.35

With Graphing Calculator

We square both sides to solve for y. $(x-2)^2 = 1 - y \rightarrow y = 1 - (x-2)^2$. Let $y1 = 1 - (x-2)^2$. Graph $y1$ on a suitable range and look only at the graph for which $x \geq 2$.

Parabolas in the Real World

* **Reflection Property**

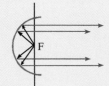

Figure 6.36

The reflective property of parabola says that if a source of light (heat) is placed at the focus of a parabola, then the rays of light (heat) are reflected parallel to the axis of the parabola. (The picture shows a cross section of a parabolic mirror).

There are many applications of parabola; we list only a few.

1. The path of a ball thrown up in a non-vertical direction is a parabola.

2. The shapes of cables in many suspension bridges are parabolic.

3. The * reflective property of parabola is used extensively in the construction of space heaters, automobile headlights, telescopes, satellite dishes etc.

EXERCISE 6.3

In exercises (1-12), find a relation that describes the parabola satisfying the given conditions.

1. The focus is at $(0, 5)$ and the directrix is $y = -5$. **2.** The focus is at $(0, 4)$ and the directrix is $y = -4$.

3. The focus is at $(0, -3)$ and the directrix is $y = 3$. **4.** The focus is at $(0, -6)$ and the directrix is $y = 6$.

5. The focus is at $(8, 0)$ and the directrix is $x = -8$. **6.** The focus is at $(5, 0)$ and the directrix is $x = -5$.

7. The focus is at $(3, 0)$ and the directrix is $x = -3$. **8.** The focus is at $(-4, 0)$ and the directrix is $x = 4$.

9. The focus is on the x-axis, the vertex is at the origin and the parabola passes through $(2, 6)$.

10. The focus is on the x-axis, the vertex is at the origin, and the parabola passes through $(-2, -4)$.

11. The focus is on the y-axis, the vertex is at the origin, and the parabola passes through $(2, -4)$.

12. The focus is on the y-axis, the vertex is at the origin, and the parabola passes through $(4, 8)$.

In exercises (13-42), verify that the relation describes a parabola and find its focus (F), vertex (V), the directrix, and the graph.

13. $x^2 = 8y$ **14.** $x^2 = -6y$ **15.** $x^2 = 12y$ **16.** $x^2 = -16y$ **17.** $y^2 = 16x$

18. $y^2 = 8x$ **19.** $y^2 = -10x$ **20.** $y^2 = -16x$ **21.** $x^2 + 18y = 0$ **22.** $x^2 + 24y = 0$

23. $y^2 + 4x = 0$ **24.** $y^2 + 8x = 0$ **25.** $(y-1)^2 = 4x$ **26.** $(y+2)^2 = -4x$ **27.** $(x+2)^2 = 8y$

28. $(x-2)^2 = -8y$ **29.** $(x-1)^2 = 12(y-2)$ **30.** $(x+2)^2 = 16(y+2)$ **31.** $(x-2)^2 = -16(y-1)$

32. $(x+2)^2 = -8(y+1)$ **33.** $(y+1)^2 = 2 - x$ **34.** $(y-3)^2 = x - 4$ **35.** $(x-1)^2 = 4 - 2y$

36. $(x+4)^2 = -8y + 8$ **37.** $y^2 - 8y - 4x = 0$ **38.** $y^2 + 6y + 9x = 0$ **39.** $x^2 + 4x + 2y + 10 = 0$

40. $x^2 - 4x + 4y - 12 = 0$ **41.** $2x^2 - 8x - y + 7 = 0$ **42.** $2y^2 - 8y + x + 2 = 0$

43. The figure shows a side view of a suspension bridge. The span of the bridge is 2200 feet long and the towers that hold the main cable are 100 feet above the roadway. For extra support there are vertical cables every 100 feet from the center (0) of the main cable. Assuming that the main cable stays in a parabolic form, find a relation that describes its shape (For the uniqueness of the answer, we suggest a coordinate system with the horizontal axis along the roadway and the vertical axis through the middle of the span.

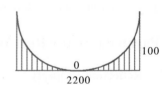

44. Consider the bridge in Exercise 43. Suppose we need to replace the second vertical supporting cable from the left tower, how long is that cable ?

45. Consider the bridge in Exercise 43. Suppose we need to replace the vertical supporting cable that is 100 feet from the right tower, how long is that cable ?

46. The figure shows a vertical cross section through the heating element (H) of a small space heater, where AB = 8 in and CD = 3 in. After repairing the heating element, we want to make sure that it is set at the focus of the parabola (Reflection Property). How far away from C should we place the heating element H ?

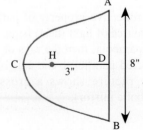

47. Refer to the heating element in Exercise 46. If AB = 6 in and CD = 2 in, then how far away from C should the heating element H be placed?

48. The music room in a modern house is designed according to the reflection property of the parabola. The vertical cross section through the deepest end (C) of the room is shown in the Figure, where CD = 36 in. If the ceiling is 96 in high, how far from the deepest end (C) should we place the speakers (facing the back wall) for the desired effect?

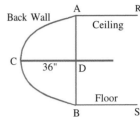

49. Refer to the music room in Exercise 46. If CD = 27 in and the ceiling is 108 in high, how far from the deepest end C should we place the speakers (facing the backwall) for the desired effect?

Writing Exercises

50. State the "reflection property" of the parabola.

51. In a parabola, describe the position of the vertex relative to the focus and the directrix.

6.4 ELLIPSE

In this section we will discuss an oval-shaped curve called an ellipse.

The cross section of a right circular cone by an inclined plane meeting the cone on both sides of the axis as shown in Figure 6.37, is an **ellipse.**

Objectives ▶ ▶

In this section you will learn about:

A. Finding an Equation of the Ellipse;

B. Graphing an Ellipse; and

C. Graphing a Half Ellipse.

A. FINDING AN EQUATION OF THE ELLIPSE

Ellipse

- An **ellipse** consists of all points in the plane, the sum of whose distances from two fixed points is a constant. The fixed points are called **foci.**

Note   The plural of **focus** is foci.

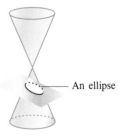

An ellipse

Figure 6.37

Let the line joining the foci be the x-axis and the midpoint of the line segment joining the foci be the origin. We will find a relation (an equation) that represents the ellipse.

Step 1   Let $F_1(c, 0)$ and $F_2(-c, 0)$ be the foci.

Step 2   The ellipse consists of all points $Q(x, y)$ satisfying the given condition (Figure 6.38).

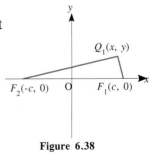

Figure 6.38

Step 3 Let a be one-half the sum of the two distances. To find a relationship between x and y, we use the fact that

> * QF_1 = distance between two points (x, y) and $(c, 0)$
>
> $= \sqrt{(x-c)^2 + (y-0)^2}$
>
> (distance formula).
>
> Similarly,
>
> $QF_2 = \sqrt{(x+c)^2 + (y-0)^2}$

* $QF_1 + QF_2 = \text{constant} = 2a$

$$\sqrt{(x-c)^2 + (y-0)^2} + \sqrt{(x+c)^2 + (y-0)^2} = 2a$$

By keeping only one square root on the left side,

we write $\sqrt{(x-c)^2 + y^2} = 2a - \sqrt{(x+c)^2 + y^2}$

By squaring both sides, we get:

$$(x - c)^2 + y^2 = 4a^2 - 4a\sqrt{(x+c)^2 + y^2} + (x + c)^2 + y^2$$

$$\cancel{x^2} - 2xc + \cancel{c^2} + \cancel{y^2} = 4a^2 - 4a\sqrt{(x+c)^2 + y^2} + \cancel{x^2} + 2xc + \cancel{c^2} + \cancel{y^2}$$

$$4a\sqrt{x^2 + 2xc + c^2 + y^2} = 4a^2 + 4xc$$

Dividing by 4 gives $a\sqrt{x^2 + 2xc + c^2 + y^2} = a^2 + xc.$

Squaring both sides again, we get:

$$a^2(x^2 + 2xc + c^2 + y^2) = a^4 + 2a^2xc + x^2c^2$$

$$a^2x^2 + \mathbf{2a^2xc} + a^2c^2 + a^2y^2 = a^4 + \mathbf{2a^2xc} + x^2c^2$$

By collecting x^2 and y^2 terms on the left side and constants on the right side, we write the above equation as

$$(a^2 - c^2)x^2 + a^2 y^2 = a^2(a^2 - c^2). \qquad \textbf{(1)}$$

To write this equation in a more convenient form we set $a^2 - c^2 = b^2$

This changes the above equation (1) to $b^2x^2 + a^2y^2 = a^2b^2.$

Dividing the equation by a^2b^2 we obtain

$$\frac{x^2}{a^2} + \frac{y^2}{b^2} = 1 \qquad \text{* } (a > b)$$

> * $a^2 - c^2 = b^2$
>
> $a^2 - b^2 = c^2$
>
> For $a > 0, b > 0$ it follows $a > b$.

The graph of $\dfrac{x^2}{a^2} + \dfrac{y^2}{b^2} = 1$, has the following properties.

1. The graph is symmetrical about the x-axis, because the equation is not affected if we change y to $-y$.

2. The graph is also symmetrical about the y-axis, since the equation is not affected if we change x to $-x$.

3.   The *x*-intercepts are the solutions (roots) of the equation.

$$\frac{x^2}{a^2} + \frac{0^2}{b^2} = 1 \quad \textbf{or} \quad x^2 = a^2 \quad \textbf{or} \quad x = \pm\, a$$

Thus, the graph meets the *x*-axis at $x = a$ and $x = -a$.

4.   The *y*-intercepts are the roots of the equation

$$\frac{0^2}{a^2} + \frac{y^2}{b^2} = 1 \quad \textbf{or} \quad y^2 = b^2 \quad \textbf{or} \quad y = \pm\, b$$

Thus, the graph meets the *y*-axis at $y = b$ and $y = -b$.

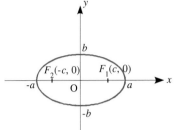

5.   Domain:

$$\frac{x^2}{a^2} + \frac{y^2}{b^2} = 1 \qquad \rightarrow \qquad b^2 x^2 + a^2 y^2 = a^2 b^2$$

$$\rightarrow \qquad a^2 y^2 = a^2 b^2 - b^2 x^2$$

$$\rightarrow \qquad a^2 y^2 = b^2 (a^2 - x^2)$$

$$\rightarrow \qquad y^2 = \frac{b^2}{a^2}(a^2 - x^2)$$

$$\rightarrow \qquad \text{so } y = \pm\frac{b}{a}\sqrt{a^2 - x^2}$$

Figure 6.39

To find the domain, set the radicand ≥ 0.

$$(a - x)\,(a + x) \geq 0$$

$$\begin{array}{ccc} & -a & a \\ \hline & | & | \end{array}$$

This gives three intervals

	sign	satisfy the inequal
$(-\infty, -a)$	pos. neg $\rightarrow$ neg	No
$[-a, a]$	pos. pos $\rightarrow$ pos	Yes
(a, ∞)	neg. pos $\rightarrow$ neg	No

Hence the domain is $[-a, a]$.

6.   By using the above results, we draw the graph of $\dfrac{x^2}{a^2} + \dfrac{y^2}{b^2} = 1$ as in Figure 6.39.

Similarly, if the foci are $(0, c)$ and $(0, -c)$, then the equation

is $\dfrac{x^2}{a^2} + \dfrac{y^2}{b^2} = 1$, where $c^2 = b^2 - a^2$ and $b > a$. The graph will look like the graph in Figure 6.40. We summarize these results as follows:

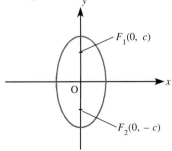

Figure 6.40

Standard Forms for the Relation Representing an Ellipse

1. $\dfrac{x^2}{a^2} + \dfrac{y^2}{b^2} = 1$, $(a > b)$

2. $\dfrac{x^2}{a^2} + \dfrac{y^2}{b^2} = 1$, $(a < b)$

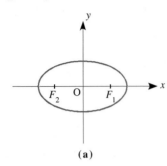

(a)

Figure 6.41

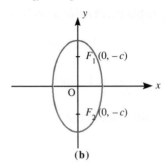

(b)

Figure 6.41

Vertices $(\pm a, 0)$ and $(0, \pm b)$

Foci $(\pm c, 0)$, where $c^2 = a^2 - b^2$

Vertices $(\pm a, 0)$, $(0, \pm b)$

Foci $(0, \pm c)$, where $c^2 = b^2 - a^2$

Remarks:

1. *The focal axis is the line passing through the foci of the ellipse. The graph is symmetrical about the focal axis.*

2. *The midpoint of the segment joining the foci is the center of the ellipse.*

3. *The focal axis is also called the **major axis**.*

4. *The line through the center perpendicular to the major axis is called the **minor axis**.*

5. *The points where the major axis and the minor axis intersect the ellipse are called the vertices.*

6. *When $a = b$, the ellipse becomes a circle.*

7. *Using the standard translations, we observe that the center of the ellipse*

$$\frac{(x-h)^2}{a^2} + \frac{(y-k)^2}{b^2} = 1 \quad is \ (h, k).$$

8. *If $a > b$, the major axis of the ellipse $\dfrac{x^2}{a^2} + \dfrac{y^2}{b^2} = 1$ is horizontal, its length is $2a$ and the length of the minor axis $2b$.*

9. *If $a < b$, the major axis of the ellipse $\dfrac{x^2}{a^2} + \dfrac{y^2}{b^2} = 1$ is vertical, its length is $2b$ and the length of the minor axis is $2a$.*

EXAMPLE 1 Find an equation of the ellipse with foci at $(-3, 0)$ and $(3, 0)$ and minor axis of length 8.

Solution: Since the midpoint of the line segment joining the foci is $(0, 0)$, the center of the ellipse is at the origin. Also by the fact that the foci are on the *x*-axis, we infer that the equation of the ellipse is

$$\frac{x^2}{a^2} + \frac{y^2}{b^2} = 1, \quad (a > b)$$

The length of the minor axis is 8, therefore, $2b = 8 \longrightarrow b = 4$

To find a, we substitute $b = 4$ and $c = 3$ in

$$c^2 = a^2 - b^2 \longrightarrow 9 = a^2 - 16 \longrightarrow a^2 = 25 \longrightarrow a = 5$$

Therefore, a relation whose graph satisfies the given condition is $\dfrac{x^2}{25} + \dfrac{y^2}{16} = 1$.

B. GRAPHING AN ELLIPSE

The following examples show that comparing the given equation with one of the standard forms of the ellipse can help in drawing its graph.

EXAMPLE   2   Determine the center, vertices, and foci of the ellipse $16x^2 + 9y^2 = 144$, and graph the ellipse.

Solution:

Step 1   Write the equation in one of the standard forms: $16x^2 + 9y^2 = 144$.

Dividing both sides by 144 gives $\dfrac{16x^2}{144} + \dfrac{9y^2}{144} = \dfrac{144}{144}$

$$\dfrac{x^2}{9} + \dfrac{y^2}{16} = 1 \quad \textbf{or} \quad \dfrac{x^2}{3^2} + \dfrac{y^2}{4^2} = 1.$$

Step 2   Compare with an appropriate standard form and find the coordinates of the center. In this case, by comparing the equation $\dfrac{x^2}{3^2} + \dfrac{y^2}{4^2} = 1$ with $\dfrac{x^2}{a^2} + \dfrac{y^2}{b^2} = 1$, we get $a = 3$, $b = 4$ and the center is $(0, 0)$.

Step 3   Plot the center and draw the major and minor axes. In this case, $(0, 0)$ is the center and the y-axis is the major axis. (Figure 6.42).

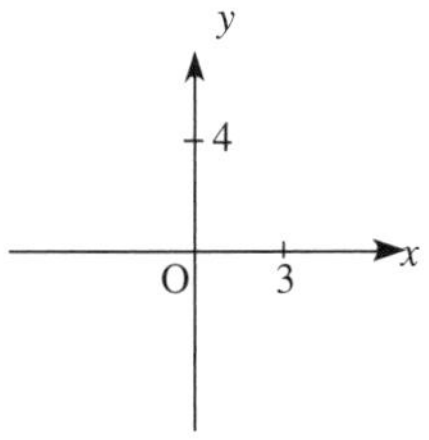

Figure 6.42

Step 4   From the center go 'a' units on each side of the center along the horizontal axis and 'b' units on each side of the center along the vertical axis. Label these as the vertices of the ellipse. Draw the ellipse through the vertices.

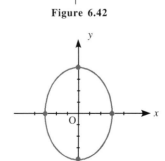

Figure 6.43

Step 5   Use the values of a and b in $c^2 = a^2 - b^2$ if $a > b$ or in $c^2 = b^2 - a^2$ if $a < b$ and find c. In this example we use $c^2 = b^2 - a^2$ because $a < b$. Using $a = 3$ and $b = 4$, we get

$$c^2 = 4^2 - 3^2 = 16 - 9 = 7.$$

This gives $c = \sqrt{7}$.

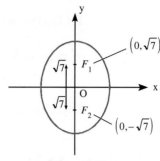

Figure 6.44

Step 6   To locate the foci go along the major axis 'c' units on both sides of the center (Figure 6.44).

Therefore, the foci of the ellipse are $\left(0, \sqrt{7}\right)$ and $\left(0, -\sqrt{7}\right)$ and the graph of the ellipse is shown in (Figure 6.44).

With Graphing Calculator

We can use a graphing calculator to verify the graph and the coordinates of the vertices of the ellipse. For this, we first write the relation in terms of two functions.

$$16x^2 + 9y^2 = 144 \longrightarrow 9y^2 = 144 - 16x^2 = 16(9 - x^2)$$

$$\longrightarrow \quad y^2 = \frac{16}{9}\left(9 - x^2\right) \longrightarrow y = \pm \frac{4}{3}\sqrt{9 - x^2}$$

Now, let $y1 = \frac{4}{3}\sqrt{9 - x^2}$ and $y2 = -\frac{4}{3}\sqrt{9 - x^2}$.

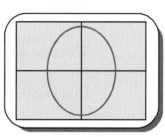

Figure 6.45

Graph $y1$ and $y2$ on the range: x-min $= -10$, x-max $= 10$, y-min $= -4$, and y-max $= 4$.

Use ZOOM-IN and TRACE to locate the vertices of the ellipse.

EXAMPLE 3   Determine the center, vertices, and foci of the ellipse $9x^2 + 25y^2 - 18x - 100y = 116$. Sketch the graph of the ellipse.

Solution:

Step 1   Before we write the equation in one of the standard forms, we complete the squares in x and y.

$$9x^2 + 25y^2 - 18x - 100y = 116 \longrightarrow (9x^2 - 18x) + (25y^2 - 100y) = 116$$

$$\longrightarrow \quad 9(x^2 - 2x) + 25(y^2 - 4y) = 116$$

$$\longrightarrow \quad 9[(x - 1)^2 - 1] + 25[(y - 2)^2 - 4] = 116$$

$$\longrightarrow \quad 9(x - 1)^2 + 25(y - 2)^2 - 9 - 100 = 116$$

$$\longrightarrow \quad 9(x - 1)^2 + 25(y - 2)^2 = 116 + 109$$

$$\longrightarrow \quad 9(x - 1)^2 + 25(y - 2)^2 = 225$$

Dividing both sides by 225: $\dfrac{(x-1)^2}{25} + \dfrac{(y-2)^2}{9} = 1$ **or** $\dfrac{(x-1)^2}{5^2} + \dfrac{(y-2)^2}{3^2} = 1$.

Step 2   Since $a > b$, we compare the equation with

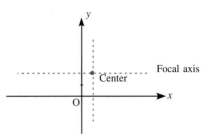

$$\frac{x^2}{a^2} + \frac{y^2}{b^2} = 1 \ (a > b).$$ We see that $a = 5$,

$b = 3$, x has been replaced with $x - 1$ and y has been replaced with $y - 2$. This means the center has moved 1 unit to the right and 2 units up from the origin.

Figure 6.46

Step 3   Plot the center and draw the axes (Figure 6.46).

Step 4   To locate the vertices along the horizontal axis, go 5 units each side of the center. Similarly, for the vertices along the vertical axis, go 3 units on each side of the center. Label the vertices and draw the graph (Figure 6.47).

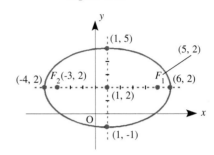

Figure 6.47

Step 5   We substitute $a = 5$, $b = 3$ in $c^2 = a^2 - b^2$ and solve for c.

$$c^2 = 5^2 - 3^2 = 25 - 9 = \mathbf{16}$$
$$c = 4$$

Step 6   Along the major axis we go 4 units on each side of the center and locate the foci. Therefore, the foci of ellipse are $(5, 2)$ and $(-3, 2)$. The graph of the ellipse is shown in Figure 6.47.

C. GRAPHING A HALF ELLIPSE

To graph a half ellipse we use the same steps as for the whole ellipse and take into consideration the restrictions.

EXAMPLE 4   Sketch the graph of $y = 1 + 2\sqrt{9 - x^2}$.

Solutions: First we re-write the equation as $y - 1 = 2\sqrt{9 - x^2}$. Now, by squaring both sides we get

$$\begin{aligned} (y - 1)^2 &= 4(9 - x^2) \\ &= 36 - 4x^2. \end{aligned}$$

- We write the equation in one of the standard forms.

$4x^2 + (y - 1)^2 = 36$.

Dividing both sides by 36 gives.

$$\frac{x^2}{9} + \frac{(y-1)^2}{36} = 1 \quad \textbf{or} \quad \frac{x^2}{3^2} + \frac{(y-1)^2}{6^2} = 1$$

- By comparing the equation with

$$\frac{x^2}{a^2} + \frac{y^2}{b^2} = 1 \ (b > a)$$ we see that $a = 3$,

$b = 6$ and y has been replaced with $y - 1$. Therefore, the center is at $(0, 1)$.

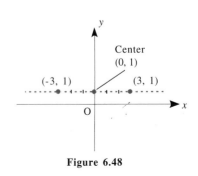

Figure 6.48

- We plot the center and draw the axes (Figure 6.48).

- To locate the vertices along the horizontal axis, go 3 units on each side of the center. Similarly, for the vertices along the vertical axis, go 6 units on each side of the center. Label the vertices and draw the ellipse (Figure 6.49).

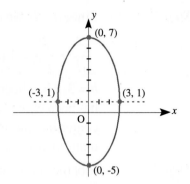

Figure 6.49

Finally, we look for the extraneous branch. Because $y - 1 = 2\sqrt{9 - x^2}$ is non-negative, so $y \geq 1$. This means that we accept only the upper half of the ellipse. Thus, the graph of $y = 1 + 2\sqrt{9 - x^2}$ is the graph in Figure 6.50.

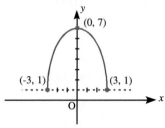

Figure 6.50

With Graphing Calculator

Let $y1 = 1 + 2\sqrt{9 - x^2}$. Graph $y1$ on the standard or any other suitable range.

Ellipse in the Real World

Among many applications of the ellipse, we mention only a few important ones.

1. Each planet in the solar system has an elliptical orbit with the sun.

2. The * reflection property of the ellipse is used in optics and acoustics.

> * The reflection property of the ellipse states that a ray of light emmited from one focus is reflected by an elliptical mirror through the other focus.
>
>
>
> **Figure 6.51**

EXERCISE 6.4

In exercises (1-14), find a relation that describes the ellipse satisfying the given conditions.

1. The foci are at $(\pm 4, 0)$ and two vertices are at $(\pm 5, 0)$.

2 The foci are at $(\pm 2, 0)$ and two vertices are at $(\pm 4, 0)$.

3. The foci are at $(\pm 3, 0)$ and two vertices are at $(\pm 5, 0)$

4. The foci are at $(\pm 5, 0)$ and two vertices are at $(\pm 7, 0)$

5. The foci are at $(0, \pm 2)$ and two vertices are at $(0, \pm 3)$

6. The foci are at $(0, \pm 4)$ and two vertices are at $(0, \pm 6)$

7. The foci are at $(0, \pm 1)$ and two vertices are at $(0, \pm 4)$

8. The foci are at $(0, \pm 3)$ and two vertices are at $(0, \pm 5)$

9.   The foci are at $(0, \pm 3)$ and the length of the major axis is 10.

10. The foci are at $(\pm 3, 0)$ and the length of the minor axis is 6.

11. The foci are at $(0, \pm 2)$ and the length of the minor axis is 10.

12. The foci are at $(\pm 2, 0)$ and the length of the major axis is 10.

13. The vertices are at $(3, -2)$ and $(3, 6)$ and the length of the minor axis is 8.

14. The vertices are at $(1, 2)$, $(5, 2)$ and the length of the major axis is 6.

In exercises (15-40), verify that the relation represents an ellipse and then find its foci, vertices, and center.

15. $\dfrac{x^2}{4} + \dfrac{y^2}{16} = 1$ 16. $\dfrac{x^2}{16} + \dfrac{y^2}{4} = 1$ 17. $\dfrac{x^2}{9} + \dfrac{y^2}{25} = 1$

18. $\dfrac{x^2}{16} + \dfrac{y^2}{9} = 1$ 19. $4x^2 + 36y^2 = 144$ 20. $4x^2 + 3y^2 = 12$

21. $x^2 + 9y^2 = 9$ 22. $2x^2 + 9y^2 = 18$ 23. $\dfrac{(x-1)^2}{3^2} + \dfrac{y^2}{1} = 1$

24. $\dfrac{(x-2)^2}{4} + \dfrac{y^2}{1} = 1$ 25. $\dfrac{x^2}{2^2} + \dfrac{(y-1)^2}{3^2} = 1$ 26. $\dfrac{x^2}{9} + \dfrac{(y-3)^2}{16} = 1$

27. $\dfrac{(x-1)^2}{2^2} + \dfrac{(y+2)^2}{3^2} = 1$ 28. $\dfrac{(x+1)^2}{2^2} + \dfrac{(y-3)^2}{3^2} = 1$ 29. $\dfrac{(x+1)^2}{3^2} + \dfrac{(y-2)^2}{2^2} = 1$

30. $\dfrac{(x-2)^2}{5^2} + \dfrac{(y-3)^2}{4^2} = 1$ 31. $x^2 + 2y^2 - 6x + 4y + 3 = 0$ 32. $x^2 + 2y^2 + 2x + 4y - 7 = 0$

33. $x^2 + 3y^2 - 4x + 6y - 2 = 0$ 34. $2x^2 + y^2 - 4x + 4y + 2 = 0$ 35. $x^2 + 5y^2 + 6x - 16 = 0$

36. $4x^2 + 5y^2 + 10y - 15 = 0$ 37. $2x^2 + 4y^2 - 20x + 8y + 46 = 0$ 38. $2x^2 + 3y^2 - 4x - 10 = 0$

39. $5x^2 + 3y^2 - 20x + 36y + 113 = 0$ 40. $3x^2 + 5y^2 + 12x - 10y + 2 = 0$

In exercises (41-49), sketch the graph of the function.

41. $y = \dfrac{2}{3}\sqrt{9 - x^2}$ 42. $y = \dfrac{3}{4}\sqrt{16 - x^2}$ 43. $y = \dfrac{-2}{3}\sqrt{9 - x^2}$

44. $y = -\dfrac{3}{2}\sqrt{4 - x^2}$ 45. $y = -2 + \dfrac{3}{2}\sqrt{4 - x^2}$ 46. $y = 1 + \dfrac{2}{5}\sqrt{25 - x^2}$

47. $y = -2 - \dfrac{3}{2}\sqrt{4 - x^2}$ 48. $y = -1 - \dfrac{2}{5}\sqrt{25 - x^2}$

49. The figure shows a side view of a bridge over a small stream in a country side. The arch of the bridge is approximately a semi ellipse. If the arch of the bridge is 60 feet wide and 18 feet high, find a relation that describes the shape of the arch.

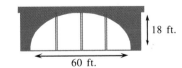

50. Refer to Exercise 49. Suppose the bridge is in need of three supporting pillars, one in the center and the other two symmetrically placed 20 ft. on each side. How high are the two pillars symmetrically placed?

51. Refer to Exercise 49. Suppose the bridge is in need of three supporting pillars, one in the center and the other two symmetrically placed 15 ft. on each side. How high are these pillars?

52. Refer to Exercise 49. Suppose the bridge is in need of three supporting pillars, one in the center and the other two symmetrically placed 22 ft. on each side. How high are the two pillars symmetrically placed?

53. On a special day of Fun and Game two first grade teachers stationed their respective groups of students 100 feet apart. Fresh apples were arranged all around the two stations as shown in the figure. Each student is supposed to run from his station and grab an apple and then run to the other station. Each participant in the game travels exactly 128 feet and is timed; the grand prize goes to the fastest runner. Give a relation that describes the path along which the apples are arranged.

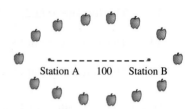

54. Refer to Exercise 53. If the respective group of students are 120 feet apart and each participant in the game travels 140 feet, then find a relation that describes the path along which the apples are arranged.

55. A music buff who is always mixing tunes and lyrics is advised to build an elliptical room. The farthest corners of the room are 25 feet apart and the points where the room is the widest are 16 feet apart. Give locations where he should place speakers facing the walls.

56. Refer to Exercise 55. If the farthest corners of the room are 36 feet apart and the points where the room is the widest are 25 feet apart, then give locations where he should place speakers facing the walls.

Writing Exercises

57. State the meaning of "reflective" property of an ellipse.

58. Describe a method of drawing an ellipse.

6.5 HYPERBOLA

Objectives ▶▶

In this section you will learn about:

A. Finding an Equation of the Hyperbola; and

B. Graphing a Hyperbola.

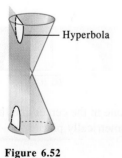

Figure 6.52

In this section, we generate a relation that describes the last of the conic sections, called **hyperbola.**

The cross section of a right circular cone by a plane parallel to the axis generates a hyperbola (Figure 6.52).

A. FINDING AN EQUATION OF THE HYPERBOLA

Hyperbola

A **hyperbola** consists of points in the plane, the difference of whose distances from two fixed points is a constant. The fixed points are called **foci.**

Let the line joining the foci be the x-axis. We will find a relation that describes the hyperbola.

We choose the y-axis to be the perpendicular bisector of the segment joining the two foci.

- Let $F_1(c, 0)$ and $F_2(-c, 0)$ be the foci. (Figure 6.53).

- The hyperbola consists of all points $Q(x, y)$ which satisfy the given condition.

- Let a be one-half of the difference of the two distances. To find a relationship between x and y, we use the fact that

$$\left| QF_2 - QF_1 \right| = \text{constant} = 2a$$

$$\sqrt{(x+c)^2 + (y-0)^2} - \sqrt{(x-c)^2 + (y-0)^2} = \pm 2a$$

By squaring and simplifying twice, we get

$$(c^2 - a^2)\, x^2 - a^2 y^2 = a^2(c^2 - a^2)$$

To write the equation in a more convenient form, we set

$$c^2 - a^2 = b^2 \quad \textbf{or} \quad c^2 = a^2 + b^2.$$

This changes the equation to $b^2 x^2 - a^2 y^2 = a^2 b^2$.

Dividing by $a^2 b^2$, we get $\dfrac{x^2}{a^2} - \dfrac{y^2}{b^2} = 1$.

This is the standard equation of the hyperbola.

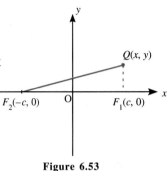

Figure 6.53

To draw the graph of $\dfrac{x^2}{a^2} - \dfrac{y^2}{b^2} = 1$, we notice the following facts.

1.   The graph is symmetrical about the x-axis.

2.   The graph is symmetrical about the y-axis.

3.   The x-intercepts of the graph are the solutions of the equation:

$$\frac{x^2}{a^2} - \frac{0^2}{b^2} = 1 \quad \longrightarrow \quad x^2 = a^2 \quad \longrightarrow \quad x = \pm\, a$$

4.   The y-intercepts of the graph are the solutions of the equation:

$$\frac{0^2}{a^2} - \frac{y^2}{b^2} = 1 \quad \longrightarrow \quad y^2 = -b^2$$

Since this equation has no real solutions (why?), the graph does not intersect the y-axis.

5.   Domain:

From $y^2 = \dfrac{b^2}{a^2}\,(x^2 - a^2)$ it follows that

$$y = \pm\frac{b}{a}\,\sqrt{x^2 - a^2}$$

To find the domain, set the radicand ≥ 0 and solve for x.

$$(x - a)\,(x + a) \geq 0$$

We consider three intervals as possible solution intervals.

		sign	satisfy inequality
A:	$(-\infty, -a]$	neg. neg → pos	Yes
B:	$(-a, a)$	neg. pos → neg	No
C:	$[a, \infty)$	pos. pos → pos	Yes

The domain is $(-\infty, -a] \cup [a, \infty)$. The hyperbola is not defined on the interval $(-a, a)$.

6.   We look into the behavior of the graph when $|x|$ is large.

The equation can be solved for y as follows.

$$\frac{y^2}{b^2} = \frac{x^2}{a^2} - 1$$

$$y^2 = b^2\left(\frac{x^2}{a^2} - 1\right) = \frac{b^2}{a^2}(x^2 - a^2) = \frac{b^2 x^2}{a^2}\left(1 - \frac{a^2}{x^2}\right)$$

Therefore, $y = \pm\dfrac{b}{a}|x|\sqrt{1 - \dfrac{a^2}{x^2}}$

Since $\dfrac{a^2}{x^2} \longrightarrow 0$ as $|x|$ increases without bound, we get:

$y = \pm\dfrac{b}{a}|x|$ or $y = \pm\dfrac{b}{a}x$, when $|x|$ is large.

In other words the graph resembles the graph of lines

$y = \pm\dfrac{b}{a}x$, when $|x|$ is large. These lines are called the

asymptotes of the graph. Since the asymptotes $y = \pm\dfrac{b}{a}x$ pass

through the origin and have slopes $\dfrac{b}{a}$ and $-\dfrac{b}{a}$, we can draw these

lines accurately by drawing the diagonals of the rectangle ABCD
(Figure 6.54), where $A(-a, b)$, $B(a, b)$, $C(a, -b)$ and $D(-a, -b)$
are the vertices of the rectangle.

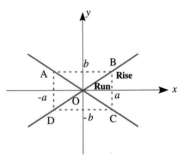

Figure 6.54

By using the above results, we draw the graph of

$\dfrac{x^2}{a^2} - \dfrac{y^2}{b^2} = 1$, as in Figure 6.55.

Similarly, the relation that describes the hyperbola with foci at

$(0, c)$ and $(0, -c)$ is $-\dfrac{x^2}{a^2} + \dfrac{y^2}{b^2} = 1$ and its graph will look

like Figure 6.56.

This is often written in the form $\dfrac{y^2}{b^2} - \dfrac{x^2}{a^2} = 1$

We summarize these results as follows:

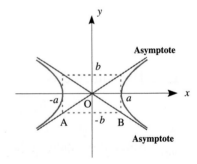

Figure 6.55

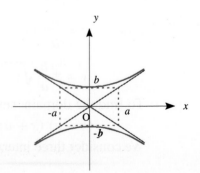

Figure 6.56

Standard Forms of Relation Representing an Hyperbola

1. $\dfrac{x^2}{a^2} - \dfrac{y^2}{b^2} = 1$

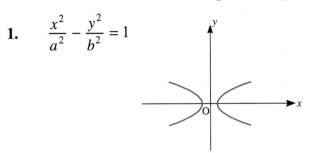

(a)

Figure 6.57 a

Vertices $(\pm a, 0)$, Foci $(\pm c, 0)$,

where $c^2 = a^2 + b^2$

Asymptote: $y = \pm\dfrac{b}{a}x$

2. $-\dfrac{x^2}{a^2} + \dfrac{y^2}{b^2} = 1$

OR $\dfrac{y^2}{b^2} - \dfrac{x^2}{a^2} = 1$

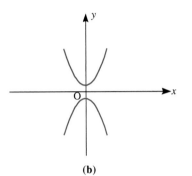

(b)

Figure 6.57 b

Vertices $(0, \pm b)$, Foci $(0, \pm c)$,

where $c^2 = a^2 + b^2$

Asymptote: $y = \pm\dfrac{b}{a}x$

Remarks:

  1. The center and the two axes of a hyperbola are defined in the same way as for ellipse.

  2. Unlike other conic sections, the hyperbola has two branches of the graph.

  3. The graph is symmetrical about the focal axis.

  4. The combined equation of the asymptotes is obtained by writing 0 for 1 in the standard form

  of the hyperbola $\dfrac{x^2}{a^2} - \dfrac{y^2}{b^2} = 1$, or $-\dfrac{x^2}{a^2} + \dfrac{y^2}{b^2} = 1$, because $\dfrac{x^2}{a^2} - \dfrac{y^2}{b^2} = 0$, gives $y = \pm\dfrac{b}{a}x$

  which are the asymptotes.

B. GRAPHING A HYPERBOLA

As in the other conic sections, we first write the given equation in one of the standard forms, then find its vertices, foci, and asymptotes to draw the graph. The following examples illustrate the procedure.

EXAMPLE 1   Find the vertices, foci and asymptotes of $9x^2 - 4y^2 = 36$. Sketch the graph of the hyperbola.

Solution:

  Step 1   Compare the equation with one of the standard forms.

In this case, we first write $9x^2 - 4y^2 = 36$ as

$$\dfrac{x^2}{4} - \dfrac{y^2}{9} = 1 \quad \textbf{or} \quad \dfrac{x^2}{2^2} - \dfrac{y^2}{3^2} = 1.$$

Now we compare with $\dfrac{x^2}{a^2} - \dfrac{y^2}{b^2} = 1$. We see that

$a = 2, b = 3$ and the center is at the origin.

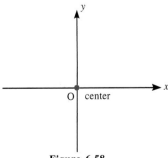

Figure 6.58

Step 2   Plot the center and draw the horizontal and vertical axes through the center of the hyperbola (Figure 6.58).

Step 3   From the center, go '*a*' units on each side along the horizontal axis and '*b*' units along the vertical axis. Complete the rectangle and draw the diagonals. The diagonals represent the asymptotes (Figure 6.59).

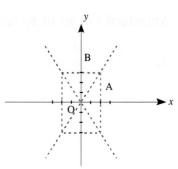

Figure 6.59

Step 4   Label the vertices and draw the graph of the hyperbola (Figure 6.60).

Step 5   Find *c* by solving the equation $c^2 = a^2 + b^2$. Now, from the center go *c* units toward each vertex and label the foci. In this case,

$$c^2 = 4 + 9 = 13$$

$$c = \sqrt{13}$$

The foci are $\left(\sqrt{13}, 0\right)$ and $\left(-\sqrt{13}, 0\right)$ (Figure 6.61)

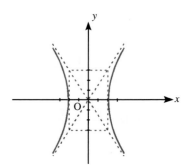

Figure 6.60

From Figure 6.61, the vertices are $(2, 0)$ and $(-2, 0)$ and, the foci are $\left(\sqrt{13}, 0\right)$ and $\left(-\sqrt{13}, 0\right)$. The equations of the asymptotes are obtained by setting each factor of $*\ \dfrac{x^2}{4} - \dfrac{y^2}{9}$ to zero. This gives

$\dfrac{x}{2} - \dfrac{y}{3} = 0$ and $\dfrac{x}{2} + \dfrac{y}{3} = 0$ as the asymptotes. The graph of the hyperbola is shown in Figure 6.61.

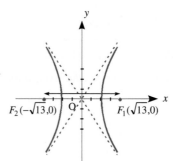

Figure 6.61

$$* \quad \frac{x^2}{4} - \frac{y^2}{9} = \left(\frac{x}{2}\right)^2 - \left(\frac{y}{3}\right)^2$$

a difference of two squares.

$$\frac{x^2}{4} - \frac{y^2}{9}$$

$$= \left(\frac{x}{2} - \frac{y}{3}\right)\left(\frac{x}{2} + \frac{y}{3}\right)$$

With Graphing Calculator

We can verify the graph as well as the coordinates of the vertices by using a graphing calculator. First write the relation $9x^2 - 4y^2 = 36$ in terms of two functions. We solve for *y*.

$$9x^2 - 36 = 4y^2 \longrightarrow \frac{9}{4}\left(x^2 - 4\right) = y^2 \longrightarrow \pm\frac{3}{2}\sqrt{x^2 - 4} = y$$

Now, let $y1 = \dfrac{3}{2}\sqrt{x^2 - 4}$ and $y2 = -\dfrac{3}{2}\sqrt{x^2 - 4}$. Graph y1 and

y2 on the standard range: By using ZOOM-IN and TRACE, we can verify the coordinates of the vertices.

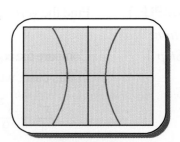

Figure 6.62

EXAMPLE 2   Find the vertices, foci, and asymptotes of the hyperbola
$-16x^2 + 9y^2 + 32x + 36y = 124$. Also sketch the graph.

Solution:

Step 1   Before we can compare the equation with one of the standard forms, we first complete the squares in x and y.

$$-16x^2 + 32x + 9y^2 + 36y = 124$$
$$-16[x^2 - 2x] + 9[y^2 + 4y] = 124$$
$$-16[(x-1)^2 - 1] + 9[(y+2)^2 - 4] = 124$$
$$-16(x-1)^2 + 16 + 9(y+2)^2 - 36 = 124$$
$$-16(x-1)^2 + 9(y+2)^2 = 144$$

Dividing by 144, we get

$$-\frac{(x-1)^2}{9} + \frac{(y+2)^2}{16} = 1 \quad \longrightarrow \quad -\frac{(x-1)^2}{3^2} + \frac{(y+2)^2}{4^2} = 1 \ .$$

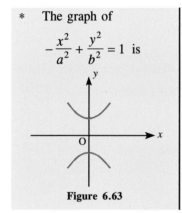

*   The graph of

$$-\frac{x^2}{a^2} + \frac{y^2}{b^2} = 1 \text{ is}$$

Figure 6.63

By comparing with * $-\dfrac{x^2}{a^2} + \dfrac{y^2}{b^2} = 1$ we

see that x has been replaced with $x - 1$ and y has been replaced with $y + 2$. Also $a = 3$ and $b = 4$.

Step 2   Since x has been replaced with $x - 1$ and y by $y + 2$, the center of the hyperbola moves to $(1, -2)$ (Figure 6.64).

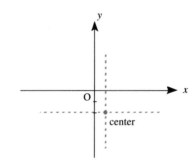

Figure 6.64

Step 3   From the center, we move three units on each side along the horizontal axis. We move four units from the center, on each side, along the vertical axis, We complete the rectangle and draw its diagonals (asymptotes) Figure 6.65.

Step 4   The vertices of the hyperbola are located at $(1, 2)$ and $(1, -6)$. The graph of the hyperbola is shown in Figure 6.66.

Step 5   To locate the foci of the hyperbola, we find c.

$$c^2 = a^2 + b^2 = 9 + 16 = \mathbf{25} \ \longrightarrow \ c = 5$$

Now, from the center we move 5 units toward each vertex. This gives the location of two foci at $(1, 3)$ and $(1, -7)$ (Figure 6.66).

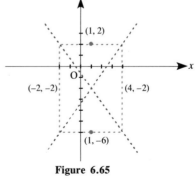

Figure 6.65

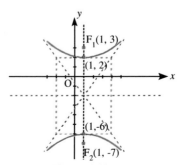

Figure 6.66

The equations of the asymptotes are given by

$* \quad -\dfrac{(x-1)^2}{9} + \dfrac{(y+2)^2}{16} = 0 \longrightarrow \left(\dfrac{y+2}{4}\right)^2 - \left(\dfrac{x-1}{3}\right)^2 = 0$

$$\left(\dfrac{y+2}{4} - \dfrac{x-1}{3}\right)\left(\dfrac{y+2}{4} + \dfrac{x-1}{3}\right) = 0$$

$\dfrac{y+2}{4} - \dfrac{x-1}{3} = 0$	$\dfrac{y+2}{4} + \dfrac{x-1}{3} = 0$
$3y + 6 - 4x + 4 = 0$	$3y + 6 + 4x - 4 = 0$
$3y - 4x + 10 = 0$	$3y + 4x + 2 = 0$

> * The combined equation of the asymptotes is derived from the standard form when we replace 1 by 0. In this case,
> $$-\dfrac{(x-1)^2}{9} + \dfrac{(y+2)^2}{16} = 0 .$$

With Graphing Calculator

To use a graphing calculator, we write the relation in terms of two functions as

$\dfrac{(y+2)^2}{16} = 1 + \dfrac{(x-1)^2}{9} \longrightarrow (y+2)^2 = 16\left(\dfrac{9+(x-1)^2}{9}\right) = \dfrac{16}{9}\left(9+(x-1)^2\right)$

$y + 2 = \pm\dfrac{4}{3}\sqrt{9+(x-1)^2} \longrightarrow y = -2 \pm \dfrac{4}{3}\sqrt{9+(x-1)^2}$

Let $y1 = -2 + \dfrac{4}{3}\sqrt{9+(x-1)^2}$ and $y2 = -2 - \dfrac{4}{3}\sqrt{9+(x-1)^2}$. Graph $y1$ and $y2$ on the standard (or any other suitable) range and verify the graph. Use ZOOM-IN and TRACE, to verify the coordinates of the vertices.

EXAMPLE 3 Sketch the graph of the relation $16x^2 - 25y^2 + 64x + 50y + 39 = 0$.

Solution: First we complete the squares in x and y.

$16x^2 + 64x - 25y^2 + 50y + 39 = 0$

$\longrightarrow \quad 16[x^2 + 4x] - 25[y^2 - 2y] + 39 = 0$

$\longrightarrow \quad 16[(x+2)^2 - 4] - 25[(y-1)^2 - 1] + 39 = 0$

$\longrightarrow \quad 16(x+2)^2 - 64 - 25(y-1)^2 + 25 + 39 = 0$

$\longrightarrow \quad 16(x+2)^2 - 25(y-1)^2 = 0$

$\longrightarrow \quad \dfrac{(x+2)^2}{25} - \dfrac{(y-1)^2}{16} = 0$

This equation can not be written in a standard form. If we factor and set each factor to zero, we get

$4(x+2) - 5(y-1) = 0$	$4(x+2) + 5(y-1) = 0$
$4x - 5y + 13 = 0$	$4x + 5y + 3 = 0$

These two lines constitute the graph.

⬤**Note** These two lines are in fact the asymptotes for the hyperbolas $\dfrac{(x+2)^2}{25} - \dfrac{(y-1)^2}{16} = \pm 1$.

The combined graph of the two asymptotes is also called a **degenerate hyperbola**.

Hyperbolas in the Real World

There are several applications of the hyperbola, such as:

1.   the use of the hyperbolic mirrors in telescopes,

2.   the use of hyperbolas in radio signals (LORAN), and

3.   the orbits of some comets.

The following summary will help us to identify a relation that describes a circle, a parabola, an ellipse, or a hyperbola.

Summary of Second Degree Relations

A second degree relation of the type $Ax^2 + By^2 + Cx + Dy + E = 0$ represents:

1.   A **parabola**, if either A **or** B is zero, but not both.

2.   An **ellipse** if A **and** B are non zero, unequal, and of the same sign.

3.   A **circle** if $A = B \neq 0$.

4.   A **hyperbola,** if A **and** B are non zero and of opposite signs.

EXERCISE   6.5

In exercises (1-14), find the relation that describes the hyperbola satisfying the given conditions.

1.   The vertices are at $(\pm 3, 0)$ and the foci are at $(\pm 5, 0)$.

2.   The vertices are at $(\pm 6, 0)$ and the foci are at $(\pm 10, 0)$.

3.   The vertices are at $(0, \pm 4)$ and the foci are at $(0, \pm 5)$.

4.   The vertices are at $(0, \pm 8)$ and the foci are at $(0, \pm 10)$.

5.   The vertices are at $(\pm 2, 0)$ and the asymptotes are $y = \pm 2x$.

6.   The vertices are at $(\pm 3, 0)$ and the asymptotes are $y = \pm 2x$.

7.   The vertices are at $(0, \pm 2)$ and the asymptotes are $y = \pm 2x$.

8.   The vertices are at $(0, \pm 3)$ and the asymptotes are $y = \pm 4x$.

9.   The vertices are at $(0, \pm 8)$ and passes through $(1, 10)$.

10.   The vertices are at $(\pm 4, 0)$ and passes through $(6, -2)$.

11.   The vertices are at $(\pm 7, 0)$ and passes through $(8, 2)$.

12.   The vertices are at $(0, \pm 3)$ and passes through $(-1, 4)$.

13.   The asymptotes are $y = \pm 2x$ and passes through $(3, 5)$.

14.   The asymptotes are $y = \pm 3x$ and passes through $(3, 4)$.

In exercises (15-48), verify that the relation represents a hyperbola and then find its foci, vertices, center, and the asymptotes. Also sketch the graph of the hyperbola.

15. $\dfrac{x^2}{9} - \dfrac{y^2}{2} = 1$ 16. $\dfrac{x^2}{16} - \dfrac{y^2}{9} = 1$ 17. $\dfrac{x^2}{25} - \dfrac{y^2}{9} = 1$ 18. $\dfrac{x^2}{16} - \dfrac{y^2}{4} = 1$

19. $-\dfrac{x^2}{4} + \dfrac{y^2}{9} = 1$ 20. $-\dfrac{x^2}{9} + \dfrac{y^2}{25} = 1$ 21. $-\dfrac{x^2}{16} + \dfrac{y^2}{25} = 1$ 22. $-\dfrac{x^2}{9} + \dfrac{y^2}{16} = 1$

23. $16x^2 - 25y^2 = 400$ 24. $4x^2 - 25y^2 = 100$ 25. $-x^2 + 4y^2 = 4$ 26. $-4x^2 + y^2 = 36$

27. $4(x-1)^2 - 9(y-2)^2 = 36$ 28. $4(x+1)^2 - (y+2)^2 = 4$ 29. $9x^2 - 4(y+1)^2 = 36$

30. $4x^2 - 9(y+2)^2 = 36$ 31. $\dfrac{(x+2)^2}{25} - \dfrac{(y-1)^2}{16} = 1$ 32. $-\dfrac{(x-2)^2}{25} + \dfrac{(y-1)^2}{9} = 1$

33. $-25x^2 + 9(y-1)^2 = 225$ 34. $25(x+1)^2 - 9y^2 = 225$ 35. $-(x-1)^2 + 4(y+2)^2 = 16$

36. $16(x-1)^2 - 25(y+1)^2 = 400$ 37. $x^2 - y^2 - 6x + 8y - 3 = 0$ 38. $x^2 - y^2 - 4x - 6y - 14 = 0$

39. $x^2 - y^2 - 8x - 8y - 1 = 0$ 40. $x^2 - y^2 + 2x + 2y - 4 = 0$ 41. $4x^2 - 9y^2 + 8x - 18y + 31 = 0$

42. $9x^2 - 4y^2 + 18x - 8y - 31 = 0$ 43. $2x^2 - 9y^2 + 8x + 36y - 46 = 0$ 44. $9x^2 - 2y^2 + 36x + 8y + 46 = 0$

45. $4x^2 - 9y^2 + 16x + 54y - 29 = 0$ 46. $9x^2 - 4y^2 + 54x + 16y + 29 = 0$

47. $16x^2 - 9y^2 - 32x + 36y - 164 = 0$ 48. $9x^2 - 16y^2 - 36x + 32y + 164 = 0$

49. A signal is sent simultaneously from each of two LORAN (LOng RAnge Navigation) radio stations A, B located along the east coast 100 miles apart to a ship off the coast. The ship receives the signal from station A approximately 400 microseconds after it receives the signal from station B. Assuming that the radio signal travels 0.2 miles per microsecond, find a relation that describes the path of the ship.

In exercises (50-63), determine (without graphing) whether the relation represents a circle, a parabola, an ellipse, or a hyperbola.

50. $3x^2 - 2y^2 + 6x - 4y = 0$ 51. $x^2 + 6y - 4x = 7$ 52. $y^2 - 2y + 3x + 5 = 0$

53. $5x^2 + 5y^2 - 4x - 40y + 10 = 0$ 54. $10x^2 + 10y^2 - 3x + 20y - 15 = 0$ 55. $4x^2 + 2y^2 - 8x + 12y = 0$

56. $3x^2 + 5y^2 - 6x + 10y + 50 = 0$ 57. $-2x^2 + 3y^2 + 4x - 18y = 0$ 58. $7x^2 + 7y^2 - 4x + 3y - 1 = 0$

59. $x^2 - y^2 - 2x + 4y - 1 = 0$ 60. $y + 2x^2 - 4x - 11 = 0$ 61. $x + 2y^2 - 4y - 11 = 0$

62. $x + 4y^2 - 8y + 8 = 0$ 63. $6x^2 + 6y^2 - 12x + 18y = 1$

64. Refer to Exercise 53 on page 6.30. On another special day of Fun and Games, the same two first grade teachers divided 40 students into 20 groups. The partners are stationed separately at stations A and B, 100 feet apart. Flag poles, displaying the group numbers around stations A and B are seen in the figure. A stopwatch is placed at the base of each flagpole. Both partners of a group start simultaneously from their respective stations and run toward their flag pole. The first one reaching the pole starts the stopwatch and the other partner stops it when he/she reaches the pole. The group whose stopwatch shows the least amount of time wins the grand prize. Is it a fair game ? Assuming that the average time on the stopwatch is 15 seconds and the average speed of the first graders is 4 ft/sec, describe the path along which the flagpoles are placed.

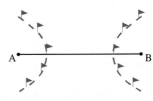

Writing Exercises

65. Describe the method of finding the asymptote of a hyperbola whose equation is given.

66. Explain how Long Range Navigation (LORAN) radio signals work.

6.6   CHAPTER SUMMARY

1. If y **varies directly** as x or if y is directly proportional to x, then $y(x) = kx$, for some constant k. The constant k is called the constant of variation or proportionality.

2. If a quantity y **varies inversely** as x(or y is inversely proportional to x), then $y(x) = \dfrac{k}{x}$ for some constant k.

3. If z **varies jointly** as x and y, or if z is directly proportional to x and y, then $z(x, y) = k\,xy$, for some constant k.

4. A function in its numerical (table) form represents a **direct variation** if all ratios $\dfrac{y}{x}$ are the same.

5. A function in its numerical (table) form, represents an **inverse variation** if all products xy are the same.

6. A **circle** consists of points in a plane equidistant from the fixed point, called the **center.** The distance from the center to a point on the circle is called the **radius.**

7. The relation that describes a circle whose center is at (h, k) and has the radius r is given by $(x - h)^2 + (y - k)^2 = r^2$.

8. The general equation of the circle is of the form: $Ax^2 + Ay^2 + Bx + Cy + E = 0$.

9. The line **tangent** to a circle at the point P is perpendicular to the radial line that joins point P to the center of the circle.

10. A **parabola** consists of all points in the plane that are equidistant from a given line called the **directrix** and a fixed point, not on the line, called the **focus.**

11. The standard forms of relation representing a parabola are:

   a. $y^2 = 4\ cx$

   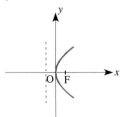

   b. $y^2 = -4\ cx$

   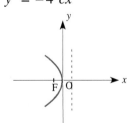

   c. $x^2 = 4\ cy$

   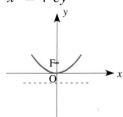

   d. $x^2 = -4\ cy$

   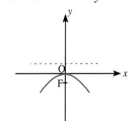

12. The vertex of a parabola is midway between the focus and the directrix.

13. An **ellipse** consist of all points in the plane, the sum of whose distances from two fixed points is a constant. The fixed points are called **foci.**

14. The standard forms of the relation representing an ellipse are:

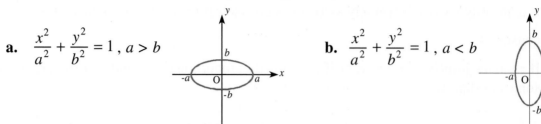

    a. $\dfrac{x^2}{a^2} + \dfrac{y^2}{b^2} = 1$, $a > b$ **b.** $\dfrac{x^2}{a^2} + \dfrac{y^2}{b^2} = 1$, $a < b$

15. If $a > b$, the length of the major axis (focal axis) is $2a$, and the length of the minor axis is $2b$. If $b > a$, the length of the major axis (focal axis) is $2b$ and the length of the minor axis is $2a$.

16. If $a = b$, the ellipse becomes a circle.

17. The distance between the foci of $\dfrac{x^2}{a^2} + \dfrac{y^2}{b^2} = 1$ is $2c$, where $c^2 = a^2 - b^2$ if $a > b$ or $c^2 = b^2 - a^2$ if $a < b$.

18. A **hyperbola** consists of points in the plane the difference of whose distances from two fixed points is a constant. The fixed points are called **foci.**

19. The standard forms of relation representing a hyperbola are:

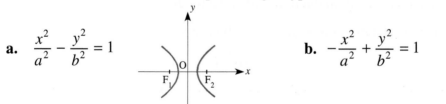
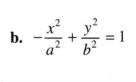
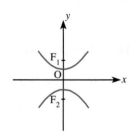

    a. $\dfrac{x^2}{a^2} - \dfrac{y^2}{b^2} = 1$ **b.** $-\dfrac{x^2}{a^2} + \dfrac{y^2}{b^2} = 1$

20. The asymptotes of the hyperbola $\dfrac{x^2}{a^2} - \dfrac{y^2}{b^2} = 1$ are $\dfrac{x^2}{a^2} - \dfrac{y^2}{b^2} = 0$ or $y = \pm\dfrac{b}{a}x$.

21. A second degree relation of the type $Ax^2 + By^2 + Cx + Dy + E = 0$ represents:

    a. A **circle**, if $A = B$.

    b. A **parabola** if either A or B is zero.

    c. An **ellipse** if A and B are non zero, unequal, and of the same sign.

    d. A **hyperbola** if A and B are non zero and of opposite signs.

6.7   CHAPTER REVIEW

In exercises (1-8), write a complete statement of the function and then use the given information to find the constant of variation.

1.   F varies directly as x, and $F = 100$ when $x = 5$.

2.   F varies directly as y, and $F = 126$ when $y = 7$.

3.   G varies inversly as the square of r, and $G = 15$ when $r = 2$.

4.   F varies inversly as x, and $F = 18$ when $x = 4$.

5.   A varies jointly as x and y, and A is 50 when $x = 5$ and $y = 2$.

6.   T varies jointly as x and y, and T is 72, when $x = 3$ and $y = 4$.

7.   The density ρ at a point $P(x,y)$ varies directly as the square of the distance from the y-axis, and ρ = 2 at (2,5).

8.   The density ρ at a point $P(x,y)$ varies directly as the square of the distance from the x-axis, and ρ = 27 at (4, 3).

In exercises (9-16), determine whether the function represents a direct, inverse, or joint variation, or none of these.

9. $S(x) = \dfrac{7}{2x}$ 10. $A(y) = 11y$ 11. $A(x) = 2 - 8x$ 12. $F(y) = 7x + 11$

13.
x	-3	-2	-1	1	2	4
y	$\dfrac{-3}{2}$	-1	$\dfrac{-1}{2}$	$\dfrac{1}{2}$	1	2

14.
x	-2	-1	1	2	3	4
y	$\dfrac{1}{2}$	2	2	$\dfrac{1}{2}$	$\dfrac{2}{9}$	$\dfrac{1}{8}$

15.
x	-3	-2	-1	1	2	3
y	$\dfrac{-1}{6}$	$\dfrac{-1}{4}$	$\dfrac{-1}{2}$	$\dfrac{1}{2}$	$\dfrac{1}{4}$	$\dfrac{1}{6}$

16.
x	-2	-1	1	2	3	4
y	12	3	3	12	27	48

In exercises (17-22), find an equation that describes the circle satisfying the given conditions.

17.   The center is at $(-1, -2)$ and is touching the y-axis.

18.   The center is at $(-2, 3)$ and is touching the x-axis.

19.   The center is at $(2, -3)$ and passing through the point $(-1, 1)$.

20.   The center is at $(-1, -6)$ and passing through the point $(5, 2)$.

21.   The diameter has end points at $(4, 7)$ and $(2, 1)$.

22.   The diameter has end points at $(-8, -7)$ and $(6, 5)$.

In exercises (23-26), verify that the relation describes a circle and then find the center and the radius of the circle.

23. $x^2 + y^2 - 2x + 4y - 4 = 0$ 24. $x^2 + y^2 + 8x - 12y - 12 = 0$

25. $2x^2 + 2y^2 - 6x + 4y - \dfrac{3}{2} = 0$ 26. $3x^2 + 3y^2 + 12x - 6y - 34 = 0$

27.   Sketch the graph of $y = -2 + \sqrt{25 - x^2}$ 28.   Sketch the graph of $y = 3 - \sqrt{9 - x^2}$

29.   Find a relation that describes the parabola whose focus is at $(-2, 0)$ and the directix is $x = 2$.

30.   Find a relation that describes the parabola whose focus is at $(0, 3)$ and the directix is $y = -3$.

In exercises (31-34), verify that the relation describes a parabola and then find its focus, vertex, and the directrix.

31. $(y + 1)^2 = -2x + 4$

32. $(x - 3)^2 = 3y - 6$

33. $x^2 + 2x + y - 1 = 0$

34. $y^2 + 2y + x - 1 = 0$

35. The main cable of a supension bridge is suspended between two towers that are 600 feet apart and 80 feet above the roadway. The main cable is in the form of a parabola with vertex at midway between the towers and touching the roadway. Find a relation that describes this parabola. (Let the horizontal axis be along the road and the vertical axis through the vertex).

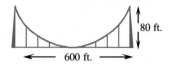

36. Refer to Exercise 35. If the two towers are 800 feet apart and 60 feet above the road way, find a relation that describes the parabola.

37. The arch of a small bridge is approximately a semi-ellipse. The span of the bridge is 80 feet and height is 20 feet. Find a relation that describes the shape of the arch.

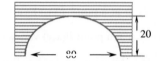

38. Refer to Exercise 37. If the span of the bridge is 100 feet and height is 30 feet, find a relation that describes the shape of the arch.

In exercises (39-44), verify that the relation represents an ellipse and then find its foci, vertices, and the center.

39. $4(x - 1)^2 + 9(y + 1)^2 = 36$

40. $9(x + 1)^2 + 4(y - 1)^2 = 36$

41. $2x^2 + 3y^2 + 4x - 12y + 8 = 0$

42. $3x^2 + 2y^2 - 12x + 4y + 8 = 0$

43. Sketch the graph of $x = 1 + \frac{1}{2}\sqrt{4 - y^2}$

44. Sketch the graph of $y = 1 + \frac{1}{2}\sqrt{4 - x^2}$

In exercises (45-48), verify that the relation represents a hyperbola and then find its foci, vertices, center, and the asymptotes. Also sketch the graph of the hyperbola.

45. $4(x + 1)^2 - 9(y - 1)^2 = 36$

46. $9(x + 1)^2 - 4(y - 1)^2 = 36$

47. $-9x^2 + 18x + 4y^2 + 16y - 29 = 0$

48. $-9y^2 + 18y + 4x^2 + 16x - 29 = 0$

In exercises (49-52), determine (without graphing) whether the relation represents a circle, a parabola, an ellipse, or a hyperbola.

49. $9x^2 - 18x - 4y^2 + 8y = 0$

50. $8x^2 + 8y^2 + 4x + 6y - 7 = 0$

51. $4x^2 - 8x + 6y + 9 = 0$

52. $4y^2 - 8y + 6x + 9 = 0$

Writing Exercise

53. Write a paragraph on conic sections as sections of a cone.

6.8   CHAPTER TEST

1.   A pyramid with a square base of side 200 feet has a height of 100 ft. If the area (A) of a horizontal cross section of the pyramid varies directly as the square of the distance (x) from the vertex, write the area (A) as a function of x.

2.   Determine whether the function represents a **direct**, **inverse**, **joint** variation or none of these.

   a.
x	-3	-2	-1	2	3	4
y	$\frac{-4}{3}$	-2	-4	2	$\frac{4}{3}$	1

   b. $f(x) = 8x + 3$

   c. $g(x) = 10x$

3.   Analyze each relation and sketch the graph.

   a. $9x^2 + 36x + 5y^2 + 30y + 36 = 0$

   b. $y^2 - 6y + 14x = 47$

   c. $-9x^2 - 36x + 4y^2 - 8y = 68$

   d. $y = -1 + \sqrt{16 - x^2}$

4.   The main cable of a suspension bridge is suspended between two towers that are 400 feet apart and 60 feet above the roadway. The main cable is in the form of a parabola with vertex at midway between the towers and touching the roadway. Let the horizontal axis of the coordinate system be along the roadway and the vertical axis along the left tower. Find a relation that describes the shape of the main cable.

Systems of Equations, Matrices, and Determinants

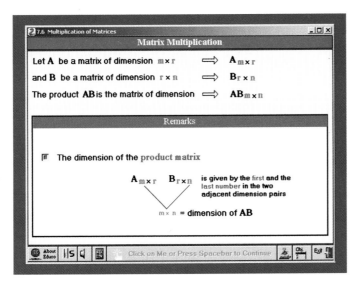

7.6 Multiplication of Matrices

Matrix Multiplication

Let **A** be a matrix of dimension $m \times r$ $\implies$ $\mathbf{A}_{m \times r}$

and **B** be a matrix of dimension $r \times n$ $\implies$ $\mathbf{B}_{r \times n}$

The product **AB** is the matrix of dimension $\implies$ $\mathbf{AB}_{m \times n}$

Remarks

☞ The dimension of the product matrix

$\mathbf{A}_{m \times r}$ $\mathbf{B}_{r \times n}$ is given by the first and the last number in the two adjacent dimension pairs

$m \times n$ = dimension of **AB**

About Educo ‖s⊲ 🔲 Click on Me or Press Spacebar to Continue ⚒ Obj. 7 Exit 11

SYSTEMS OF EQUATIONS, MATRICES, AND DETERMINANTS

7

Until now we have discussed mathematical models resulting in one equation. However, models of real life situations often have more than one equation, e.g.

$$5x - 2y + z = 8$$
$$x + 3y - 2z = -4$$
$$2x + y + z = 2, \qquad \text{where } x, y, \text{ and } z \text{ are unknowns.}$$

This set of equations is called a **system of equations.** The equations may be linear or non-linear. First, we will discuss algebraic methods of solving a system of linear equations. Then we apply those to a system of non-linear equations. The algorithm in one of the methods uses only the coefficients of the unknowns in the equations. The array of these coefficients (numbers) when written in rows and columns is called a matrix. In this chapter, we will develop an algebra of matrices (plural of matrix) and show its use in solving a system of **linear** equations. We will also define the **determinant** of a matrix and show its application (Cramer's Rule) in solving a system of linear equations.

The discussion in this chapter is organized into eight sections.

7.1	*Systems of Linear Equations;*	**7.5**	*Matrix Algebra;*
7.2	*Systems of Non-Linear Equations;*	**7.6**	*Multiplication of Matrices;*
7.3	*Parametric Representations of Relations;*	**7.7**	*Inverse of Matrix; and*
7.4	*Gauss-Jordan Method;*	**7.8**	*Determinants.*

7.1 SYSTEMS OF LINEAR EQUATIONS

We know functions (relations) consist of ordered pairs (input, output) or (x, y). In several real life situations we deal with more than one function (relation) simultaneously and need to find the ordered pairs that are common to these functions (relations). For example, in economics we deal with demand and supply functions. One important ordered pair in these functions is the pair that represents the equilibrium point which is a point common to the graphs of the demand and supply functions. Finding such common ordered pairs of more than one function (relation) is equivalent to solving systems of equations. In this section we will consider system of linear equations.

Objectives ▶ ▶

In this section you will learn about:

A. Linear Equations in Two Unknowns;

B. Linear Equations in Three Unknowns; and

C. Applications of Linear Systems.

TERMINOLOGY

The ordered pairs (x, y) common to the given functions (relations) are also called the **solutions to the system** (set) **of equations** representing the functions (relations). For example, the pair (x, y) common to the linear functions

$$f(x) = 7x - 8 \quad \text{and} \quad g(x) = 2x + 9$$

is the same as the solution to the system of equations $y = 7x - 8$ and $y = 2x + 9$.

A. LINEAR EQUATIONS IN TWO UNKNOWNS

To solve a system of linear equations in two variables we have a choice of three methods:

    1.   Graphing Method

    2.   Elimination by Addition Method

    3.   Elimination by Substitution Method

1.   Graphing Method

Graphically, the ordered pair (x, y) common to the linear functions represents the point of intersection of the graphs. Since the graph of a linear function (relation) is always a straight line, therefore, the coordinates of the points of intersection of the lines is the solution to the system of linear equations. We may draw the graphs of straight lines either by hand or with graphing calculator.

By Hand

Find at least two points on the first line by completing the table

x		
y		

Plot the points and connect the points to draw the first line. Similarly, draw the graph of the second line. Now we may have one of the following situations:

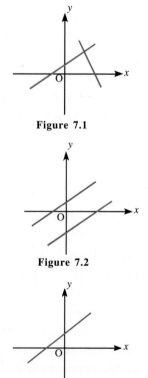

(i)   The lines intersect in a point (Figure 7.1). Find the coordinates (x, y) of the point of intersection. This is the solution to the system of equations.

Figure 7.1

(ii)   The lines are parallel (Figure 7.2). Since parallel lines do not intersect in a finite plane, there is **no solution** to this system of equations. Such a system of equations is called an **inconsistent system.**

Figure 7.2

(iii)   The lines coincide (Figure 7.3). Since the two lines meet each other in infinitely many points, there are **many solutions.** Such a system of equations is called a **dependent** system.

With Graphing Calculator

Solve each equation for y, that is, write each relation as a function. Let $y1$ and $y2$ be the two functions. Graph $y1$ and $y2$ on a suitable range. Use ZOOM-IN and TRACE and locate the points of intersection. If the two graphs coincide, then the system is dependent and there are many solutions. If the lines look parallel (m_1 must be equal to m_2), then the system is inconsistent and there is no solution.

Figure 7.3

● **Note** The graphing method may not always give us the exact solution.

EXAMPLE 1   Solve the following system of equations graphically.

$$5x + 2y = 3$$
$$3x - 5y = 8$$

Solution: Solving the first equation for y, we get:

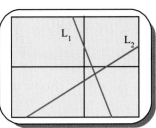

$$2y = 3 - 5x \longrightarrow y = \frac{3}{2} - \frac{5}{2}x .$$

Let $y1 = \frac{3}{2} - \frac{5}{2}x$ in a graphing calculator.

Figure 7.4

Similarly, the second equation gives

$$y2 = \frac{3}{5}x - \frac{8}{5}$$

Graph $y1$ and $y2$ on the standard range (Lines L_1 and L_2). We see that the lines intersect in a point. To estimate the coordinates of the point of intersection, we use ZOOM-IN and TRACE successively. The coordinates of the point of intersection are $(1, -1)$. Thus, the solution to the system of equations is $x = 1$ and $y = -1$ or $(1, -1)$.

2.   Elimination by Addition Method

Since we know how to solve an equation in one unknown, we try to eliminate one of the unknowns (x or y) by adding the two equations. But before we add, we must make sure that the coefficients of the unknown to be eliminated from the two equations are equal but with opposite signs (i.e. additive inverses). The phrase "adding two equations" is an informal but useful way of saying that a new equation is formed by adding the **left** sides and **right** sides of the two equations and then setting the results equal to each other. We explain this procedure in steps as follows:

EXAMPLE 2   Solve the system of equations by the addition method.

$$5x + 2y = 3$$
$$3x - 5y = 8$$

Solution:

*   *Step* 1   Align the x, y terms in the two equations.

$$5x + 2y = 3$$
$$3x - 5y = 8$$

> *   Suppose the first equation was given as $5x = 3 - 2y$. Then, we write it as
> $$5x + 2y = 3$$
> This is the standard form of a line.
>
> x is the targeted unknown.

Step 2   Choose a target unknown. Let us eliminate x.

Step 3   Multiply both equations by appropriate numbers so that the coefficients of the targeted unknown become the lcm of the two coefficients but with opposite signs. In this example, we get 15 and -15 as the coefficients of x in the two equations. In order to do this, we multiply the first equation by 3 and the second equation by -5 (or -3 times the first and 5 times the second). This gives

$$5x + 2y = 3 \quad (3) \qquad \longrightarrow \qquad 15x + 6y = 9$$
$$3x - 5y = 8 \quad (-5) \qquad \longrightarrow \qquad -15x + 25y = -40$$

Step 4   Now add the equations to eliminate the target unknown.

$$15x + 6y = 9$$
$$\underline{-15x + 25y = -40}$$
$$31y = -31 \qquad \text{add}$$

Step 5   Solve the resultant equation

$$31y = -31 \quad \longrightarrow \quad y = -\frac{31}{31} = \mathbf{-1}$$

Step 6   To find the other unknown, we substitute this value of the unknown in one of the given equations and solve for the other unknown. Let us substitute $y = -1$ in the first equation.

$$5x + 2(-1) = 3 \quad \longrightarrow \quad 5x - 2 = 3 \quad \longrightarrow \quad 5x = 5 \quad \longrightarrow \quad \mathbf{x = 1}$$

Thus, $(1, -1)$ is the solution to the system of equations.

EXAMPLE 3   Use the elimination by addition method to solve the following system of equations.

$$7x - 3y = 2$$
$$-14x + 6y = 7$$

Solution:

- Let us eliminate y.

- We multiply only the first equation by 2 **(WHY?)**

$$7x - 3y = 2 \quad \times 2 \quad \longrightarrow \quad 14x - 6y = 4$$
$$14x + 6y = 7 \qquad \longrightarrow \quad -14x + 6y = 7$$

- By adding the two equations, we eliminate the x-terms.

$$14x - 6y = 4$$
$$\underline{-14x + 6y = 7}$$
$$0 = 11 \qquad \text{add}$$

- We arrive at a contradiction. Therefore, there is **no solution** to the system of equations. The two lines are parallel.

⬤Note   We can use a graphing calculator to check whether the straight lines are actually parallel.

EXAMPLE 4   Solve the system of equations

$$y = \frac{2}{3}x - \frac{1}{2}$$
$$8x - 12y = 6$$

Solution:

- We remove fractions and rewrite the first equation as

$$6y = 6\left(\frac{2}{3}x\right) - 6\left(\frac{1}{2}\right)$$

$$6y = 4x - 3 \quad \longrightarrow \quad -4x + 6y = -3$$

Now we can align the x and y terms in the two equations as
$$-4x + 6y = -3$$
$$8x - 12y = 6$$

- Let us eliminate x.

- We multiply only the first equation by 2.
$$-4x + 6y = -3 \quad \times(2) \quad \longrightarrow \quad -8x + 12y = -6$$
$$8x - 12y = 6 \quad\quad\quad \longrightarrow \quad 8x - 12y = 6$$

- We add the equations to eliminate x.

$$\begin{array}{r} -8x + 12y = -6 \\ 8x - 12y = 6 \\ \hline 0 = 0 \end{array}$$

We arrive at a universal truth, therefore, there are many solutions.

Note   Check to verify that the graphs of the straight lines coincide. The slopes of both lines are $\frac{2}{3}$.

3.   Elimination by Substitution

To eliminate the target unknowns by substitution instead of addition, we solve one of the given equations for the target unknown and substitute the expression into the other equation. The resultant equation will be in one variable. We solve the equation and find the target unknown by substitution again. We show the strategy in the following example.

EXAMPLE 5   Solve the following system of equations by the substitution method.
$$2x - y = 1$$
$$5x + 3y = 8$$

Solution:

Step 1   Solve one of the equations for the target unknown. In this example, we solve the first equation for y. Therefore, y is the target unknown.
$$2x - 1 = y \quad\quad \text{or} \quad\quad \boxed{y = 2x - 1}$$

Step 2   Substitute this expression for the target unknown into the other equation. In this case, we substitute $2x - 1$ for y in the second equation. This gives
$$5x + 3(\mathbf{2x - 1}) = 8$$

Step 3   We solve the resultant equation.
$$5x + 6x - 3 = 8 \quad \longrightarrow \quad 11x = 11 \quad \longrightarrow \quad \mathbf{x = 1}$$

Step 4   Go back to Step 1 and substitute the value of this unknown and compute the value of the target unknown.
$$\mathbf{y} = 2(1) - 1 = 2 - 1 = \mathbf{1}$$

This $(1, 1)$ is the solution to the system of equations.

In the next objective, we extend the method of elimination by addition to a system of three equations in three unknowns.

B. LINEAR EQUATIONS IN THREE UNKNOWNS

Here, we will use a very common mathematical approach of reducing the new problem (of solving three equations in three unknowns) to an old problem (of solving two equations in two unknowns) and then using the old method to arrive at the solution. Suppose x, y and z are the unknowns. We will form two pairs of equations out of the given three equations. We will eliminate one of the unknowns (say z) in two pairs of equations. This will result in two equations in two unknowns (x and y) - a system we know how to solve. In case of a system of three equations in three variables, the solution, if one exists, will be an ordered triple. We explain this strategy in the following examples.

Method of Elimination

EXAMPLE 6   Solve the following system of equations.

$$3x - 2y + z = 8$$
$$2x + y - 2z = -5$$
$$x + 3y + 5z = 13$$

Solution:

Step 1   Label the equations as **(1)**, **(2)** and **(3)**.

$$3x - 2y + z = 8 \quad \textbf{(1)} \qquad 2x + y - 2z = -5 \quad \textbf{(2)} \qquad x + 3y + 5z = 13 \quad \textbf{(3)}$$

Step 2   Eliminate (by addition) one of the unknowns in **(1)** and **(2)** and label the resulting equation as **(4)**.

*   Let us eliminate z in **(1)** and **(2)**.

$$3x - 2y + z = 8 \ \times (2) \longrightarrow 6x - 4y + 2z = 16$$
$$2x + y - 2z = -5 \longrightarrow \underline{2x + \ y - 2z = -5}$$
$$8x - 3y \quad\ = 11 \quad \textbf{(4)}$$

add

> *   To eliminate z in (1) and (2), we multiply (1) by 2 so that the coefficients of z in the resulting equations are equal but with opposite signs.

Step 3   Eliminate the same unknown in **(1)** and **(3)** or **(2)** and **(3)** and label the resultant equation as **(5)**.

*   In this case we eliminate z in **(1)** and **(3)**.

$$3x - 2y + z = 8 \ \times (-5) \longrightarrow -15x + 10y - 5z = -40$$
$$x + 3y + 5z = 13 \longrightarrow \underline{\quad x + 3y + \ 5z = 13}$$
$$-14x + 13y \quad\ = -27 \quad \textbf{(5)}$$

add

> *   To eliminate z in **(1)** and **(3)**, we multiply **(1)** by -5. This makes -5 as the coefficient of z in the equation **(1)**.

Step 4   Solving **(4)** and **(5)**, we get

$$8x - 3y \ = 11 \quad \times (7) \longrightarrow 56x - 21y = 77$$
$$-14x + 13y = -27 \quad \times (4) \longrightarrow \underline{-56x + 52y = -108}$$
$$31y = -31$$

add

$$\longrightarrow \qquad y = -1$$

We substitute $y = -1$ in **(4)** and solve for x.

$$8x - 3(-1) = 11 \longrightarrow 8x + 3 = 11 \longrightarrow 8x = 8 \longrightarrow \ \textbf{\textit{x = 1}}$$

Step 5   Substitute these values of the two unknowns in **(1)** or **(2)** or **(3)** and find the third unknown.

Let us substitute $x = 1$ and $y = -1$ in **(1)**, we get

$$3(1) - 2(-1) + z = 8 \quad \longrightarrow \quad 3 + 2 + z = 8 \quad \longrightarrow \quad z = 3$$

Thus, the solution to the system of equations is $(1, -1, 3)$.

Substitute 1 for x, -1 for y, and 3 for z in equations (1), (2), and (3) to verify that $(1, -1, 3)$ is a common solution.

EXAMPLE 7   Solve: $3x - 5y + 7z = 9$
$$3y + 5z = 26$$
$$2z = 8$$

Solution: If the system of equations is given in this special (**triangular**) form, then we do not have to use the above steps. Instead, start from the last equation and find z.

$$2z = 8 \quad \longrightarrow \quad z = 4$$

Use this value of z in the next equation and find the unknown y.

$$3y + 5(4) = 26 \quad \longrightarrow \quad 3y + 20 = 26 \quad \longrightarrow \quad 3y = 6 \quad \longrightarrow \quad y = 2$$

Finally, use these values in the first equation and find the remaining unknown.

$$3x - 5(2) + 7(4) = 9 \quad \longrightarrow \quad 3x - 10 + 28 = 9 \quad \longrightarrow \quad 3x = -9 \quad \longrightarrow \quad x = -3$$

Thus, the solution to the system of equations is $(-3, 2, 4)$.

Remark: *We observe that it is easier to solve a system of equations in a triangular form. Later in this chapter (Section 7.4), we will discuss the Gauss-Jordan method which uses matrices to reduce a given system of equations to a special type of triangular form (diagonal form). That will give us the solution more conveniently.*

C. APPLICATIONS OF A LINEAR SYSTEM

We have seen, earlier, a numerical (table) form of a function which shows linear tendencies has a formula representation in the form of a linear function. Suppose a numerical (table) form has a non-linear tendency like a parabola. Then we can find a formula representation of the data by solving a system of linear equations as discussed in the following example.

EXAMPLE 8   Hourly temperatures in a green house are recorded as follows:

t	6AM	7	8	9	10	11	12	1PM	2	3
T	55	63	69.3	75	78	80	83.5	84	84	83.1

    a.   Plot the points and check to see if it has a non-linear tendency.

    b.   Find a second degree expression that describes the data.

Solutions: Let x be the number of hours after 6 AM and $f(x)$ be the temperature at the x-th hour. The table takes the following form:

x	0	1	2	3	4	5	6	7	8	9
$f(x)$	55	63	69.3	75	78	80	83.5	84	84	83.1

a. We plot the points. The graph of these points is called a scatter diagram.

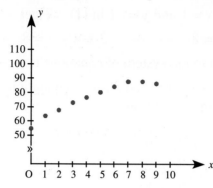

Figure 7.5

We observe that the shape of the scatter diagram is non-linear, and has the general (but not exact) shape of a parabola.

b. Let $f(x) = ax^2 + bx + c$ be the second degree expression that "best" describes the data. In other words, the graph will contain, or come close to, the 10 points. In particular, let us find the values of a, b, and c so that $y = ax^2 + bx + c$ contains three of the points, say $(1, 63)$, $(4, 78)$, and $(8, 84)$. Applying the condition to point $(1, 63)$, we get

$$63 = a(1)^2 + b(1) + c.$$

Since the point $(4, 78)$ is on the graph, it follows that

$$78 = a(4)^2 + b(4) + c$$

Similarly,

$$84 = a(8)^2 + b(8) + c$$

Let us solve these equations for a, b, and c.

Step 1   We label the equations as (1), (2) and (3).

$$a + b + c = 63 \qquad \textbf{(1)}$$
$$16a + 4b + c = 78 \qquad \textbf{(2)}$$
$$64a + 8b + c = 84 \qquad \textbf{(3)}$$

Step 2   We eliminate c in **(1)** and **(2)**

$$a + b + c = 63 \quad \times(-1) \longrightarrow \quad -a - b - c = -63$$
$$16a + 4b + c = 78 \quad\quad\quad \longrightarrow \quad 16a + 4b + c = 78$$

$$\overline{} \text{add}$$
$$15a + 3b = 15 \qquad \textbf{(4)}$$

Step 3   We eliminate c in **(2)** and **(3)**.

$$16a + 4b + c = 78 \quad \times(-1) \longrightarrow \quad -16a - 4b - c = -78$$
$$64a + 8b + c = 84 \quad\quad\quad \longrightarrow \quad 64a + 8b + c = 84$$

$$\overline{} \text{add}$$
$$48a + 4b = 6 \qquad \textbf{(5)}$$

Step 4   We solve **(4)** and **(5)** for a by eliminating b.

(4)× $\quad 15a + 3b = 15 \quad \times (4) \quad \longrightarrow \quad 60a + 12b = 60$

$\qquad\quad 48a + 4b = 6 \quad \times (-3) \quad \longrightarrow \quad \underline{-144a - 12b = -18}$

$$-84a \qquad = 42 \qquad \text{add} \quad \textbf{(6)}$$

$$a = \frac{42}{-84} = -\frac{1}{2}$$

Step 5   Substitute a into (4) [or (5)] and solve for b.

$$15\left(-\frac{1}{2}\right) + 3b = 15 \quad \longrightarrow \quad -\frac{15}{2} + 3b = 15$$

$$\longrightarrow \quad 3b = \frac{15}{2} + 15$$

$$\longrightarrow \quad 3b = \frac{45}{2}$$

$$\longrightarrow \quad \boldsymbol{b = \frac{15}{2}}$$

Step 6   Substitute a and b into **(1)** [or **(2)** or **(3)**]. Solve for c.

$$-\frac{1}{2} + \frac{15}{2} + c = 63 \quad \longrightarrow \quad 7 + c = 63 \quad \longrightarrow \quad \boldsymbol{c = 56}$$

Thus, the second degree formula that describes the data fairly well is $f(x) \approx -\frac{1}{2}x^2 + \frac{15}{2}x + 56$.

 Note   We made an arbitrary choice of three points and found an equation of the parabola that contains those points. Therefore, this is an estimate to the expression of the actual function.

EXERCISE 7.1

In exercises (1–5), solve the system of equations by the substitution method.

1. $2x + 5y = -3$
    $y = -2x + 1$

2. $3x - 2y = -5$
    $5x + 3y = -2$

3. $7x + 3y = -1$
    $4x - 5y = 33$

4. $\frac{2}{3}x - 3y = -2$

    $x + \frac{1}{2}y = 7$

5. $-\frac{2}{5}x + \frac{1}{2}y = 0$

    $\frac{1}{4}x - \frac{1}{5}y = \frac{9}{10}$

In exercises (6–16), use the method of elimination by addition to solve the system of equations.

6. $5x - 2y = 12$
    $6x + 4y = 8$

7. $6x + 5y = -9$
    $2x - 4y = 14$

8. $5x + 7y = 11$
    $3x - 2y = -12$

9. $3x - 5y = 51$

    $2x + 7y = -59$

10. $2\sqrt{3}x + 5y = 7$

    $2x - 3y = \sqrt{3}$

11. $7x - 5y = 12$

    $\pi x + 2y = 10$

12.
$$x - y + z = 0$$
$$2x + 3y + 2z = 0$$
$$3x - 2y - z = -4$$

13.
$$-2x + y - z = -4$$
$$x - 2y + 3z = 6$$
$$5x + 3y + 4z = 6$$

14.
$$3x + y + 2z = 0$$
$$4x - 3y + z = -7$$
$$9x - 2y + 4z = -8$$

15.
$$3x - y - 5z = 11$$
$$-6x + 2y + 10z = 10$$
$$7x + 2y - 3z = 2$$

16.
$$4x - 2y + 3z = -1$$
$$3x + 5y + 2z = 5$$
$$5x - y + z = 1$$

17. Bob's cash gifts on his birthday amount to $105. He wants to spend all his money on buying tapes and CDs; each CD is twice as expensive as a tape. If each tape costs $5.25 and he comes home with 12 pieces of tapes and CDs, how many of these were tapes and how many were CDs?

18. Refer to Exercise 17. Suppose Bob had $180.50 and he bought 20 pieces of tapes and CD's. How much money was left over?

19. Joe and his brother finish a job in 16 hours and are paid an amount of $320. His brother, who works 1.3 times as fast as Joe, demands that he be paid at the rate he would have earned had he done the whole job alone for $320. What rate per hour will he demand?

20. To raise money for the upcoming band competition Jim loaded 50 pizzas in his car and drove to his neighborhood to sell them. He notices that there were two kinds of pizzas, regular and deluxe. Each regular pizza was priced at $10.99 and the deluxe for $12.99. Jim sold all 50 pizzas and brought in $585.50. When asked how many regular and how many deluxe pizzas he sold, he had no record but pretended that he left the paper in his car. He sat in his car and did some math and came up with the numbers. What were those two numbers?

21. The profits (in millions) of a company are recorded as follows:

year	1990	1991	1992	1993	1994	1995
profit	4	8.8	12.6	15.4	17.2	18

Plot the points in a scatter diagram. Estimate a formula for the profit (P) function in terms of the number (x) of years after 1990. Find either a quadratic formula or a linear formula, depending on which fits the data best.

22. Early morning temperatures ($F°$) recorded at the airport on July 20 are as follows:

Time	4 AM	5	6	7	8	9	10	11	12
Temp	69.9	64.4	61.1	60	61.1	64.4	69.9	77.6	87.5

Plot the points in a scatter diagram. Estimate a formula for the temperature (T) function in terms of number (x) hours after 4 AM. Find either a quadratic formula or a linear formula, depending on which fits the data best.

23. Find the equilibrium point if the supply (S) and demand (D) functions are as follows:
$S(x) = x + 1$ and $D(x) = 10 - x$.

24. Sue feeds her cat a combination of two cat foods, Brands A and B. One ounce of Brand A contains 8 units of protein and 6 units of fat. One ounce of Brand B contains 4 units of protein and 9 units of fat. Sue's cat requires 16 units of protein and 28 units of fat daily. How many ounces of each brand should Sue feed her cat daily so that the cat gets his daily requirements of protein and fat?

Writing Exercises

25. Distinguish between the methods of "elimination by addition" and "elimination by substitution".

26. Describe a method of finding an approximation as a second degree formula form of the given numerical form of a function.

7.2 SYSTEMS OF NON-LINEAR EQUATIONS

In the previous section, we learned how to find a pair (x, y) common to two linear functions. In this section, we will investigate pairs (x, y) common to non-linear functions (relations). By the same terminology this is equivalent to finding the solutions of a system of equations which are not necessarily linear.

A. SOLVING SYSTEMS OF NON-LINEAR EQUATIONS

To solve a system of non-linear equations, we eliminate one of the unknowns, either by addition or by substitution, and solve the resulting equation for the possible values of other unknown. Then, we substitute each value in one of the given equations and find the corresponding value(s) of the first unknown. We illustrate this strategy in the following examples:

EXAMPLE 1   Solve the following system of equations.
$$y + 2x - 3 = 0$$
$$y + x^2 - 6 = 0$$

Solution:

Step 1   Eliminate one of the unknowns by addition or by substitution. In this example we show both the methods. Let us eliminate y.

By addition

$y + 2x - 3 = 0$ $\times(-1)$ $\longrightarrow$ $-y - 2x + 3 = 0$
$y + x^2 - 6 = 0$ $\longrightarrow$ $y + x^2 - 6 = 0$
Add: $x^2 - 2x - 3 = 0$

By substitution

We first solve the first equation for y.
$$y = 3 - 2x$$
Substitute this expression for y in the second equation.
$$3 - 2x + x^2 - 6 = 0 \text{ or}$$
$$x^2 - 2x - 3 = 0$$

Step 2   Solve the resulting equation for the possible values of the unknown. In this case, we solve $x^2 - 2x - 3 = 0$ for x. This is a second degree (quadratic) equation, and hence we can use either the factoring method or the quadratic formula method. We will use the factoring method here.

$$x^2 - 2x - 3 = 0 \longrightarrow (x - 3)(x + 1) = 0$$
$$\longrightarrow x - 3 = 0 \text{ or } x + 1 = 0 \longrightarrow x = 3 \text{ or } -1$$
Therefore $x = 3$ and $x = -1$.

Step 3   For each value found in Step 2, we find the corresponding value of the other unknown. For this, we substitute each value in one of the given equations (use the lowest degree equation) and solve for the unknown. In this example we substitute each x-value in the first equation.

$$x = 3$$
$$y + 2(3) - 3 = 0$$
$$y + 6 - 3 = 0$$
$$y = -3$$

$$x = -1$$
$$y + 2(-1) - 3 = 0$$
$$y - 2 - 3 = 0$$
$$y = 5$$

Thus, the solutions to the given system of equations are $(3, -3)$ and $(-1, 5)$.

With Graphing Calculator

We write each relation (equation) in a function form; that is, we solve for y.

$y = 3 - 2x$ and $y = 6 - x^2$.

Let $y1 = 3 - 2x$ and $y2 = 6 - x^2$. Graph $y1$ and $y2$ on the standard range. Use ZOOM-IN and TRACE to locate the points of intersection.

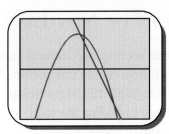

Figure 7.6

EXAMPLE 2   Solve the following system of equations.
$$4x^2 + y^2 = 13$$
$$x + y = 2$$

Solution:

Step 1   Since we can not eliminate x or y by the addition method, we will use the substitution method. By solving the second equation for y, we get $y = 2 - x$. We substitute this expression for y in the first equation.

$$4x^2 + (\mathbf{2 - x})^2 = 13 \quad \longrightarrow \quad 4x^2 + 4 - 4x + x^2 = 13 \quad \longrightarrow \quad 5x^2 - 4x - 9 = 0$$

Step 2   We solve $5x^2 - 4x - 9 = 0$ by factoring

$$(5x - 9)(x + 1) = 0 \quad \longrightarrow \quad x = \frac{\mathbf{9}}{\mathbf{5}}, \; x = \mathbf{-1}.$$

Step 3   We substitute each x-value in the second equation and find the corresponding y value.

$x = \dfrac{\mathbf{9}}{\mathbf{5}}$	$x = \mathbf{-1}.$
$\dfrac{9}{5} + y = 2$	$-1 + y = 2$
$y = 2 - \dfrac{9}{5} = \dfrac{\mathbf{1}}{\mathbf{5}}$	$y = \mathbf{3}$

Thus, the solutions are $\left(\dfrac{9}{5}, \dfrac{1}{5}\right)$ and $(-1, 3)$.

With Graphing Calculator

The first relation, when written in functional form, gives

$y^2 = 13 - 4x^2 \rightarrow y = \pm\sqrt{13 - 4x^2}$.

The second relation gives $y = 2 - x$.

Now let $y1 = \sqrt{13 - 4x^2}$, $y2 = -\sqrt{13 - 4x^2}$, $y3 = 2 - x$.

Graph $y1$, $y2$ and $y3$ on the standard range. Use ZOOM-IN and TRACE to locate the points of intersection of $y1$ and $y3$.

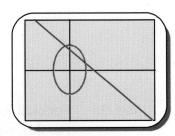

Figure 7.7

EXAMPLE 3   Solve
$$x = y^2$$
$$x^2 + y^2 = 6$$

Solution:

Step 1   We can eliminate y either by addition or by substitution.

Addition

$$x - y^2 = 0$$
$$x^2 + y^2 = 6$$
$$\overline{} \text{ add}$$
$$x^2 + x = 6$$

Substitution

We substitute $y^2 = x$ in the second equation, we get:

$$x^2 + x = 6$$

Step 2   By using the factoring method, we obtain

$$x^2 + x - 6 = 0$$
$$(x + 3)(x - 2) = 0 \quad \longrightarrow \quad x = -3, \ x = 2$$

Step 3   To find the values of y corresponding to these values of x, we use the simpler of the given two equations.

$x = -3$
$$-3 = y^2$$
No solution

$x = 2$
$$2 = y^2$$
$$\pm\sqrt{2} = y$$

Therefore, $\left(2, \sqrt{2}\right)$ and $\left(2, -\sqrt{2}\right)$ are the solutions.

With Graphing Calculator

We solve the first equation for y, and get $y = \pm\sqrt{x}$

By solving the second equation for y, and get

$y^2 = 6 - x^2 \rightarrow y = \pm\sqrt{6 - x^2}$. Now let

$y1 = \sqrt{x}$, $y2 = -\sqrt{x}$, $y3 = \sqrt{6 - x^2}$ and $y4 = -\sqrt{6 - x^2}$.
Graph $y1$, $y2$, $y3$ and $y4$ on the standard range.
Use ZOOM-IN and TRACE to locate the points of
intersection of $y1$ and $y3$, and $y2$ and $y4$.

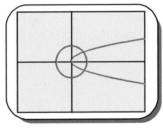

Figure 7.8

EXAMPLE 4   Solve $x^2 + 4y^2 = 16$ Note that the solutions will be intersections of an
$ x^2 + y^2 = 9$ an ellipse and a circle, both with centers at the origin

Solution:

Step 1   We can eliminate x either by addition or by substitution.

Addition

$$x^2 + 4y^2 = 16 \quad \longrightarrow \quad x^2 + 4y^2 = 16$$
$$x^2 + y^2 = 9 \quad \times(-1) \quad \longrightarrow \quad -x^2 - y^2 = -9$$
$$\overline{ 3y^2 = 7}$$

Substitution

We solve the second equation for x^2 and substitute in the first equation.

$$x^2 = 9 - y^2$$
$$(9 - y^2) + 4y^2 = 16$$
$$3y^2 = 7$$

Step 2   We solve $3y^2 = 7 \quad \longrightarrow \quad y^2 = \dfrac{7}{3} \quad \longrightarrow \quad y = \pm\sqrt{\dfrac{7}{3}} = \pm\sqrt{\dfrac{7 \cdot 3}{3 \cdot 3}}$

$$= \pm\frac{\sqrt{21}}{3}$$

Step 3　　　　We substitute each value of y in the second equation and solve for x.

$$y = \pm \frac{\sqrt{21}}{3}$$

$$x^2 + y^2 = x^2 + \frac{21}{9} = 9$$

$$x^2 = 9 - \frac{21}{9} = \frac{60}{9} = \frac{20}{3}$$

$$x = \pm \sqrt{\frac{20}{3}} = \pm 2\sqrt{\frac{5}{3}}$$

$$= \pm 2 \frac{\sqrt{15}}{3}$$

Thus, the solutions are

$$\left(2\frac{\sqrt{15}}{3}, \frac{\sqrt{21}}{3}\right), \left(-2\frac{\sqrt{15}}{3}, \frac{\sqrt{21}}{3}\right), \left(2\frac{\sqrt{15}}{3}, -\frac{\sqrt{21}}{3}\right), \left(-2\frac{\sqrt{15}}{3}, -\frac{\sqrt{21}}{3}\right).$$

With Graphing Calculator

Write each relation in terms of two functions, graph all four functions and estimate the points of intersection of the graphs.

EXAMPLE 5　　　Solve:　　$\dfrac{2}{x^2} - \dfrac{5}{y^2} = 2$

$$\frac{3}{x^2} + \frac{2}{y^2} = 22$$

Solution:

Step 1　　　　We eliminate $\dfrac{1}{x^2}$ by addition as follows:

Addition

$$\frac{2}{x^2} - \frac{5}{y^2} = 2 \quad \times(-3) \quad \longrightarrow \quad \frac{-6}{x^2} + \frac{15}{y^2} = -6$$

$$\frac{3}{x^2} + \frac{2}{y^2} = 22 \quad \times(2) \quad \longrightarrow \quad \frac{6}{x^2} + \frac{4}{y^2} = 44$$

$$\underline{\hspace{6cm}} \text{ add}$$

$$\frac{19}{y^2} = 38$$

Step 2　　　　We solve $\dfrac{19}{y^2} = 38 \quad \longrightarrow \quad 38y^2 = 19 \quad \longrightarrow \quad y^2 = \dfrac{1}{2}$

$$\longrightarrow \quad y = \pm\sqrt{\frac{1}{2}} = \pm\frac{\sqrt{2}}{2}$$

Step 3 To find the corresponding values of x, we substitute each value of y in the first equation.

$$y = \pm\sqrt{\frac{1}{2}}.$$

$$\frac{2}{x^2} - \frac{5}{y^2} = 2$$

$$\frac{2}{x^2} - 5(2) = 2 \quad *$$

$$\frac{2}{x^2} - 10 = 2 \longrightarrow \frac{2}{x^2} = 12 \longrightarrow 2 = 12x^2$$

$$* \qquad y = \pm\sqrt{\frac{1}{2}} \longrightarrow y^2 = \frac{1}{2}$$

$$\longrightarrow \frac{1}{y^2} = 2$$

$$\longrightarrow \frac{1}{6} = x^2$$

$$\longrightarrow \pm\sqrt{\frac{1}{6}} = x \longrightarrow x = \pm\frac{\sqrt{6}}{6}$$

Thus, the solutions are $\left(\dfrac{\sqrt{6}}{6}, \dfrac{\sqrt{2}}{2}\right)$, $\left(-\dfrac{\sqrt{6}}{6}, \dfrac{\sqrt{2}}{2}\right)$, $\left(\dfrac{\sqrt{6}}{6}, -\dfrac{\sqrt{2}}{2}\right)$, $\left(-\dfrac{\sqrt{6}}{6}, -\dfrac{\sqrt{2}}{2}\right)$.

⬤ Note   Use the regular graphing method to verify the points of intersection.

With Graphing Calculator

Set the range: x-min $= -1$, x-max $= 1$, y-min $= -1$ and y-max $= 1$.
$x$scl $= .2$, $y$scl $= .2$

By solving the given two equations for y we get the following four equations.

$$y_1 = \sqrt{\frac{5x^2}{2 - 2x^2}} \, , y_2 = -\sqrt{\frac{5x^2}{2 - 2x^2}} \, , y_3 = \sqrt{\frac{2x^2}{22x^2 - 3}} \text{ and } y_4 = -\sqrt{\frac{2x^2}{22x^2 - 3}}$$

(Four points of intersection). Graph these functions and use ZOOM-IN
and TRACE to find the four points of intersection.

B. Applications of Systems of Non-Linear Equations

In economics the concept of an equilibrium point is important.

Equilibrium Point

The equilibrium point is the point of intersection of the
graphs of demand and supply functions.

EXAMPLE 6 Find the equilibrium point if the supply and demand functions are as follows:
Supply: $S(x) = 0.5x^2 + 1$
Demand: $D(x) = 7 - 0.5x$

Solution: To find the point where the two functions meet, we solve the following system of equations
$$y = 0.5x^2 + 1 \text{ and } y = 7 - 0.5x$$

Step 1   We can use either addition or substitution to eliminate *y*. Let us use the substitution method. We substitute $y = 7 - 0.5x$ in the first equation. We get:

$$7 - 0.5x = 0.5x^2 + 1$$
$$0 = 0.5x^2 + 0.5x - 6$$

Step 2   To solve the equation, we multiply both sides by 10 (why?)

$$0 = 5x^2 + 5x - 60$$

By factoring, we get:

$$0 = 5(x^2 + x - 12) = 5(x + 4)(x - 3)$$

Therefore, ***x* = −4** or ***x* = 3**

Since *x* is the number of items produced, so $x = -4$ does not make sense.

Step 3   We substitute $x = 3$ in $y = 7 - 0.5x$ and we get:

$$y = 7 - 0.5(3) = 7 - 1.5 = \mathbf{5.5}$$

Thus, the solution of the system of equations or the equilibrium point is (3, 5.5).

Remark: *At the equilibrium price $5.50, the demand equals the supply.*

With Graphing Calculator

Let $y1 = .5x^2 + 1$ and $y2 = 7 - .5x$. Graph $y1$ and $y2$ on x-min $= 0, x$-max $= 10, y$-min $= 0, y$-max $= 10$. Use ZOOM-IN and TRACE to estimate the point of intersection. Note that we set x-min ≥ 0, since negative inputs are out of context.

EXERCISE 7.2

In exercises (1–15), solve the equations.

1. $y = x^2$
    $y = 2x - x^2$

2. $y = x - 1$
    $y^2 - 2x - 6 = 0$

3. $y = x$
    $y = x^2$

4. $y = -x^2 + 5x - 4$
    $y + x + 4 = 0$

5. $y = 2x^2$
    $y = x^4 + 1$

6. $y = x$
    $x - y^2 + 2 = 0$

7. $y = 2x - 6$
    $y = -2x^2 + 8x - 6$

8. $y = 2 + x$
    $y + x^2 = 4$

9. $y = 3x$
    $y^2 = 6 + 3x$

10. $x^2 + y = 2$
     $x^4 - y = 0$

11. $x - y^2 + 1 = 0$
     $x - y - 2 = 0$

12. $y = 2x + 5$
     $y = -x^2 + 8x$

13. $xy = 12$

     $y = x^2 - 6x + 2$

14. $\dfrac{x^2}{12} + \dfrac{y^2}{16} = 1$

     $\dfrac{3x^2}{35} + \dfrac{2y^2}{35} = 1$

15. $\dfrac{x^2}{9} + \dfrac{y^2}{4} = 1$

     $\dfrac{x^2}{36} - \dfrac{y^2}{36} = 1$

16. Find the equilibrium point if the supply (*S*) and demand (*D*) functions are given by

$$S(x) = x^2 + 1, \qquad D(x) = 13 - x$$

Writing Exercises

17. Describe a method of solving non-linear systems of equations.

18. Explain situations where elimination by addition is preferred to elimination by substitution or vice versa.

7.3 PARAMETRIC REPRESENTATIONS OF RELATIONS

Imagine that the point $P(x, y)$ is moving along the path $y = f(x)$ (Figure 7.10). The position of the point P depends upon time t ($t = 0$ at the start). This means that the coordinates of the point P depend on time t. By using the dependency statements we get

$$x = x(t) \quad \text{and}$$
$$y = y(t).$$

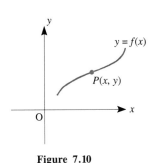

Figure 7.10

Note that the letters x and y are being used here in two different ways: first to represent a function and second to represent the output of the function.

Since the position of the point P is given by the graph of $y = f(x)$, so the equation $y = f(x)$ must be equivalent to two equations $x = x(t)$ and $y = y(t)$.

> **A Parametric Representation**
>
> A pair of equations such as $x = x(t)$ and $y = y(t)$ is called a parametric representation of the function $y = f(x)$. The variable t is called a **parameter.**

Recall that the change from other forms (numerical) of a function to the graphical form was extremely useful in interpreting the behavior of the function. Now we will observe the same advantage when a function is given in its parametric form.

EXAMPLE 1   Sketch the path of a particle whose position after time t (seconds) is given by
$$x = t^2, \quad y = 2t; \quad 0 \le t \le 5.$$

Solution: To find points on the graph (path), we change the parametric form into a numerical (table) form.

t	0	1	2	3	4	5
x	0	1	4	9	16	25
y	0	2	4	6	8	10

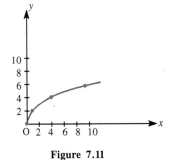

Figure 7.11

We plot the points and connect them by a smooth curve (Figure 7.11). The curve represents the path of the particle in the x-y plane. The parameter t is not represented in Figure 7.11.

A. CHANGING PARAMETRIC EQUATIONS TO RECTANGULAR FORM

To take advantage of our past experience with the graphs of functions like $y = f(x)$, we discuss changing a parametric form of a function to a relation in x and y (rectangular form). The following examples illustrate the method.

EXAMPLE 2   Change the parametric representation $x = t^2$, $y = 2t$ into a relation between x and y.

Solution: To find an equivalent relation between x and y, we eliminate t, either by addition or by substitution.

In this case, we use the substitution method to eliminate t.

Solving $y = 2t$ for t, we get: $t = \dfrac{y}{2}$

By substituting $t = \dfrac{y}{2}$ in $x = t^2$, we get $x = \left(\dfrac{y}{2}\right)^2 = \dfrac{y^2}{4} \longrightarrow 4x = y^2$

This shows that for any t, $x = t^2$ and $y = 2t$ is a solution of $y^2 = 4x$.

Conversely, given a solution (x, y) of $4x = y^2$, we can set $t = \dfrac{y}{2}$, or **$y = 2t$**, then

$4x = y^2 = 4t^2$ or **$x = t^2$**. Hence $\begin{cases} x = t^2 \\ y = 2t \end{cases}$ and $y^2 = 4x$ are equivalent.

EXAMPLE 3   Change the parametric representation $x = t$, $y = 2t - 3$ to a relationship between x and y and then draw the graph.

Solution: We eliminate t by substitution (or addition). Substitute $t = x$ in the second equation. We get $y = 2x - 3$.

This is linear function; its graph is a straight line. Two points are given by

x	0	1
y	−3	−1

We plot the points and connect them to draw the line (Figure 7.12).

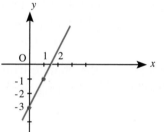

Figure 7.12

With Graphing Calculator

We can draw the graph of a function in parametric form. Select MODE. Choose 'Param' on the line that gives choices like Func Pol Param DifEq. Press Exit after selecting Param. Now Press GRAPH and choose $E(t) =$. Let $x1t = t$ and $y1t = 2t - 3$. Graph on any suitable range.

B. CHANGING RECTANGULAR EQUATIONS TO PARAMETRIC FORM

The following example explains how to change a relation in x and y into a parametric form.

EXAMPLE 4   Change $y = \sqrt{x}$ into a parametric form.

Solution: There can be more than one parametric representation. However, the easiest one is obtained by setting $x = t$ and substituting t in the given relation. This gives $y = \sqrt{t}$.

Thus, $\left.\begin{array}{c} x = t \\ y = \sqrt{t} \end{array}\right\}$ gives a parametric representation of $y = \sqrt{x}$.

● Note   Another parametric representation can be $x = t^2$ and $y = t$, $t \geq 0$.

EXERCISE 7.3

In exercises (1-7), change the parametric representation into a relation in *x* and *y* and then sketch the graph.

1. $x = t^2$, $y = t^4 + 2$ **2.** $x = t - 1$, $y = t^2$ **3.** $x = t$, $y = \dfrac{1}{t}$ **4.** $x = \sqrt{t}$, $y = t$

5. $x = t^2 - 1$, $y = t^2 + 1$ **6.** $x = \sqrt{t}$, $y = \sqrt{4 - t}$ **7.** $x = t^2$, $y = t^3$

In exercises (8-10), find parametric equations of the graph of the function.

8. $y = x^3$ **9.** $y = x^2 - 3x$ **10.** $x = y^3 - 2y$

7.4 GAUSS-JORDAN METHOD

In the elimination method, the computations involve only the coefficients and constant terms of the equations. Since the unknowns (variables) do not play any role in the calculations, so we can speed up the computations by writing the system of equations without the variables. In this section we will show how to simplify the elimination method by writing the system of equations as a **Matrix.**

Objectives ▶▶

In this section you will learn about:

A. The Matrix of Coefficients;

B. Row Operations; and

C. The Gauss-Jordan Method.

A. THE MATRIX OF COEFFICIENTS

Matrix

A rectangular array of numbers written within brackets is called a **matrix.** The numbers are called the **entries** of the matrix.

Consider the system of equations

$$5x + 3y + z = 1$$
$$x + 2y + 3z = 10$$
$$-2x + y + 7z = 24$$

The array of numbers $\begin{bmatrix} 5 & 3 & 1 \\ 1 & 2 & 3 \\ -2 & 1 & 7 \end{bmatrix}$ consisting of the coefficients of *x*, *y*, and *z* is called the **matrix of**

coefficients of the system. If we extend this matrix by adding a column consisting of the constants 1, 10, and 24, we obtain a matrix called the **augmented matrix** of the system.

$$\begin{bmatrix} 5 & 3 & 1 & \vdots & 1 \\ 1 & 2 & 3 & \vdots & 10 \\ -2 & 1 & 7 & \vdots & 24 \end{bmatrix}$$

The matrix of coefficients is separated from the column of constants by a dotted vertical line. Each number in the array is an **element** or **entry** of the matrix. The location of an element of the matrix is denoted as (r, c), where r is the row and c is the column on which it lies.

EXAMPLE 1   Find the entries at the indicated locations of the matrix.

$$\begin{bmatrix} -1 & 2 & 3 \\ 4 & 0 & 9 \\ -1 & -2 & 3 \end{bmatrix}$$

a. (1, 1)   **b.** (2, 3)   **c.** (3, 2)

Solutions: **a.** **(1, 1):**   The location in the given matrix is intersection of the first row and the first column. The corresponding entry is **–1**.

b. **(2, 3):**   This location in the given matrix is the intersection of the second row and the third column. The corresponding entry is **9.**

c. **(3, 2):**   This location in the given matrix is the intersection of the third row and the second column. The corresponding entry is **–2.**

EXAMPLE 2   Write each system as an augmented matrix.

a. $2x - 5y = 9$
        $x + y = 2$

b. $3x + 5y - z = 2$
        $4y + 3z = 7$
        $-2x - y + 2z = 12$

c. $x - y + 2z = 7$
        $5y + x - 3z = 8$
        $z - x + y = 10$

d. $2x - 5y = 7$
        $7y + x + 8 = 0$

Solutions: Before we represent the given system of equations by an augmented matrix, the terms with variables should be on the left side and constants on the right side of each equation, with variables aligned in the same order.

a. $\begin{array}{l} 2x - 5y = 9 \\ x + y = 2 \end{array}$ $\longrightarrow$ $\left[\begin{array}{cc:c} 2 & -5 & 9 \\ 1 & 1 & 2 \end{array}\right]$

b. $\begin{array}{l} 3x + 5y - z = 2 \\ 4y + 3z = 7 \\ -2x - y + 2z = 12 \end{array}$ $\longrightarrow$ $\left[\begin{array}{ccc:c} 3 & 5 & -1 & 2 \\ 0 & 4 & 3 & 7 \\ -2 & -1 & 2 & 12 \end{array}\right]$

c. $\begin{array}{l} x - y + 2z = 7 \\ x + 5y - 3z = 8 \\ -x + y + z = 10 \end{array}$ $\longrightarrow$ $\left[\begin{array}{ccc:c} 1 & -1 & 2 & 7 \\ 1 & 5 & -3 & 8 \\ -1 & 1 & 1 & 10 \end{array}\right]$

d. $\begin{array}{l} 2x - 5y = 7 \\ x + 7y = -8 \end{array}$ $\longrightarrow$ $\left[\begin{array}{cc:c} 2 & -5 & 7 \\ 1 & 7 & -8 \end{array}\right]$

EXAMPLE 3   Write a system of equations for each augmented matrix.

a. $\begin{bmatrix} 5 & -1 & \vdots & 3 \\ 2 & 9 & \vdots & 1 \end{bmatrix}$ **b.** $\begin{bmatrix} 1 & 0 & -1 & \vdots & 3 \\ 2 & 1 & 8 & \vdots & 5 \\ 3 & -1 & 0 & \vdots & 7 \end{bmatrix}$

Solutions:

a. $\begin{bmatrix} 5 & -1 & \vdots & 3 \\ 2 & 9 & \vdots & 1 \end{bmatrix}$ $\begin{aligned} 5x - y &= 3 \\ 2x + 9y &= 1 \end{aligned}$

b. $\begin{bmatrix} 1 & 0 & -1 & \vdots & 3 \\ 2 & 1 & 8 & \vdots & 5 \\ 3 & -1 & 0 & \vdots & 7 \end{bmatrix}$ $\begin{aligned} x - z &= 3 \\ 2x + y + 8z &= 5 \\ 3x - y &= 7 \end{aligned}$

Since the augmented matrix is simply a convenient form of the given system of equations, therefore, the **admissible operations on equations** translate into **admissible operations on the rows** of the augmented matrix. We refer to these as **row operations.**

B. ROW OPERATIONS

The operations that produce a row - equivalent matrix of an augmented matrix are :

1.   multiplying a row by a non-zero number,
2.   adding a multiple of one row to another row, and
3.   interchanging any two rows.

Notation

The operation $\frac{1}{2}R_1$ multiplies each element of the first row of matrix by $\frac{1}{2}$ and leaves the other rows unchanged. For example:

$$\begin{bmatrix} 4 & -2 & 3 & \vdots & 6 \\ 2 & 1 & 4 & \vdots & 7 \\ -3 & 0 & 5 & \vdots & 10 \end{bmatrix} \xrightarrow{\frac{1}{2}R_1} \begin{bmatrix} \frac{1}{2}(4) & \frac{1}{2}(-2) & \frac{1}{2}(3) & \vdots & \frac{1}{2}(6) \\ 2 & 1 & 4 & \vdots & 7 \\ -3 & 0 & 5 & \vdots & 10 \end{bmatrix} = \begin{bmatrix} 2 & -1 & \frac{3}{2} & \vdots & 3 \\ 2 & 1 & 4 & \vdots & 7 \\ -3 & 0 & 5 & \vdots & 10 \end{bmatrix}$$

The row operation $R_3 + 2R_2$ replaces the third row with the row obtained by adding two times the elements of the second row to the corresponding elements of third row. For example:

$$\begin{bmatrix} 4 & -2 & 3 & \vdots & 6 \\ 2 & 1 & 4 & \vdots & 7 \\ -3 & 0 & 5 & \vdots & 10 \end{bmatrix} \xrightarrow{R_3 + 2R_2} \begin{bmatrix} 4 & -2 & 3 & \vdots & 6 \\ 2 & 1 & 4 & \vdots & 7 \\ -3+2(2) & 0+2(1) & 5+2(4) & \vdots & 10+2(7) \end{bmatrix} = \begin{bmatrix} 4 & -2 & 3 & \vdots & 6 \\ 2 & 1 & 4 & \vdots & 7 \\ 1 & 2 & 13 & \vdots & 24 \end{bmatrix}$$

In general $R_i + kR_j$ replaces the ith row by the ith row + $k(j^{\text{th}}$ row).

The operation $R_1 \longleftrightarrow R_2$ interchanges the first and second rows. For example:

$$\begin{bmatrix} 4 & -2 & 3 & \vdots & 6 \\ 2 & 1 & 4 & \vdots & 7 \\ 1 & 2 & 13 & \vdots & 24 \end{bmatrix} \xrightarrow{R_1 \leftrightarrow R_2} \begin{bmatrix} 2 & 1 & 4 & \vdots & 7 \\ 4 & -2 & 3 & \vdots & 6 \\ 1 & 2 & 13 & \vdots & 24 \end{bmatrix}.$$

EXAMPLE 4   Perform, in sequence, the operations

$$R_1 \leftrightarrow R_3, \; R_2 + (-2) \, R_1, \; \text{and} \; R_3 + (3) \, R_1 \; \text{on the matrix}$$

$$\begin{bmatrix} -3 & 1 & -2 & \vdots & 8 \\ 2 & -4 & 6 & \vdots & 2 \\ 1 & -2 & 5 & \vdots & 3 \end{bmatrix}$$

Solution:

$$\begin{bmatrix} -3 & 1 & -2 & \vdots & 8 \\ 2 & -4 & 6 & \vdots & 2 \\ 1 & -2 & 5 & \vdots & 3 \end{bmatrix} \xrightarrow{R_1 \leftrightarrow R_3} \begin{bmatrix} 1 & -2 & 5 & \vdots & 3 \\ 2 & -4 & 6 & \vdots & 2 \\ -3 & 1 & -2 & \vdots & 8 \end{bmatrix}.$$

$$\xrightarrow{R_2 + (-2) R_1} \begin{bmatrix} 1 & -2 & 5 & \vdots & 3 \\ 2+(-2)1 & -4+(-2)(-2) & 6+(-2)5 & \vdots & 2+(-2)(3) \\ -3 & 1 & -2 & \vdots & 8 \end{bmatrix} = \begin{bmatrix} 1 & -2 & 5 & \vdots & 3 \\ 0 & 0 & -4 & \vdots & -4 \\ -3 & 1 & -2 & \vdots & 8 \end{bmatrix}.$$

$$\xrightarrow{R_3 + 3 R_1} \begin{bmatrix} 1 & -2 & 5 & \vdots & 3 \\ 0 & 0 & -4 & \vdots & -4 \\ -3+3(1) & 1+3(-2) & -2+3(5) & \vdots & 8+3(3) \end{bmatrix} = \begin{bmatrix} 1 & -2 & 5 & \vdots & 3 \\ 0 & 0 & -4 & \vdots & -4 \\ 0 & -5 & 13 & \vdots & 17 \end{bmatrix}.$$

◢ C. THE GAUSS-JORDAN METHOD

The Gauss-Jordan method transforms the augmented matrix of the system into a diagonal form. This form of the augmented matrix when written as a system of equations, gives the solution of the system. We provide the steps used in this method as follows:

Step **1**   Write the augmented matrix of the system that has variable terms, in the same order on the left, and constants on the right.

Step **2**   Get 1 in (1, 1) entry either by interchanging rows or by the row operation:

$$(\blacktriangle) \, R_1 \quad \rule{1.5cm}{0.4pt} \quad \text{Multiplicative inverse of (1, 1) entry.}$$

Step **3**   Get zero in (2, 1) and (3, 1) entries by the operations.

$$R_2 + (\blacktriangle) \, R_1 \quad \rule{1.5cm}{0.4pt} \quad \text{Additive inverse of (2, 1) entry.}$$

$$R_3 + (\blacktriangle) \, R_1 \quad \rule{1.5cm}{0.4pt} \quad \text{Additive inverse of (3, 1) entry.}$$

Step **4**   Get 1 in (2,2) entry either by interchanging rows below the first row or by the row operation:

$$(\ \blacktriangle\ )\ R_2 \quad \rule{2cm}{0.4pt} \quad \text{Multiplicative inverse of } (2, 2) \text{ entry.}$$

Step **5**   Get zero in (1, 2) and (3, 2) entries by the operations.

$$R_1 + (\ \blacktriangle\ )\ R_2 \quad \rule{2cm}{0.4pt} \quad \text{Additive inverse of } (1, 2) \text{ entry.}$$

$$R_3 + (\ \blacktriangle\ )\ R_2 \quad \rule{2cm}{0.4pt} \quad \text{Additive inverse of } (3, 2) \text{ entry.}$$

Step **6**   Get 1 in (3, 3) entry either by interchanging rows or by row operation.

$$(\ \blacktriangle\ )\ R_3 \quad \rule{2cm}{0.4pt} \quad \text{Multiplicative inverse of } (3, 3) \text{ entry.}$$

Step **7**   Get zero in (1, 3), (2, 3), entries by operations

$$R_1 + (\ \blacktriangle\ )\ R_3 \quad \rule{2cm}{0.4pt} \quad \text{Additive inverse of } (1, 3) \text{ entry.}$$

$$R_2 + (\ \blacktriangle\ )\ R_3 \quad \rule{2cm}{0.4pt} \quad \text{Additive inverse of } (2, 3) \text{ entry.}$$

and so on.

Step **8**   Write the system corresponding to the new augmented matrix.

EXAMPLE 5   Solve the system:

$$x + y \quad + z = 0$$
$$3x + 2y - 2z = -17$$
$$-4x - y + 3z = 27$$

Solution:

Step 1   The augmented matrix corresponding to the system is: $\begin{bmatrix} 1 & 1 & 1 & \vdots & 0 \\ 3 & 2 & -2 & \vdots & -17 \\ -4 & -1 & 3 & \vdots & 27 \end{bmatrix}.$

Step 2   There is 1 in (1, 1) entry.

Step 3   We get zero in (2, 1) and (3, 1) entries by the operations.

$$R_2 + (-3)R_1 \text{ and } R_3 + (4)\ R_1: \quad \xrightarrow[R_3 + (4)R_1]{R_2 + (-3)R_1} \quad \begin{bmatrix} 1 & 1 & 1 & \vdots & 0 \\ 0 & -1 & -5 & \vdots & -17 \\ 0 & 3 & 7 & \vdots & 27 \end{bmatrix}$$

Step 4   To get 1 in (2, 2) entry, we perform the operation $(-1)\ R_2$:

$$\xrightarrow{(-1)R_2} \quad \begin{bmatrix} 1 & 1 & 1 & \vdots & 0 \\ 0 & 1 & 5 & \vdots & 17 \\ 0 & 3 & 7 & \vdots & 27 \end{bmatrix}$$

Step 5   To get zero in (1, 2) and (3, 2) entries, we use the operations

$$R_1 + (-1)R_2 \text{ and } R_3 + (-3)R_2: \quad \xrightarrow[R_3 + (-3)R_2]{R_1 + (-1)R_2} \quad \begin{bmatrix} 1 & 0 & -4 & \vdots & -17 \\ 0 & 1 & 5 & \vdots & 17 \\ 0 & 0 & -8 & \vdots & -24 \end{bmatrix}$$

Step 6   To get 1 in (3, 3) entry, we use the operation $\left(-\dfrac{1}{8}\right)R_3$:

$$\xrightarrow{-\frac{1}{8}R_3} \quad \begin{bmatrix} 1 & 0 & -4 & \vdots & -17 \\ 0 & 1 & 5 & \vdots & 17 \\ 0 & 0 & 1 & \vdots & 3 \end{bmatrix}$$

Step 7   To get zero in (1, 3) and (2, 3) entries, we use the operations

$$R_1 + (4)\, R_3 \text{ and } R_2 + (-5)\, R_3: \quad \xrightarrow[R_2 + (-5)R_3]{R_1 + (4)R_3} \quad \begin{bmatrix} 1 & 0 & 0 & \vdots & -5 \\ 0 & 1 & 0 & \vdots & 2 \\ 0 & 0 & 1 & \vdots & 3 \end{bmatrix}$$

Step 8   The system that represents the above augmented matrix is

$$\begin{array}{lll} x + 0y + 0z = -5 & & x = -5 \\ 0x + y + 0z = 2 & \text{or} & y = 2 \\ 0x + 0y + z = 3 & & z = 3 \end{array}$$

Thus, the solution of the system is $x = -5$, $y = 2$, and $z = 3$ or $(-5, 2, 3)$.

Substitute these values in the original system of equations to check the solution.

EXAMPLE 6   Solve the system: $\begin{array}{l} 2x - y = 3 \\ 4x - 2y = 5 \end{array}$

Solution:

Step 1   The augmented matrix representing the system is $\begin{bmatrix} 2 & -1 & \vdots & 3 \\ 4 & -2 & \vdots & 5 \end{bmatrix}$

Step 2   We get 1 in (1, 1) entry by performing the operation $\left(\dfrac{1}{2}\right)R_1$: $\begin{bmatrix} 1 & -\dfrac{1}{2} & \vdots & \dfrac{3}{2} \\ 4 & -2 & \vdots & 5 \end{bmatrix}$

Step 3   We get zero in (2, 1) entry by using the operation $R_2 + (-4)\, R_1$:

$$\xrightarrow{R_2 + (-4)R_1} \quad \begin{bmatrix} 1 & \dfrac{-1}{2} & \vdots & \dfrac{3}{2} \\ 0 & 0 & \vdots & -1 \end{bmatrix}$$

We stop here and write the system of equations $x - \dfrac{1}{2}y = \dfrac{3}{2}$ and $0x + 0y = -1$

The second equation gives a mathematical contradiction

$$0 = -1$$

Therefore, there are no values of x and y that can satisfy both equations. Thus, there is no solution of the system. In other words, the system is **inconsistent.**

Remark: *In the process of applying row operations to an augmented matrix, if we get a row where all elements on the left of the dotted line are zero, and the element on the right of the dotted line is non-zero, then the system of equations is* **inconsistent** *(with no solution).*

EXAMPLE 7 Solve the system:
$$x + y\ \ \ + 4z = 1$$
$$3x + 2y + 11z = 1$$
$$x\ \ \ \ \ \ + 3z = -1$$

Solution:

Step 1 The augmented matrix representing the system is $\begin{bmatrix} 1 & 1 & 4 & \vdots & 1 \\ 3 & 2 & 11 & \vdots & 1 \\ 1 & 0 & 3 & \vdots & -1 \end{bmatrix}$.

Step 2 The $(1, 1)$ entry is already 1.

Step 3 To get zero in $(2, 1)$ and $(3, 1)$ entries we use the operations

$R_2 + (-3)\ R_1$ and $R_3 + (-1)R_1$: $\xrightarrow[R_3 + (-1)R_1]{R_2 + (-3)R_1}$ $\begin{bmatrix} 1 & 1 & 4 & \vdots & 1 \\ 0 & -1 & -1 & \vdots & -2 \\ 0 & -1 & -1 & \vdots & -2 \end{bmatrix}$

Step 4 To get 1 in $(2, 2)$ entry we use the operation $(-1)\ R_2$:

$\xrightarrow{(-1)\,R_2}$ $\begin{bmatrix} 1 & 1 & 4 & \vdots & 1 \\ 0 & 1 & 1 & \vdots & 2 \\ 0 & -1 & -1 & \vdots & -2 \end{bmatrix}$

Step 5 To get zero in $(1, 2)$ and $(3, 2)$ entries we use operations

$R_1 + (-1)\ R_2$ and $R_3 + (1)\ R_2$: $\xrightarrow[R_3 + (1)R_2]{R_1 + (-1)R_2}$ $\begin{bmatrix} 1 & 0 & 3 & \vdots & -1 \\ 0 & 1 & 1 & \vdots & 2 \\ 0 & 0 & 0 & \vdots & 0 \end{bmatrix}$

We stop here and write the system of equations
$$x + 0y + 3z = -1 \qquad \textbf{(1)}$$
$$0x + y + z = 2 \qquad \textbf{(2)}$$
$$0x + 0y + 0z = 0 \qquad \textbf{(3)}$$

The third equation is true for any choice of x, y and z. Thus all numbers $x, y,$ and z that satisfy the first two equations are solutions of the system. The second equation gives

$y + z = 2$ or $y = 2 - z$

and the first equation gives

$x + 3z = -1$ or $x = -1 - 3z$

Hence, $x = -1 - 3z$, $y = 2 - z$, $z = z$ is the general solution of the system. The given system has an infinite number of solutions corresponding to each value assigned to z. The values of x and y are given in parametric form with parameter z.

In short, all ordered triples $(-1-3z,\ 2-z,\ z)$, where z is an arbitrary number, are the solutions of the system.

Remark: *In the process of applying row operations to an augmented matrix, if there is a row where all entries are zero then the system has infinite number of solutions, provided the system has the same number of rows as columns to the left of the dotted line.*

EXAMPLE 8

A furniture manufacturer makes three kinds of dressers; small, medium, and large. For delivery, the company uses three types of vehicles; small pickups, large pickups, and large trucks. These vehicles can carry the dressers according to the following table.

Vehicle/Dressers	Small	Medium	Large
Small Pickup	3	2	1
Large Pickup	5	3	2
Large Truck	8	6	3

If the manufacturer needs to deliver 63 small, 41 medium, and 24 large dressers, how many vehicles of each kind should be used so that all vehicles operate at full capacity?

Solution:

For a mathematical model, we assume that the manufacturer uses x small pickups, y large pickups, and z large trucks. Together the vehicles must carry 63 pieces of small dressers, so $3x+5y+8z=63$. Similarly, the vehicles must carry 41 and 24 pieces of medium and large dressers, respectively, so we obtain the next two equations:

$$2x + 3y + 6z = 41 \quad \text{and} \quad x + 2y + 3z = 24$$

Thus, we have generated a system of three equations

$$3x + 5y + 8z = 63$$
$$2x + 3y + 6z = 41$$
$$x + 2y + 3z = 24$$

Now, we solve the system.

$$\begin{bmatrix} 3 & 5 & 8 & \vdots & 63 \\ 2 & 3 & 6 & \vdots & 41 \\ 1 & 2 & 3 & \vdots & 24 \end{bmatrix} \xrightarrow{R_1 \leftrightarrow R_3} \begin{bmatrix} 1 & 2 & 3 & \vdots & 24 \\ 2 & 3 & 6 & \vdots & 41 \\ 3 & 5 & 8 & \vdots & 63 \end{bmatrix} \xrightarrow[R_3 + (-3)R_1]{R_2 + (-2)R_1}$$

$$\begin{bmatrix} 1 & 2 & 3 & \vdots & 24 \\ 0 & -1 & 0 & \vdots & -7 \\ 0 & -1 & -1 & \vdots & -9 \end{bmatrix} \xrightarrow{(-1)R_2} \begin{bmatrix} 1 & 2 & 3 & \vdots & 24 \\ 0 & 1 & 0 & \vdots & 7 \\ 0 & -1 & -1 & \vdots & -9 \end{bmatrix} \xrightarrow[R_3 + R_2]{R_1 + (-2)R_2}$$

$$\begin{bmatrix} 1 & 0 & 3 & \vdots & 10 \\ 0 & 1 & 0 & \vdots & 7 \\ 0 & 0 & -1 & \vdots & -2 \end{bmatrix} \xrightarrow{(-1)R_3} \begin{bmatrix} 1 & 0 & 3 & \vdots & 10 \\ 0 & 1 & 0 & \vdots & 7 \\ 0 & 0 & 1 & \vdots & 2 \end{bmatrix} \xrightarrow{R_1 + (-3)R_3} \begin{bmatrix} 1 & 0 & 0 & \vdots & 4 \\ 0 & 1 & 0 & \vdots & 7 \\ 0 & 0 & 1 & \vdots & 2 \end{bmatrix}$$

The corresponding system is $x = 4$, $y = 7$, and $z = 2$. Therefore, the manufacturer should use 4 small pickups, 7 large pickups, and 2 large trucks to deliver the dressers.

EXERCISE 7.4

In exercises (1-5), write the augmented matrix representing the system.

1. $5x - 7y = -1$
   $2x + y = 2$

2. $5y + 2x - 7 = 0$
   $x - 3y + 8 = 0$

3. $y - 2z = 9$
   $x + 2y = 5$
   $3z - x = 7$

4. $9x - y + z + 1 = 0$
   $2y + x - z + 9 = 0$
   $y + z - 3 = 0$

5. $2x_1 - 3x_2 + x_3 - x_4 + 7x_5 = 1$
   $x_1 + 2x_2 = 5$
   $2x_3 + 2x_4 = 4$
   $x_1 - x_2 + 3x_4 + x_5 = 8$

In exercises (6-7), write the system of equations for the augmented matrix.

6. $\begin{bmatrix} 3 & -2 & \vdots & 5 \\ 2 & 1 & \vdots & 3 \end{bmatrix}$

7. $\begin{bmatrix} 0 & -1 & 2 & \vdots & 7 \\ 1 & 0 & 3 & \vdots & 2 \\ -5 & -1 & 8 & \vdots & 1 \end{bmatrix}$

In exercises (8-30), solve the system by using the Gauss-Jordan method.

8. $x + 6y = -16$
   $5x - 3y = 19$

9. $2x + 4y = 2$
   $3x - 5y = -8$

10. $6u + 8v + 5 = 0$
    $4u + 10v + 8 = 0$

11. $8p - 9q - 61 = 0$
    $3p + 2q + 4 = 0$

12. $4r + 12s = 7$
    $2r + 6s = 1$

13. $2x - 7y = 20$
    $6x - 21y = 60$

14. $\dfrac{x}{2} - \dfrac{y}{3} = -\dfrac{1}{6}$
    $x + \dfrac{y}{2} = 2$

15. $x - y + 2z = -2$
    $-2x + 3y + z = 5$
    $-x + y + 3z = 2$

16. $5x + y - 2z = 2$
    $x + 7y + 3z = -3$
    $-2x - y + z = 0$

17. $3x + 5y + 2z = 1$
    $2x - y - z = 3$
    $-x + y + 3z = 2$

18. $-4x + 3y + z = 6$
    $x - y + 7z = -9$
    $2x + y - 6z = 5$

19. $3x + y + z = -2$
    $x + 2y + 3z = 0$
    $2x + z = -3$

20. $y - 2z = -8$
    $x + z = 4$
    $2x - y = -4$

21. $x - y - z = 1$
    $2x - y - z = 0$
    $3x - y - z = 2$

22. $2x - y + z = 6$
    $3x - y + z = 6$
    $4x - 2y + 2z = 12$

23. $2x + 7y + 3z = 8$
    $4x + 15y + 7z = 10$
    $x + 4y + 2z = 1$

24. $x - y + z = 7$
    $-2x - 3y - z = -7$

25. $x + y - z = 1$
    $2x - y + 7z = 2$

26. $2x - y + 2z + w = 1$
    $x + y + z - w = -1$
    $3x + 2y - z + 2w = 6$
    $x - 3y + z - 3w = -3$

27. $x + 3y + 4z = 0$
    $2x + 5y + 6z = 0$
    $2x + 7y + 7z = 0$

28. $2x - y + 3z = 0$
    $6x - 2y + 7z = 0$
    $4x - 2y + 6z = 0$

29. $x + 4y + 2z = 0$
    $3x - 2y + z = 0$
    $7x + 4z = 0$

30. $3x + y - 2z = 0$
    $x + 2y - 3z = 0$
    $2x - y + z = 0$

31. A patient must receive 152 units of vitamin A, 210 units of vitamin C, and 232 units of vitamin E. There are three types of pills containing these vitamins. Pill #1, contains 20 units of vitamin A, 12 units of vitamin C, and 36 units of vitamin E. Pill #2 contains 10 units, 15 units, and 10 units of vitamins A, C, and E, respectively. And pill #3 contains, 8, 30, and 8 units of vitamins A, C, and E, respectively. How many pills of each type the patient must take in order to receive the minimum units of each vitamin?

32. A patient must receive 25 units of fat, 38 units of protein, and 58 units of carbohydrate in a meal consisting of three types of food, A, B, and C. Each ounce of food A contains 2, 5, and 6 units of fat, protein, and carbohydrate, respectively. Each ounce of food B contains 3, 3, and 4 units of fat, protein, and carbohydrate, respectively. And each ounce of food C contains 1, 2, and 5 units of fat, protein, and carbohydrates, respectively. How many ounces of each types of food should the patient consume in order to receive the minimum requirement of fat, protein, and carbohydrate?

Writing Exercises

33. Explain what is meant by (a) consistent system, (b) a dependent system, and (c) inconsistent system.

34. Describe the Gauss-Jordan method.

7.5 MATRIX ALGEBRA

Objectives ▶▶

In this section you will learn about:

A. Special Matrices;

B. Equality of Matrices;

C. Addition of Matrices;

D. Subtraction of Matrices; and

E. Scalar Multiplication

In addition to using matrices to solve a system of equations, there are many situations in both pure and applied mathematics that deal directly with rectangular array of numbers. Therefore, it is important to learn the basic operations on matrices. In this section, we will see that two matrices can be added, subtracted, and multiplied by a number (scalar).

Matrix

Suppose ABC-Electronics manufactures three types of TVs, Black and White, color, and Color TV with VCR. A black and white TV uses 5 units of material and 6 units of labor, a color TV uses 12 units of materials and 8 units of labor, and a color TV with VCR uses 17 units of material and 13 units of labor. A convenient way to organize the above data is

	B/W	Color	with VCR
Material	5	12	17
Labor	6	8	13

The data has been organized in two rows and three columns. The rows represent the use of material and labor, and the columns represent different types of products the company manufacturers. This information can also be written as the matrix:

$$\begin{bmatrix} 5 & 12 & 17 \\ 6 & 8 & 13 \end{bmatrix}$$

The size of a matrix is indicated by its dimensions.

Dimension

The dimension of a matrix is determined by the number of rows and the number of columns. It is denoted as (# of rows) × (# of columns).

For example, a matrix with 5 rows and 3 columns has the dimension 5 × 3.

A. SPECIAL MATRICES

1. **Row Matrix**   A matrix consisting of only one row is called a **row matrix.**

   For example, [3 2 5 2] is a row matrix of dimension 1×4.

2. **Column Matrix** A matrix consisting of only one column is called a **column matrix.**

   For example, $\begin{bmatrix} 2 \\ -1 \\ 5 \end{bmatrix}$ is a column matrix of dimension 3×1.

3. **Square Matrix** If a matrix has the same number of rows as the number of columns, it is called a square matrix.

   For example, $\begin{bmatrix} 1 & 3 & 5 \\ 2 & 1 & 2 \\ 0 & 1 & 3 \end{bmatrix}$ is a square matrix, because it has 3 rows and 3

   columns.

4. **Diagonal Matrix** A square matrix with its non zero entries only along the principal diagonal from the left hand top corner to the right hand bottom corner is called a diagonal matrix.

   For example, $\begin{bmatrix} 1 & 0 & 0 \\ 0 & 8 & 0 \\ 0 & 0 & 5 \end{bmatrix}$ is a diagonal matrix.

   → Principal diagonal

5. **Identity Matrix** A diagonal matrix that has all diagonal entries equal to 1 is called an identity matrix.

   For example, $\begin{bmatrix} 1 & 0 \\ 0 & 1 \end{bmatrix}$ is an identity matrix of dimension 2×2.

   Notation: $l_{3 \times 3}$ represents an identity matrix of dimension 3×3.

   $$l_{3 \times 3} = \begin{bmatrix} 1 & 0 & 0 \\ 0 & 1 & 0 \\ 0 & 0 & 1 \end{bmatrix}$$

6. **Zero Matrix** A matrix with all of its entries zero is called a zero matrix.

   For example, $\begin{bmatrix} 0 & 0 & 0 \\ 0 & 0 & 0 \\ 0 & 0 & 0 \end{bmatrix}$ is a zero matrix of a dimension 3×3.

EXAMPLE 1   Give the dimension and identify the kind of special matrix, if it is so.

a. $\begin{bmatrix} 2 & 3 & -1 \\ 5 & 2 & 0 \end{bmatrix}$ b. $\begin{bmatrix} 5 & 0 & 0 \\ 0 & 0 & 0 \\ 0 & 0 & 1 \end{bmatrix}$ c. $[7 \quad 9 \quad 2]$ d. $\begin{bmatrix} 0 \\ 1 \\ 0 \end{bmatrix}$

e. $\begin{bmatrix} 0 & 0 & 0 \\ 0 & 0 & 0 \\ 0 & 0 & 0 \end{bmatrix}$ f. $\begin{bmatrix} 1 & 1 \\ 1 & 1 \end{bmatrix}$ g. $\begin{bmatrix} 1 & 0 & 0 \\ 0 & 1 & 0 \\ 0 & 0 & 0 \end{bmatrix}$

Solutions:

a.   dimension = 2×3,

b.   dimension = 3×3, a diagonal matrix, square matrix

c.   dimension = 1×3, a row matrix

d.   dimension = 3×1, a column matrix

e.   dimension = 3×3, a zero matrix, square matrix

f.   dimension = 2×2, a square matrix

g.   dimension = 3×3, a diagonal matrix, square matrix

B. EQUALITY OF MATRICES

As with two numerical algebraic expressions, we now want to determine under what conditions two matrices are equal.

> **Equality of Matrices**
> Two matrices if they are of the same dimension and if corresponding entries are equal.

EXAMPLE 2   Find x, y, a, and b in:

$$\begin{bmatrix} -3 & 2 \\ a & b \end{bmatrix} = \begin{bmatrix} y & x \\ 5 & 9 \end{bmatrix}$$

Solution: For the matrices to be equal, the corresponding entries must be equal. Therefore, $-3 = y$, $2 = x$, $a = 5$, and $b = 9$.

C. ADDITION OF MATRICES

The following is the rule for addition of matrices.

The **sum** of two $m \times n$ matrices is the $m \times n$ matrix in which each element is the sum of the corresponding elements in the given matrices.

Note   We can not add matrices of different dimensions.

EXAMPLE 3   Find the sums   **a.** $A + B$ **b.** $B + A$,

if $A = \begin{bmatrix} -2 & 7 \\ 5 & 9 \end{bmatrix}$ and $\begin{bmatrix} 8 & -1 \\ 0 & -2 \end{bmatrix}$

Solutions: **a.** $A + B = \begin{bmatrix} -2 & 7 \\ 5 & 9 \end{bmatrix} + \begin{bmatrix} 8 & -1 \\ 0 & -2 \end{bmatrix} = \begin{bmatrix} -2+8 & 7+(-1) \\ 5+0 & 9+(-2) \end{bmatrix} = \begin{bmatrix} 6 & 6 \\ 5 & 7 \end{bmatrix}$

b. $B + A = \begin{bmatrix} 8 & -1 \\ 0 & -2 \end{bmatrix} + \begin{bmatrix} -2 & 7 \\ 5 & 9 \end{bmatrix} = \begin{bmatrix} 8+(-2) & -1+7 \\ 0+5 & -2+9 \end{bmatrix} = \begin{bmatrix} 6 & 6 \\ 5 & 7 \end{bmatrix}$

Remark: *If A and B are two matrices of the same dimension, then A + B = B + A. That is, matrix addition is* **commutative.**

EXAMPLE 4   Find the sums   **a.** $A + B$ **b.** $B + A$

if $A = \begin{bmatrix} 2 & 1 & 3 \\ 0 & -2 & 1 \end{bmatrix}$ and $B = \begin{bmatrix} -2 & 5 & 1 \\ 2 & -2 & 8 \end{bmatrix}$

Solutions:

a. $A + B = \begin{bmatrix} 2 & 1 & 3 \\ 0 & -2 & 1 \end{bmatrix} + \begin{bmatrix} -2 & 5 & 1 \\ 2 & -2 & 8 \end{bmatrix} = \begin{bmatrix} 2+(-2) & 1+5 & 3+1 \\ 0+2 & -2+(-2) & 1+8 \end{bmatrix}$

$= \begin{bmatrix} 0 & 6 & 4 \\ 2 & -4 & 9 \end{bmatrix}$

b. $B + A = \begin{bmatrix} -2 & 5 & 1 \\ 2 & -2 & 8 \end{bmatrix} + \begin{bmatrix} 2 & 1 & 3 \\ 0 & -2 & 1 \end{bmatrix} = \begin{bmatrix} -2+2 & 5+1 & 1+3 \\ 2+0 & -2+(-2) & 8+1 \end{bmatrix}$

$= \begin{bmatrix} 0 & 6 & 4 \\ 2 & -4 & 9 \end{bmatrix}$

Additive inverse

The additive inverse of a matrix A is the matrix $-A$ in which each entry is the additive inverse of the corresponding entry of A.

For example, if $A = \begin{bmatrix} 2 & -1 \\ 0 & 8 \\ -2 & 7 \end{bmatrix}$, then $-A = \begin{bmatrix} -2 & 1 \\ 0 & -8 \\ 2 & -7 \end{bmatrix}$

Property of Zero Matrix

If 0 is the $m \times n$ zero matrix and A is any $m \times n$ matrix, then $A + 0 = 0 + A = A$.

D. Subtraction of Matrices

The difference of two matrices is defined the same way as addition. We subtract the corresponding elements of matrices. We can not subtract matrices of different dimensions.

EXAMPLE 5 Given $A = \begin{bmatrix} 1 & -3 & 2 \\ 0 & 1 & 5 \\ -2 & 3 & 4 \end{bmatrix}$, and $B = \begin{bmatrix} 3 & 1 & 4 \\ -1 & 3 & 2 \\ 4 & 5 & 6 \end{bmatrix}$

Find **a.** $A - B$, **b.** $B - A$

Solution:

a. $A - B = \begin{bmatrix} 1 & -3 & 2 \\ 0 & 1 & 5 \\ -2 & 3 & 4 \end{bmatrix} - \begin{bmatrix} 3 & 1 & 4 \\ -1 & 3 & 2 \\ 4 & 5 & 6 \end{bmatrix} = \begin{bmatrix} 1-3 & -3-1 & 2-4 \\ 0+1 & 1-3 & 5-2 \\ -2-4 & 3-5 & 4-6 \end{bmatrix}$

$$= \begin{bmatrix} -2 & -4 & -2 \\ 1 & -2 & 3 \\ -6 & -2 & -2 \end{bmatrix}$$

b. $B - A = \begin{bmatrix} 3 & 1 & 4 \\ -1 & 3 & 2 \\ 4 & 5 & 6 \end{bmatrix} - \begin{bmatrix} 1 & -3 & 2 \\ 0 & 1 & 5 \\ -2 & 3 & 4 \end{bmatrix} = \begin{bmatrix} 3-1 & 1+3 & 4-2 \\ -1-0 & 3-1 & 2-5 \\ 4+2 & 5-3 & 6-4 \end{bmatrix}$

$$= \begin{bmatrix} 2 & 4 & 2 \\ -1 & 2 & -3 \\ 6 & 2 & 2 \end{bmatrix}$$

E. Scalar Multiplication

The product of a scalar c and a matrix A is the matrix whose entries are c times the corresponding entries in A and is written as cA.

For Example, $3\begin{bmatrix} -2 & 1 \\ 5 & 7 \end{bmatrix} = \begin{bmatrix} -6 & 3 \\ 15 & 21 \end{bmatrix}$.

EXAMPLE 6 Find: **a.** $2A + B$ **b.** $3A - 2B$

if $A = \begin{bmatrix} -2 & 1 & 5 \\ 3 & 0 & -1 \end{bmatrix}$, and $B = \begin{bmatrix} 3 & 2 & -4 \\ 9 & -7 & 8 \end{bmatrix}$

Solution:

a. $2A + B = 2\begin{bmatrix} -2 & 1 & 5 \\ 3 & 0 & -1 \end{bmatrix} + \begin{bmatrix} 3 & 2 & -4 \\ 9 & -7 & 8 \end{bmatrix}$

$$= \begin{bmatrix} -4 & 2 & 10 \\ 6 & 0 & -2 \end{bmatrix} + \begin{bmatrix} 3 & 2 & -4 \\ 9 & -7 & 8 \end{bmatrix} = \begin{bmatrix} -1 & 4 & 6 \\ 15 & -7 & 6 \end{bmatrix}$$

b. $3A - 2B = 3\begin{bmatrix} -2 & 1 & 5 \\ 3 & 0 & -1 \end{bmatrix} - 2\begin{bmatrix} 3 & 2 & -4 \\ 9 & -7 & 8 \end{bmatrix}$

$$= \begin{bmatrix} -6 & 3 & 15 \\ 9 & 0 & -3 \end{bmatrix} - \begin{bmatrix} 6 & 4 & -8 \\ 18 & -14 & 16 \end{bmatrix}$$

$$= \begin{bmatrix} -6-6 & 3-4 & 15-(-8) \\ 9-18 & 0-(-14) & -3-16 \end{bmatrix} = \begin{bmatrix} -12 & -1 & 23 \\ -9 & 14 & -19 \end{bmatrix}$$

EXAMPLE 7   Refer to ABC Electronics (Page 7.28) consumption matrix C:

$$C = \begin{bmatrix} 5 & 12 & 17 \\ 6 & 8 & 13 \end{bmatrix}$$

If the company manufactures 100 units of each type of TV, find the matrix that describes the total consumption of material and labor for each type.

Solution: The matrix that describes the consumption of material and labor for one unit of each type of

TV is $C = \begin{bmatrix} 5 & 12 & 17 \\ 6 & 8 & 13 \end{bmatrix}$.

Therefore, the consumption of material and labor in 100 units of each is

$$100\ C = 100\begin{bmatrix} 5 & 12 & 17 \\ 6 & 8 & 13 \end{bmatrix} = \begin{bmatrix} 500 & 1200 & 1700 \\ 600 & 800 & 1300 \end{bmatrix}$$

EXAMPLE 8   Suppose ABC Electronics has two divisions, one makes 13" models and the other makes 19" models. The consumption of materials and labor for the 13-inch and 19-inch models are:

$$A = \begin{bmatrix} 5 & 12 & 17 \\ 6 & 8 & 13 \end{bmatrix} \text{ and } B = \begin{bmatrix} 7 & 15 & 20 \\ 8 & 11 & 19 \end{bmatrix}$$

respectively. If the company manufactures 20 units of 13" and 30 units of 19" models, find a matrix that describes the total consumption of the material and labor for each kind of TV.

Solution: The matrix that describes the number of units of material and labor needed to manufacture 20 units of 13-inch and 30 units of 19-inch models is given by

$$20\ A + 30\ B = 20\begin{bmatrix} 5 & 12 & 17 \\ 6 & 8 & 13 \end{bmatrix} + 30\begin{bmatrix} 7 & 15 & 20 \\ 8 & 11 & 19 \end{bmatrix}$$

$$= \begin{bmatrix} 100 & 240 & 340 \\ 120 & 160 & 260 \end{bmatrix} + \begin{bmatrix} 210 & 450 & 600 \\ 240 & 330 & 570 \end{bmatrix}$$

$$= \begin{bmatrix} 310 & 690 & 940 \\ 360 & 490 & 830 \end{bmatrix}.$$

EXERCISE 7.5

In exercises (1-6), write the dimensions of the matrix.

1. $\begin{bmatrix} 1 & 5 \\ 0 & -1 \end{bmatrix}$ 2. $\begin{bmatrix} 4 \\ 7 \end{bmatrix}$ 3. $\begin{bmatrix} 1 & -1 & 3 \\ 2 & 7 & 8 \end{bmatrix}$ 4. $[5 \ 3 \ 1 \ 5]$ 5. $[4]$ 6. $\begin{bmatrix} 2 & -1 \\ 3 & 7 \\ 5 & 0 \end{bmatrix}$

In exercises (7-10), determine if the matrices are equal.

7. $\begin{bmatrix} 2 & -5 \\ 9 & 1 \end{bmatrix}, \begin{bmatrix} -5 & 2 \\ 9 & 1 \end{bmatrix}$ 8. $[5 \ 7 \ 1], \begin{bmatrix} 5 \\ 7 \\ 1 \end{bmatrix}$ 9. $\begin{bmatrix} 5 & 9 \\ 3 & -2 \end{bmatrix}, \begin{bmatrix} 5 & 6+3 \\ 3 & -2 \end{bmatrix}$ 10. $\begin{bmatrix} 2 & 1 & 0 \\ 3 & 7 & 0 \end{bmatrix}, \begin{bmatrix} 2 & 1 \\ 3 & 7 \end{bmatrix}$

In exercises (11-12), find the unknown(s).

11. $\begin{bmatrix} x & 5 \\ -7 & t \end{bmatrix} = \begin{bmatrix} -1 & y \\ z & 9 \end{bmatrix}$

12. $\begin{bmatrix} x-y & 6 \\ 5 & 7 \end{bmatrix} = \begin{bmatrix} 4 & x+y \\ 5 & z \end{bmatrix}$

In exercises (13-24), use matrices A, B, and C to express the indicated expressions as a single matrix.

$$A = \begin{bmatrix} 1 & -2 & 3 \\ 7 & 9 & -5 \end{bmatrix}, \ B = \begin{bmatrix} 0 & -9 & 8 \\ 7 & 2 & 3 \end{bmatrix}, \ C = \begin{bmatrix} 11 & 1 & -1 \\ 0 & 2 & -3 \end{bmatrix}$$

13. $A + C$ 14. $B + C$ 15. $A + B$ 16. $3A + 2B$

17. $5A - 3B$ 18. $(A + B) - 3C$ 19. $2(A + B) - C$ 20. $2C - (A + B)$

21. $3C - 2(A+B)$ 22. $2A + 3(B + C)$ 23. $0 + 2A$ 24. $-3A + 0$

25. Find x and y so that $\begin{bmatrix} 2 & -3 & 1 \\ 5 & -4 & -1 \end{bmatrix} + \begin{bmatrix} x+y & 1 & -1 \\ 3 & x & 9 \end{bmatrix} = \begin{bmatrix} -2 & -2 & 0 \\ 8 & 2x+y & 8 \end{bmatrix}$

26. A small steel factory produces two kinds of screws, regular and phillips, in four different sizes. One week it produces 25, 30, 20, and 35 units of regular screws of size $\frac{1}{2}$ inch, $\frac{3}{4}$ inch, 1– inch, and $1\frac{1}{2}$ inches, respectively.

The same week it produces 40, 25, 35, and 25 units of phillips screws of size $\frac{1}{2}$ inch, $\frac{3}{4}$ inch, 1-inch and $1\frac{1}{2}$ inches respectively. Write a matrix describing production of the factory.

27. In a large corporation, the following data was collected:

120 females employees earn less than $ 20,000
280 male employees earn less than $20,000
150 male employees earn more than $20,000
72 female employees earn more than $20,000

Write a matrix that describes the above data.

Writing Exercises

28. Can we add any two matrices? Explain.

29. When are two matrices equal?

30. Distinguish between the row operation cR_1, and the scalar multiplication cA, where R_1 is row 1 of the matrix A and c is a number.

7.6 MULTIPLICATION OF MATRICES

In the previous section we discussed the product of a number (scalar) and a matrix. In this section we will discuss the product of two matrices.

A. MATRIX MULTIPLICATION

Matrix multiplication is based on the following definition of the product of a row matrix times a column matrix or simply a row times a column.

> **Row times Column**
>
> A row times a column (with the same number of entries) is the number obtained by adding the products of the corresponding entries.

EXAMPLE 1   Multiply $[5 \quad 3 \quad 2] \begin{bmatrix} 7 \\ 2 \\ 1 \end{bmatrix}$

Solution: $[5 \quad 3 \quad 2] \begin{bmatrix} 7 \\ 2 \\ 1 \end{bmatrix}$ = sum of the products of the corresponding entries

$$= 5(7) + 3(2) + 2(1) = 35 + 6 + 2 = \mathbf{43}$$

EXAMPLE 2   Multiply $[-3 \quad 9 \quad 7] \begin{bmatrix} 5 \\ -2 \\ 3 \end{bmatrix}$

Solution: $[-3 \quad 9 \quad 7] \begin{bmatrix} 5 \\ -2 \\ 3 \end{bmatrix} = (-3)5 + 9(-2) + 7(3)$

$$= -15 - 18 + 21$$
$$= -12$$

Matrix Multiplication

We extend the above definition of a row times a column to the following definition of a matrix A times matrix B.

> **Matrix Multiplication**
>
> Let A be a matrix of dimension $m \times r$ and B be a matrix of dimension $r \times n$. The product AB is the matrix of dimension $m \times n$ whose (i, j) entry is the product of the i-th row of A times the j-th column of B.

Remarks: 1. *We can multiply matrices only if the number of columns of the first matrix equals the number of rows of the second. If we indicate the dimensions of the matrices like $A_{m \times r}$ $B_{r \times n}$, then the adjacent numbers in the dimensions must be equal.*

2. *The i-th row of the first matrix, when multiplied with all the columns of the second matrix, will generate the i-th row of the product matrix.*

3. *The dimension of the product matrix*

$$A_{m \times r} \quad B_{r \times n}$$

$$is \qquad m \times n$$

EXAMPLE 3

Find: **a.** (1, 2) entry of AB **b.** (2, 1) entry of AB,

where $A = \begin{bmatrix} 5 & 2 \\ 1 & -1 \end{bmatrix}$, $B = \begin{bmatrix} 7 & 4 \\ 3 & 8 \end{bmatrix}$.

Solutions: **a.** The (1, 2) entry of AB is obtained by multiplying the first row of the first matrix with the second column of the second matrix.

$$\begin{bmatrix} 5 & 2 \end{bmatrix} \begin{bmatrix} 4 \\ 8 \end{bmatrix} = 5(4) + 2(8) = 20 + 16 = 36$$

Thus, the (1, 2) entry of AB is **36.**

b. The (2, 1) entry of AB is given by the product of the second row of A and the first column of B.

$$\begin{bmatrix} 1 & -1 \end{bmatrix} \begin{bmatrix} 7 \\ 3 \end{bmatrix} = 1(7) + (-1)3 = 7 - 3 = 4$$

Thus, the (2, 1) entry of AB is **4.**

EXAMPLE 4

Write the first row of the product AB if $A = \begin{bmatrix} 1 & 3 & 2 \\ 5 & 4 & 7 \end{bmatrix}$, and $B = \begin{bmatrix} 2 & 1 \\ 4 & 6 \\ 5 & 3 \end{bmatrix}$.

Solution: The first row of the product AB is obtained by multiplying the first row of A by each column of B.

$$(1, 1) \text{ entry of } AB = \begin{bmatrix} 1 & 3 & 2 \end{bmatrix} \begin{bmatrix} 2 \\ 4 \\ 5 \end{bmatrix} = 1(2) + 3(4) + 2(5) = 2 + 12 + 10 = \textbf{24}$$

$$(1, 2) \text{ entry of } AB = \begin{bmatrix} 1 & 3 & 2 \end{bmatrix} \begin{bmatrix} 1 \\ 6 \\ 3 \end{bmatrix} = 1(1) + 3(6) + 2(3) = 1 + 18 + 6 = \textbf{25}$$

Thus, the first row of AB is [24   25].

EXAMPLE 5   Compute: **a.** AB and   **b.** BA if

$$A = \begin{bmatrix} 3 & 1 \\ 2 & 5 \end{bmatrix}, \text{ and } B = \begin{bmatrix} 2 & 4 \\ 7 & 3 \end{bmatrix}.$$

Solutions: We will find each row of the product matrices AB and BA.

a.   For the first row of AB, i.e. $\begin{bmatrix} 3 & 1 \\ 2 & 5 \end{bmatrix}\begin{bmatrix} 2 & 4 \\ 7 & 3 \end{bmatrix}$, we compute

$$[3 \quad 1]\begin{bmatrix} 2 \\ 7 \end{bmatrix} = \mathbf{13} \text{ and } [3 \quad 1]\begin{bmatrix} 4 \\ 3 \end{bmatrix} = \mathbf{15}$$

For the second row of AB, we find

$$[2 \quad 5]\begin{bmatrix} 2 \\ 7 \end{bmatrix} = \mathbf{39} \text{ and } [2 \quad 5]\begin{bmatrix} 4 \\ 3 \end{bmatrix} = \mathbf{23}$$

Thus, the product matrix AB is $\begin{bmatrix} \mathbf{13} & \mathbf{15} \\ \mathbf{39} & \mathbf{23} \end{bmatrix}$.

b.   For the first row of BA, i.e. $\begin{bmatrix} 2 & 4 \\ 7 & 3 \end{bmatrix}\begin{bmatrix} 3 & 1 \\ 2 & 5 \end{bmatrix}$, we compute

$$[2 \quad 4]\begin{bmatrix} 3 \\ 2 \end{bmatrix} = \mathbf{14} \text{ and } [2 \quad 4]\begin{bmatrix} 1 \\ 5 \end{bmatrix} = \mathbf{22}$$

The second row of BA is given by

$$[7 \quad 3]\begin{bmatrix} 3 \\ 2 \end{bmatrix} = \mathbf{27} \text{ and } [7 \quad 3]\begin{bmatrix} 1 \\ 5 \end{bmatrix} = \mathbf{22}$$

Therefore, the product matrix $BA = \begin{bmatrix} \mathbf{14} & \mathbf{22} \\ \mathbf{27} & \mathbf{22} \end{bmatrix}$.

Remark: *Observe that $AB \neq BA$, so we conclude that matrix multiplication is not commutative.*

EXAMPLE 6   Find the product AB if $A = \begin{bmatrix} 2 & 1 \\ -1 & 0 \\ 3 & 4 \end{bmatrix}$, $B = \begin{bmatrix} 1 & 3 & -2 \\ 4 & 2 & -1 \end{bmatrix}$.

Solution: The dimensions (3×2) (2×3) when written side by side have same adjacent numbers, that is, number of columns (2) in the first matrix is the same as number of rows (2) in the second matrix. Therefore, the product AB is defined and the product is a 3×3 matrix. We find the rows of the product AB.

For the first row of AB we multiply

$$[2 \quad 1]\begin{bmatrix} 1 \\ 4 \end{bmatrix} = \mathbf{6}, \quad [2 \quad 1]\begin{bmatrix} 3 \\ 2 \end{bmatrix} = \mathbf{8}, \text{ and } [2 \quad 1]\begin{bmatrix} -2 \\ -1 \end{bmatrix} = \mathbf{-5}$$

For the second row, we compute

$$[-1 \quad 0]\begin{bmatrix} 1 \\ 4 \end{bmatrix} = \mathbf{-1}, \quad [-1 \quad 0]\begin{bmatrix} 3 \\ 2 \end{bmatrix} = \mathbf{-3} \quad \text{and} \quad [-1 \quad 0]\begin{bmatrix} -2 \\ -1 \end{bmatrix} = \mathbf{2}$$

And for the third row, we find

$$[3 \quad 4]\begin{bmatrix} 1 \\ 4 \end{bmatrix} = \mathbf{19}, \quad [3 \quad 4]\begin{bmatrix} 3 \\ 2 \end{bmatrix} = \mathbf{17} \quad \text{and} \quad [3 \quad 4]\begin{bmatrix} -2 \\ -1 \end{bmatrix} = \mathbf{-10}$$

Thus, the product matrix AB is $\begin{bmatrix} 6 & 8 & -5 \\ -1 & -3 & 2 \\ 19 & 17 & -10 \end{bmatrix}$.

Note that the product matrix BA is $\begin{bmatrix} -7 & -7 \\ 3 & 0 \end{bmatrix}$.

EXAMPLE 7 Refer to ABC Electronics (Section 7.5). The number of units of material and labor used in the production of different types of TV's is given by

	B/W	Color	with VCR
Material	5	12	17
Labor	6	8	13

or by the matrix $\begin{bmatrix} 5 & 12 & 17 \\ 6 & 8 & 13 \end{bmatrix}$.

If the cost of each unit of material is $3 and the cost of each unit of labor is $5, find the matrix that represents the cost per unit of each type of TV.

Solution: The cost matrix is given by

$$[3 \quad 5]\begin{bmatrix} 5 & 12 & 17 \\ 6 & 8 & 13 \end{bmatrix} = [45 \quad 76 \quad 116].$$

Think how the units are associated with the unit cost in the matrix multiplication.

EXAMPLE 8 Let $A = \begin{bmatrix} 2 & 1 & 5 \\ -2 & 0 & 8 \\ 1 & 4 & 6 \end{bmatrix}$ and $I_{3\times3}$ be the 3×3 identity matrix. Find AI and IA.

Solution: $AI = \begin{bmatrix} 2 & 1 & 5 \\ -2 & 0 & 8 \\ 1 & 4 & 6 \end{bmatrix}\begin{bmatrix} 1 & 0 & 0 \\ 0 & 1 & 0 \\ 0 & 0 & 1 \end{bmatrix} = \begin{bmatrix} 2 & 1 & 5 \\ -2 & 0 & 8 \\ 1 & 4 & 6 \end{bmatrix}$

$IA = \begin{bmatrix} 1 & 0 & 0 \\ 0 & 1 & 0 \\ 0 & 0 & 1 \end{bmatrix}\begin{bmatrix} 2 & 1 & 5 \\ -2 & 0 & 8 \\ 1 & 4 & 6 \end{bmatrix} = \begin{bmatrix} 2 & 1 & 5 \\ -2 & 0 & 8 \\ 1 & 4 & 6 \end{bmatrix}$

We generalize the result of this example in the following property of identity matrix.

Identity Matrix Property

If A is a square matrix of dimension n, and $I_{n \times n}$ is an identity matrix of order $n \times n$.

$$A\, I_{n \times n} = A \text{ and } I_{n \times n}\, A = A.$$

EXERCISE 7.6

In exercises (1-8), let matrix A be of dimension 5×3, let matrix B be of dimension 5×5, let matrix C be of dimension 2×5 and let matrix D be of dimension 5×2. Determine if the product is defined and if so then give its dimensions.

1. AB 2. BA 3. CD 4. AC 5. CB 6. $(CB)D$ 7. $(BD)C$ 8. $C(BD)$

In exercises (9-10), find the (2, 3) entry of the product matrix AB.

9. $A = \begin{bmatrix} 1 & 2 \\ -1 & 0 \end{bmatrix}$, $B = \begin{bmatrix} 1 & 1 & 5 \\ 0 & 1 & -1 \end{bmatrix}$

10. $A = \begin{bmatrix} 1 & -1 & 0 \\ 2 & 3 & 1 \\ -1 & 1 & 2 \end{bmatrix}$, $B = \begin{bmatrix} 1 & -2 & 2 \\ 0 & 1 & 7 \\ 1 & 5 & 3 \end{bmatrix}$

In exercises (11-14), find the second row of the product matrix AB.

11. $A = \begin{bmatrix} 1 & 5 \\ 2 & 3 \end{bmatrix}$, $B = \begin{bmatrix} -1 & 2 \\ 3 & 7 \end{bmatrix}$

12. $A = \begin{bmatrix} 1 & 3 & -1 \\ 2 & 0 & 4 \end{bmatrix}$, $B = \begin{bmatrix} 1 & 2 \\ -1 & 0 \\ 2 & -3 \end{bmatrix}$

13. $A = \begin{bmatrix} 3 \\ 2 \\ 1 \end{bmatrix}$, $B = [5 \ -1 \ 7]$

14. $A = \begin{bmatrix} 1 & 0 \\ 2 & -1 \\ -1 & 1 \end{bmatrix}$, $B = \begin{bmatrix} 1 & 5 \\ 3 & -1 \end{bmatrix}$

In exercises (15-25), let $A = \begin{bmatrix} 2 & 3 \\ 1 & 5 \end{bmatrix}$, $B = \begin{bmatrix} -2 & 1 & 0 \\ 1 & -1 & 3 \end{bmatrix}$, $C = \begin{bmatrix} 2 & -1 \\ 3 & 4 \\ 5 & -2 \end{bmatrix}$, $D = \begin{bmatrix} 1 & 0 & -2 \\ -1 & 5 & 0 \\ 0 & 1 & -3 \end{bmatrix}$, and $E = \begin{bmatrix} 5 & -1 \\ 2 & 3 \end{bmatrix}$.

Find each of the following matrices, if I is the 3×3 identity matrix.

15. BC 16. BD 17. DC 18. AE 19. AB 20. CE

21. ID 22. $(BC)E$ 23. $(CB)D$ 24. $(EB)I$ 25. $(EB)D$

26. Eric bought 4 pairs of pants, 5 shirts, and 2 neckties. John bought 5 pairs of pants, 3 shirts, and 4 neckties. If the pants cost $28 each, shirts $15 each, and neckties $10 each, use matrix multiplication to compute the amount each person spent.

27. A produce wholesaler receives oranges, mandarins, and tangelos from three different growers. The number of crates received is shown as follows:

	Grower #1	Grower #2	Grower #3
Oranges	25	10	15
Mandarins	5	3	7
Tangelos	9	10	2

If oranges cost $5 per crate, mandarins $6 per crate, and tangelos $8 per crate, express the cost matrix as a product of two matrices.

Writing Exercises

28. Can we multiply any two matrices? Explain.

29. Is the matrix multiplication commutative? Give examples in support of your answer.

7.7 INVERSE OF MATRIX

<table>
<tr><td>

Objective ▶ ▶

In this section you will learn about:

A. Inverse of a Matrix.

</td><td>

In real numbers, division by a number is equivalent to multiplication by its reciprocal, i.e. the multiplicative inverse. In the same way, division by a matrix is also accomplished by multiplying by the inverse of the matrix, if it exists. In this section we will learn how to find the inverse of a matrix. **The inverse of a matrix is defined only for square matrices.**

</td></tr>
</table>

A. INVERSE OF A MATRIX

Let A be a matrix of dimension $n \times n$. Then the matrix B of dimension $n \times n$ is called the inverse of a matrix A if

$$AB = BA = I_{n \times n}$$

We denote the inverse of a matrix A by A^{-1}.

Remark: *For real numbers, zero does not have its multiplicative inverse. In the same way there are matrices that do not have inverses. Such matrices are called **singular** matrices.*

EXAMPLE 1 Determine whether or not the matrices are inverses of each other.

$$\begin{bmatrix} 3 & 5 \\ 1 & 5 \end{bmatrix} \text{ and } \begin{bmatrix} \dfrac{1}{2} & -\dfrac{1}{2} \\ -\dfrac{1}{10} & \dfrac{3}{10} \end{bmatrix}$$

Solution:
$$\begin{bmatrix} 3 & 5 \\ 1 & 5 \end{bmatrix}\begin{bmatrix} \dfrac{1}{2} & -\dfrac{1}{2} \\ -\dfrac{1}{10} & \dfrac{3}{10} \end{bmatrix} = \begin{bmatrix} 1 & 0 \\ 0 & 1 \end{bmatrix} \text{ and } \begin{bmatrix} \dfrac{1}{2} & -\dfrac{1}{2} \\ -\dfrac{1}{10} & \dfrac{3}{10} \end{bmatrix}\begin{bmatrix} 3 & 5 \\ 1 & 5 \end{bmatrix} = \begin{bmatrix} 1 & 0 \\ 0 & 1 \end{bmatrix}$$

Hence by definition the matrices are inverses of each other.

EXAMPLE 2 Find the inverse of matrix A, if it exists: $A = \begin{bmatrix} 2 & 1 \\ 3 & 4 \end{bmatrix}$.

Solution: Suppose $A^{-1} = \begin{bmatrix} a & b \\ c & d \end{bmatrix}$. By definition, the product of A and A^{-1} must be the identity matrix:

$$\begin{bmatrix} 2 & 1 \\ 3 & 4 \end{bmatrix}\begin{bmatrix} a & b \\ c & d \end{bmatrix} = \begin{bmatrix} 1 & 0 \\ 0 & 1 \end{bmatrix}.$$

Multiplying the matrices on the left side gives $\begin{bmatrix} 2a+c & 2b+d \\ 3a+4c & 3b+4d \end{bmatrix} = \begin{bmatrix} 1 & 0 \\ 0 & 1 \end{bmatrix}.$

In order for the matrices to be equal,

$2a + c = 1$, $2b + d = 0$, $3a + 4c = 0$, and $3b + 4d = 1$

Solving $2a + c = 1$ and $3a + 4c = 0$ gives $a = \dfrac{4}{5}$ and $c = \dfrac{-3}{5}$.

Solving $3b + 4d = 1$ and $2b + d = 0$ gives $b = -\dfrac{1}{5}$ and $d = \dfrac{2}{5}$.

Thus, the inverse of $\begin{bmatrix} 2 & 1 \\ 3 & 4 \end{bmatrix}$ is $\begin{bmatrix} \dfrac{4}{5} & -\dfrac{1}{5} \\ -\dfrac{3}{5} & \dfrac{2}{5} \end{bmatrix}$ or $\dfrac{1}{5}\begin{bmatrix} 4 & -1 \\ -3 & 2 \end{bmatrix}$.

Observation: Observe that in the inverse of the matrix $\begin{bmatrix} 2 & 1 \\ 3 & 4 \end{bmatrix}$, the entries along the principal diagonal are interchanged and the entries along the other diagonal are additive inverses (negative of entries in the given matrix). The scalar $\dfrac{1}{5}$ is the reciprocal of the difference:

$$\underset{\substack{\text{Product of elements in} \\ \text{the principal diagonal}}}{2(4)} \quad - \quad \underset{\substack{\text{Product of elements} \\ \text{in the other diagonal.}}}{1(3)} = 5$$

This observation leads us to the following short cut method of finding an inverse of a 2×2 matrix.

Inverse of a 2×2 Matrix (Short Cut)

The inverse of a 2×2 matrix $\begin{bmatrix} a & b \\ c & d \end{bmatrix}$ is $\dfrac{1}{ad - bc}\begin{bmatrix} d & -b \\ -c & a \end{bmatrix}$.

EXAMPLE 3   Use the shortcut to find the inverse of the matrix $A = \begin{bmatrix} 5 & 2 \\ 3 & 4 \end{bmatrix}$.

Solution: *By using the shortcut*

$$A^{-1} = \dfrac{1}{20 - 6}\begin{bmatrix} 4 & -2 \\ -3 & 5 \end{bmatrix} = \dfrac{1}{14}\begin{bmatrix} 4 & -2 \\ -3 & 5 \end{bmatrix}$$

$$= \begin{bmatrix} \dfrac{4}{14} & -\dfrac{2}{14} \\ -\dfrac{3}{14} & \dfrac{5}{14} \end{bmatrix} \text{ or } \begin{bmatrix} \dfrac{2}{7} & -\dfrac{1}{7} \\ -\dfrac{3}{14} & \dfrac{5}{14} \end{bmatrix}$$

In order to find a general method of finding the inverse of a matrix, we go back to Example

2 where we attempted to find the inverse of a 2×2 matrix $A = \begin{bmatrix} 2 & 1 \\ 3 & 4 \end{bmatrix}$. By looking at the equation

$$\begin{bmatrix} 2a+c & 2b+d \\ 3a+4c & 3b+4d \end{bmatrix} = \begin{bmatrix} 1 & 0 \\ 0 & 1 \end{bmatrix}$$

we get a system of four equations:

$$2a+c = 1 \quad \text{and} \quad 2b+d = 0$$
$$3a+4c = 0 \qquad\qquad 3b+4d = 1$$

Their augmented matrices are

$$\begin{bmatrix} 2 & 1 & \vdots & 1 \\ 3 & 4 & \vdots & 0 \end{bmatrix} \quad \text{and} \quad \begin{bmatrix} 2 & 1 & \vdots & 0 \\ 3 & 4 & \vdots & 1 \end{bmatrix}$$

The row operations that are performed on these two matrices can be performed more conveniently on one doubly augmented matrix

$$\begin{bmatrix} 2 & 1 & \vdots & 1 & 0 \\ 3 & 4 & \vdots & 0 & 1 \end{bmatrix} \xrightarrow{R_1\left(\frac{1}{2}\right)} \begin{bmatrix} 1 & \frac{1}{2} & \vdots & \frac{1}{2} & 0 \\ 3 & 4 & \vdots & 0 & 1 \end{bmatrix}$$

$$\xrightarrow{R_2 + (-3)R_1} \begin{bmatrix} 1 & \frac{1}{2} & \vdots & \frac{1}{2} & 0 \\ 0 & \frac{5}{2} & \vdots & -\frac{3}{2} & 1 \end{bmatrix} \xrightarrow{R_2\left(\frac{2}{5}\right)} \begin{bmatrix} 1 & \frac{1}{2} & \vdots & \frac{1}{2} & 0 \\ 0 & 1 & \vdots & -\frac{3}{5} & \frac{2}{5} \end{bmatrix}$$

By using the Gauss-Jordan method we can transform this matrix to

$$\xrightarrow{R_1 + \left(-\frac{1}{2}\right)R_2} \begin{bmatrix} 1 & 0 & \vdots & \frac{4}{5} & -\frac{1}{5} \\ 0 & 1 & \vdots & -\frac{3}{5} & \frac{2}{5} \end{bmatrix}.$$

The matrix on the right side of the dotted vertical bar is A^{-1}. We generalize the above procedure as follows:

Strategy

To find the **inverse** of an $n\times n$ matrix A.

Step **1**   Write the augmented matrix $[A \mid I]$, where the identity matrix I is of the same dimension as A.

Step **2**   Use the steps in the Gauss-Jordan method to transform A into identity matrix, if possible.

Step **3**   If the resultant matrix is of the form $[I \mid B]$, then B is the inverse of A.

EXAMPLE 4   Find the inverse of the matrix $A = \begin{bmatrix} 3 & 1 & 3 \\ 1 & 2 & 1 \\ 2 & 1 & 0 \end{bmatrix}$.

Solution:

Step 1   We augment the matrix by the identity matrix $I_{3 \times 3}$.

$$\left[\begin{array}{ccc:ccc} 3 & 1 & 3 & 1 & 0 & 0 \\ 1 & 2 & 1 & 0 & 1 & 0 \\ 2 & 1 & 0 & 0 & 0 & 1 \end{array}\right]$$

Step 2   Using the steps in the Gauss-Jordan method, we transform matrix A into an identity matrix.

$$\left[\begin{array}{ccc:ccc} 3 & 1 & 3 & 1 & 0 & 0 \\ 1 & 2 & 1 & 0 & 1 & 0 \\ 2 & 1 & 0 & 0 & 0 & 1 \end{array}\right] \xrightarrow{R_1 \leftrightarrow R_2} \left[\begin{array}{ccc:ccc} 1 & 2 & 1 & 0 & 1 & 0 \\ 3 & 1 & 3 & 1 & 0 & 0 \\ 2 & 1 & 0 & 0 & 0 & 1 \end{array}\right]$$

$$\xrightarrow[R_3 + (-2)R_1]{R_2 + (-3)R_1} \left[\begin{array}{ccc:ccc} 1 & 2 & 1 & 0 & 1 & 0 \\ 0 & -5 & 0 & 1 & -3 & 0 \\ 0 & -3 & -2 & 0 & -2 & 1 \end{array}\right] \xrightarrow{-\frac{1}{5}R_2} \left[\begin{array}{ccc:ccc} 1 & 2 & 1 & 0 & 1 & 0 \\ 0 & 1 & 0 & -\frac{1}{5} & \frac{3}{5} & 0 \\ 0 & -3 & -2 & 0 & -2 & 1 \end{array}\right]$$

$$\xrightarrow[R_3 + (3)R_2]{R_1 + (-2)R_2} \left[\begin{array}{ccc:ccc} 1 & 0 & 1 & \frac{2}{5} & -\frac{1}{5} & 0 \\ 0 & 1 & 0 & -\frac{1}{5} & \frac{3}{5} & 0 \\ 0 & 0 & -2 & -\frac{3}{5} & -\frac{1}{5} & 1 \end{array}\right] \xrightarrow{-\frac{1}{2}R_3} \left[\begin{array}{ccc:ccc} 1 & 0 & 1 & \frac{2}{5} & -\frac{1}{5} & 0 \\ 0 & 1 & 0 & -\frac{1}{5} & \frac{3}{5} & 0 \\ 0 & 0 & 1 & \frac{3}{10} & \frac{1}{10} & -\frac{1}{2} \end{array}\right]$$

$$\xrightarrow{R_1 + (-1)R_3} \left[\begin{array}{ccc:ccc} 1 & 0 & 0 & \frac{1}{10} & -\frac{3}{10} & \frac{1}{2} \\ 0 & 1 & 0 & -\frac{1}{5} & \frac{3}{5} & 0 \\ 0 & 0 & 1 & \frac{3}{10} & \frac{1}{10} & -\frac{1}{2} \end{array}\right]$$

Step 3   Since the identity matrix $I_{3 \times 3}$ appears on the left side of the dotted vertical bar, the matrix that appears on the right side is the inverse of the given matrix.

Thus, $A^{-1} = \begin{bmatrix} \frac{1}{10} & -\frac{3}{10} & \frac{1}{2} \\ -\frac{1}{5} & \frac{3}{5} & 0 \\ \frac{3}{10} & \frac{1}{10} & -\frac{1}{2} \end{bmatrix}$.

EXAMPLE 5   Find the inverse of the matrix $A = \begin{bmatrix} 6 & 3 \\ 1 & 2 \end{bmatrix}$ by row operations and then verify the result by using the shortcut.

Solution:

Step 1   We use $I_{2\times2}$ to write the augmented matrix: $\begin{bmatrix} 6 & 3 & 1 & 0 \\ 1 & 2 & 0 & 1 \end{bmatrix}$

Step 2   Using the steps in the Gauss-Jordan method, we get

$$\begin{bmatrix} 6 & 3 & 1 & 0 \\ 1 & 2 & 0 & 1 \end{bmatrix} \xrightarrow{R_1 \leftrightarrow R_2} \begin{bmatrix} 1 & 2 & 0 & 1 \\ 6 & 3 & 1 & 0 \end{bmatrix}$$

$$\xrightarrow{R_2+(-6)R_1} \begin{bmatrix} 1 & 2 & 0 & 1 \\ 0 & -9 & 1 & -6 \end{bmatrix} \xrightarrow{-\frac{1}{9}R_2} \begin{bmatrix} 1 & 2 & 0 & 1 \\ 0 & 1 & -\frac{1}{9} & \frac{6}{9} \end{bmatrix}$$

$$\xrightarrow{R_1+(-2)R_2} \begin{bmatrix} 1 & 0 & \frac{2}{9} & -\frac{3}{9} \\ 0 & 1 & -\frac{1}{9} & \frac{6}{9} \end{bmatrix}.$$

Step 3   Since the matrix A has been transformed to the identity matrix $I_{2\times2}$, the matrix that appears on the right side is the inverse of the given matrix.

$$A^{-1} = \begin{bmatrix} \frac{2}{9} & -\frac{1}{3} \\ -\frac{1}{9} & \frac{2}{3} \end{bmatrix} \qquad (1)$$

We verify the answer by using the short cut

$$A^{-1} = \frac{1}{12-3}\begin{bmatrix} 2 & -3 \\ -1 & 6 \end{bmatrix} = \frac{1}{9}\begin{bmatrix} 2 & -3 \\ -1 & 6 \end{bmatrix} = \begin{bmatrix} \frac{2}{9} & -\frac{1}{3} \\ -\frac{1}{9} & \frac{2}{3} \end{bmatrix} \qquad (2)$$

The matrices in **(1)** and **(2)** obtained by two different methods are the same.

EXAMPLE 6   Find the inverse of the matrix $A = \begin{bmatrix} 9 & 6 \\ 3 & 2 \end{bmatrix}$ by row operations, if it exists.

Solution:

Step 1   We proceed with the augmented matrix $\begin{bmatrix} 9 & 6 & 1 & 0 \\ 3 & 2 & 0 & 1 \end{bmatrix}.$

Step 2   Using the steps of the Gauss-Jordan method gives

$$\begin{bmatrix} 9 & 6 & 1 & 0 \\ 3 & 2 & 0 & 1 \end{bmatrix} \xrightarrow{\frac{1}{9}R_1} \begin{bmatrix} 1 & \frac{2}{3} & \frac{1}{9} & 0 \\ 3 & 2 & 0 & 1 \end{bmatrix} \xrightarrow{R_2+(-3)R_1} \begin{bmatrix} 1 & \frac{2}{3} & \frac{1}{9} & 0 \\ 0 & 0 & -\frac{1}{3} & 1 \end{bmatrix}$$

Step 3   The zeros in row 2 of the matrix on the left of the dotted vertical bar tell us that we cannot get the identity matrix. Therefore, in this case, the inverse of *A* does not exist. The matrix *A* is a **singular** matrix.

Compare this result with the matrix obtained by using the short cut formula for the inverse.

$$A^{-1} = \frac{1}{ad-bc}\begin{bmatrix} d & -b \\ -c & a \end{bmatrix} = \frac{1}{18-18}\begin{bmatrix} 2 & -6 \\ -3 & 9 \end{bmatrix} = \frac{1}{0}\begin{bmatrix} 2 & -6 \\ -3 & 9 \end{bmatrix}$$ $\frac{1}{0}$ is not defined

Since the denominator is 0, A^{-1} does not exist.

Remark: *If a matrix A or its equivalent form has a row (column) of zeros, then A does not have an inverse, i.e. A is singular.*

EXERCISE 7.7

In exercises (1-8), determine whether or not the given matrices are inverses of each other.

1. $\begin{bmatrix} 5 & 2 \\ 7 & 3 \end{bmatrix}$ and $\begin{bmatrix} 3 & -2 \\ -7 & 5 \end{bmatrix}$

2. $\begin{bmatrix} 4 & 1 \\ 7 & 2 \end{bmatrix}$ and $\begin{bmatrix} 2 & -1 \\ -7 & 4 \end{bmatrix}$

3. $\begin{bmatrix} 7 & 2 \\ 11 & 3 \end{bmatrix}$ and $\begin{bmatrix} -3 & 2 \\ 11 & -7 \end{bmatrix}$

4. $\begin{bmatrix} 8 & -2 \\ -7 & 2 \end{bmatrix}$ and $\begin{bmatrix} 1 & 1 \\ \frac{7}{2} & 4 \end{bmatrix}$

5. $\begin{bmatrix} 5 & 8 \\ 3 & 5 \end{bmatrix}$ and $\begin{bmatrix} 3 & 7 \\ 5 & 8 \end{bmatrix}$

6. $\begin{bmatrix} 2 & 3 & 4 \\ 1 & 2 & 1 \\ 1 & 2 & 3 \end{bmatrix}$ and $\begin{bmatrix} 2 & -\frac{1}{2} & -\frac{5}{2} \\ -1 & 1 & 1 \\ 0 & -\frac{1}{2} & \frac{1}{2} \end{bmatrix}$

7. $\begin{bmatrix} 1 & 1 & 0 \\ 2 & 0 & 1 \\ 3 & 4 & 5 \end{bmatrix}$ and $\begin{bmatrix} 1 & 1 & 2 \\ 0 & 0 & 1 \\ 0 & -2 & -2 \end{bmatrix}$

8. $\begin{bmatrix} 1 & 3 & 3 \\ 1 & 4 & 3 \\ 1 & 3 & 4 \end{bmatrix}$ and $\begin{bmatrix} 7 & -3 & -3 \\ -1 & 1 & 0 \\ -1 & 0 & 1 \end{bmatrix}$

In exercises (9-12), use the shortcut method to find the inverse of the given 2 × 2 matrix.

9. $\begin{bmatrix} -3 & -1 \\ 5 & 2 \end{bmatrix}$

10. $\begin{bmatrix} 5 & 4 \\ 6 & 5 \end{bmatrix}$

11. $\begin{bmatrix} 10 & 6 \\ 3 & 2 \end{bmatrix}$

12. $\begin{bmatrix} 9 & 2 \\ 4 & 2 \end{bmatrix}$

In exercises (13-24) find the inverse of the matrix using row operations.

13. $\begin{bmatrix} 3 & 1 \\ 5 & 2 \end{bmatrix}$

14. $\begin{bmatrix} 1 & -1 \\ 4 & -5 \end{bmatrix}$

15. $\begin{bmatrix} 4 & 2 \\ 5 & 3 \end{bmatrix}$

16. $\begin{bmatrix} 5 & 2 \\ 5 & 3 \end{bmatrix}$

17. $\begin{bmatrix} 1 & 2 & 1 \\ 1 & 1 & 1 \\ 1 & 1 & 2 \end{bmatrix}$

18. $\begin{bmatrix} -1 & 1 & 1 \\ 1 & -2 & 1 \\ 1 & 0 & -1 \end{bmatrix}$

19. $\begin{bmatrix} -1 & 0 & 1 \\ 2 & 1 & 1 \\ -3 & -2 & -1 \end{bmatrix}$

20. $\begin{bmatrix} 1 & 1 & 2 \\ 0 & 1 & 1 \\ 2 & -2 & -1 \end{bmatrix}$

21. $\begin{bmatrix} -2 & 4 & 6 \\ 0 & 1 & 1 \\ 1 & 0 & 1 \end{bmatrix}$

22. $\begin{bmatrix} 0 & 1 & 2 \\ 2 & 1 & 3 \\ -1 & 1 & -1 \end{bmatrix}$

23. $\begin{bmatrix} -1 & 2 & 1 & 1 \\ 0 & 0 & 2 & -1 \\ 2 & 1 & -1 & 0 \\ -2 & 1 & 0 & 3 \end{bmatrix}$

24. $\begin{bmatrix} -1 & 1 & 0 & 1 \\ 1 & -1 & 1 & 1 \\ 1 & 1 & 1 & -1 \\ -1 & 0 & -1 & 1 \end{bmatrix}$

In exercises (25-30), show that the matrix has no inverse.

25. $\begin{bmatrix} 3 & 6 \\ 2 & 4 \end{bmatrix}$

26. $\begin{bmatrix} 1 & -2 \\ -4 & 8 \end{bmatrix}$

27. $\begin{bmatrix} 2 \\ 3 \end{bmatrix}$

28. $\begin{bmatrix} 1 & -3 & 2 \\ 4 & 9 & 2 \\ 2 & -6 & 4 \end{bmatrix}$

29. $\begin{bmatrix} 1 & 3 & -2 \\ -2 & 7 & 4 \\ 5 & 9 & -10 \end{bmatrix}$

30. $\begin{bmatrix} 1 & -1 & 5 & 9 \\ -3 & 7 & 0 & 2 \\ 0 & 0 & 0 & 0 \\ 2 & 3 & 5 & 1 \end{bmatrix}$

Writing Exercises

31. Does every matrix have an inverse matrix? State reasons and give examples.

32. Describe a procedure for finding the inverse of a matrix.

7.8 DETERMINANTS

Objectives ▶ ▶

In this section you will learn about:

A. The Determinant of a 2×2 Matrix;

B. The Determinant of a 3×3 Matrix;

C. The Effects of Row Operations on Determinants; and

D. Applications involving Determinants.

There are several ways to associate a number with a square matrix. Of particular importance is the **determinant** of the matrix. In this section, we will learn how to compute the determinant of a square matrix and also how to use determinants to solve a system of linear equations.

Notation: The determinant of a matrix A is denoted as

$$\det(A) \text{ or } |A|.$$

A. THE DETERMINANT OF A 2×2 MATRIX

Let the matrix A be $\begin{bmatrix} a & b \\ c & d \end{bmatrix}$. The determinant of matrix A is defined as follows:

$$|A| = \begin{vmatrix} a & b \\ c & d \end{vmatrix} = ad - bc.$$

EXAMPLE 1 Compute $|A|$ if $A = \begin{bmatrix} 5 & -2 \\ 3 & 7 \end{bmatrix}$.

Solution: Using the definition, the determinant of the 2×2 matrix A is given by

$$|A| = \begin{vmatrix} 5 & -2 \\ 3 & 7 \end{vmatrix} = 5(7) - (3)(-2)$$

$$= 35 - (-6)$$

$$= 35 + 6 = \mathbf{41}$$

EXAMPLE 2   Compute $|A|$ if $A = \begin{bmatrix} 2 & 8 \\ 7 & 5 \end{bmatrix}$.

Solution: Using the definition;

$$|A| = \begin{vmatrix} 2 & 8 \\ 7 & 5 \end{vmatrix} = 2(5) - (7)(8)$$

$$= 10 - 56 = \mathbf{-46.}$$

EXAMPLE 3   Compute det (A) if $A = \begin{bmatrix} 6 & 4 \\ 3 & 2 \end{bmatrix}$.

Solution: $\det (A) = \begin{vmatrix} 6 & 4 \\ 3 & 2 \end{vmatrix} = 6(2) - 3(4)$

$$= 12 - 12 = \mathbf{0}$$

Remark: *The determinant of a matrix can be positive or negative or zero. A matrix whose determinant is zero is a **singular** matrix as defined earlier.*

B. THE DETERMINANT OF A 3×3 MATRIX

Before we discuss a general method of finding the determinant of a 3×3 matrix, we give a special method (short-cut method).

A Special Method for a 3×3 Matrix

Consider a 3×3 matrix $A = \begin{bmatrix} 2 & -3 & 1 \\ 4 & 0 & 5 \\ -1 & 7 & 3 \end{bmatrix}$.

To evaluate its determinant, we extend the matrix by rewriting the first two columns on the right of the matrix as shown below:

$$\begin{bmatrix} 2 & -3 & 1 \\ 4 & 0 & 5 \\ -1 & 7 & 3 \end{bmatrix} \begin{matrix} 2 & -3 \\ 4 & 0 \\ -1 & 7 \end{matrix}$$

Multiply the numbers along the diagonals (top left to bottom right) shown below and add the products:

$$\begin{bmatrix} 2 & -3 & 1 \\ 4 & 0 & 5 \\ -1 & 7 & 3 \end{bmatrix} \begin{matrix} 2 & -3 \\ 4 & 0 \\ -1 & 7 \end{matrix}$$

$[2(0)(3) + (-3)(5)(-1) + (1)(4)(7)]$
$= 0 + 15 + 28 = \mathbf{43}$

Multiply the numbers along the other diagonals (top right to bottom left) as shown below and add the products:

$$\begin{bmatrix} 2 & -3 & 1 \\ 4 & 0 & 5 \\ -1 & 7 & 3 \end{bmatrix} \begin{matrix} 2 & -3 \\ 4 & 0 \\ -1 & 7 \end{matrix}$$

$[(1)(0)(-1) + (2)(5)(7) + (-3)(4)(3)]$
$= 0 + 70 - 36 = \mathbf{34}$

Subtract the two products: $|A| = 43 - 34 = 9$

EXAMPLE 4   Compute the determinant of $A = \begin{bmatrix} 3 & -2 & -5 \\ 1 & 2 & 4 \\ -6 & 2 & -1 \end{bmatrix}$.

Solution: We show the scheme of the special method of finding the determinant.

$$\begin{bmatrix} 3 & -2 & -5 \\ 1 & 2 & 4 \\ -6 & 2 & -1 \end{bmatrix} \begin{matrix} 3 & -2 \\ 1 & 2 \\ -6 & 2 \end{matrix}$$

$$|A| = [3(2)(-1) + (-2)(4)(-6) + (-5)(1)(2)] - [(-5)(2)(-6) + 3(4)(2) + (-2)(1)(-1)]$$
$$= [-6 + 48 - 10] - [60 + 24 + 2] = 32 - 86 = -54.$$

Cofactor method

The method of finding the determinant of a matrix that is also applicable to determinants of higher order uses cofactors of its elements.

Cofactor of an Element

Consider a matrix $A = \begin{bmatrix} -1 & 5 & 7 \\ 2 & 1 & 4 \\ 3 & 2 & -3 \end{bmatrix}$. The cofactor of the element in $(1, 3)$ position written as C_{13} is

$(-1)^{1+3}$ times the determinant of the matrix obtained by deleting the first row and third column of matrix A.

In short,

$$C_{13} = (-1)^{1+3} \begin{vmatrix} 2 & 1 \\ 3 & 2 \end{vmatrix} = (-1)^4 (4 - 3) = 1(1) = \mathbf{1}$$

In general, the cofactor of the element in (i, j)-th position is obtained as follows:

> **Cofactor of the element in (i, j)-th position**
>
> The cofactor (C_{ij}) of the element in (i, j)-th position of the matrix A is given by
> $C_{ij} = (-1)^{i+j} \cdot \det$ (of a matrix obtained by deleting the i-th row and the j-th column).

Thus,

$$C_{11} = (-1)^{1+1} \begin{vmatrix} 1 & 4 \\ 2 & -3 \end{vmatrix} = (-1)^2 (-3 - 8) = 1(-11) = \mathbf{-11}$$

$$C_{12} = (-1)^{1+2} \begin{vmatrix} 2 & 4 \\ 3 & -3 \end{vmatrix} = (-1)^3 (-6 - 12) = -1(-18) = \mathbf{18}$$

$$C_{23} = (-1)^{2+3} \begin{vmatrix} -1 & 5 \\ 3 & 2 \end{vmatrix} = (-1)^5 (-2 - 15) = -1(-17) = \mathbf{17}$$

EXAMPLE 5   Compute the cofactor C_{22}, C_{13}, and C_{32} of det A, where

$$A = \begin{bmatrix} 5 & -1 & 1 \\ 2 & 3 & 4 \\ 1 & 0 & 3 \end{bmatrix}.$$

Solution: The cofactor C_{22} is given by

$$C_{22} = (-1)^{2+2} \begin{vmatrix} 5 & 1 \\ 1 & 3 \end{vmatrix} = (-1)^4 (15 - 1) = 1(14) = \mathbf{14}$$

The cofactors C_{13} and C_{32} are given by

$$C_{13} = (-1)^{1+3} \begin{vmatrix} 2 & 3 \\ 1 & 0 \end{vmatrix} = (-1)^4 (0 - 3) = (1)(-3) = \mathbf{-3,}$$

$$C_{32} = (-1)^{3+2} \begin{vmatrix} 5 & 1 \\ 2 & 4 \end{vmatrix} = (-1)^5 (20 - 2) = (-1)(18) = \mathbf{-18.}$$

To find the determinant of a matrix A, we add the products of elements of any one row (column) by their cofactors. Consider the matrix:

$$A = \begin{bmatrix} a_{11} & a_{12} & a_{13} \\ a_{21} & a_{22} & a_{23} \\ a_{31} & a_{32} & a_{33} \end{bmatrix}$$

In general, we state the rule as follows

$$|A| = a_{11}C_{11} + a_{12}C_{12} + a_{13}C_{13}, \text{ if we expand by row 1 or}$$

$$= a_{21}C_{21} + a_{22}C_{22} + a_{23}C_{23}, \text{ if we expand by row 2 or}$$

$$= a_{13}C_{13} + a_{23}C_{23} + a_{33}C_{33}, \text{ if we expand by column 3 and so on.}$$

Cofactor Method

The determinant of a $n \times n$ matrix $A = [a_{ij}]$ is obtained by expanding the matrix by i-th row as:

$$|A| = a_{i1} C_{i1} + a_{i2}C_{i2} + \ldots + a_{in} C_{in}. \text{ A similar formula holds for columns.}$$

EXAMPLE 6   Compute the determinant of the matrix

$$A = \begin{bmatrix} -1 & 5 & 2 \\ 0 & -2 & 3 \\ 4 & 1 & -3 \end{bmatrix}$$

Solution: We expand the matrix by a row (column) that has largest number of zeros (why?). In this case, we can expand by the first column or second row. Let us expand by the first column.

$$|A| = (-1)C_{11} + (0)C_{21} + 4\,C_{31}$$

$$= (-1)^{1+1}\begin{vmatrix} -2 & 3 \\ 1 & -3 \end{vmatrix} + 0 + 4(-1)^{3+1}\begin{vmatrix} 5 & 2 \\ -2 & 3 \end{vmatrix}$$

$$= -(1)(6-3) + 4(1)(15-(-4)) = -3 + 76 = \mathbf{73}$$

C. The Effects of Row Operations on Determinants

Before we expand a matrix by any row (column) we can get zeros in a maximum number of its locations by using row operations. Let us first see the effect of each row operation on the value of the determinant of a matrix.

1. Consider the matrix $A = \begin{bmatrix} 1 & 5 \\ 3 & 7 \end{bmatrix}$. Its determinant $|A| = 7 - 15 = \mathbf{-8}$.

    Let us **interchange the rows** and see the effect on the value of the determinant.

    $$\begin{bmatrix} 1 & 5 \\ 3 & 7 \end{bmatrix} \xrightarrow{R_1 \leftrightarrow R_2} \begin{bmatrix} 3 & 7 \\ 1 & 5 \end{bmatrix} \text{ and } \begin{vmatrix} 3 & 7 \\ 1 & 5 \end{vmatrix} = 15 - 7 = \mathbf{8}.$$

    We observe that the sign of the determinant has changed.

    Therefore, interchanging rows in a matrix changes the sign of the value of the determinant.

2. Suppose we multiply a row of a matrix by a non zero number.

    $$\begin{bmatrix} 1 & 5 \\ 3 & 7 \end{bmatrix} \xrightarrow{2R_1} \begin{bmatrix} 2 & 10 \\ 3 & 7 \end{bmatrix}.$$

    The determinant of the new matrix is $\begin{vmatrix} 2 & 10 \\ 3 & 7 \end{vmatrix} = 2(7) - 3(10) = 14 - 30 = \mathbf{-16}$ and this is 2 times the

    original value (−8). **Therefore, if a row of a matrix is multiplied by a non zero number c, the determinant of the new matrix is c times the determinant of the original matrix.**

3. Finally, we check the effect of the row operation when a multiple of one row is added to another row.

    $$\begin{bmatrix} 1 & 5 \\ 3 & 7 \end{bmatrix} \xrightarrow{R_2 + (-3)R_1} \begin{bmatrix} 1 & 5 \\ 0 & -8 \end{bmatrix}.$$

    The determinant of the new matrix is given by: $\begin{vmatrix} 1 & 5 \\ 0 & -8 \end{vmatrix} = 1(-8) - 0(5) = -8$. The same value as

    of the original determinant.

    Therefore, adding a multiple of one row to another row does not change the value of the determinant. We summarize our results as follows.

Effect of Row operations on Determinants

Let A be $n \times n$ matrix.

1. If two rows in A are interchanged, then the determinant of the new matrix $= -|A|$.

2. If a row of A is multiplied by a non zero number c, then the determinant of the new matrix is $c|A|$.

3. If a multiple of a row of A is added to another row, then the determinant of the new matrix is $= |A|$.

We can use row operations to bring zeros to the maximum number of rows and then evaluate the determinant of the matrix by the cofactor method.

In the following example we demonstrate the use of row operations with the cofactor method.

EXAMPLE 7   Compute the determinant of $A = \begin{bmatrix} 1 & 0 & -1 & 2 \\ 0 & 3 & 1 & 5 \\ -2 & 1 & 4 & -1 \\ 3 & 2 & 0 & 1 \end{bmatrix}$.

Solution: Let us expand the matrix by the first column. First, we use row operations to bring zeros in all but $(1, 1)$ position of column 1.

$$A = \begin{bmatrix} 1 & 0 & -1 & 2 \\ 0 & 3 & 1 & 5 \\ -2 & 1 & 4 & -1 \\ 3 & 2 & 0 & 1 \end{bmatrix} \xrightarrow[R_4 + (-3)R_1]{R_3 + (2)R_1} \begin{bmatrix} 1 & 0 & -1 & 2 \\ 0 & 3 & 1 & 5 \\ 0 & 1 & 2 & 3 \\ 0 & 2 & 3 & -5 \end{bmatrix}$$

The value of determinant does not change under such row operations.

$$|A| = \begin{vmatrix} 1 & 0 & -1 & 2 \\ 0 & 3 & 1 & 5 \\ 0 & 1 & 2 & 3 \\ 0 & 2 & 3 & -5 \end{vmatrix} = 1(-1)^{1+1} \begin{vmatrix} 3 & 1 & 5 \\ 1 & 2 & 3 \\ 2 & 3 & -5 \end{vmatrix} = \begin{vmatrix} 3 & 1 & 5 \\ 1 & 2 & 3 \\ 2 & 3 & -5 \end{vmatrix}$$

We use row operations again to get two zeros in the first column.

$$\begin{bmatrix} 3 & 1 & 5 \\ 1 & 2 & 3 \\ 2 & 3 & -5 \end{bmatrix} \xrightarrow{R_1 \leftrightarrow R_2} \begin{bmatrix} 1 & 2 & 3 \\ 3 & 1 & 5 \\ 2 & 3 & -5 \end{bmatrix} \xrightarrow[R_3 + (-2)R_1]{R_2 + (-3)R_1} \begin{bmatrix} 1 & 2 & 3 \\ 0 & -5 & -4 \\ 0 & -1 & -11 \end{bmatrix}$$

The determinant of the new matrix is (-1) times the determinant of the old matrix because of the operation $R_1 \leftrightarrow R_2$ used on the matrix. Therefore,

$$|A| = \begin{vmatrix} 3 & 1 & 5 \\ 1 & 2 & 3 \\ 2 & 3 & -5 \end{vmatrix} = (-1) \begin{vmatrix} 1 & 2 & 3 \\ 0 & -5 & -4 \\ 0 & -1 & -11 \end{vmatrix}$$

$$= -1(1)(-1)^{1+1}(55 - 4)$$

$$= -1(1)(1)(51) = \mathbf{-51}$$

D. APPLICATIONS INVOLVING DETERMINANTS

1. Cramer's Rule for Solving Equations

Cramer's rule shows one of the applications of determinants in solving a system of linear equations. In order to write Cramer's rule in short, we introduce the following notations:

In a system of equations:

$$a_{11}x + a_{12}y + a_{13}z = b_1$$
$$a_{21}x + a_{22}y + a_{23}z = b_2$$
$$a_{31}x + a_{32}y + a_{33}z = b_3$$

the matrix of coefficients is denoted by: $A = \begin{bmatrix} a_{11} & a_{12} & a_{13} \\ a_{21} & a_{22} & a_{23} \\ a_{31} & a_{32} & a_{33} \end{bmatrix}$. Let $X = \begin{bmatrix} x \\ y \\ z \end{bmatrix}$ and $B = \begin{bmatrix} b_1 \\ b_2 \\ b_3 \end{bmatrix}$.

The system can be written as $AX = B$.

If the first column of A is replaced with the column of constants $\begin{bmatrix} b_1 \\ b_2 \\ b_3 \end{bmatrix}$ of the right side of the equations, then

we write

$$A_1 = \begin{bmatrix} b_1 & a_{12} & a_{13} \\ b_2 & a_{22} & a_{23} \\ b_3 & a_{32} & a_{33} \end{bmatrix}. \text{ Similarly, } A_2 = \begin{bmatrix} a_{11} & b_1 & a_{13} \\ a_{21} & b_2 & a_{23} \\ a_{31} & b_3 & a_{33} \end{bmatrix} \text{ and } A_3 = \begin{bmatrix} a_{11} & a_{12} & b_1 \\ a_{21} & a_{22} & b_2 \\ a_{31} & a_{32} & b_3 \end{bmatrix}.$$

The determinants of matrices A_1, A_2 and A_3 are used to find the solution of the system of equations as stated in the following rule.

Cramer's Rule

The solution of the system of equations is given by:

$$x = \frac{|A_1|}{|A|}, \quad y = \frac{|A_2|}{|A|}, \quad z = \frac{|A_3|}{|A|}, \text{ provided } |A| \neq 0.$$

EXAMPLE 8　　Solve the following system of equations:

$$2x - y + 3z = -6$$
$$x + y - 2z = 2$$
$$-3x + 2y - z = 6$$

Solution:　　We compute the values of $|A|$, $|A_1|$, $|A_2|$ and $|A_3|$, and use Cramer's rule to find the solution of the system.

$$|A| = \begin{vmatrix} 2 & -1 & 3 \\ 1 & 1 & -2 \\ -3 & 2 & -1 \end{vmatrix} = \mathbf{14}, \qquad |A_1| = \begin{vmatrix} -6 & -1 & 3 \\ 2 & 1 & -2 \\ 6 & 2 & -1 \end{vmatrix} = \mathbf{-14},$$

$$|A_2| = \begin{vmatrix} 2 & -6 & 3 \\ 1 & 2 & -2 \\ -3 & 6 & -1 \end{vmatrix} = \mathbf{14}, \quad \text{and} \quad |A_3| = \begin{vmatrix} 2 & -1 & -6 \\ 1 & 1 & 2 \\ -3 & 2 & 6 \end{vmatrix} = \mathbf{-14},$$

Therefore, $x = \dfrac{|A_1|}{|A|} = \dfrac{-14}{14} = -1$, $y = \dfrac{|A_2|}{|A|} = \dfrac{14}{14} = 1$, and $z = \dfrac{|A_3|}{|A|} = \dfrac{-14}{14} = -1$

2. **Area of a Triangle**

The determinants can also be used to find the area of a triangle whose vertices are at (x_1, y_1), (x_2, y_2), and (x_3, y_3).

Area of a Triangle

The area of a triangle with vertices (x_1, y_1), (x_2, y_2), and (x_3, y_3) is given by the determinant.

$\pm \dfrac{1}{2} \begin{vmatrix} x_1 & y_1 & 1 \\ x_2 & y_2 & 1 \\ x_3 & y_3 & 1 \end{vmatrix}$, where the sign is chosen so that the answer is positive.

EXAMPLE 9   Find the area of the triangle whose vertices are $(-2, 3)$, $(-5, -7)$ and $(10, 13)$.

Solution: The determinant that gives the area of the triangle is

$$\pm \frac{1}{2} \begin{vmatrix} -2 & 3 & 1 \\ -5 & -7 & 1 \\ 10 & 13 & 1 \end{vmatrix} \xrightarrow[R_3 + (-1)R_1]{R_2 + (-1)R_1} \pm \frac{1}{2} \begin{vmatrix} -2 & 3 & 1 \\ -3 & -10 & 0 \\ 12 & 10 & 0 \end{vmatrix} \quad \text{Expand by column 3.}$$

$$= \pm \frac{1}{2} (1)(-1)^{1+3} \begin{vmatrix} -3 & -10 \\ 12 & 10 \end{vmatrix}$$

$$= \pm \left(\frac{1}{2}\right) 1 (-1)^4 (-30 + 120)$$

$$= \frac{1}{2}(90) = \mathbf{45} \text{ square units.}$$

EXAMPLE 10   Prove using determinants that the three points $A(0, 2)$, $B(-3, 4)$, and $C(6, -2)$ are collinear.

Solution: The points A, B, and C are collinear if the area of the triangle ABC is zero.

Area of the triangle ABC

$$= \pm \frac{1}{2} \begin{bmatrix} 0 & 2 & 1 \\ -3 & 4 & 1 \\ 6 & -2 & 1 \end{bmatrix} \xrightarrow[R_3 + (-1)R_1]{R_2 + (-1)R_1} \pm \frac{1}{2} \begin{bmatrix} 0 & 2 & 1 \\ -3 & 2 & 0 \\ 6 & -4 & 0 \end{bmatrix}$$

Evaluate the determinant with respect to the last column.

$$\text{Area of the triangle} = \pm \frac{1}{2} \begin{bmatrix} 0 & 2 & 1 \\ -3 & 2 & 0 \\ 6 & -4 & 0 \end{bmatrix} = \pm \frac{1}{2} [1 \cdot C_{13}]$$

$$= \pm \frac{1}{2} [12 - 12] = \pm \frac{1}{2} (0) = \mathbf{0}$$

Therefore the three points are collinear.

EXERCISE 7.8

In exercises (1-5), compute the determinant of the 2×2 matrix.

1. $\begin{bmatrix} 5 & 2 \\ 9 & 7 \end{bmatrix}$ 2. $\begin{bmatrix} -1 & 0 \\ 5 & 10 \end{bmatrix}$ 3. $\begin{bmatrix} 2 & 3 \\ 4 & 6 \end{bmatrix}$ 4. $\begin{bmatrix} 5 & -9 \\ 2 & 1 \end{bmatrix}$ 5. $\begin{bmatrix} 1 & 0 \\ 0 & 9 \end{bmatrix}$

In exercises (6-9), use the special method to compute the determinant of 3×3 matrix.

6. $\begin{bmatrix} -1 & 0 & 2 \\ 3 & 5 & 9 \\ 1 & 2 & 5 \end{bmatrix}$ 7. $\begin{bmatrix} 2 & -1 & 3 \\ -3 & 2 & 5 \\ 4 & 0 & 7 \end{bmatrix}$ 8. $\begin{bmatrix} 7 & -3 & 0 \\ 2 & 1 & 4 \\ -1 & 0 & 5 \end{bmatrix}$ 9. $\begin{bmatrix} 1 & 1 & 1 \\ 2 & -2 & 3 \\ 4 & 1 & 0 \end{bmatrix}$

In exercises (10-17), compute the determinant.

10. $\begin{bmatrix} 5 & -1 & 0 \\ 2 & 1 & 7 \\ -1 & 0 & 1 \end{bmatrix}$ 11. $\begin{bmatrix} -1 & 2 & -1 \\ 3 & -1 & 3 \\ 0 & 5 & 2 \end{bmatrix}$ 12. $\begin{bmatrix} 0 & 1 & 5 \\ 7 & 2 & -3 \\ 9 & -1 & -5 \end{bmatrix}$ 13. $\begin{bmatrix} 1 & 5 & -7 \\ 2 & 0 & 2 \\ 1 & 0 & -3 \end{bmatrix}$

14. $\begin{bmatrix} 5 & 0 & 0 \\ 2 & 1 & 5 \\ 1 & 1 & -3 \end{bmatrix}$ 15. $\begin{bmatrix} 10 & 0 & 0 \\ 0 & -5 & 0 \\ 0 & 0 & -1 \end{bmatrix}$ 16. $\begin{bmatrix} 2 & -1 & 5 & 3 \\ -1 & 0 & 7 & -2 \\ 3 & 1 & -2 & 1 \\ 1 & 2 & -1 & 0 \end{bmatrix}$ 17. $\begin{bmatrix} 1 & -1 & 1 & -1 \\ 2 & 1 & -1 & 2 \\ -3 & 0 & 1 & -1 \\ 4 & -1 & 0 & 2 \end{bmatrix}$

In exercises (18-28), use Cramer's rule to solve the system of equations.

18. $3x - 2y = -7$
$4x + 5y = 6$

19. $2x - 5y = -9$
$3x + y = -5$

20. $x - 3y = -8$
$2x + 4y = 4$

21. $7x - 3y = 38$
$2x + y = 9$

22. $4x + 5y = -11$
$3x - 7y = -19$

23. $x - 2y + z = -5$
$2x + y - z = -2$
$3x + 2y + 3z = -7$

24. $2x + 3y - 5z = -17$
$-x + 2y + z = 4$
$3x - y + 2z = 3$

25. $5x - 2y - 4z = 8$
$x + 3z = 5$
$2y + 7z = 5$

26. $4x - 3y - z = -4$
$2x + y + 2z = -7$
$3x - y = -4$

27. $x + y - z = -3$
$-x + y + 2z = 0$
$3x - 2y + 3z = 7$

28. $x - y + z - w = -1$
$2x + y - z + 3w = 8$
$3x - 2y + 3z + w = 4$
$-4x + y - 2z + 2w = 1$

In exercises (29-30), find the area of the triangle whose vertices are given.

29. $(-2, 3)$, $(-1, 5)$, $(3, 7)$ 30. $(-1, -1)$, $(0, 7)$, $(-5, 9)$

Writing Exercises

31. Explain the effects of row operations on determinant. Give examples.

32. Explain the Cramer's Rule of Solving a system of equations.

33. What is the determinant of

    (a) an identity matrix   **(b)** a diagonal matrix   **(c)** a triangular matrix

    Explain with examples.

34. Use row-operations to solve

$$a_{11}x_1 + a_{12}x_2 + a_{13}x_3 = b_1$$
$$a_{21}x_1 + a_{22}x_2 + a_{23}x_3 = b_2$$
$$a_{31}x_1 + a_{32}x_2 + a_{33}x_3 = b_3$$

for x_1. Show that this agrees with the general formula for $x_1 = \dfrac{|A_1|}{|A|}$ in Cramer's Rule.

35. Let the vertices of a triangle be (x_1, y_1), (x_2, y_2), and (x_3, y_3) where $y_1 = y_2$. Find a formula for the area the triangle and show that this agrees with the determinant formula for this special case.

7.9 CHAPTER SUMMARY

1. A system of equations can have a **unique** solution, **no solution,** or **infinitely many** solutions.

2. Algebraically, we can solve a system by elimination using **addition,** or by elimination using **substitution.**

3. A contradiction of the form "0 = non-zero number" implies that the system is an **inconsistent** system.

4. The universal truth of the form "0 = 0" indicates that the system has many solutions. Such a system is called **dependent** system.

5. The solutions of a system of non-linear equations give the points of intersection of the graphs represented by the equations.

6. If we write the coefficients of the variables of equations written in the standard form in rows and columns, we get an array of numbers called the **matrix of coefficients.**

7. Each number in the array is called an entry of the matrix.

8. The **Gauss-Jordan method** attempts to transform the matrix of coefficients to the identity matrix.

9. The size of a matrix is indicated by its **dimension.**

10. The dimension of a matrix is written as (number of rows) × (number of columns).

11. If the number of rows in a matrix is the same as the number of columns, the matrix is called a **square** matrix.

12. A matrix with only one row is called a **row matrix.**

13. A matrix with only one column is called a **column matrix**.

14. A square matrix with its non zero entries only along the principal diagonal is called a **diagonal matrix.**

15. A diagonal matrix that has all diagonal entries 1's called an **identity matrix.**

16. Two matrices are equal if they are of the same dimensions and if corresponding entries are equal.

17. The **sum** of two matrices A and B is defined as the matrix obtained by taking the sum of the corresponding entries of A and B. The **difference** of two matrices is defined as the matrix obtained by taking the difference of the corresponding entries of A and B.

18. The **additive inverse** of a matrix A is the matrix $-A$ in which each entry is the additive inverse of the corresponding entry of A.

19. If 0 is the $m \times n$ zero matrix (a matrix with all entries zeros) and A is any $m \times n$ matrix then $0 + A = A + 0 = A$.

20. The **product** of a **scalar** (a number) c and a **matrix** A is the matrix whose entries are c times the corresponding entries in A and is written as cA.

21. A row times a column (with the same number of entries in each) is the number obtained by adding the products of the corresponding entries.

22. A matrix A of dimension $m \times r$ times a matrix B of dimensions $r \times n$ is a matrix of dimension $m \times n$ whose (i, j) entry is the i-th row of A times the j-th column of B.

23. The product of two matrices is defined only if the number of columns of the first matrix is equal to the number of rows of the second matrix.

$$A_{m \times r} \, B_{r \times n} = C_{m \times n}$$

24. The addition of matrices is **commutative**. However, the subtraction and product are **not** commutative.

25. The product of any square matrix A with the identity matrix of the same dimension is A.

$$AI = IA = A,$$

I is of suitable size or $\quad AI_{m \times m} = I_{m \times m} A = A$ if A is $m \times m$.

26. The matrix B is called the **inverse** of a square matrix A if and only if $AB = BA = I$.

We write: $B = A^{-1}$.

27. A matrix that does not have the inverse is called a **singular matrix.**

28. If $A = \begin{bmatrix} a & b \\ c & d \end{bmatrix}$, then $A^{-1} = \dfrac{1}{ad-bc} \begin{bmatrix} d & -b \\ -c & a \end{bmatrix}$.

29. To find the inverse of an $n \times n$ matrix A, start with $[A \,|\, I]$, where I is the identity matrix of the same dimension as A. With row operations we transform $[A \,|\, I]$ into the matrix $[I/B]$. Then the matrix B is the inverse of matrix A or $B = A^{-1}$.

30. A matrix with a row (column) of zeros has no inverse.

31. The determinant of a 2×2 matrix $A = \begin{bmatrix} a & b \\ c & d \end{bmatrix}$ is given by $|A| = \begin{vmatrix} a & b \\ c & d \end{vmatrix} = ad - bc$.

32. A special method of finding the determinant of a 3×3 matrix is

$$\begin{vmatrix} a_{11} & a_{12} & a_{13} \\ a_{21} & a_{22} & a_{23} \\ a_{31} & a_{32} & a_{33} \end{vmatrix} \begin{matrix} a_{11} & a_{12} \\ a_{21} & a_{22} \\ a_{31} & a_{32} \end{matrix}$$

$$= [a_{11}a_{22}a_{33} + a_{12}a_{23}a_{31} + a_{13}a_{21}a_{32}] - [a_{13}a_{22}a_{31} + a_{11}a_{23}a_{32} + a_{12}a_{21}a_{33}]$$

33. The cofactor C_{ij} of the element in (i, j)th position of the matrix A is

$C_{ij} = (-1)^{i+j}$ det (matrix obtained by deleting the i-th row and the j-th column of A).

34. The determinant of a $n \times n$ matrix $A = \begin{bmatrix} a_{ij} \end{bmatrix}$ is obtained by expanding the matrix by its i-th row as $|A| = a_{i1}C_{i1} + a_{i2}C_{i2} + \ldots + a_{in}C_{in}$ or by its i-th column.

35. If two rows of A are interchanged, then the determinant of the new matrix is $= -|A|$.

36. If a row of A is multiplied by a non-zero number c, then the determinant of the new matrix $= c|A|$.

37. If a multiple of a row of A is added to another row of A, the determinant of the new matrix $= |A|$.

38. Consider a system of equations in matrix form $AX = B$, where $X = \begin{vmatrix} x_1 \\ x_2 \\ \vdots \\ x_n \end{vmatrix}$ and $B = \begin{vmatrix} b_1 \\ \vdots \\ b_n \end{vmatrix}$. If

A_i is the matrix in which i-th column has been replaced with the column of constants B of the system

of equations, then Cramer's rule gives $x_1 = \dfrac{|A_1|}{|A|}$, $x_2 = \dfrac{|A_2|}{|A|}$, ...

39. The area of a triangle whose vertices are (x_1, y_1), (x_2, y_2), and (x_3, y_3) is $\pm \dfrac{1}{2} \begin{vmatrix} x_1 & y_1 & 1 \\ x_2 & y_2 & 1 \\ x_3 & y_3 & 1 \end{vmatrix}$.

40. Three points (x_1, y_1), (x_2, y_2), (x_3, y_3) are collinear if $\begin{vmatrix} x_1 & y_1 & 1 \\ x_2 & y_2 & 1 \\ x_3 & y_3 & 1 \end{vmatrix} = 0$.

7.10 CHAPTER REVIEW

In exercises (1-4), solve the system algebraically using elimination by addition or substitution.

1. $5x - 8y = 18$
$7x + 9y = 5$

2. $y = 7x - 5$
$2x + 3y = 7$

3. $\frac{2}{5}x - \frac{3}{10}y = 1$
$3x + 2y = -1$

4. $0.25x + .5y = 5$
$1.5x - .2y = 14$

5. A farmer has 1000 acres of land for cultivating soybeans and corn. The cost of planting and cultivating soybeans and corn is $60 and $30, respectively. If the farmer has only $42,000 available one season and wishes to use all of his land and money, how many acres of each crop should he plant?

In exercises (6-16), solve the system using Gauss Jordan Method. If the system is dependent, write the solution in terms of z.

6. $x + 2y + 3z = 0$
$2x + 3y + 2z = 3$
$-x + y + 2z = -2$

7. $x + 2y - 3z = -5$
$-2x + 2y + z = -6$
$3x - 2y + 8z = 27$

8. $x + 2y + 3z = 2$
$2x - y + z = 3$
$3x + y + 4z = 1$

9. $x + 2y + 3z = 2$
$2x - y + z = 4$
$3x + y + 4z = 6$

10. $3x - y = -5$
$2x + 5y = -9$

11. $8x - 4y = 20$
$7x + 3y = 37$

12. $x + y + z = 0$
$2x - y + z = 1$
$-x + y + 2z = -3$

13. $x - 3y + 2z = 5$
$2x + y - z = 2$
$-3x + 2y - z = -1$

14. $x + 3y + z = -4$
$2x + 6y + 4z = 8$
$3x + 9y + 5z = 0$

15. $x + 3y + z = 0$
$2x + 4y + 6z = 1$
$3x + 7y + 7z = 1$

16. $-x + 2y + z = -7$
$2x - 3y + 2z = 6$
$x + 3z = 7$

17. Jack invested $4000 in two accounts. One pays simple interest at the rate of 5% and the other pays simple interest at the rate of 6%. If Jack earned a total of $224 in interest in the first year, how much did he invest in each account?

18. Sue invested $25,000 in three accounts paying simple interest at the rates 5%, 6% and 8%. If her investment at 6% was twice as much as at 5% and the total annual interest earned was $1,720, find how much money did she put in each account?

In exercises (19-20), use the matrices A, B, and C to find the matrix of the given expression.

$$A = \begin{bmatrix} 1 & 5 \\ 2 & 3 \\ 4 & 9 \end{bmatrix}, \quad B = \begin{bmatrix} 1 & -1 & 2 \\ 5 & -2 & 2 \end{bmatrix}, \quad C = \begin{bmatrix} 11 & -10 \\ 8 & 6 \end{bmatrix}$$

19. AB

20. $BA + 3C$

21. The Stuffed - Stuff Company manufactures stuffed animals - bears, pandas, and rabbits at two locations I and II. At location I, 300 bears, 500 pandas, and 1000 rabbits are to be manufactured. At location II, the corresponding numbers are 400, 600 and 500, respectively. Each bear needs 2 units of fabric, 5 units of stuffing and 3 units of trim. Each panda needs 3 units of fabric, 7 units of stuffing, and 4 units of trim. Each rabbit uses 3 units of fabric, 8 units of stuffing, and 4 units of trim.

The fabric costs $2 per unit, the stuffing costs $ 0.20 per unit, and the trim costs $1 per unit.

a. How much of each material is needed at each location?

b. What is the total cost at each location?

In exercises (22-24), use the Cramer's rule to solve the system of equations.

22. $2x + y + z = 7$
$3x + 2y + z = 9$
$2x + y + 2z = 9$

23. $x + 2y + 3z = 2$
$2x + y + 2z = 4$
$3x + 3y + 5z = 2$

24. $x - y + 3z = -4$
$2x + y + 2z = -5$
$-2x - 2y + z = -1$

In exercises (25-26), solve the system of equations.

25. $3x - y = 4, \quad x^2 - x - y = 1$ **26.** $2x + y = 5, \quad x^2 + y^2 - 2x = 1$

27. The sales (S) in millions of a company are recorded as follows:

Year	1990	1991	1992	1993	1994
Sale(s)	0.7	0.3	0.7	1.9	3.9

Estimate a formula for the sales (S) function in terms of the number (x) of years after 1990.

28. Change the parametric representation into a relation in x and y. $x = 2\sqrt{t}, \quad y = \sqrt{4-t}$.

7.11 CHAPTER TEST

1. Use elimination by addition or substitution to solve the system $\quad 2x - 3y = 7$
$$3x + 5y = 1$$

2. Use the Gauss-Jordan method to solve the system
$$x + 3y + 3z = -4$$
$$2x - y + 3z = 10$$
$$3x + 2y - z = -1$$

3. Solve the system of equations by using Cramer's rule
$$x - 2y + 3z = 9$$
$$2x + y + z = 3$$
$$3x - 4y + 2z = 11$$

4. Solve the system of equations: $y^2 - 2x = 0$ and $x - y = 4$

5. Estimate a second degree formula that fits into the following numerical form of the function $f(x)$.

x	0	1	2	3	4
$f(x)$	4	5	10	19	32

6. A patient on a special diet must consume 26 grams of protein and 80 grams of carbohydrates daily. The patient's meal consist of two major foods, food A and B. Each ounce of food A contains 10 grams of protein and 18 grams of carbohydrates. Each ounce of food B contains 4 grams of protein and 1 gram of carbohydrates. How many ounces of each food should the patient consume so that he receives his daily requirements of protein and carbohydrates?

7. If $A = \begin{bmatrix} 2 & -1 & 3 \\ 5 & 0 & 4 \end{bmatrix}$, $B = \begin{bmatrix} 1 & -1 \\ 3 & 2 \\ -1 & 4 \end{bmatrix}$, and $C = \begin{bmatrix} 5 & 7 \\ 12 & 8 \end{bmatrix}$, find $AB + 2C$.

8. Find the inverse of the matrix $\begin{bmatrix} 1 & 1 & 1 \\ 4 & 5 & 0 \\ 0 & 1 & -3 \end{bmatrix}$.

9. Transform the pair of parametric equations to a relation in x and y.
$$x = 5 \cos t, \quad y = 3 \sin t.$$

Sequences, Series, and Binomial Expansion

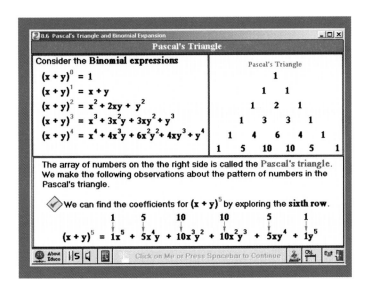

8.6 Pascal's Triangle and Binomial Expansion

Pascal's Triangle

Consider the Binomial expressions

$(x + y)^0 = 1$

$(x + y)^1 = x + y$

$(x + y)^2 = x^2 + 2xy + y^2$

$(x + y)^3 = x^3 + 3x^2y + 3xy^2 + y^3$

$(x + y)^4 = x^4 + 4x^3y + 6x^2y^2 + 4xy^3 + y^4$

Pascal's Triangle

```
          1
        1   1
      1   2   1
    1   3   3   1
  1   4   6   4   1
1   5  10  10   5   1
```

The array of numbers on the the right side is called the Pascal's triangle. We make the following observations about the pattern of numbers in the Pascal's triangle.

We can find the coefficients for $(x + y)^5$ by exploring the **sixth row**.

$$1 \quad 5 \quad 10 \quad 10 \quad 5 \quad 1$$

$(x + y)^5 = 1x^5 + 5x^4y + 10x^3y^2 + 10x^2y^3 + 5xy^4 + 1y^5$

About Educo | | S | | | Click on Me or Press Spacebar to Continue | | Obj. | Exit

8

SEQUENCES, SERIES, AND BINOMIAL EXPANSION

Sequences are collections of numbers or objects where the order or the position of the objects is well defined. Sequences can be finite or infinite. Sequences whose terms follow some pattern are of special interest. Arithmetic and geometric sequences are two such types of sequences. A series is the sum of the terms of a sequence.

The discussion in this chapter is divided into six sections.

8.1   *Sequences;*

8.2   *Arithmetic sequences;*

8.3   *Geometric sequences;*

8.4   *Arithmetic series;*

8.5   *Geometric series; and*

8.6   *Pascal's Triangle and Binomial Theorem.*

8.1 SEQUENCES

Introduction

We come across sequences of numbers in several situations.

For example

1. The number of touch downs per hour at Atlanta airport between 8:00 am and 4:00 pm on Monday:

   34, 35, 41, 40, 12, 18, 37, 25

2. The amount of decaying matter left at each stage in the decaying process in an experiment:

   $1, \dfrac{1}{2}, \dfrac{1}{4}, \dfrac{1}{8}, \cdots$

3. Even numbers written in increasing order: 2, 4, 6, 8, 10, …

4. A Fibonacci sequence where the first two numbers are each equal to one, and after that each number is a sum of the preceding two numbers:

   1, 1, 2, 3, 5, 8, 13, …

We will discuss several other types of sequences.

> **Objectives** ▶ ▶
>
> In this section you will learn about:
>
> A. Finite and infinite sequences;
>
> B. Identifying patterns for the terms of a sequence; and
>
> C. Sequence as a function.

A. FINITE AND INFINITE SEQUENCES

A sequence is classified according to the number of terms it has.

Finite Sequence: A sequence is **finite** if it has finite number of terms (members).

For example,

1. The sequence 5, 10, 15, 20, 25, 30 has only six terms.

2. The sequence of touch-downs per hour at Atlanta airport given earlier is a finite sequence. It has eight terms :

$$34, 35, 41, 40, 12, 18, 37, 25.$$

Infinite Sequence: A sequence is **infinite** if it has infinite number of terms (members).

For example,

3. The sequence 5, 10, 15, 20, 25, 30, … has unlimited number of terms.

4. The sequence $1, \dfrac{1}{2}, \dfrac{1}{4}, \dfrac{1}{8}, \ldots$ has infinite number of terms.

5. The Fibonacci sequence 1, 1, 2, 3, 5, 8, 11, is infinite.

   Observe how we write finite and infinite sequences :

Finite sequence	**Infinite sequence**
5, 10, 15, 20, 25, 30	5, 10, 15, 20, 25, 30, …
The last term is 30	There is no last term.

B. IDENTIFYING PATTERNS FOR THE TERMS OF A SEQUENCE

It is impossible to list all terms of an infinite sequence. Terms of an infinite sequence must have some pattern. Knowing the pattern helps us to determine the subsequent terms.

Notation : We write the first few terms until the pattern is clear. Ellipsis (…) are inserted to denote the continuation of the terms in that pattern. If the sequence is finite then we write the last term at the end.

In this notation

1. Finite sequence 5, 10, 15, 20, 25, 30 may also be written as 5, 10, 15, …, 30.
2. Infinite sequence 5, 10, 15, 20, 25, 30, … is already written in the notation described above. Each term of a sequence has a place associated with it. Thus, in the sequence 5, 10, 15, 20, 25, 30, …

   The first term = 5, second term = 10, third term = 15, fourth term = 20, fifth term = 25 and so on.

Notation : Terms of a sequence will be named as a_1, a_2, a_3, etc. In general nth term of a sequence will be named as a_n.

EXAMPLE 1   Identify a pattern for the terms of the sequence
5, 10, 15, 20, 25, 30, …

Solution:

Step 1   Observe the first few terms carefully. First four terms of the given sequence are 5, 10, 15, and 20.

Step 2   Decide on a pattern or a formula which gives these terms. Observe that each subsequent term is 5 more than the preceding term.

Step 3   Check your pattern on the remaining terms. The pattern is the same. The next unlisted two terms are 35 and 40.

EXAMPLE 2   Identify a pattern for the sequence $1, \dfrac{1}{2}, \dfrac{1}{4}, \dfrac{1}{8}, \dfrac{1}{16}, \cdots$

Solution:

Step 1   First few terms of the sequence are $1, \dfrac{1}{2}, \dfrac{1}{4}, \dfrac{1}{8}$, and $\dfrac{1}{16}$.

Step 2   Here first term is 1, second term is $\dfrac{1}{2}$, third term is $\dfrac{1}{4}$, and fourth term is $\dfrac{1}{8}$.

Notice that the denominators of terms are 1, 2, 4, and 8. These are various powers of 2 $\left(2^0, 2^1, 2^2, 2^3 \ldots\right)$.

The last listed term is $\dfrac{1}{16}$ or $\dfrac{1}{2^4}$. The next term is $\dfrac{1}{2^5}$ or $\dfrac{1}{32}$ and so on.

Thus $a_1 = \dfrac{1}{2^0}$, $a_2 = \dfrac{1}{2^1}$, $a_3 = \dfrac{1}{2^2}$, and $a_4 = \dfrac{1}{2^3}$.

It follows that nth term is a reciprocal of $(n-1)^{\text{th}}$ power of 2, or $a^n = \dfrac{1}{2^{n-1}}$.

Step 3   Fifth term is $\dfrac{1}{16}$. From the pattern $a_5 = \dfrac{1}{2^{5-1}} = \dfrac{1}{2^4} = \dfrac{1}{16}$.

C. SEQUENCE AS A FUNCTION

A sequence can be defined as a function.

Definition :   A sequence is a function whose domain consists of consecutive positive integers.

    a.   Domain of an infinite sequence is the set of all positive integers.

    b.   If a finite sequence has n terms then its domain consists of first n positive integers.

To write a sequence as a function

> **Step 1**   Identify a pattern for successive terms of the sequence.
>
> **Step 2**   Using this pattern, express the nth term a_n in the form of a formula in n.
>
> **Step 3**   Then the sequence can be written in function form as $f(n) = a_n$.

EXAMPLE 3   Write the sequence $1, \dfrac{1}{2}, \dfrac{1}{4}, \dfrac{1}{8}, \ldots$ in the function form.

Solution:

    Step 1   In Example 2, we identified a pattern for the sequence where the nth term is a reciprocal of $(n-1)^{\text{th}}$ power of 2.

    Step 2 $a_n = \dfrac{1}{2^{n-1}}$

    Step 3   Since this sequence is infinite, its domain is the set of all positive integers and in the function form this sequence is written as $\boldsymbol{f(n) = \dfrac{1}{2^{n-1}}}$.

EXAMPLE 4   Write in the function form the sequence $-3, -1, 1, 3, 5, 7, \ldots$.

Solution:

    Step 1   Here, first term $= -3$,   second term $= -1$,

                 third term $= 1$,   fourth term $= 3$, and so on.

                 As we look for a pattern, we find that the difference between two consecutive terms is 2. Thus, these terms can be rewritten as

                 1st   term $= -3 = -3 + 2(\mathbf{0}) = -3 + 2(\mathbf{1} - 1)$

                 2nd   term $= -1 = -3 + 2(\mathbf{1}) = -3 + 2(\mathbf{2} - 1)$

                 3rd   term $= 1 \;\; = -3 + 2(\mathbf{2}) = -3 + 2(\mathbf{3} - 1)$

                 4th   term $= 3 \;\; = -3 + 2(\mathbf{3}) = -3 + 2(\mathbf{4} - 1)$

    Step 2   Using the above pattern we get :

             1   2   3   4... n...

           $\downarrow$ $\downarrow$ $\downarrow$ $\downarrow$ $\downarrow$

    $-3 + 2(1 - 1)$ $-3 + 2(2 - 1)$ $-3 + 2(3 - 1)$ $-3 + 2(4 - 1)$ $-3 + 2(n - 1)$

                 Therefore, the general term is $\boldsymbol{a_n = -3 + 2(n - 1)}$.

    Step 3   In the function form we can rewrite the sequence as

                 $f(n) = -3 + 2(n - 1)$ or $\boldsymbol{f(n) = 2n - 5}$.

EXAMPLE 5   Write the first seven terms of sequence $f(n) = \dfrac{(-1)^n \, 2n}{3n - 1}$.

Solution: The nth term a_n is the same as $f(n)$.

Therefore, $a_n = (-1)^n \dfrac{2n}{3n - 1}$

$a_1 = \dfrac{(-1)^1 2(1)}{3(1) - 1} = \dfrac{-2}{2} = -1$ Substitute $n = 1$

$a_2 = \dfrac{(-1)^2 2(2)}{3(2) - 1} = \dfrac{4}{5}$ Substitute $n = 2$

$a_3 = \dfrac{(-1)^3 2(3)}{3(3) - 1} = -\dfrac{3}{4}$, $a_4 = \dfrac{(-1)^4 2(4)}{3(4) - 1} = \dfrac{8}{11}$, $a_5 = \dfrac{(-1)^5 2(5)}{3(5) - 1} = -\dfrac{5}{7}$

$a_6 = \dfrac{(-1)^6 2(6)}{3(6) - 1} = \dfrac{12}{17}$, $a_7 = \dfrac{(-1)^7 2(7)}{3(7) - 1} = -\dfrac{7}{10}$

It is difficult to identify the pattern of terms of this sequence.

EXAMPLE 6   A machine depreciates by one-fifth of its value each year. If the cost of the new machine is $5,000 then

   a.   What is the value of the machine at the end of the first year ?

   b.   Write a sequence of 5 terms representing value of the machine at the end of each successive year.

   c.   What is the value of the machine at the end of five years?

Solutions: **a.**   Depreciation during the first year $= 5000 \times \dfrac{1}{5}$

Value of the machine at the end of the first year

$= 5000 - 5000 \cdot \dfrac{1}{5} = 5000\left(1 - \dfrac{1}{5}\right) = 5000 \times \dfrac{4}{5} = \$4,000$

   b.   Value of the machine at the end of the second year $= 4000 \times \dfrac{4}{5} = \$3,200.00$

Value of the machine at the end of the third year $= 3200 \times \dfrac{4}{5} = \$2,560.00$

Value of the machine at the end of the fourth year $= 2560 \times \dfrac{4}{5} = \$2,048.00$

Value of the machine at the end of the fifth year $= 2048 \times \dfrac{4}{5} = \$1,638.40$

The required sequence of five terms is 4000, 3200, 2560, 2048, and 1638.40

   c.   Value of the machine at the end of five years $= \$ 1,638.40$.

EXERCISE 8.1

In exercises (1-6), identify a pattern for the terms of the sequence and write next four terms.

1. $2, 5, 8, 11, \ldots$

2. $10, 8, 6, 4, \ldots$

3. $3, 8, 13, 18, 23, \ldots$

4. $2, -4, 8, -16, \ldots$

5. $1, 3, 9, 27, \ldots$

6. $4, 2, 1, \dfrac{1}{2}, \ldots$

In exercises (7-16), determine the indicated terms of the sequence whose first few terms are given.

7. $1, 3, 5, 7, \ldots$; fifth term

8. $1, -1, 2, -2, 3, -3, \ldots$; ninth term

9. $1, 0, 1, 0, 0, 1, 0, 0, 0, 1, \ldots$; eighteenth term

10. $-2, 1, 4, 7, \ldots$; eighth term

11. $1, -\dfrac{1}{2}, \dfrac{1}{4}, -\dfrac{1}{8}, \dfrac{1}{16}, \ldots$; tenth term

12. $2, 6, 18, 54, \ldots$; seventh term

13. $1, 3, 8, 16, 27, \ldots$; seventh term

14. $1, 3, 7, 15, 31, \ldots$; seventh term

15. $1, -2, -5, -8, \ldots$; eighth term

16. $\dfrac{1}{3}, \dfrac{2}{9}, \dfrac{4}{27}, \ldots$; eighth term

In exercises (17-22), write each sequence in function form.

17. $1, \dfrac{1}{4}, \dfrac{1}{16}, \dfrac{1}{64}, \ldots$

18. $3, 6, 12, 24, \ldots, 384$

19. $5, 8, 11, 14, 17, \ldots, 32$

20. $-6, -1, 4, 9, 14, 19, \ldots$

21. $2, -2, 2, -2, \ldots$

22. $5, -10, 15, -20, \ldots$

8.2 ARITHMETIC SEQUENCES

Objectives ▶ ▶

In this section you will learn about:

A. Definition of an arithmetic sequence;

B. General term of an arithmetic sequence;

C. Arithmetic means; and

D. Graph of an arithmetic sequence.

We know that some sequences have patterns while others do not. If we know that pattern, we can find the terms that are not listed. For example, consider the sequence 10, 25, 40, 55, 70, 85, …

The pattern suggests that the difference between two consecutive terms is 15. Therefore, the next term of the sequence is 85 + 15 = 100. A sequence of this type is an example of an arithmetic sequence.

A. DEFINITION OF AN ARITHMETIC SEQUENCE

A sequence in which the **difference between any two consecutive terms is a constant (same number)** is called an **Arithmetic Sequence** (Progression). The **common difference** is generally represented by the letter d.

Thus the sequence $a_1, a_2, a_3, a_4, a_5, a_6, \ldots, a_n, \ldots$

is an arithmetic sequence if $(a_2 - a_1) = (a_3 - a_2) = \ldots = (a_{n+1} - a_n) = \ldots$

For example,

a. 5,   9,   13,   17,   21, … is an arithmetic sequence.

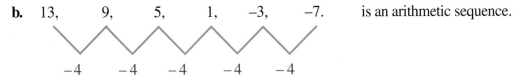

4   4   4   4

The common difference is 4.

b. 13,   9,   5,   1,   −3,   −7.   is an arithmetic sequence.

−4   −4   −4   −4   −4

The common difference is − 4.

B. General term of an Arithmetic Sequence

It is possible to determine the unknown (unlisted) members of a sequence if the sequence has a definite pattern. Since arithmetic sequence has a definite pattern, we can find a formula which gives various terms of an arithmetic sequence.

Suppose we want to find the 10th term of the sequence:

$$11, 14, 17, 20, \dots$$

This sequence is certainly arithmetic (why?). Here d, the common difference = 3.

We can determine 10th term a_{10} by listing each successive term as follows.

a_1 a_2 a_3 a_4 … a_{10}

11   14   17   20

+   +   +

3   3   3

Verify that the 10th term = 38

$$\boxed{11, \ 14, \ 17, \ 20, \ 23, \ 26, \ 29, \ 32, \ 35, \ 38}$$

But if we had to determine a_{100}, or a_{1000} the above method will be very time consuming. So we need a formula for the nth term a_n. Consider the arithmetic sequence,

11, 14, 17, 20, …

Here a_1 = 11
a_2 = 14 = 11 + 3
a_3 = 17 = 11 + 6
a_4 = 20 = 11 + 9
…   …
…   …

We may rewrite these terms using the pattern as ,

$$a_1 = 11 + 0(3) = 11 + (\mathbf{1} - 1)3$$
$$a_2 = 11 + 1(3) = 11 + (\mathbf{2} - 1)3$$
$$a_3 = 11 + 2(3) = 11 + (\mathbf{3} - 1)3$$
$$a_4 = 11 + 3(3) = 11 + (\mathbf{4} - 1)3$$

Continuing this pattern,

$$a_{10} = 11 + (\mathbf{10} - 1)3 = 11 + 9(3)$$
$$= 11 + 27 = 38$$

Thus to get **tenth** term of an arithmetic sequence we add **nine** times the common difference to the first term. Generalizing this pattern we get the formula for the nth term.

$$a_n = 11 \quad + \quad (n - 1)3$$

first term   common difference

Formula for the nth term of an arithmetic sequence:

For an arithmetic sequence with **first** term a_1 and **common difference** d, the general term or the nth term a_n is given by

$$\boxed{a_n = a_1 + (n - 1)d}$$

● Note   Arithmetic sequence with common difference zero is a constant sequence, for example 2, 2, 2, 2, ...

EXAMPLE 1   Which of the following sequences is arithmetic ?

        a. $5, 2, -1, -4, -7, -10, \ldots$ **b.** $3, 7, 11, 16, 21, 25, \ldots$

Solution: Recall $a_1, a_2, a_3, \ldots$ is an arithmetic sequence if $(a_2 - a_1) = (a_3 - a_2) = (a_4 - a_3) = (a_5 - a_4) = \ldots$

    a. $a_1 = 5, a_2 = 2, a_3 = -1, a_4 = -4, a_5 = -7, a_6 = -10$

        $a_2 - a_1 = 2 - 5 = \mathbf{-3}$; $a_3 - a_2 = -1 - 2 = \mathbf{-3}$

        $a_4 - a_3 = -4 - (-1) = \mathbf{-3}$; $a_5 - a_4 = -7 - (-4) = \mathbf{-3}$

        We observe that the given sequence is arithmetic with $\mathbf{-3}$ as the common difference.

    b. $a_1 = 3, a_2 = 7, a_3 = 11, a_4 = 16, a_5 = 21, a_6 = 25$

        Here $a_2 - a_1 = 4, a_3 - a_2 = 4, a_4 - a_3 = 5 , a_5 - a_4 = 5$

        Since the difference between consecutive terms is not always the same, this is not an arithmetic sequence.

EXAMPLE 2   Find the general term of the arithmetic sequence:

        $-7, -2, 3, 8, \ldots$

Solution: Here,

        $a_1 = -7, \quad$ and $\quad \mathbf{d} = -2 - (-7) = 5$

Therefore,

$$a_n = a_1 + (n-1)d = -7 + (n-1)5$$
$$= -7 + 5n - 5 = 5n - 12$$

EXAMPLE 3   Find 136th term of the arithmetic sequence whose first term is -12 and the common difference is $\frac{1}{3}$.

Solution: Here, $a_1 = -12$ and $d = \frac{1}{3}$

Therefore, $\quad a_n = -12 + (n-1) \cdot \frac{1}{3} = -12 + \frac{n-1}{3}$

Substituting $\quad n = 136$, we get

$$a_{136} = -12 + \frac{136-1}{3}$$

$$= -12 + \frac{135}{3} = -12 + 45 = 33$$

EXAMPLE 4   Find the number of terms in the sequence 5, 11, 17, 23, ... 77.

Solution: The sequence 5, 11, 17, 23, ... 77 is a finite arithmetic sequence with $a_1 = 5$ and $d = 11 - 5 = 6$.

Suppose that this sequence has n terms. Then $a_n = 77$.

We substitute these values in the formula for the general term and solve for the unknown n.

$a_n = a_1 + (n-1)d \qquad$ Formula for n^{th} term of an arithmetic sequence.

$77 = 5 + (n-1)6 \qquad$ Substitute values for a_1, d, and a_n.

$77 = 5 + 6n - 6 \qquad$ Simplify.

$77 = 6n - 1$

$6n = 77 + 1 = 78 \qquad$ Solve for n.

$n = \dfrac{78}{6} = 13$

Hence, the given sequence has 13 terms.

C. Arithmetic Means

Given two numbers, we can always insert numbers between them so that the new set of numbers form an arithmetic sequence. The inserted numbers are called **arithmetic means** (AM) between the given two numbers.

We shall discuss two cases of AM.

1.   To find **a single** AM between two numbers.

2.   To find **more than one** AM between two numbers.

Case 1: Let M be the single AM between a and b.

Then by definition of AM, the three numbers a, M, and b form an arithmetic sequence.

or $M - a = b - M$.

or $2M = a + b \longrightarrow M = \dfrac{a+b}{2}$

EXAMPLE 5 Find the arithmetic mean of -3 and 5.

Solution: Arithmetic mean of -3 and $5 = \dfrac{-3+5}{2} = \dfrac{2}{2} = 1$

Case 2: Let A_1, A_2, A_3 and A_4, be the four arithmetic means between a and b.

Then by definition a, A_1, A_2, A_3 A_4, and b form an arithmetic sequence.

a is the first term and b is the sixth term.

Therefore, by the formula for general term.

$$b = a + (6-1)d \quad \text{or} \quad b = a + 5d \quad \text{or} \quad d = \dfrac{b-a}{5}$$

This gives us the value of the common difference. Since a and b are known, we can find the four arithmetic means using the first term a, and the common difference d.

$$A_1 = a + d, \qquad A_2 = a + 2d, \qquad A_3 = a + 3d, \qquad A_4 = a + 4d$$

$$A_1 = a + \dfrac{b-a}{5}, \quad A_2 = a + 2 \cdot \dfrac{b-a}{5}, \qquad A_3 = a + 3 \cdot \dfrac{b-a}{5}, \quad A_4 = a + 4 \cdot \dfrac{b-a}{5}$$

$$A_1 = \dfrac{4a+b}{5}, \quad A_2 = \dfrac{3a+2b}{5}, \qquad A_3 = \dfrac{2a+3b}{5}, \qquad A_4 = \dfrac{a+4b}{5}$$

EXAMPLE 6 Insert three arithmetic means between 2 and 8.

Solution:

Suppose that the three arithmetic between 2 and 8 are x, y, and z (in this order).

Then $2, x, y, z, 8$ is an arithmetic sequence such that

$$a_1 = 2, \quad a_2 = x, \quad a_3 = y, \quad a_4 = z, \quad a_5 = 8.$$

To determine a_2, a_3 and a_4 we need to know the common difference d.

Now $\quad 8 = a_5 = a_1 + (5-1)d = 2 + 4d$ \hfill Use formula for general term.

$\qquad\qquad 4d = 8 - 2 = 6$ \hfill Solve for d.

$$d = \dfrac{6}{4} = \dfrac{3}{2}$$

Once again using the formula for the general term we get:

$$x = a_2 = a_1 + (2-1)d = 2 + \dfrac{3}{2} = \dfrac{7}{2}$$

$$y = a_3 = a_1 + (3-1)d = 2 + 2\left(\dfrac{3}{2}\right) = 5$$

$$z = a_4 = a_1 + (4-1)d \;=\; 2 + 3\left(\frac{3}{2}\right) = \frac{13}{2}$$

Therefore, three arithmetic means between 2 and 8 are $\dfrac{7}{2}$, 5, and $\dfrac{13}{2}$.

D. GRAPH OF AN ARITHMETIC SEQUENCE

An arithmetic sequence can be expressed as a function of **n** using its **n^{th}** term where a_1 and d are known from the given sequence.

$$f(n) = a_n = a_1 + (n-1)d$$

Given the function, we can always draw its graph.

EXAMPLE 7   Draw the graph of the sequence 0, 2, 4, 6, …

Solution:

  Step 1   Express the sequence as a function.

This is an arithmetic sequence with $a_1 = 0$ and $d = 2 - 0 = 2$.

Therefore, $\begin{aligned} a_n &= a_1 + (n-1)d \\ &= 0 + (n-1)2 = 2n - 2 \qquad \text{\small Formula for general term.} \end{aligned}$

Hence, this sequence can be written in the function form as $f(n) = 2n - 2$.

  Step 2   **Plot the points.** Observe that the domain of this function is the set $\{1, 2, 3, …, n, …\}$ of all positive integers.

Plot the points $(1, 0)$, $(2, 2)$, $(3, 4)$, $(4, 6)$, and so on. Notice that these points are (n, a_n) for different values of n. In Figure 8.1 the four points, shown as dots, form the graph of the sequence.

Remark:	*To draw the graph of f(n) = 2n – 2, we replace n by x and obtain f(x) = 2x – 2 or y = 2x – 2.*
	The graph of y = 2x – 2 contains the four points as shown in Figure 8.1

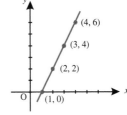

Figure 8.1

Observe that: **a.** The graph of the sequence $f(n) = 2n - 2$ is a set of discrete points. These points also lie on the graph of $f(x) = 2x - 2$ which is a straight line.

  b. Slope of the line $f(x) = 2x - 2$ is the same as the common difference **d** of the arithmetic sequence.

$$\begin{aligned} f(n) = a_n &= a_1 + d(n-1) \\ &= a_1 + dn - d \\ &= dn + (a_1 - d) \\ f(x) &= mx + c \qquad \text{\small $d = m$.} \end{aligned}$$

EXERCISE 8.2

In exercises (1-5), find the first five terms of the arithmetic sequence, using the given information.

1. First term = 2, common difference (c.d.) = −1.

2. First term = −2, (c.d.) = 3. 3. First term = 0, (c.d.) = 4.

4. First term = 1, difference between the fifth and the fourth terms equals 2.

5. First term = 3, difference between the fifth and the third terms equals 5.

In exercises (6-9), write the first three terms of the arithmetic sequence using the given information.

6. 3rd term = 7 and 8th term = 22. 7. 8th term = 21 and 15th term = 35.

8. 7th term = 18 and 20th term = −34. 9. 11th term = 2 and the 21st term = 7.

In exercises (10-15), find the general term of the arithmetic sequence.

10. $1, 2, 3, 4, \ldots$ 11. $-1, 1, 3, 5, \ldots$ 12. $2, 5, 8, 11, \ldots$

13. $-3, 0, 3, 6, \ldots$ 14. $-25, -13, -1, 11, \ldots$ 15. $15, \dfrac{27}{2}, 12, \dfrac{21}{2}, \ldots$

In exercises (16-19), find the arithmetic mean of the numbers.

16. $3, 10$ 17. $-5, 7$ 18. $-8, 8$ 19. $\dfrac{19}{2}, 35$

20. Insert three arithmetic means between 10 and −2.

21. Insert five arithmetic means between 3 and 10.

22. Insert four arithmetic means between −5 and 13.

In exercises (23–28), find the number of terms of the sequence.

23. $-1, 10, 21, 32, \ldots, 186$. 24. $-4, -1, 2, 5, \ldots, 53$. 25. $8, 15, 22, 29, \ldots, 120$.

26. $7, 20, 33, 46, \ldots, 176$. 27. $-4, 10, 24, 38, \ldots, 206$. 28. $35, 32, 29, 26, \ldots, -25$.

In exercises (29–34), draw the graph of the arithmetic sequence.

29. $-1, 2, 5, 8, 11$. 30. $-6, -4, -2, 0, 2, 4, 6$. 31. $0, 1.5, 3, 4.5, 6$.

32. $1, -1, -3, -5, -7$. 33. $-3, 0, 3, 6, \ldots$. 34. $-1, -3.5, -6, \ldots$.

8.3 GEOMETRIC SEQUENCES

In an arithmetic sequence each successive term is obtained by adding a fixed number (called common difference) to the previous term. We now consider sequences for which successive terms are obtained by multiplying the previous term by a fixed non-zero number. Such a sequence is known as a geometric sequence. For example, in the sequence

$$1, 2, 4, 8, 16, 32, \ldots$$

Objectives ▶▶

In this section you will learn about:

A. Definition of a geometric sequence;

B. General term of a geometric sequence;

C. Geometric mean(s); and

D. Graphs of geometric sequences.

each term is obtained by multiplying the previous term by 2. Equivalently, the ratio of each term to its preceding term is 2. This pattern suggests that the term next to 32 is $32 \times 2 = 64$.

A. DEFINITION OF A GEOMETRIC SEQUENCE

A sequence in which the ratio of every pair of successive terms is the same number, say r, is called a "Geometric sequence" (Progression). The number r is called the **common ratio**.

Thus, a sequence

$a_1, a_2, a_3, a_4, a_5, a_6, \ldots, a_n, \ldots$ is a geometric sequence if $\dfrac{a_2}{a_1} = \dfrac{a_3}{a_2} = \ldots = \dfrac{a_{n+1}}{a_n} = \ldots$ (= r, say)

For example:

a. 3, 9, 27, 81, ... is a geometric sequence. The common ratio is **3**, since $\dfrac{9}{3} = \dfrac{27}{9} = \dfrac{81}{27} = 3$.

b. 4, 2, 1, $\dfrac{1}{2}$, $\dfrac{1}{4}$, ... is a geometric sequence.

The common ratio is $\dfrac{1}{2}$, since $\dfrac{2}{4} = \dfrac{1}{2}$, $\dfrac{\frac{1}{2}}{1} = \dfrac{1}{2}$, $\dfrac{\frac{1}{4}}{\frac{1}{2}} = \dfrac{1}{2} \ldots$

EXAMPLE 1   Which of the following is a geometric sequence?

   a.   1, 3, 9, 27, 9   **b.**   −2, 4, −8, 16, −32

Solution: A sequence $a_1, a_2, a_3, \ldots$ is geometric if $\dfrac{a_2}{a_1} = \dfrac{a_3}{a_2} = \dfrac{a_4}{a_3} = \dfrac{a_5}{a_4} = \ldots$

   a.   1, 3, 9, 27, 9.

   Here, $a_1 = 1$, $a_2 = 3$, $a_3 = 9$, $a_4 = 27$, and $a_5 = 9$.

   Therefore, $\dfrac{a_2}{a_1} = \mathbf{3}, \dfrac{a_3}{a_2} = \mathbf{3}, \dfrac{a_4}{a_3} = \mathbf{3}, \dfrac{a_5}{a_4} = \dfrac{\mathbf{1}}{\mathbf{3}}$

   Since the ratios $\dfrac{a_2}{a_1}, \dfrac{a_3}{a_2}, \dfrac{a_4}{a_3}, \dfrac{a_5}{a_4}$ are not all equal, this is not a geometric sequence.

b. $-2, 4, -8, 16, -32$

Here, $a_1 = -2$, $a_2 = 4$, $a_3 = -8$, $a_4 = 16$, $a_5 = -32$.

Therefore, $\dfrac{a_2}{a_1} = -\mathbf{2}$, $\dfrac{a_3}{a_2} = -\mathbf{2}$, $\dfrac{a_4}{a_3} = -\mathbf{2}$, $\dfrac{a_5}{a_4} = -\mathbf{2}$

Since the ratio of any two successive terms is the same number, this is a geometric sequence.

B. GENERAL TERM OF A GEOMETRIC SEQUENCE

Consider the sequence 3, 6, 12, 24, …

This sequence is geometric because $\dfrac{6}{3} = \dfrac{12}{6} = \dfrac{24}{12} = 2$.

Each successive term in this geometric sequence is twice the previous term. Therefore, we can find any term of this sequence by following this pattern. For example, to find the 6th term, we list all the terms upto the 6th term as follows.

$$a_1 = 3 \ , \quad a_2 = 6 \ , \quad a_3 = 12 \ , \quad a_4 = 24 \ , \quad a_5 = 2 \times 24 = 48 \ , \quad a_6 = 2 \times 48 = 96$$

But if we had to determine a_{100} or a_{1000}, this method will consume too much time and space. So we need a formula for the general term or the nth term of the geometric sequence.

Here $a_1 = 3 = 3 \times 1 = 3 \times 2^0 = 3 \times 2^{\mathbf{1-1}}$

$a_2 = 6 = 3 \times 2 = 3 \times 2^1 = 3 \times 2^{\mathbf{2-1}}$

$a_3 = 12 = 3 \times 4 = 3 \times 2^2 = 3 \times 2^{\mathbf{3-1}}$

$a_4 = 24 = 3 \times 8 = 3 \times 2^3 = 3 \times 2^{\mathbf{4-1}}$

Continuing this pattern we get

$$a_6 = 3 \times 2^{\mathbf{6-1}}$$

$$\cdots \qquad \text{Common ratio}$$

$$a_n = 3 \times 2^{n-1}$$

$$\downarrow$$

$$\text{First term}$$

Formula for nth term of a geometric sequence

For the geometric sequence with first term a_1 and the **common ratio** r, the general term or the nth term a_n is given by

$$a_n = a_1 \ r^{n-1}$$

Note   Geometric sequence with common ratio one is a constant sequence, for example, 2, 2, 2, 2.

EXAMPLE 2   Find the general term of the geometric sequence
$$2, -6, 18, -54, \ldots$$

Solution: Here, $a_1 = 2$ and $r = -\dfrac{6}{2} = -3$.

$$a_n = a_1 \ r^{n-1} \qquad \text{Formula for general term of a geometric sequence.}$$
$$a_n = 2 \ (-3)^{n-1} \qquad \text{Substitute for } a_1 \text{ and } r.$$
$$= (-1)^{n-1} \cdot 2 \cdot 3^{n-1}$$

EXAMPLE 3 Find the 15th term of the geometric sequence whose first term is 12 and

the common ratio is $\dfrac{1}{2}$.

Solution: Here, $a_1 = 12$, and $r = \dfrac{1}{2}$.

$$a_n = a_1 \ r^{n-1} \qquad \text{Formula for } n\text{th term of a geometric sequence.}$$

$$a_{15} = 12 \cdot \left(\dfrac{1}{2}\right)^{15-1} \qquad \text{Substitute for } a_1, r, \text{ and } n.$$

$$= 12 \left(\dfrac{1}{2}\right)^{14} = 12 \cdot \dfrac{1}{2^{14}} = \dfrac{3}{4096}$$

EXAMPLE 4 Find the 10th term of a geometric sequence whose first two terms are 3 and -6.

Solution: Here, $a_1 = 3$ and $a_2 = -6$. Therefore, $r = \dfrac{a_2}{a_1} = \dfrac{-6}{3} = -2$

$$a_n = a_1 \ r^{n-1} \qquad \text{Formula for } n\text{th term of a geometric sequence.}$$
$$a_{10} = a_1 \ r^{10-1} = a_1 \ r^9 = 3(-2)^9 = -1536 \qquad \text{Substitute for } a_1, r, \text{ and } n.$$

EXAMPLE 5 Find the number of terms of the geometric sequence
5, 10, 20, 40, ..., 5120.

Solution: The sequence 5, 10, 20, 40, ..., 5120 is a finite geometric sequence with

$a_1 = 5$ and $r = \dfrac{10}{5} = 2$.

Suppose that this sequence has n terms. Then $a_n = 5120$. We substitute these values in the
formula for the general term and solve for the unknown n.

$$a_n = a_1 \ r^{n-1} \qquad \text{Formula for } n\text{th term of a geometric sequence.}$$
$$5120 = 5(2^{n-1}) \qquad \text{Substitute } a_1 = 5, \ r = 2, \text{ and } a_n = 5120.$$
$$2^{n-1} = 1024 \qquad \text{Simplify.}$$
$$2^{n-1} = 2^{10} \qquad \text{Solve for } n.$$
$$n - 1 = 10 \ ;$$
$$n = 10 + 1 = 11$$

C. GEOMETRIC MEAN(S)

Given any two numbers, we can always insert numbers between them so that the new set of numbers forms a geometric sequence. The inserted numbers are called geometric means (GM) between two given numbers.

We shall discuss two cases of GM.

1. To find **a single** GM between two numbers.
2. To find **more than one** GM between two numbers.

Case 1: Let M be the single GM between a and b. Then by definition of GM, the three numbers a, M, b form a geometric sequence.

$$\frac{M}{a} = \frac{b}{M}$$

$$M^2 = ab \qquad \text{Cross multiply.}$$

$$M = \pm\sqrt{ab} \qquad \text{Take square root of both sides.}$$

If a an b are both positive then we take $M = +\sqrt{ab}$ and if they are both negative then we take $M = -\sqrt{ab}$.

Case 2: Let $M_1, M_2, M_3,$ and M_4 be the four geometric means between a and b. Then by definition of GM, the six numbers a, M_1, M_2, M_3, M_4, b form a geometric sequence with

a as the **first** term and b as the **sixth** term of the geometric sequence.

$$a_n = a_1 r^{n-1} \qquad \text{Formula for } n\text{th term of a geometric sequence.}$$

$$b = a \cdot r^{6-1} = a r^5 \qquad \text{Substitute } a_1 = a, \ n = 6, \text{ and } a_6 = b.$$

or $\quad r^5 = \dfrac{b}{a} \qquad \text{Solve for } r.$

$$r = \left(\frac{b}{a}\right)^{1/5}$$

This gives us the value of the common ratio r, since a and b are known.

Using this value of r and the first term a, we get the four geometric means as

$$M_1 = a r, \quad M_2 = a r^2, \quad M_3 = a r^3, \quad M_4 = a r^4.$$

EXAMPLE 6 Find the geometric mean of

    a. 8 and 18   **b.** -6 and -150

Solution:

    a. Geometric mean of 8 and 18

$$= \sqrt{8 \times 18} \qquad \text{Since 8 and 18 are both positive.}$$

$$= \sqrt{144} = \mathbf{12}$$

b.   Geometric mean of -6 and -150

$$= -\sqrt{6 \times 150}$$ Since -6 and -150 are both negative.

$$= -\sqrt{900} = \mathbf{-30}$$

EXAMPLE 7   Insert three positive geometric means between 10 and 250.

Solution: Suppose that the three positive geometric means between 10 and 250 are M_1, M_2, and M_3 (in this order). Then 10, M_1, M_2, M_3, 250 is a geometric sequence such that $a_1 = 10$, $a_2 = M_1$, $a_3 = M_2$, $a_4 = M_3$, and $a_5 = 250$.

To determine M_1, M_2, and M_3 we need to know the common ratio **r**.

$$a_5 = a_1 r^{5-1}$$
$$250 = 10 r^4$$

or $10 r^4 = 250 \longrightarrow r^4 = 25 \longrightarrow r^2 = 5 \longrightarrow r = \pm\sqrt{5}$

Since we want **positive** geometric means, we take positive value of **r**.

Once again using the formula for the general term and $r = \sqrt{5}$, we get

$$M_1 = a_2 = a_1 r = 10 \times \sqrt{5} = 10\sqrt{5}$$

$$M_2 = a_3 = a_1 r^2 = 10 \times \left(\sqrt{5}\right)^2 = 50$$

$$M_3 = a_4 = a_1 r^3 = 10 \times \left(\sqrt{5}\right)^3 = 50\sqrt{5}$$

Therefore, three positive geometric means between 10 and 250 are **$10\sqrt{5}$, 50, and $50\sqrt{5}$**.

D. GRAPHS OF GEOMETRIC SEQUENCES

As in the case of an arithmetic sequence, we can draw the graph of a geometric sequence. Once again, the basic idea is that geometric sequences can be expressed as functions, and therefore they can be graphed.

$$f(n) = a_n = a_1 r^{n-1} \quad \text{or} \quad f(x) = a_1 r^{x-1}$$

where a_1 and r are known for a given sequence. This is a function with the set of **natural numbers** as the domain.

EXAMPLE 8   Draw the graph of the sequence 9, 3, 1, $\frac{1}{3}$ ...

Solution:

Step 1   **Express the sequence as a function**

This is a geometric sequence with $a_1 = 9$ and $r = \frac{3}{9} = \frac{1}{3}$.

Therefore, $a_n = a_1 r^{n-1}$ Formula for general term of a geometric sequence.

$$= 9\left(\frac{1}{3}\right)^{n-1} = 27\left(\frac{1}{3}\right)^n \quad \text{\small Substitute for } a_1 \text{ and } r.$$

Hence this sequence can be written as $f(n) = 27\left(\frac{1}{3}\right)^n$ or $f(x) = 27\left(\frac{1}{3}\right)^x$

Step 2   Observe that the domain of this function is the set $\{1, 2, 3, \dots, n, \dots\}$ of all **positive integers**.

Make a table of values of x and $f(x)$ using the function relation.

$f(x) = 27\left(\frac{1}{3}\right)^x$.

Plot the points $(1, 9)$, $(2, 3)$, $(3, 1)$,

x	1	2	3	4...
$f(x)$	9	3	1	$\frac{1}{3}$ ...

$\left(4, \frac{1}{3}\right)$ and so on. Notice that these points are

(n, a_n) for different values of n. In the Figure 8.2 these points shown as dots form the graph of the sequence.

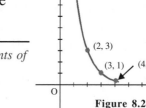

Figure 8.2

Remark :   *The graph of the sequence is the graph of plotted discrete points of the exponential function* $f(x) = 27\left(\frac{1}{3}\right)^x$.

EXERCISE 8.3

In exercises (1-5), find the first five terms of a geometric sequence using the given information.

1. First term $= 1$, common ratio $(r) = -2$.

2. First term $= 2$, $r = -1$.

3. First term $= -2$, $r = 3$.

4. First term $= 3$, $\dfrac{a_4}{a_3} = 2$.

5. First term $= 5$, $\dfrac{a_4}{a_2} = 16$, given that all terms are positive.

In exercises (6-8), find the first five terms of the geometric sequence.

6. $a_3 = 24$, $a_7 = 384$, given that all terms are positive.

7. $a_2 = 18$, $a_5 = -486$.

8. $a_4 = -1$, $a_{10} = -1$, given that the terms are alternately positive and negative.

In exercises (9-14), find the general term of the given geometric sequence.

9. $1, 2, 4, 8, \dots$

10. $-2, 2, -2, 2, \dots$

11. $4, 12, 36, 108, \dots$

12. $-3, 6, -12, 24, \dots$

13. $4, 2, 1, \dfrac{1}{2}, \dfrac{1}{4}, \dots$

14. $-\dfrac{1}{4}, -\dfrac{1}{12}, -\dfrac{1}{36}, -\dfrac{1}{108}, \dots$

In exercises (15-17), find the geometric mean of the numbers.

15. 4 and 9. **16.** -3 and -27. **17.** 2 and 18.

18. Insert two geometric means between 5 and 40.

19. Insert three geometric means between 3 and $\frac{1}{27}$.

In exercises (20-24), find the number of terms in the given sequence.

20. $4, -8, 16, -32, \ldots, -512$ **21.** $4, 12, 36, 108, \ldots, 8748$ **22.** $2, 6, 18, 54, \ldots, 13122$

23. $-3, 6, -12, 24, \ldots, 1536$ **24.** $5, 15, 45, 135, \ldots, 98415$

In exercises (25-28), draw the graph of the geometric sequence.

25. $-2, 2, -2, 2, -2, \ldots$ **26.** $1, 2, 4, 8, \ldots$ **27.** $1, -2, 4, -8, \ldots$ **28.** $3, 3, 3, 3, \ldots$

8.4 ARITHMETIC SERIES

When the terms of an arithmetic sequence are added together, the resulting expression is called an arithmetic series.

For example,

| **Arithmetic sequence** | : | **1, 4, 7, 10, 13, 16, 19** |
| **Arithmetic series** | : | **1 + 4 + 7 + 10 + 13 + 16 + 19** |

| **Arithmetic sequence** | : | **–3, –1, 1, 3, 5, 7, 9** |
| **Arithmetic series** | : | **(–3) + (–1) + 1 + 3 + 5 + 7 + 9** |

A series is called a **finite series** if it has only a finite number of terms. For example, $1 + 3 + 5 + 7 + 9 + 11 + 13$ is a finite series because it has only 7 terms.

A series is called an **infinite series** if it has an infinite number of terms. For example, $2 + 4 + 8 + 16 + 32 + \ldots$ is an infinite series.

Objectives ▶ ▶

In this section you will learn about:

A. Sigma notation; and

B. Sum of first n terms of an arithmetic series.

A. SIGMA NOTATION (ANATOMY)

A series can be written in short form using the upper case Greek letter sigma Σ.

For example, consider the series $3 + 6 + 9 + 12 + \ldots + 300$

$$3 \quad + \quad 6 \quad + \quad 9 \quad + \quad 12 \quad + \quad \ldots \quad + \quad 300$$
$$3.1 \quad + \quad 3.2 \quad + \quad 3.3 \quad + \quad 3.4 \quad + \quad \ldots \quad + \quad 3.100$$

This is the **sum of 100 terms** of the type $3n$ where, $n = 1$ for the first term, $n = 2$ for the second term, $\ldots$, and $n = 100$ for the last term.

We write this sum as $\displaystyle\sum_{n=1}^{100} 3n$ = sum of all the terms of the type $3n$ starting from $n = 1$

and ending at $n = 100$.

$$= 3 \cdot 1 + 3 \cdot 2 + 3 \cdot 3 + \ldots + 3 \cdot 100$$

1. $\sum$ is called a **summation sign**.

2. n is called the **index.** The letter n can be replaced by any letter without changing the series.

Thus $\displaystyle\sum_{n=1}^{100} 3n = \sum_{k=1}^{100} 3k = 3 + 6 + 9 + 12 + \ldots + 300$ represents the same series.

3.   The expression **3n** after the summation sign is called the **summand.**

EXAMPLE 1   Write the summation in the expanded form (without sigma sign).

a. $\displaystyle\sum_{n=1}^{7} \frac{3n}{n+1}$ **b.** $\displaystyle\sum_{n=1}^{\infty} (4n - 1)$

Solution:

a. $\displaystyle\sum_{n=1}^{7} \frac{3n}{n+1}$

For $n = 1$, the summand = $a_1 = \dfrac{3(1)}{1+1} = \dfrac{3}{2}$.

Similarly,

For $n = 2$, the summand = $a_2 = \dfrac{3(2)}{2+1} = 2$;   **for $n = 3$**, the summand = $a_3 = \dfrac{3(3)}{3+1} = \dfrac{9}{4}$;

for $n = 4$, the summand = $a_4 = \dfrac{3(4)}{4+1} = \dfrac{12}{5}$;   **for $n = 5$**, the summand = $a_5 = \dfrac{3(5)}{5+1} = \dfrac{5}{2}$;

for $n = 6$, the summand = $a_6 = \dfrac{3(6)}{6+1} = \dfrac{18}{7}$; and   **for $n = 7$**, the summand = $a_7 = \dfrac{3(7)}{7+1} = \dfrac{21}{8}$.

Therefore, $\displaystyle\sum_{n=1}^{7} \frac{3n}{n+1} = \frac{3}{2} + 2 + \frac{9}{4} + \frac{12}{5} + \frac{5}{2} + \frac{18}{7} + \frac{21}{8}$.

b. $\displaystyle\sum_{n=1}^{\infty} (4n - 1)$

For $n = 1$, the summand = $a_1 = 4(1) - 1 = 3$;
for $n = 2$, the summand = $a_2 = 4(2) - 1 = 7$;
for $n = 3$, the summand = $a_3 = 4(3) - 1 = 11$; and
for $n = 4$, the summand = $a_4 = 4(4) - 1 = 15$.

Therefore, $\displaystyle\sum_{n=1}^{\infty} (4n - 1) = 3 + 7 + 11 + 15 + \ldots$

B. Sum of First *n* Terms of an Arithmetic Series

Recall that when terms of a sequence are added the resulting expression is called an arithmetic series. We can derive a formula to find the sum of finite number of terms of such a series.

Formula

Let S_n be the sum of the first n terms of an arithmetic series $a_1 + a_2 + a_3 + \ldots$

Then $S_n = a_1 + a_2 + \ldots + a_n$

If d is the common difference of this series then $a_2 = a_1 + d$, $a_3 = a_1 + 2d$, ..., $a_n = a_1 + (n-1)d$

Therefore, $S_n = a_1 + (a_1 + d) + (a_1 + 2d) + \ldots + [a_1 + (n-1)d]$ **(1)**

Similarly, by writing the terms of S_n in reverse order, we obtain

$$S_n = a_n + a_{n-1} + \ldots + a_1$$
$$= a_n + (a_n - d) + (a_n - 2d) + \ldots + [a_n - (n-1)d] \quad \textbf{(2)}$$

$$S_n = a_1 + (a_1 + d) + (a_1 + 2d) + \ldots + [a_1 + (n-1)d]$$
$$S_n = a_n + \quad + (a_n - 2d) + \ldots + [a_n - (n-1)d]$$

If we add **(1)** and **(2)** we get,

$$2S_n = (a_1 + a_n) + (a_1 + a_n) + (a_1 + a_n) + \ldots + (a_1 + a_n)$$
$$= n(a_1 + a_n)$$

$$\text{or} \quad S_n = \frac{n}{2}(a_1 + a_n)$$

$$= \frac{n}{2}\left[\textbf{First term} + \textbf{last term}\right]$$

This is one of the formulae for the sum of the first n terms of the arithmetic series.
But we know that $a_n = a_1 + (n-1)d$.

Therefore, $$S_n = \frac{n}{2}(a_1 + a_n)$$

$$= \frac{n}{2}\left[a_1 + a_1 + (n-1)d\right]$$

$$S_n = \frac{n}{2}\left[2a_1 + (n-1)d\right]$$

This is the second formula for the sum of the first n terms of a series. Thus, to find the sum of the first n terms of a series we use $S_n = \frac{n}{2}(a_1 + a_n)$ if we are given the first and the last term of a series.

Otherwise we use $S_n = \frac{n}{2}\left[2a_1 + d(n-1)\right]$.

Observe : We can find the sum of only finite number of terms. If n is infinitely large then $|S_n|$ is also infinitely large.

EXAMPLE 2 Find the sum of the first 22 terms of the arithmetic series whose first term is 10 and the common difference is 5.

Solution: Here, $a_1 = 10$ and $d = 5$.

Since the last term a_{22} is not given, we use the formula $S_n = \dfrac{n}{2}\left[2a_1 + (n-1)d\right]$.

Thus, $S_{22} = \dfrac{22}{2}\left[2(10) + (22-1)5\right]$ Substitute $n = 22$, and $a_1 = 10$, $d = 5$ in the formula for S_n.

$= 11(20 + 105) = 1375$.

EXAMPLE 3 Find the value of $\displaystyle\sum_{n=1}^{24}(3n+1)$.

Solution: $a_n = 3n + 1$; $\boldsymbol{a_1} = 3(1) + 1 = 4$ and $\boldsymbol{a_{24}} = 3(24) + 1 = \boldsymbol{73}$

Therefore, using the formula

$S_n = \dfrac{n}{2}\left[a_1 + a_n\right]$, we get $S_{24} = \dfrac{24}{2}\left[4+73\right] = 12 \times 77 = 924$.

EXAMPLE 4 Find the sum of the first n natural numbers.

Solution: Sum of the first n natural numbers is the sum of the n terms of the sequence 1, 2, 3, ..., n.

Observe that the above sequence is an arithmetic sequence with common difference 1.

Therefore, $S_n = \dfrac{n}{2}\left[a_1 + a_n\right] = \dfrac{n}{2}[1+n] = \dfrac{n(n+1)}{2}$.

EXAMPLE 5 Find the sum of odd integers from 1 through 57.

Solution: Sum of odd integers from 1 through 57 can be written as $1 + 3 + 5 + 7 + 9 + 11 + \ldots + 57$.

$1, 3, 5, 7, 9, 11, \ldots$ is an arithmetic sequence with common difference 2. At this point we cannot use any formula since we do not know $\boldsymbol{n}$, the number of terms. Suppose 57 is the nth term of the above sequence.

Thus, $a_n = a_1 + (n-1)d$ Formula for the nth term.

$57 = 1 + (n-1)2$ Substitute $a_n = 57$, $a_1 = 1$, and $d = 2$.

$57 = 1 + 2n - 2$ Simplify.

$2n = 58$ Solve for n.

$n = \dfrac{58}{2} = 29$

Thus, $1 + 3 + 5 + 7 + \ldots + 57$ is the sum of the first 29 terms of the series.

Therefore, $S_n = \dfrac{n}{2}\left(a_1 + a_n\right)$ Formula for the sum of first n terms of an arithmetic series.

$= \dfrac{29}{2}(1+57)$ Substitute $n = 29$, $a_1 = 1$, and $a_n = 57$.

$= \dfrac{29}{2} \times 58 = 29 \times 29 = 841$

EXAMPLE 6 Suppose you are offered a job at $1,200 per month with an increase of $10 every month. How much money would you make in the first year?

Solution: You will make $1200, $1210, $1220, ... in successive months.

This forms an arithmetic sequence with $a_1 = 1200$ and $d = 10$

Total money made in 12 months is the sum of the first 12 terms of the sequence.

Substitute $a_1 = 1200$, $d = 10$, and $n = 12$ in $S_n = \dfrac{n}{2}\left[2a_1 + (n-1)\,d\right]$.

$S_{12} = \dfrac{12}{2}\left[2 \times 1200 + (12-1)\,10\right]$

$= 6(2400 + 110) = 6 \times 2510 = 15060$

Thus total money made in the first year is $15060.

EXERCISE 8.4

In exercises (1-12), write the series in expanded form.

1. $\displaystyle\sum_{n=1}^{10} 2n$ 2. $\displaystyle\sum_{n=1}^{8}(2n+3)$ 3. $\displaystyle\sum_{n=1}^{6}(4-3n)$ 4. $\displaystyle\sum_{k=1}^{7}(-1)^k k$

5. $\displaystyle\sum_{n=1}^{7}\left(n^2+1\right)$ 6. $\displaystyle\sum_{n=1}^{6}\left(n^2+n-3\right)$ 7. $\displaystyle\sum_{n=1}^{8}3\cdot 2^{n-1}$ 8. $\displaystyle\sum_{k=1}^{6}(-2)^k$

9. $\displaystyle\sum_{n=1}^{7}5(-3)^{n+1}$ 10. $\displaystyle\sum_{n=1}^{5}(-1)^{n-1}n$ 11. $\displaystyle\sum_{k=1}^{5}(-1)^{k-1}\left(1-k^2\right)$ 12. $\displaystyle\sum_{k=1}^{4}\left(-\dfrac{1}{2}\right)^k$

In exercises (13-18), write the series using sigma notation.

13. $2+5+8+11+\ldots 35$ terms

14. $3+7+11+15+\ldots 63$ terms

15. $(-5)+5+(-5)+5+(-5)+5+\ldots, 20$ terms

16. $(-10)+(-5)+0+5+\ldots, 120$ terms

17. $3+1+\dfrac{1}{3}+\dfrac{1}{3^2}+\cdots\dfrac{1}{243}$

18. $18+6+2+\dfrac{2}{3}+\dfrac{2}{9}+\ldots+\dfrac{2}{729}$

In exercises (19-24), identify whether the series is arithmetic or not.

19. $-2+1+4+7+10+\ldots+28$

20. $2+6+12+20+\ldots$

21. $\dfrac{1}{2}+\left(-\dfrac{1}{2}\right)+\dfrac{1}{2}+\left(-\dfrac{1}{2}\right)+\ldots$

22. $3+5+7+9+11+\ldots$

23. $1+9+25+49+81+\ldots$

24. $1^2+2^2+3^2+\ldots$

In exercises (25-30), find the sum of the first one hundred terms of the series whose first few terms are given.

25. $2 + 4 + 6 + 8 + 10 + \ldots$ **26.** $(-5) + (-3) + (-1) + 1 + 3 + \ldots$ **27.** $7 + 8.5 + 10 + 11.5 + \ldots$

28. $1 + 2 + 3 + 4 + \ldots$ **29.** $25 + 21 + 17 + 13 + \ldots$ **30.** $8 + 3 - 2 - 7 - 12 \ldots$

In exercises (31-33), find the sum of the arithmetic series.

31. $2 + 7 + 12 + \ldots + 102$ **32.** $-1 + 3 + 7 + 11 + \ldots + 151$ **33.** $28 + 26 + 24 + \ldots + (-6)$

In exercises (34-36), find a formula for the sum of the first n terms of a series whose first few terms are given.

34. $1 + 3 + 5 + 7 + \ldots$ **35.** $-3 + 0 + 3 + 6 + \ldots$ **36.** $6 + 9 + 12 + 15 + \ldots$

In exercises (37-40), find a formula for S_n using the given information.

37. $S_{12} = 222$, $S_{14} = 301$ **38.** $S_{10} = 55$, $S_{13} = 130$

39. $a_1 = 5$, $S_{18} = 549$ **40.** $a_1 = -4$, $S_{15} = 675$

8.5 GEOMETRIC SERIES

Objectives ▶ ▶

In this section you will learn about:

A. Sum of first n terms of a geometric series; and

B. Sum of an infinite geometric series.

When the terms of a geometric sequence are added together, the resulting expression is called a geometric series.

For example,

Geometric sequence	:	2, 4, 8, 16, 32, 64, 128
Geometric series	:	2 + 4 + 8 + 16 + 32 + 64 + 128

Geometric sequence	:	1/3, 1/6, 1/12, 1/24, 1/48
Geometric series	:	1/3 + 1/6 + 1/12 + 1/24 + 1/48

Unlike arithmetic series, it is possible to find the sum of an infinite geometric series in some cases.

A. SUM OF FIRST n TERMS OF A GEOMETRIC SERIES

Let S_n be the sum of the first n terms of a geometric sequence. If a_1 is the first term of this sequence, and r is its common ratio, then using the formula for the nth term of a geometric sequence we get:

$$a_2 = a_1 r, \quad a_3 = a_1 r^2, \quad a_4 = a_1 r^3 \ldots, \quad a_n = a_1 r^{n-1}$$

Thus $S_n = a_1 + a_1 r + a_1 r^2 + a_1 r^3 + \ldots + a_1 r^{n-1}$ **(1)**

Multiplying both sides by r we get $rS_n = a_1 r + a_1 r^2 + a_1 r^3 + a_1 r^4 + \ldots + a_1 r^{n-1} + a_1 r^n$ **(2)**

Re-writing **(1)** and **(2)** by aligning the like terms on the right side, and subtracting **(2)** from **(1)** we get :

$$S_n = a_1 + a_1 r + a_1 r^2 + \ldots + a_1 r^{n-1}$$

$$rS_n = \quad\quad a_1 r + a_1 r^2 + \ldots + a_1 r^{n-1} + a_1 r^n$$

$$S_n - rS_n = a_1 - a_1 r^n$$

$$S_n(1 - r) = a_1(1 - r^n) \quad \longrightarrow \quad S_n = \frac{a_1\left(1 - r^n\right)}{1 - r}, \quad (r \neq 1)$$

◉ Notes **1.** The formula $S_n = \frac{a_1\left(1 - r^n\right)}{1 - r}$ gives the sum of the first n terms of a sequence with first term a_1 and common ratio r if $r \neq 1$.

2. When $r = 1$, the geometric sequence becomes the constant sequence $a_1, a_1, a_1, \ldots, a_1$. Thus, $a_1 + a_2 + \ldots + a_n = \underbrace{a_1 + a_1 + \ldots + a_1}_{a_1 \text{ repeated } n \text{ times}} = n\, a_1$

EXAMPLE 1 Find the sum of the first 10 terms of the series.
$$3 + 9 + 27 + 81 + \ldots$$

Solution: This is a geometric series because the ratio of any two consecutive terms is 3. Therefore, we substitute $a_1 = 3$, $r = 3$, $n = 10$ in the formula for S_n.

$$S_n = \frac{a_1\left(1 - r^n\right)}{1 - r} = \frac{3\left(1 - 3^{10}\right)}{1 - 3} = \frac{3}{-2}\left(1 - 3^{10}\right) = \frac{3}{2}\left(3^{10} - 1\right)$$

EXAMPLE 2 Find the sum of the first 15 terms of the series $4 + 2 + 1 + \dfrac{1}{2} + \dfrac{1}{4} + \ldots$

Solution: This is a geometric series because the ratio of any two consecutive terms is $\dfrac{1}{2}$.

Therefore, we substitute $a_1 = 4$, $r = \dfrac{1}{2}$ and $n = 15$ in the formula for S_n.

$$S_n = \frac{a_1\left(1 - r^n\right)}{1 - r} = \frac{4\left(1 - \dfrac{1}{2^{15}}\right)}{1 - \dfrac{1}{2}} = 8\left(1 - \frac{1}{2^{15}}\right)$$

EXAMPLE 3 Find the sum of the series $\displaystyle\sum_{n=1}^{7} (2) \times (3)^{n-1}$.

Solution: This is a geometric series with $a_1 = 2$, $r = 3$, and $n = 7$.

$$S_n = \frac{a_1\left(1 - r^n\right)}{1 - r}$$ Formula for the sum of first n terms of a geometric sequence.

$$S_7 = \frac{2\left(1 - (3)^7\right)}{1 - 3}$$ Substitute $a_1 = 2$, $r = 3$, and $n = 7$.

$$= \frac{2\left(1 - (2187)\right)}{-2} = \mathbf{2186}$$

B. Sum of an Infinite Geometric Series

Consider the following geometric series:

1. $1 + 2 + 4 + 8 + 16 + \dots$

2. $1 + \dfrac{1}{2} + \dfrac{1}{4} + \dfrac{1}{8} + \dots$

3. $2 + 2 + 2 + \dots$

1. The series $1 + 2 + 4 + 8 + 16 + \dots$ is a geometric series with common ratio $2 (r > 1)$. The terms of this series are becoming larger and larger. The sum of this infinite series is infinitely large and therefore does not exist.

2. The series $1 + \dfrac{1}{2} + \dfrac{1}{4} + \dfrac{1}{8} + \dots$ is an infinite geometric series with common ratio $\dfrac{1}{2} (r < 1)$. The terms of this series are becoming smaller and smaller. The sum of this series is a finite number and is given by:

$$* \quad S = \frac{a_1}{1-r} = \frac{1}{1-\dfrac{1}{2}} = \frac{1}{\dfrac{1}{2}} = 2$$

$$* \quad S_n = \frac{a_1(1-r^n)}{1-r} \text{ , if } |r| < 1 \text{ then for large } n, \ r^n \approx 0.$$

$$\text{Therefore, } \ S_n = \frac{a_1(1-0)}{1-r} = \frac{a_1}{1-r} \text{ for very large } n.$$

3. The series $2 + 2 + 2 + \dots$ is an infinite geometric series with common ratio $1 (r = 1)$. The sum of this series means adding 2 infinite times. As we can see, this also does not exist. We summarize the above discussion in the following rule.

> **The sum of the infinite geometric series $a_1 + a_1 r + a_1 r^2 + \dots$**
>
> **a.** does not exist if $|r| \geq 1$
>
> **b,** equals $\dfrac{a_1}{1-r}$ if $|r| < 1$

The geometric series $a_1 + a_1 r + a_1 r^2 + \dots$ is written in Sigma notation as $\displaystyle\sum_{n=1}^{\infty} a_1 r^{n-1}$.

$$\sum_{n=1}^{\infty} a_1 r^{n-1} = a_1 + a_1 r + a r^2 + \dots$$

EXAMPLE 4 Find the sum of the infinite geometric series with first term 2 and common ratio $\dfrac{2}{5}$.

Solution: The first term and the common ratio are given.

$$a_1 = 2, \text{ and } r = \frac{2}{5}. \quad |r| = \left|\frac{2}{5}\right| = \frac{2}{5} < 1$$

Therefore, the sum is given by $S = \dfrac{a_1}{1-r} = \dfrac{2}{1-\dfrac{2}{5}} = \dfrac{2}{\dfrac{3}{5}} = \dfrac{10}{3}$

EXAMPLE 5   Convert repeating decimal 0.363636... into an equivalent fraction.

Solution: $.363636... = 0.36 + 0.0036 + 0.000036 + ...$

$$= 0.36 + 0.36(.01) + 0.36(.01)^2 + ...$$

This is an infinite geometric series with $a_1 = 0.36$, and $r = 0.01$.

Since $|r| = |0.01| = 0.01 < 1$, the sum is given by $S = \dfrac{a_1}{1-r}$

$$S = \frac{a_1}{1-r} = \frac{0.36}{1-0.01} = \frac{0.36}{0.99} = \frac{36}{99} = \frac{4}{11}$$

EXERCISE 8.5

In exercises (1-6), identify whether the series is geometric or not.

1. $1 + 3 + 5 + 7 + 9 + ...$ **2.** $1 + 4 + 9 + 16 + 25 + ... + 81$ **3.** $1 + 2 + 4 + 8 + 16 + ... + 1024$

4. $3 + \dfrac{1}{2} + \dfrac{1}{4} + \dfrac{1}{8} + \dfrac{1}{16} + ...$ **5.** $\dfrac{1}{5} + \left(-\dfrac{1}{5}\right) + \dfrac{1}{5} + \left(-\dfrac{1}{5}\right) + ...$ **6.** $4 + \dfrac{4}{9} + \dfrac{4}{81} + \dfrac{4}{729} + ...$

In exercises (7-9), determine the sum of the first fifteen terms of the geometric series.

7. $1 + \dfrac{1}{3} + \dfrac{1}{9} + \dfrac{1}{27} + ...$ **8.** $64 + 32 + 16 + 8 + ...$ **9.** $3 + 6 + 12 + 24 + ...$

In exercises (10-15), find the expression for the sum of n terms of the geometric series.

10. $1 + 2 + 4 + 8 ...$ **11.** $2 + \dfrac{1}{2} + \dfrac{1}{8} + \dfrac{1}{32} + ...$ **12.** $3 - 6 + 12 - 24 + ...$

13. $2 + (-6) + 18 + (-54) + ...$ **14.** $4 + (-4) + 4 + (-4) + ...$ **15.** $\dfrac{3}{4} + \dfrac{3}{16} + \dfrac{3}{64} + ...$

In exercises (16-21), find the sum of the infinite geometric series, if it exists.

16. $1 + \dfrac{1}{3} + \dfrac{1}{9} + \dfrac{1}{27} + \dfrac{1}{81} + ...$ **17.** $2 + \dfrac{1}{2} + \dfrac{1}{4} + \dfrac{1}{8} + \dfrac{1}{16} + ...$ **18.** $\dfrac{1}{4} - \dfrac{1}{16} + \dfrac{1}{64} - \dfrac{1}{256} + ...$

19. $1 + 2 + 4 + 8 + 16 + ...$ **20.** $3 - 3^2 + 3^3 - 3^4 + ...$ **21.** $\dfrac{3}{5} + \dfrac{3}{25} + \dfrac{3}{125} + ...$

22. A king, who was very fond of chess, was saved by a person in a forest. The king was very happy and grateful, and asked the person for a wish. This person said very humbly "Oh my master ! If you want to grant me a wish then please give me 1 grain of rice for the first square of the chessboard, 2 for the second, 4 for the third, 8 for the fourth and so on." The king was amazed at this wish and promptly granted the same. It is said that the king ran out of rice and could not fulfill the fish. Explain !

[*Hint:*   **1.**   There are 64 squares on a chessboard.

   2.   You may assume that 100 grains of rice weighs one gram].

8.6 PASCAL'S TRIANGLE AND BINOMIAL THEOREM

Objectives ▶ ▶

In this section you will learn about:

A. Expanding a binomial raised to certain power using Pascal's Triangle;

B. n factorial ($n!$);

C. Binomial Theorem; and

D. General term of a binomial expansion.

Recall that

$$(x + y)^2 = x^2 + 2xy + y^2$$

$$(x + y)^3 = x^3 + 3x^2y + 3xy^2 + y^3$$

These are particular cases of the general binomial expansion for $(x + y)^n$, where n is a positive integer. The expression $x + y$ itself is called a binomial, since this expression has two terms.

A. EXPANDING A BINOMIAL RAISED TO CERTAIN POWER USING PASCAL'S TRIANGLE

Consider the expressions

$$(x + y)^0 = 1$$
$$(x + y)^1 = x + y$$
$$(x + y)^2 = x^2 + 2xy + y^2$$
$$(x + y)^3 = x^3 + 3x^2y + 3xy^2 + y^3$$
$$(x + y)^4 = x^4 + 4x^3y + 6x^2y^2 + 4xy^3 + y^4$$

Observations:

1. Total number of terms in the expansion of $(x + y)^n$ is $n + 1$.

2. The first term is always x^n and the last term is y^n.

3. The sum of the exponents of the variables in each term is always n.

4. The exponents of x decrease by 1 in each successive term, while the exponents of y increase by 1.

5. The coefficients of the binomial expansion has a pattern described below.

Binomial	**Coefficients**

$(x + y)^0 = 1$

$(x + y)^1 = x + y = 1 \cdot x + 1 \cdot y$

$(x + y)^2 = 1 \cdot x^2 + 2 \cdot xy + 1 \cdot y^2$

$(x + y)^3 = 1 \cdot x^3 + 3 \cdot x^2y + 3 \cdot xy^2 + 1 \cdot y^3$

$(x + y)^4 = 1 \cdot x^4 + 4 \cdot x^3y + 6 \cdot x^2y^2 + 4 \cdot xy^3 + 1 \cdot y^4$

```
              1
            1   1
          1   2   1
        1   3   3   1
      1   4   6   4   1
```

The array of numbers on the right side is called the **Pascal's Triangle.** We make the following observations about the pattern of numbers in Pascal's triangle.

a. Each number in this triangle is **the sum of the two numbers just above it** (one on the left and the other to the right). For example,

  gives the picture of the first 3 in the **fourth row**

and the numbers just abve it in the **third row**.

b. Numbers in **first** row are coefficients in the expansion of $(x + y)^0 = 1$.

Numbers in the second row are coefficients in the expansion of $(x + y)^1 = 1 \cdot x + 1 \cdot y$.

Numbers in the **third row** are the coefficients in the expansion of

$(x + y)^2 = 1 \cdot x^2 + 2 \cdot xy + 1 \cdot y^2$ and so on.

Thus we can find the coefficients in the expansion of $(x + y)^5$ by exploring the sixth row.

Sixth row in Pascal triangle will be

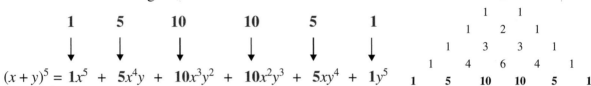

c. Observe that we have multiplied each number in the row by $x^m y^n$, where m decreases and n increases.

Starting value of $m = 5$, Starting value of $n = 0$

Last value of $m = 0$ Last value of $n = 5$

EXAMPLE 1 Write the following binomials in the expanded form.

  a. $(3 + x)^4$ **b.** $(2x + 3y)^5$

Solutions:

a. $(3 + x)^4$: There are five terms in its expansion.

The first term is $(3)^4$ and the last term (fifth) is $(x)^4$

As we write, 2nd, 3rd, and 4th terms, the exponent of 3 will decrease by 1 at each stage, and exponent of x will increase by 1, wheareas the sum of the exponents will remain 4. The coefficients in the expansion are given by the fifth line in pascal's triangle.

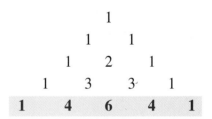

  1 4 6 4 1

Thus, the expansion is

$(3 + x)^4 = $ **1** $\cdot 3^4 x^0 + $ **4** $\cdot 3^{4-1} x^1 + $ **6** $\cdot 3^{4-2} x^2 + $ **4** $\cdot 3^{4-3} x^3 + $ **1** $\cdot 3^{4-4} x^4$

  $= 3^4 + 4 \cdot 3^3 x + 6 \cdot 3^2 x^2 + 4 \cdot 3x^3 + x^4$

b. $(2x + 3y)^5$: There are six terms in its expansion.

The first term is $(2x)^5$, and the last term (6th term) is $(3y)^5$. As we write 2nd, 3rd, 4th, and 5th terms of the expansion, exponents of $(2x)$ will decrease by 1, and those of $(3y)$ will increase by 1, whereas sum of the exponents will always be 5. The coefficients are given by the numbers in the 6th row of Pascal's Triangle. (1, 5, 10, 10, 5, 1).

Therefore,

$$(2x + 3y)^5 = \mathbf{1} \cdot (2x)^5 + \mathbf{5} \cdot (2x)^4(3y)^1 + \mathbf{10} \cdot (2x)^3(3y)^2 + \mathbf{10} \cdot (2x)^2(3y)^3 + \mathbf{5} \cdot (2x)^1(3y)^4 + \mathbf{1} \cdot (3y)^5$$

$$= 2^5\,x^5 + (5 \cdot 2^4 \cdot 3)\,x^4y + (10 \cdot 2^3 \cdot 3^2)x^3y^2 + (10 \cdot 2^2 \cdot 3^3)x^2y^3 + 5 \cdot 2 \cdot 3^4\,xy^4 + 3^5\,y^5$$

B. n FACTORIAL ($n!$)

Pascal's triangle is useful to find the coefficients in the expansion of $(a + b)^n$, when n is a small positive integer. But it may not be convenient to use Pascal's triangle if n is large. In that case, we use Binomial theorem. This theorem, discussed below in objective C, will require the use of factorial of a positive integer, say n, usually denoted by $n!$. We now define factorial and workout a few examples to practice the use of this symbol.

Definition : For any **positive integer n.**

$$n! = n(n - 1)\,(n - 2)\,(n - 3) \ldots (2)\,(1) \text{ and}$$
$$0! = 1$$

EXAMPLE 2   Find the value of :

    a. $4!$ **b.** $\dfrac{7!}{4!\,3!}$ **c.** $\dfrac{5!}{3!\,0!}$

Solutions:

    a. $4! = (4)\,(3)\,(2)\,(1) = 24$

    b. $\dfrac{7!}{4!\,3!} = \dfrac{7(6)\,(5)\,\mathbf{(4)\,(3)\,(2)\,(1)}}{\mathbf{(4)\,(3)\,(2)\,(1)}\,(3)\,(2)\,(1)} = \dfrac{7(6)\,(5)}{(3)\,(2)\,(1)} = 35$

    c. $\dfrac{5!}{3!\,0!} = \dfrac{(5)\,(4)\,\mathbf{(3)\,(2)\,(1)}}{\mathbf{(3)\,(2)\,(1)}\,(1)} = 20$

C. Binomial Theorem

Let us look at the expansion of $(x + y)^4$ once again.

$(x + y)^4 = \mathbf{1}x^4y^0 + \mathbf{4}x^3y^1 + \mathbf{6}x^2y^2 + \mathbf{4}x^1y^3 + \mathbf{1}x^0y^4.$

Observations :

1. $(x + y)^4$ is expressed in terms of monomials x^my^n

    $m = 4, 3, 2, 1, 0 \ ; \ n = 0, 1, 2, 3, 4$

2.   • Exponents in x^4y^0 are 4 and 0. Also , $\dfrac{4!}{4!\,0!} = \dfrac{(4)\,(3)\,(2)\,(1)}{(4)\,(3)\,(2)\,(1)\,(1)} = \mathbf{1}$

        The coefficient of x^4y^0 is **1** : $1x^4y^0 = \dfrac{4!}{4!\,0!}\,x^4y^0$

- Exponents in x^3y^1 are 3 and 1. Also, $\dfrac{4!}{3!\,1!} = \dfrac{(4)\,(3)\,(2)\,(1)}{(3)\,(2)\,(1)\,(1)} = \mathbf{4}$

  The coefficient of x^3y^1 is **4**: $4x^3y^1 = \dfrac{4!}{3!\,1!}x^3y^1$

- Exponents in x^2y^2 are 2 and 2. Also, $\dfrac{4!}{2!\,2!} = \dfrac{(4)\,(3)\,(2)\,(1)}{(2)\,(1)\,(2)\,(1)} = \mathbf{6}$

  The coefficient of x^2y^2 is **6**: $6x^2y^2 = \dfrac{4!}{2!\,2!}x^2y^2$

and so on. Observe the pattern of coefficients expressed using factorials. The numerator of all the coefficients is **factorial of power of the binomial.** The denominator is a product of two factorials, one is the factorial of the power of x and the other is the factorial of the power of y.

This is not a coincidence. We may verify the same patterns in some other expansions, such as $(x+y)^2 = x^2 + 2xy + y^2$ and $(x+y)^3 = x^3 + 3x^2y + 3xy^2 + y^3$.

We generalize the above observations in the following statements.

a. The general term, the $(k+1)^{\text{th}}$ term, in the expansion of $(x+y)^n$ is (coefficient) $x^{n-k} \cdot y^k$

b. The coefficient $= \dfrac{n!}{(n-k)!\,k!}$ $\longrightarrow$ n is the power of the binomial

$\longrightarrow$ $n-k$ and k are the exponents of the two factors of the term.

With these two statements, we can now state the **Binomial Theorem.**

Binomial Theorem

For any positive integer n

$$(x+y)^n = x^n + \dfrac{n!}{(n-1)!\,1!}x^{n-1}y^1 + \dfrac{n!}{(n-2)!\,2!}x^{n-2}y^2$$

$$+ \dots + \dfrac{n!}{2!\,(n-2)!}x^2y^{n-2} + \dfrac{n!}{1!\,(n-1)!}x^1y^{n-1} + y^n \qquad \text{The coefficients of } x^n \text{ and } y^n \text{ are } \tfrac{n!}{n!\,0!}=1.$$

$$= \sum_{k=0}^{n} \dfrac{n!}{(n-k)!\,k!}x^{n-k}y^k$$

EXAMPLE 3 Verify that coefficients in the expansion of $(x+y)^3$ obtained by using Pascal's triangle are the same as coefficients obtained by using binomial theorem.

Solution:
$$(x+y)^3 = 1 \cdot x^3 + 3 \cdot x^2y + 3 \cdot xy^2 + 3 \cdot xy^2 + y^3$$

$$= 1 \cdot x^3y^0 + 3x^2y^1 + 3x^1y^2 + 1 \cdot x^0y^3 \qquad \text{Coefficients in the expansion using Pascal's Triangle.}$$

$$= \dfrac{3!}{(3!)\,(0!)} \quad \dfrac{3!}{(2!)\,(1!)} \quad \dfrac{3!}{(1!)\,(2!)} \quad \dfrac{3!}{(0!)\,(3!)} \qquad \text{Coefficients in the expansion using Binomial theorem.}$$

$$= \quad \frac{3 \cdot 2 \cdot 1}{3 \cdot 2 \cdot 1 \cdot 1} \qquad \frac{3 \cdot 2 \cdot 1}{2 \cdot 1 \cdot 1} \qquad \frac{3 \cdot 2 \cdot 1}{1 \cdot 2 \cdot 1} \qquad \frac{3 \cdot 2 \cdot 1}{1 \cdot 3 \cdot 2 \cdot 1}$$

$$= \quad 1 \qquad\qquad 3 \qquad\qquad 3 \qquad\qquad 1$$

EXAMPLE 4   Expand $(2a - b)^4$, using Binomial Theorem

Solution: Binomial Theorem States

$$(x + y)^n = x^n y^0 + \frac{n!}{(n-1)!1!}x^{n-1}y^1 + \frac{n!}{(n-2)!2!}x^{n-2}y^2 + \ldots + \frac{n!}{2!(n-2)!}x^2 y^{n-2}$$

$$+ \frac{n!}{1!(n-1)!}x^1 y^{n-1} + x^0 y^n \ .$$

$$(2a - b)^4 = (2a)^4(-b)^0 + \frac{4!}{(4-1)!1!}(2a)^{4-1}(-b)^1 \qquad \text{Substitute } n = 4, \ x = 2a, \text{ and } y = -b.$$

$$+ \frac{4!}{(4-2)!2!}(2a)^{4-2}(-b)^2 + \frac{4!}{(4-3)!3!}(2a)^{4-3}(-b)^3 + (2a)^{4-4}(-b)^4$$

$$= (2a)^4 b^0 - \frac{4!}{3!1!}(2a)^3 b^1 + \frac{4!}{2!2!}(2a)^2 b^2 - \frac{4!}{1!3!}(2a)^1 b^3 + b^4$$

$$(2a - b)^4 = 16a^4 - 4(8a^3)b + 6(4a^2)b^2 - 4(2a)b^3 + 1\,b^4$$

$$= 16a^4 - 32a^3 b + 24a^2 b^2 - 8ab^3 + b^4$$

D. GENERAL TERM OF A BINOMIAL EXPANSION

Let us look at the expansion of $(x + y)^4$ once again.

$$(x + y)^4 = 1x^4 y^0 + 4x^3 y^1 + 6x^2 y^2 + 4x^1 y^3 + 1x^0 y^4$$

↓   ↓   ↓   ↓   ↓

1st term   2nd term   3rd term   4th term   5th term

Observations:

Each term in the expansion of $(x + 4)^4$ is a product of three factors.

The 3rd term in the expansion is $6 \cdot x^2 y^2 = 6 \cdot x^{4-2}y^2 = \frac{4!}{2!2!}x^{4-2}\,y^2$

In general, the coefficient of $(k + 1)$th term in the expansion of $(x + y)^n$ is the coefficient of $x^{n-k}y^k$ which is

$$\frac{n!}{(n-k)!k!} \longrightarrow \quad n \text{ is the power of the binomial}$$
$$\longrightarrow \quad n - k \text{ and } k \text{ are the exponents of } x \text{ and } y$$

$(k + 1)$th term in the expansion of $(x + y)^n$ is $T_{k+1} = \dfrac{n!}{(n-k)!k!}x^{n-k} \cdot y^k$

EXAMPLE 5 Find the 4th term in the expansion of $(a + 2b)^{10}$.

Solution: For the fourth $(= 3 + 1)$th term in the expansion of $(a + 2b)^{10}$,

substitute $n = 10$, $k = 3$, $x = a$, and $y = 2b$ in $T_{k+1} = \dfrac{n!}{(n-k)!k!} x^{n-k} y^k$

$$T_4 \text{ of } (a + 2b)^{10} = \frac{10!}{(10-3)!3!} a^{10-3}(2b)^3$$

$$= \frac{10!}{7!3!} a^7 (2b)^3$$

$$= 120\, a^7\left(8b^3\right) = 960\ a^7 b^3 \qquad \frac{10!}{7!3!} = \frac{10 \cdot 9 \cdot 8 \cdot 7!}{7! \cdot 3 \cdot 2 \cdot 1} = 120$$

EXAMPLE 6 **a.** Which term in the expansion of $\left(2x^2 - \dfrac{1}{x}\right)^6$ is constant?

  b. Find the constant term.

Solutions:

a. A term is a constant term if it contains no variable after simplification.

Let $(k+1)$th term be the constant term in the expansion of $\left(2x^2 - \dfrac{1}{x}\right)^6$.

$1 \le k + 1 \le 6 + 1 \quad \rightarrow \quad 1 \le k + 1 \le 7 \quad \rightarrow \quad 0 \le k \le 6$.

$$T_{k+1} = \frac{6!}{(6-k)!k!}\left(2x^2\right)^{6-k}\left(-\frac{1}{x}\right)^k$$

$$= \frac{6!}{(6-k)!k!} 2^{6-k}\left(x^2\right)^{6-k}(-1)^k\left(\frac{1}{x}\right)^k$$

$$= \frac{6!}{(6-k)!k!}\left(2^{6-k}\right)(-1)^k\left(x^2\right)^{6-k}\left(\frac{1}{x}\right)^k$$

Variable part of the term is $\left(x^2\right)^{6-k}\left(\dfrac{1}{x}\right)^k = x^{12-2k}\cdot\left(\dfrac{1}{x}\right)^k = x^{12-2k}\cdot x^{-k} = x^{12-2k-k} = x^{12-3k}$

The $(k + 1)$th term will become constant if the exponent of the variable x is zero.
Thus for the constant term $12 - 3k = 0$ or $k = 4$.

Therefore, $(4 + 1)$th term or the 5th term in the expansion of $\left(2x^2 - \dfrac{1}{x}\right)^6$ is constant.

b. To find the constant term, substitute $k = 4$ (obtained in part (a)) in the expression for $(K + 1)$th term T_{K+1}, or directly find the 5th term.

$$T_5 = \frac{6!}{(6-4)!\cdot 4!}\cdot\left(2x^2\right)^{6-4}\left(-\frac{1}{x}\right)^4$$

$$= \frac{6!}{2!4!}\left(2x^2\right)^2\left(\frac{1}{x^4}\right) = \frac{(6)\,(5)(4)(3)(2)(1)}{(2)(1)(4)(3)(2)(1)}\cdot(4)x^4\cdot\frac{1}{x^4} = \mathbf{60}$$

EXERCISE 8.6

[**Note :** In the following exercises you may use calculator to calculate factorial values of numbers.]

In exercises (1-8), use Pascal's triangle to expand the binomial.

1. $(a+2)^4$

2. $(r+s)^3$

3. $(p-q)^5$

4. $(p-2q)^4$

5. $\left(\dfrac{x}{4}+2y\right)^4$

6. $\left(x^2-2\right)^4$

7. $(ab-2c)^5$

8. $\left(r^2+2s^2\right)^6$

In exercises (9-12), use binomial theorem to write the first four terms of the expansion.

9. $(2x+3y)^{10}$

10. $\left(a^2+b^3\right)^{11}$

11. $\left(2x-\dfrac{y}{3}\right)^7$

12. $\left(3-\dfrac{2}{x}\right)^6$

In exercises (13-21), find the indicated term(s) in the binomial expansion.

13. $(3x-y)^8$; 3rd term

14. $(m+4n)^{15}$; 6th term

15. $\left(x^2+2\right)^{11}$; 10th term

16. $\left(4x^2+5y\right)^6$; middle term

17. $\left(a^2-2b^3\right)^{10}$; middle term

18. $\left(4x^2+3y\right)^7$; 2 middle terms

19. $\left(2x^2+\dfrac{1}{x^2}\right)^6$; constant term

20. $\left(2x^3-\dfrac{3}{x^2}\right)^{10}$; constant term

21. $\left(x^4-\dfrac{3}{x^2}\right)^6$; constant term

8.7 CHAPTER SUMMARY

1. A **sequence** is a collection of numbers or objects where the order or position of an object is well defined. A **finite sequence** has a finite number of terms. An **infinite sequence** has an infinite number of terms.

    Examples : 5, 10, 15, 20, 25, 30   is a finite sequence

    5, 10, 15, 20, 25, 30, …   is an infinite sequence

2. Terms of an infinite sequence **have a pattern**.

    Example :   Pattern for the terms of the infinite sequence 5, 10, 15, 20, 25, 30, … is that its *n*th term is five times *n*.

3. A sequence is a function whose domain is the set of consecutive positive integers.

    Examples :

    a.   Finite sequence 5, 10, 15, 20, 25, 30 can be written in the function form as
    $$f(n) = 5n, \ n \in \{1, 2, \ldots , 6\}$$

    b.   Infinite sequence 5, 10, 15, 20, 25, 30, … can be written in the function form as
    $$f(n) = 5n , \ n \in \{1, 2, 3, 4, \ldots\}$$

4. A sequence (finite or infinite) $a_1, a_2, a_3, a_4, \ldots$ is called an **arithmetic sequence**
    if $a_2 - a_1 = a_3 - a_2 = a_4 - a_3 = \ldots$
    Examples : Arithmetic Sequence :   1, 3, 5, 7, 9, 11
                   Non-Arithmetic Sequence :   1, 3, 5, 7, 10, 13

5. **Formula for the nth term of an arithmetic sequence is $a_n = a_1 + (n-1)d$** where a_1 is the first
    term and d is the common difference.
    Example : nth term of the arithmetic sequence
              1, 3, 5, 7, 9, 11, … is given by $a_n = 1 + (n-1)2 = 2n - 1$ [Here $a_1 = 1$ and $d = 2$]

6. The Arithmetic mean of two numbers a and b is $\dfrac{a+b}{2}$

    Example :   Arithmetic mean of 2 and 8 is $\dfrac{2+8}{2} = 5$.

7. Numbers $m_1, m_2, \ldots m_n$ are called **n arithmetic means** between two numbers a and b
    if $a, m_1, m_2, \ldots, m_n, b$ is an arithmetic sequence.

8. To **insert n arithmetic means** between **a** and **b**, find **d** from the formula $b = a + (n-1)d$ then all
    the terms of the resulting arithmetic sequence from a to b are the arithmetic means.
    The means are: $a + d, a + 2d, a + 3d, \ldots$

9. **Graph of an arithmetic sequence** $a_1, a_2, \ldots, a_n, \ldots$ is a set of discrete points on the line
    $y = dx + (a_1 - d)$ where d is the common difference.

10. A sequence $a_1, a_2, a_3, \ldots, a_n, \ldots$ is a **geometric sequence** if $\dfrac{a_2}{a_1} = \dfrac{a_3}{a_2} = \ldots = \dfrac{a_{n+1}}{a_n} = \ldots$

    Examples :   Geometric Sequence :   2, 8, 32, 128, …
                   Non-Geometric Sequence :   2, 4, 16, 64, 256, …

11. Formula for the **nth term of a geometric sequence** is $a_n = a_1 r^{n-1}$ where a_1 is the first term
    and r is the common ratio.
    Example : n^{th} term of the geometric sequence 2, 8, 32, 128, … is given by
             $a_n = 2(4)^{n-1} = 2 \cdot 2^{2(n-1)} = 2^{2n-1}$.

12. The **Geometric mean** of two positive numbers a and b is $\sqrt{ab}$.

    Example :   Geometric mean of 3 and 27 is $\sqrt{3 \cdot 27} = \sqrt{81} = 9$.

13. The **Geometric mean** of two negative numbers a and b is $-\sqrt{ab}$.

    Example :   Geometric mean of –3 and –27 is $-\sqrt{(-3)(-27)} = -\sqrt{81} = -9$.

14. Positive numbers $x_1, x_2, \ldots, x_n$ are called **n geometric means** between two positive integers a and
    b, if $a, x_1, x_2, \ldots, x_n, b$ is a geometric sequence.

15. To **insert n geometric means** between two positive real numbers a and b, find r from the formula $b = a\,r^{(n+2)-1} = a\,r^{n+1}$, then all the terms of the resulting geometric sequence between a and b are the geometric means: $ar,\ ar^2,\ \ldots$.

16. Graph of the geometric sequence $a_1, a_2, \ldots, a_n$ is a set of discrete points on the exponential curve $y = a_1 r^{x-1}$, where r is the common ratio.

17. Sigma Notation: $\displaystyle\sum_{i=1}^{n} a_i = a_1 + a_2 + \ldots + a_n$

18. When the terms of an arithmetic sequence are added together the resulting expression is called an **arithmetic series.**

    Examples :   Arithmetic Sequence :   1, 4, 7, 10, 13, 16, 19
                        Arithmetic Series :   1 + 4 + 7 + 10 + 13 + 16 + 19

19. A series is called a finite series if it has only a finite number of terms.

    Example :   1 + 3 + 5 + 7 + 9 + 11 + 13

20. A series is called an **infinite series** if it has infinitely many terms.

    Example :   1 + 3 + 5 + 7 + 9 + 11 + 13 + …

21. Sum of the first n terms of an arithmetic sequence $a_1, a_2, \ldots, a_n$ is given by the formulae

    1. $S_n = \dfrac{n}{2}\left(a_1 + a_n\right)$,   **or**   **2.** $S_n = \dfrac{n}{2}\left[2a_1 + (n-1)d\right]$, where d is the common difference

22. Sum of the first n natural numbers is $\dfrac{n(n+1)}{2}$.

23. When the terms of a geometric sequence are added together the resulting expression is called a geometric series.

    Examples :   Geometric Sequence :   2, 4, 8, 16, 32, 64, 128
                        Geometric Series :   2 + 4 + 8 + 16 + 32 + 64 + 128

24. **Sum of the first n terms of a geometric sequence** $a_1, a_2, a_3, \ldots, a_n, \ldots$ is given by the formula

     $S_n = \dfrac{a_1\left(1-r^n\right)}{1-r}$, if $r \neq 1$, and $S_n = n\,a_1$, if $r = 1$ where r is the common ratio.

25. **Sum of an infinite geometric series** $a_1 + a_2 + a_3 + \ldots + a_n + \ldots$ is given by $S_n = \dfrac{a_1}{1-r}$ if the common ratio r is such that $\left|r\right| < 1$.

    Example: Sum of $1 + \dfrac{1}{2} + \dfrac{1}{4} + \dfrac{1}{8} + \ldots = \dfrac{1}{1-\dfrac{1}{2}} = \dfrac{1}{\dfrac{1}{2}} = 2$

26. $n! = n(n-1)(n-2)\ldots 1$, $n > 0$

Example: $5! = 5 \cdot 4 \cdot 3 \cdot 2 \cdot 1 = 120$

27. $0! = 1$

28. Coefficients of the binomial expansion $(x+y)^n$, $n = 0, 1, 2, 3, \ldots$ are given by the numbers in the rows of Pascal's Triangle

$$
\begin{array}{ccccccccccc}
 & & & & & 1 & & & & & \\
 & & & & 1 & & 1 & & & & \\
 & & & 1 & & 2 & & 1 & & & \\
 & & 1 & & 3 & & 3 & & 1 & & \\
 & 1 & & 4 & & 6 & & 4 & & 1 & \\
1 & & 5 & & 10 & & 10 & & 5 & & 1 \\
\end{array}
$$

$\ldots$

29. Every number in the **Pascal Triangle** is the sum of the two numbers right above it.

30.
- Binomial expansion of $(x+y)^n$ has $n+1$ terms.
- Any term in the **Binomial expansion** of $(x+y)^n$ is of the form (coefficient) $x^{n-k} \cdot y^k$, $k = 0, 1, 2, \overline{\ldots}, n$.
- **Coefficient of $x^{n-k}y^k$**, in the expansion of $(x+y)^n$ is $\dfrac{n!}{(n-k)!k!}$.

31. Examples of binomial expansion are:

$(x+y)^2 = x^2 + 2xy + y^2$

$(x+y)^3 = x^3 + 3x^2y + 3xy^2 + y^3$

$(x+y)^4 = x^4 + 4x^3y + 6x^2y^2 + 4xy^3 + y^4$

$(x+y)^5 = x^5 + 5x^4y + 10x^3y^2 + 10x^2y^3 + 5xy^4 + y^5$

$(x+y)^6 = x^6 + 6x^5y + 15x^4y^2 + 20x^3y^3 + 15x^2y^4 + 6xy^5 + y^6$

8.8 CHAPTER REVIEW

In exercises (1-5), identify a pattern (arithmetic, geometric, or none) for the terms of the sequence.

1. $1, 0, 1, 0, 1, \ldots$

2. $4, 1, -2, -5, \ldots$

3. $2, 1, 3, 4, 7, 11, \ldots$

4. $1, \dfrac{1}{2}, \dfrac{1}{4}, \dfrac{1}{8}, \ldots$

5. $3, 3.01, 3.0001, 3.000001, \ldots$

In exercises (6-11), write the sequence in function form.

6. $6, 3, 0, -3, \ldots$

7. $5, 9, 13, 17, \ldots$

8. $2, 1, \dfrac{1}{2}, \dfrac{1}{4}, \ldots$

9. $4, 16, 64, 256, \ldots$

10. $2, 10, 50, 250, \ldots$

11. $2, -4, 8, -16, 32, \ldots$

In exercises (12-17), find the first five terms of the sequence.

12. Arithmetic sequence: $a_1 = 4, d = -2$

13. Arithmetic sequence : $a_1 = 3, S_7 = 189$

14. Arithmetic sequence : $S_4 = -4, S_9 = 81$

15. Geometric sequence : $a_1 = 3, \ r = \dfrac{1}{2}$

16. Geometric sequence : $a_3 = 15. \ a_7 = \dfrac{5}{27}$

17. Geometric sequence : $a_1 = 6, r = -\dfrac{1}{2}$

18. Find the arithmetic mean of -20 and 7.

19. Find the geometric mean of 3 and 27.

20. Find the geometric mean of -8 and -32.

21. Insert five arithmetic means between 3 and 12.

22. Insert four geometric means between 3 and $\dfrac{1}{81}$.

In exercises (23-26), write the summation in expanded form.

23. $\displaystyle\sum_{n=1}^{4} \dfrac{n+1}{2n+1}$

24. $\displaystyle\sum_{n=1}^{5} \dfrac{1}{3n}$

25. $\displaystyle\sum_{n=1}^{\infty} \dfrac{2^{n+1}}{3^n}$

26. $\displaystyle\sum_{n=1}^{\infty} \dfrac{2n}{(2n-1)^2}$

In exercises (27-32), identify the series as arithmetic or geometric, and find the nth term.

27. $1 + 4 + 7 + 10 + \ldots$

28. $-1 - 5 - 9 - 13 \ldots$

29. $1 + \dfrac{3}{2} + 2 + \dfrac{5}{2} + \ldots$

30. $1 + \dfrac{1}{3} + \dfrac{1}{9} + \ldots$

31. $4 - 2 + 1 - \dfrac{1}{2} + \ldots$

32. $1 - \dfrac{2}{3} + \dfrac{4}{9} - \dfrac{8}{27} + \ldots$

In exercises (33-38), find the sum of the first n terms of the series.

33. $3 + 7 + 11 + 15 + \ldots$

34. $15 + 12 + 9 + 6 + \ldots$

35. $3 + 6 + 12 + 24 + \ldots$

36. $4 + \dfrac{8}{3} + \dfrac{16}{9} + \dfrac{32}{27} + \ldots$

37. $\displaystyle\sum_{k=1}^{n} 4\left(-\dfrac{1}{2}\right)^k$

38. $\displaystyle\sum_{k=1}^{n} 5(2k-3)$

In exercises (39-40), find the sum of the first n terms of the series using the given information.

39. Arithmetic series : $S_4 = 42, S_7 = 42$

40. Arithmetic series : $a_2 = 7, S_5 = 60$

In exercises (41-43), find the sum of the infinite geometric series, if it exists.

41. $2 + \dfrac{4}{3} + \dfrac{8}{9} + \dfrac{16}{27} + \ldots$

42. $\dfrac{1}{9} - \dfrac{1}{3} + 1 - 3 + \ldots$

43. $1 + 0.2 + 0.04 + 0.008 + \ldots$

44. A ball is dropped from a height of 6 feet. Every time the ball hits the ground it bounces back $\dfrac{3}{4}$ of the distance it had fallen. Find the distance traveled by the ball until it comes to rest.

45. Write the binomial $(3x + 2y)^4$ in expanded form using both methods:
   a. Pascal's Triangle
   b. Binomial Theorem
   Verify that the coefficients in both expansions are the same.

46. Determine the constant term in the expansion of $\left(3x^3 - \dfrac{2}{x}\right)^4$.

8.9 CHAPTER TEST

1. Find the formula for the nth term of the following sequences.

   a) $5, -1, -7, -13, \ldots$ **b)** $0.4, 0.04, 0.004, 0.0004, \ldots$

2. Find the sum of the first twenty-seven terms of an arithmetic series whose first term is -8 and the sum of the first seven terms is 28.

3. The first and the tenth terms of a geometric sequence are 192 and $\dfrac{3}{8}$. Find the seventh term.

4. An auditorium has fifty rows of seats. The row nearest to the stage has 20 seats. Each row has 2 seats more than the one in front of it. What is the seating capacity of the auditorium.

5. A ball is let go from a height of 5 feet. Each time it hits the floor it bounces back $\dfrac{2}{3}$ of the distance it fell. Find the distance the ball travels before it comes to rest.

6. Express $.4\overline{31}$ as a fraction.

7. Expand $(3 - 2a)^5$ either by using Pascal's triangle or Binomial Theorem.

ANSWERS

ANSWERS

SECTION 1.1

1. integer, rational **3.** rational **5.** rational **7.** irrational **9.** integer, rational **11.** integer, rational **13.** rational

15. rational **17.** rational **19.** irrational **21.** irrational **23.** irrational **25.** rational **27.** rational **29.** irrational

31. irrational **33.** rational **35.** rational **37.** irrational **39.** irrational

41. 1.75

43. −2.5

45. 2.24
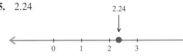

47. 3.65
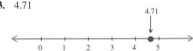

49. 4.41
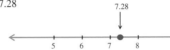

51. 1.57

53. 4.71

55. 7.28

57. 1.05

59. 2.09
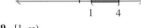

61. $5 > 0$ **63.** $-2 < 0$ **65.** $x^2 \geq 0$ **67.** $\sqrt{x} \geq 0$ **69.** $2 \leq x \leq 5$ **71.** $x > -2$

73. $x \leq 9$ **75.** $x > 10$ or $x < -10$ **77.** $-5 \leq x < -1$ **79.** $t < 5$ or $t \geq 10$

81. (1, 4] **83.** [− 4, 2) **85.** [− 3, 3] **87.** (0, 5)

89. [1, ∞) **91.** (−2, ∞) **93.** (−∞, 3) **95.** (−∞, 0]

97. $(1,\infty) \cap (-\infty, 3]$ or (1, 3] **99.** $(-\infty, 2) \cup (5, \infty)$ **101.** $(-\infty, 10] \cap [2, \infty)$ or [2, 10]

103. $(-\infty, -2) \cup (2, \infty)$ **105.** $(-\infty, -2) \cap [2, \infty)$ Empty Set **107.** $1 \leq x < 5$

109. $-1 < x < 3$ **111.** $-7 \leq x < 2$ **113.** $3 < x < 7.5$

115. $x < -2$ or $x > 3$ **117.** $-4 < x < -1$ or $x > -3$ **119.** $x < 3$ and $x > 2$

SECTION 1.2

1. 20 **3.** 10 **5.** 7 **7.** 2 **9.** −3 **11.** −12 **13.** 4 **15.** 6 **17.** $\frac{1}{4}$ **19.** $\frac{1}{3}$

21. 4 **23.** 12 **25.** − 2 **27.** −1 **29.** 3 **31.** 4 **33.** $\sqrt{3} - 1$ **35.** $3 - \sqrt{3}$ **37.** $12 - \sqrt{7}$ **39.** $7 - \sqrt{10}$

41. $\pi - 5$ **43.** $6 + \sqrt{5} - \pi$ **45.** $7 - 2\pi + \sqrt{3}$ **47.** $9 + \pi$ **49.** $\sqrt{5} + 1 - \sqrt{2}$ **51.** $-1 - \sqrt{3}$ **53.** y^2

55. $\sqrt{x}$ **57.** $y^2 + 6$ **59.** $x^2 + 4$ **61.** $9 - x$ **63.** $x - 5$ **65.** $|y-3| = \begin{cases} 3-y & \text{if } y<3 \\ y-3 & \text{if } y\geq3 \end{cases}$ **67.** $|1-x| = \begin{cases} 1-x & \text{if } x\leq1 \\ x-1 & \text{if } x>1 \end{cases}$

69. $|y+7| = \begin{cases} -y-7 & \text{if } y<-7 \\ y+7 & \text{if } y\geq-7 \end{cases}$ **71.** $|5+x| = \begin{cases} -5-x & \text{if } x<-5 \\ 5+x & \text{if } x\geq-5 \end{cases}$ **73.** $2x + 3$ **75.** 1 **77.** $2x - 2$ **79.** 2

81. $|x-1|-|x-5| = \begin{cases} -4 & \text{if } x\leq1 \\ 2x-6 & \text{if } 1<x<5 \\ 4 & \text{if } x\geq5 \end{cases}$ **83.** $|(x+1)(x-2)| = \begin{cases} (x+1)(x-2) & \text{if } x\leq-1 \text{ or } x\geq2 \\ -(x+1)(x-2) & \text{if } -1<x<2 \end{cases}$

85. $|5-2x|+|x-4| = \begin{cases} 9-3x & \text{if } x\leq\frac{5}{2} \\ x-1 & \text{if } \frac{5}{2}<x<4 \\ 3x-9 & \text{if } x\geq4 \end{cases}$ **87.** $|(2x-1)(x-3)| = \begin{cases} (2x-1)(x-3) & \text{if } x\leq\frac{1}{2} \text{ or } x\geq3 \\ -(2x-1)(x-3) & \text{if } \frac{1}{2}<x<3 \end{cases}$

89. $|x|$ **91.** $|x+1|$ **93.** $|y+3|$ **95.** $|7+4|$ **97.** $|-8+3|$ **99.** $|7-y|$ **101.** $|y+4|$ **103.** $|y-5|=7$

105. $|y+2|=5$ **107.** $|y-7|\geq3$ **109.** $|y+3|\geq2$ **111.** $|x-2|\leq4$ **113.** $|x+5|\leq6$ **115.** $2\,\delta$ **117.** $6\,\delta$

119. $\dfrac{8\delta}{7}$ **121.** $3\,\delta$ **123.** $|x+5|\leq\delta+7$ **125.** $|-x+7|\leq\delta+5$

Section 1.3

1. $63x^8$ **3.** $36x^8$ **5.** $-27x^3$ **7.** 2 **9.** $\dfrac{16y^5}{x^5}$ **11.** $\dfrac{x^6}{2y^8}$ **13.** $20(x+2)^5$ **15.** 5 **17.** $2(2x+3)^2$

19. $(3x+5)^9$ **21.** $25x^2 - 9$ **23.** $4x^2y^2 - 49$ **25.** $9x^4 - 25$ **27.** $x - 7$ **29.** $81x^4 - 4y^2 z^2$ **31.** $49x^2 + 42xz + 9z^2$

33. $16x^2 - 24xy + 9y^2$ **35.** $4x^4 + 20x^2 + 25$ **37.** $9x^6 - 30x^3y^2 + 25y^4$ **39.** $x^3 + 3x^2 + 3x + 1$

41. $8x^3 + 12x^2 + 6x + 1$ **43.** $27x^3 - 54x^2 + 36x - 8$ **45.** $(4-x)(4+x)$ **47.** $(b-a)(b+a)$ **49.** $(1+x)(5-x)$

51. $(5+x)(3-x)$ **53.** $h(2x+h)$ **55.** $3(x+h)^2(x+h-2)(x+h+2)$ **57.** $2x^2(1-2x)(1+2x)$ **59.** $3x^2(1+9x^2)$

61. $(x+2)(x^2-2x+4)$ **63.** $(x-2)(x^2+2x+4)$ **65.** $(x-2)(x+2)(x^2+4)$ **67.** prime   **69.** $\left(y-\dfrac{2}{3}\right)\left(y+\dfrac{2}{3}\right)\left(y^2+\dfrac{4}{9}\right)$

71. $\left(x-\dfrac{3}{2}\right)\left(x^2+\dfrac{3}{2}x+\dfrac{9}{4}\right)$ **73.** $(x-8)(x+3)$ **75.** $(x-15)(x+2)$ **77.** $(2x-1)(x-3)$ **79.** $(3x-1)(2x+5)$ **81.** $(x-3)(x-2)(x+2)$

83. $(2x+1)(x-2)(x+2)$ **85.** $(x+1)(9x+1)$ **87.** $-15(2x+1)^2(x-2)^2$ **89.** $68(x+5)^2(3x-2)^2$ **91.** prime

93. $(x^2+5)^{1/2}(x^2+6)$ **95.** $(4x+5)^{-1/2}(6x-7)^{-1/2}(10x-2)$ **97.** $7(3x-4)^{1/2}(4x-3)(x-1)$ **99.** -1 **101.** -115

103. 49 **105.** 1.6241×10^{10} **107.** 6.2320×10^{12}

Section 1.4

1. $\dfrac{x-2}{x+2}$ for $x\neq-2$ **3.** $\dfrac{h-3}{h+3}$ for $h\neq-3$ **5.** $\dfrac{x-4}{2x-1}$ for $x\neq-4$ **7.** $\dfrac{x^2}{(x+1)}$ for $x\neq-3/2$ **9.** $\dfrac{x+2}{x+3}$ for $x\neq-3$

11. $\dfrac{2x-1}{x}$ for $x\neq-2/3$ **13.** $\dfrac{-3x-2}{x+1}$ for $x\neq3$ **15.** $\dfrac{3(x+2)^5(x-4)}{(x-1)^4}$ for $x\neq1$ **17.** $\dfrac{12t(t^2-1)^2}{(t^2+1)^4}$ **19.** $\dfrac{-2(3x-1)(x+2)}{(3x-4)^4}$ for $x\neq\dfrac{4}{3}$

21. $\dfrac{(x+4)(x-2)}{x^2}$ **23.** $\dfrac{1}{x+1}$ for $x\neq1$ **25.** $\dfrac{2(x-4)}{(x-2)^2}$ **27.** $\dfrac{2x+11}{(x-1)(x-2)(x+3)}$ **29.** $\dfrac{3x-7}{(x+3)(x-2)(x+1)}$

31. $\dfrac{-5x-2}{x^2(x+2)}$ **33.** $\dfrac{x^2+5x-1}{(x+3)^2}$ **35.** $\dfrac{2(x^2-2)}{(2x+1)(x+1)(x-1)}$ **37.** $\dfrac{5x+1}{4(x-1)(3x-1)}$ **39.** $\dfrac{4x-9}{(x+1)(x+2)(x-3)}$

41. $\dfrac{1}{(x-1)(x+2)}$ for $x\neq-5$ **43.** $\dfrac{x-5}{x-3}$, $x\neq-2$ **45.** $\dfrac{-5}{x(x+h)}$, $h\neq0$ **47.** $\dfrac{-6}{(2x+1)(2x+2h+1)}$, $h\neq0$

49. $\dfrac{-(2x+h)}{x^2(x+h)^2}$, $h \neq 0$ **51.** 0 **53.** indeterminate **55.** undefined **57.** indeterminate **59.** undefined

61. 3 **63.** 2 **65.** $\dfrac{7}{2}$ **67.** 0 **69.** 0 **71.** 3,700 **73.** 5

SECTION 1.5

1. $x - 3 + \dfrac{2}{x-2}$ **3.** $x^2 - 4x - 9 - \dfrac{32}{x-3}$ **5.** $5x + 8 + \dfrac{6}{x-1}$ **7.** $x^3 - 3x^2 + 1 - \dfrac{5}{x-2}$ **9.** $5x + 4 + \dfrac{8x-11}{x^2-x+1}$

11. $4x - 6 + \dfrac{9x-7}{x^2+2x-1}$ **13.** $1 + \dfrac{-x^2-9x+6}{x^3-x+3}$ **15.** $2x - 1 + \dfrac{6-6x}{x^2+1}$ **17.** $x + \dfrac{x^2+2x-2}{x^3-x^2}$ **19.** $x^2 + 3x + 9 + \dfrac{26}{x-3}$

21. $x^2 + x + 1 + \dfrac{x^2-3}{x^3-x^2}$ **23.** $x^2 + x + 2 + \dfrac{2}{x-1}$ **25.** $5x^4 + x^2 + \dfrac{13}{2} + \dfrac{19}{2x^2-4}$ **27.** $x - 4 - \dfrac{10}{x-3}$ **29.** $2x - 6 + \dfrac{3}{x-1}$

31. $4x - 3 + \dfrac{13}{x+1}$ **33.** $3x - 8 + \dfrac{24}{x+2}$ **35.** $8x^2 + 21x + 67 + \dfrac{210}{x-3}$ **37.** $6x^2 + 14x + 28 + \dfrac{52}{x-2}$ **39.** $x^2 + x + 1$

41. $x^2 + 2x + 4$ **43.** $x^2 - 5x + 19 - \dfrac{93}{x+5}$ **45.** $2x^2 + 9x + 27 + \dfrac{82}{x-3}$ **47.** $5x^2 + \dfrac{1}{2}x + \dfrac{5}{4} + \dfrac{21}{4(2x-1)}$ **49.** $2x^2 + 2x - 3 + \dfrac{23}{2x+1}$

51. $x^2 + 4x + 9 + \dfrac{11}{x-2}$ **53.** $2x^2 + 3x + 6 + \dfrac{37}{3x-6}$ **55.** $Q(x) = x^2 + 10x + 28$, $R(x) = 85$ **57.** $Q(x) = 3x^2 - 16x + 56$, $R(x) = -159$

59. $Q(x) = x^3 - 3$, $R(x) = 2x - 2$ **61.** $x^2 + x - 5$ **63.** $x^3 - 4x^2 + 2x - 2$ **65.** -69 **67.** -273 **69.** $x^3 - 2x^2 + 2$ **71.** $-2x$

73. $4x^2 + 4x - 2$ **75.** $\dfrac{1}{2}x^2 + \dfrac{1}{4}$ **77.** $x^2 - 3x + 2$ **79.** $3x - 17$ **81.** 7,226,505 **83.** $-143,880$ **85.** 2,881,197

SECTION 1.6

1. $8\sqrt{2}$ **3.** $-4\sqrt[3]{2}$ **5.** $\dfrac{4\sqrt{2}}{5}$ **7.** $2x^2|y|\sqrt{6x}$ **9.** $3xy^2\sqrt[3]{3x^2}$ **11.** $4\sqrt{3}\,x^2|y|$ **13.** $2x^2z^2\sqrt[3]{2x^2}$

15. $\dfrac{2p^2|q|\sqrt{q}}{|r|}$ **17.** $\dfrac{5x^2}{2z}\sqrt[3]{\dfrac{x^2}{y^2z}}$ **19.** $3x - 5$ **21.** $3|y-1|$ **23.** $\dfrac{1}{216}$ **25.** 625 **27.** $5x^2|x|y^6$

29. $\dfrac{27}{125}$ **31.** $-1,024$ **33.** $25a^4b^2c^6$ **35.** $16x^4y^2$ **37.** $4x^4y^2$ **39.** $\dfrac{(5x+7)^{1/3}}{(5x-3)^{1/3}}$ **41.** $(x+2)(x^2+4)^{1/2}$

43. $y^{3/5}(y+1)^{1/5}$ **45.** $3^{1/3}y(y+7)^{1/3}$ **47.** $\dfrac{(3x-4)^{1/5}}{(4x+3)^{1/3}}$ **49.** $6^{1/3}x^{2/3}y^{2/5}$ **51.** $(3x+5)^{-1/2}(5x+4)^{-1/2}(11x+14)$

53. $(x+5)^{1/2}(16x^2+60x+3)$ **55.** $\dfrac{8x-3}{(x-3)^{7/6}}$ **57.** $(3x+8)(3x+4)^{11/6}$ **59.** $\dfrac{-(3x^2+17x)}{(3x+5)^{3/2}}$ **61.** $\dfrac{x^2+7x+11}{(x+2)^{1/2}(x+5)^{4/3}}$

63. $9 - 25x$ **65.** $9x - 61$ **67.** $18x - 52$ **69.** $2x + 28 + 10\sqrt{2x+3}$ **71.** $2x + 2h + 2\sqrt{x^2+2xh}$ **73.** $\dfrac{5x\sqrt{3x}}{3|x|}$

75. $\dfrac{2}{3}x\sqrt[3]{3b^2x^2y}$ **77.** $\dfrac{2(\sqrt{x}-2)}{x-4}$ **79.** $3\sqrt{x}-5$ **81.** $\dfrac{1}{\sqrt{x+h+1}+\sqrt{x+1}}$ **83.** $\dfrac{3}{\sqrt{3x+3h-5}+\sqrt{3x-5}}$

85. $\dfrac{-2}{\sqrt{x+1}\,\sqrt{x+2h+1}\left(\sqrt{x+1}+\sqrt{x+2h+1}\right)}$ **87.** $\dfrac{-5x}{x-\sqrt{5x+x^2}}$ **89.** $\dfrac{9x-15x^2}{\sqrt{x^2+9x}+4x}$ **91.** 3 **93.** 5

95. $3i$; which is not a real number. **97.** 3 **99.** $\dfrac{7x}{2|x|}$ **101.** $\dfrac{5x}{2\sqrt{2}\,|x|}$

CHAPTER REVIEW 1.8

1. 0, 3, and $\sqrt{25}$

3. 2π, $\sqrt{7}$, $3.1223157...$

5. $.524$ $\quad$ $.524$

7. 4.646 $\qquad\qquad$ 4.646

9. 2.667 $\qquad$ 2.667

11. $(-1, 3]$

13. $[2, 5]$

15. $[-1, \infty)$

17. $(-\infty, 2)$

19. $(-\infty, 1) \cup [7, \infty)$

21. $(2, 6]$

23. 4 $\qquad$ **25.** $\sqrt{26} - 5$ $\qquad$ **27.** $8 - 2\pi$ $\qquad$ **29.** $\sqrt{x+5}$ $\qquad$ **31.** $t^2 + 2$ $\qquad$ **33.** $y - 1$ $\qquad$ **35.** $1 - y$

37. $\left| x - 5 \right| = \begin{cases} 5 - x & \text{if } x < 5 \\ x - 5 & \text{if } x \geq 5 \end{cases}$ $\qquad$ **39.** 1 $\qquad$ **41.** $\left| x + 20 \right|$ $\qquad$ **43.** $\left| x + 1 \right|$ $\qquad$ **45.** $\left| x - 2 \right| \geq 5$ $\qquad$ **47.** 5δ $\qquad$ **49.** $\dfrac{2}{5}\delta$

51. $\left| x - 2 \right| \leq \delta + 1$ $\qquad$ **53.** $5x^{5/2}\, y^{1/2}$ $\qquad$ **55.** 10 $\qquad$ **57.** $125x^6 y^3$ $\qquad$ **59.** h $\qquad$ **61.** $2x + 7 - 2\sqrt{x}\,\sqrt{x+7}$

63. $3x^2(1 - 2x)\,(1 + 2x)$ $\qquad$ **65.** $(x - 3)\,(x + 3)\,(x^2 + 9)$ $\qquad$ **67.** $(x - 6)\,(x + 1)$ $\qquad$ **69.** $(4x - 5)\,(3x - 4)$

71. $(2x + 1)\,(x - 3)\,(x + 3)$ $\qquad$ **73.** $\dfrac{6x+5}{(5x+3)^{1/2}\,(x+2)^{1/2}}$ $\qquad$ **75.** $\dfrac{2x+3}{5x+2}$ for $x \neq 1$ $\qquad$ **77.** $\dfrac{-2(x+1)^2\,(x+7)}{(x-3)^6}$, $x \neq 3$

79. $\dfrac{2(x-6)}{(2x-3)\,(x-2)}$ $\qquad$ **81.** $\dfrac{-5}{(x+h+3)\,(x+3)}$ $\qquad$ **83.** indeterminate $\qquad$ **85.** indeterminate

87. 0 $\qquad$ **89.** $3x$ $\qquad$ **91.** $x^2 - 3x + 17 + \dfrac{-72x+75}{x^2+3x-5}$ $\qquad$ **93.** $3x^2 - 2x + 3 + \dfrac{8}{x-2}$ $\qquad$ **95.** $7x^2 - 2x + \dfrac{-11}{x-1}$

97. $\dfrac{3}{(4x+5)^{3/2}\,(2x+1)^{1/2}}$ $\qquad$ **99.** $\sqrt{x} + 5$

CHAPTER TEST 1.9

1. a. $\sqrt{4}\ (= 2)$ $\qquad$ **b.** $\dfrac{2}{7}$, $\sqrt{4}$, -2.98, $2\% = .02$, $5.\overline{32}$ $\qquad$ **c.** $-\sqrt{3}$, $\dfrac{\pi}{2}$, $-1.731523...$ $\qquad$ **3. a.** $5 - \pi$ $\qquad$ **b.** $9 + x^2$

c. $\left| x - 4 \right| = \begin{cases} 4 - x & \text{if } x < 4 \\ x - 4 & \text{if } x \geq 4 \end{cases}$ $\qquad$ **5. a.** $x + 18 - 6\sqrt{x+9}$ $\qquad$ **b.** $h + 5$ $\qquad$ **c.** $x^3 - 6x^2 + 12x - 8$

7. a. $\dfrac{5x+2}{3x+5}$ for $x \neq 3$ $\qquad$ **b.** $\dfrac{x+4}{(x+3)^{3/2}\,(x+2)^{2/3}}$ $\qquad$ **9. a.** undefined $\qquad$ **b.** 2 $\qquad$ **c.** indeterminate $\qquad$ **11.** $2x^2 + x - 1 - \dfrac{2}{x-3}$

Chapter 2

Section 2.1

1. Yes   **3.** Yes   **5.** Yes   **7.** No   **9.** Yes   **11.** {0, 1, 2, 3, 4, ... } **13.** {3, 6, 9, 12, 15, ... }

15. {a, e, r, o, p, l, n}   **17.** {S, M, T, W, F}   **19.** $\left\{\frac{1}{2}, \frac{2}{3}, \frac{3}{4}, \frac{4}{5}, ...\right\}$ **21.** {x | x is a natural number less than 20 and is divisible by 3}

23. {x | x is an integer divisible by 2}   **25.** {x | |x| = 1}

27. $A \cup B$ = {0, 1, 2, 3, 4, 5}   **29.** $A \cup B$ = {Sunday, Monday, Tuesday, Wednesday, Thursday, Saturday}

$A \cap B$ = {1, 2, 3, 4, 5} $A \cap B$ = {Tuesday, Saturday}

$A \setminus B$ = { } or ϕ $A \setminus B$ = {Sunday, Thursday}

$B \setminus A$ = {0} $B \setminus A$ = {Monday, Wednesday}

31. $A \not\subseteq B$, $B \subseteq A$ **33.** $A \subseteq B$ & $B \not\subset A$ **35.** $A \subseteq B$, $B \not\subset A$

37. $A \times B$ = {(x,l), (x,m), (x, a), (x, b), (y,l), (y,m), (y, a), (y,b), (u,l), (u,m), (u, a), (u,b), (v,l), (v,m), (v,a), (v,b)}

$B \times A$ = {(l, x), (l, y), (l, u), (l, v), (m,x), (m,y), (m, u), (m,v), (a,x), (a,y), (a, u), (a,v), (b,x), (b,y), (b,u), (b,v)}

$A \times A$ = {(x, x), (x, y), (x, u), (x, v), (y,x), (y,y), (y, u), (y,v), (u,x), (u,y), (u, u), (u,v), (v,x), (v,y), (v,u), (v,v)}

39. $A \times B$ = {(Sunday, 20), (Sunday, 30), (Sunday, 40), (Tuesday, 20), (Tuesday, 30), (Tuesday, 40), (Friday, 20), (Friday, 30), (Friday, 40)}

$B \times A$ = {(20, Sunday), (20, Tuesday), (20, Friday), (30, Sunday), (30, Tuesday), (30, Friday), (40, Sunday), (40, Tuesday), (40, Friday)}

$A \times A$ = {(Sunday, Sunday) , (Sunday, Tuesday), (Sunday, Friday), (Tuesday, Sunday), (Tuesday, Tuesday), (Tuesday, Friday), (Friday, Sunday), (Friday, Tuesday), (Friday, Friday)}

41. **(i)** {a, b, c, l, x, y}   **(ii)** {a, b, c, l, x, y}   **(iii)** {l}   **(iv)** {l}

43. **(i)** Set of integers   **(ii)** Set of integers   **(iii)** Set of natural numbers   **(iv)** Set of natural numbers

45. **(i)** {Monday, Tuesday, Wednesday, Thursday, Friday, Saturday, Sunday}

(ii) {Monday, Tuesday, Wednesday, Thrusday, Friday, Saturday, Sunday}   **(iii)** {Tuesday}   **(iv)** {Tuesday}

Section 2.2

1. $S(r) = 4\pi r^2$ **3.** $V(r) = \frac{4}{3}\pi r^3$ **5.** $A(a) = a^2$ **7.** $V(x) = x^3$ **9.** $p(x) = 3x$ **11.** $C(F) = \frac{5}{9}(F - 32)$

13. It represents a function.   **15.** It represents a function.   **17.** It represents a function.   **19.** It represents a function

21. It defines a function.   **23.** It defines a function.   **25.** It does not define a function. **27.** It defines a function.

29. It defines a function.   **31.** Yes   **33.** No   **35.** Yes   **37.** Yes   **39.** No

41. Yes **43.** Yes   **45.** Yes   **47.** Yes   **49.** No   **51.** No   **53.** No

55. No **57.** Absolute value   **59.** Rational   **61.** Radical   **63.** Absolute value   **65.** Piecewise

67. Polynomial   **69.** Piecewise   **71.** Piecewise **73.** Absolute value   **75.** Rational

77. $4(3x - 1)$ **79.** $5(x - 2)(x + 2)$ **81.** $(3x - 2)(x - 1)$ **83.** $f(x) = 2 + x^2$

85. $h(x) = \begin{cases} x - 5 & if \ x \geq 5 \\ -(x - 5) & if \ x < 5 \end{cases}$ **87.** $H(x) = \begin{cases} -2x + 7 & if \ x \leq 3 \\ 1 & if \ 3 < x < 4 \\ 2x - 7 & if \ x \geq 4 \end{cases}$ **89.** $f(x) = \sqrt{x + 9}$ **91.** $\frac{x + 2}{x + 1}$, $x \neq 2$

93. $\frac{x - 5}{(x + 3)(x + 2)}$, $x \neq 0$ **95.** $\frac{x + 1}{x^2 + x + 1}$, $x \neq 1$ **97.** $\frac{3x}{|x|(x + 1)^{\frac{1}{2}}}$ **99.** $(x + 3)^{\frac{2}{5}}$

SECTION 2.3

1. a. 8 **b.** 29 **c.** -6 **d.** $7a + 15$ **e.** $7h$ **3. a.** 10 **b.** 10 **c.** 10 **d.** 10 **e.** 0

5. a. 7 **b.** -11 **c.** -1 **d.** $-2a^2 - 4a + 5$ **e.** $-2h\,(2x + h)$ **7. a.** 0 **b.** 72 **c.** 22 **d.** $7a^2 + 17a + 10$ **e.** $h\,(7h + 14x + 3)$

9. a. $\sqrt{15}$ **b.** $2\sqrt{3}$ **c.** $\sqrt{17}$ **d.** $\sqrt{14-a}$ **e.** $\sqrt{15-x-h} - \sqrt{15-x}$ **11. a.** $-\dfrac{5}{2}$ **b.** -5 **c.** 5 **d.** undefined

13. a. 0 **b.** $\dfrac{1}{2}$ **c.** $\dfrac{3}{4}$ **d.** $\dfrac{2}{3}$ **15. a.** $\dfrac{1}{5}$ **b.** $-\dfrac{1}{4}$ **c.** $\dfrac{-5}{2}$ **d.** -1

17. a. $\dfrac{3}{25}$ **b.** $\dfrac{1}{12}$ **c.** 0 **d.** $\dfrac{1}{21}$ **19. a.** $\dfrac{1}{2}$ **b.** $\dfrac{1}{3}$ **c.** $\dfrac{1}{5}$ **d.** indeterminate

21. a. 5 **b.** 7 **c.** 4 **d.** $5 + h$ **23. a.** 2 **b.** 4 **c.** 1 **d.** $2 + h$

25. a. 1 **b.** 1 **c.** 1 **d.** 1 **27. a.** indeterminate **b.** 1 **c.** -1 **d.** 1

29. a. 1 **b.** 2 **c.** -3 **d.** $-h$ **31. a.** -3 **b.** 5 **c.** 25 **d.** $(2 + h)^2$

33. a. -1 **b.** 0 **c.** 25 **d.** $(2 + h)^2$ **35. a.** -2 **b.** -2 **c.** 2 **d.** 2

37. a. \$2,250 **b.** \$11,042.50 **c.** \$31,039.50 **d.** \$99,439.50 **39.** Cost = \$40,000 ; Revenue = \$120,000; Profit = \$80,000

41. $300x - \dfrac{x^2}{4000}$; Revenue = \$119,960 ; Cost per DVD = \$299.90 **43.** $Y(x) = (x + 24)(600 - 12x)$; Total yield = 15,660

45. The farmer should sell after **2 weeks** for the highest price per bushel. **47.** Domain : $(-\infty, \infty)$; Range : $(-\infty, \infty)$

49. Domain : $(-\infty, \infty)$; Range : $\left[\dfrac{2}{3}, \infty\right]$ **51.** Domain : $(-\infty, \infty)$; Range : $[1, \infty)$

53. Domain : $(-\infty, \infty)$; Range : $(-\infty, \infty)$ **55.** Domain : $[-1, \infty)$; Range : $[0, \infty)$

57. Domain : $(-\infty, 8) \cup (8, \infty)$; Range : $(-\infty, 1) \cup (1, \infty)$

59. Domain : $(-\infty, \infty)$; Range : $[-3, \infty)$

SECTION 2.4

1.
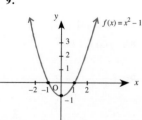

3.
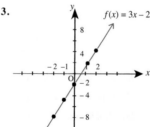

5.
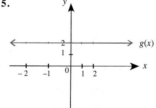

7.
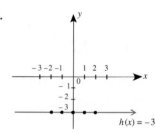

9.
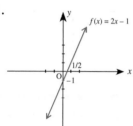

11.
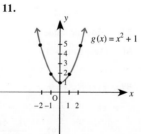

13.
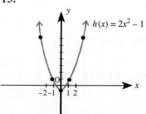

15.
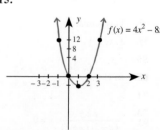

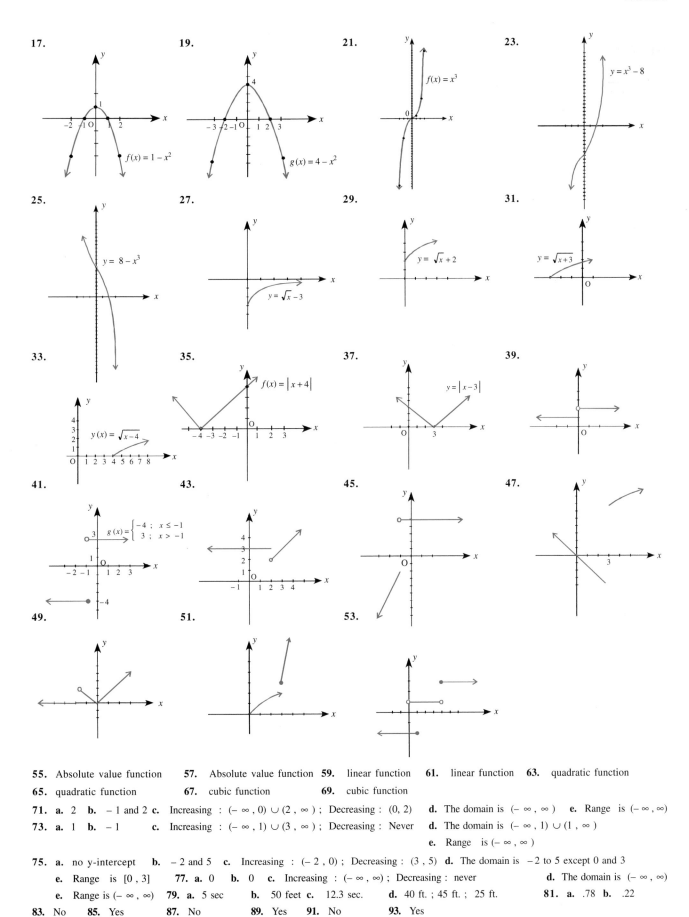

17.

19.

21. $f(x) = x^3$

23. $y = x^3 - 8$

25. $y = 8 - x^3$

27. $y = \sqrt{x} - 3$

29. $y = \sqrt{x} + 2$

31. $y = \sqrt{x+3}$

33. $y(x) = \sqrt{x-4}$

35. $f(x) = |x+4|$

37. $y = |x-3|$

39.

41. $g(x) = \begin{cases} -4 \; ; \; x \le -1 \\ 3 \; ; \; x > -1 \end{cases}$

43.

45.

47.

49.

51.

53.

55. Absolute value function   **57.** Absolute value function **59.** linear function   **61.** linear function   **63.** quadratic function

65. quadratic function   **67.** cubic function   **69.** cubic function

71. a. 2 **b.** -1 and 2 **c.** Increasing : $(-\infty, 0) \cup (2, \infty)$; Decreasing : $(0, 2)$ **d.** The domain is $(-\infty, \infty)$ **e.** Range is $(-\infty, \infty)$

73. a. 1 **b.** -1 **c.** Increasing : $(-\infty, 1) \cup (3, \infty)$; Decreasing : Never   **d.** The domain is $(-\infty, 1) \cup (1, \infty)$
e. Range is $(-\infty, \infty)$

75. a. no y-intercept   **b.** -2 and 5 **c.** Increasing : $(-2, 0)$; Decreasing : $(3, 5)$ **d.** The domain is -2 to 5 except 0 and 3
e. Range is $[0, 3]$ **77. a.** 0 **b.** 0 **c.** Increasing : $(-\infty, \infty)$; Decreasing : never   **d.** The domain is $(-\infty, \infty)$
e. Range is $(-\infty, \infty)$ **79. a.** 5 sec   **b.** 50 feet **c.** 12.3 sec.   **d.** 40 ft. ; 45 ft. ; 25 ft.   **81. a.** .78 **b.** .22
83. No   **85.** Yes   **87.** No   **89.** Yes   **91.** No   **93.** Yes

SECTION 2.5

1. $\sqrt{74}$ **3.** 5   **5.** $\left|\sqrt{x}-x^2\right|$ **7.** $\left|x^2-x^3\right|$ **9.** $\sqrt{(x-c)^2+y^2}$ **11.** Yes

13. No   **15.** Yes   **17.** Yes   **19.** Yes   **21.** $x+2-x^2$

23. x^2-x^3 **25.** $\sqrt{x-1}+x-5$ **27.** $4-2x^2$ **29.** $5-2x$ **31.** $(2,8)$

33. $\left(\dfrac{3}{2},\dfrac{3}{2}\right)$ **35.** $\left(\dfrac{1}{2},-1\right)$ **37.** $\left(x,\dfrac{\sqrt{x}+x^2}{2}\right)$ **39.** $\left(x,\dfrac{x^2+x^3}{2}\right)$ **41.** $\left(x,\dfrac{x^2-x^3+2}{2}\right)$ **43.** $M=\left(x,\dfrac{x^2-x+2}{2}\right)$

45. $M=\left(x,\dfrac{3-x^2+\sqrt{1-x^2}}{2}\right)$ **47.** $M=\left(x,\dfrac{\sqrt{1-x^2}+x^2}{2}\right)$ **49.** $M=(x,3)$ **51.** $M=\left(x,\dfrac{\sqrt{x}+x}{2}\right)$

53. 0   **55.** -1 **57.** undefined   **59.** $\dfrac{4}{3}$ **61.** undefined   **63.** $2x-h$

65. $h-1$ **67.** $h-2a$ **69.** $3+3h+h^2$ **71.** $3x^2+3xh+h^2$ **73.** $3x^2+h^2$ **75.** 1.25 million per year

77. a. $4,035   **b.** $80   **c.** $4,115   **79. a.** 22.67   **b.** -0.7 **81. a.** 70.8 in   **b.** 0.5 in

SECTION 2.6

1. a. x^2+x ; Domain : $(-\infty,\infty)$ **b.** x^2-3x+2 ; Domain : $(-\infty,\infty)$ **c.** $2x^3-3x^2+3x-1$; Domain : $(-\infty,\infty)$

    d. $\dfrac{x^2-x+1}{2x-1}$; Domain : $x\neq\dfrac{1}{2}$ **e.** $2x^2-2x+2$; Domain : $(-\infty,\infty)$ **f.** $6x-3$; Domain : $(-\infty,\infty)$

    g. $2x^2+4x-1$; Domain : $(-\infty,\infty)$ **h.** $2x^2-8x+5$; Domain : $(-\infty,\infty)$

3. a. $2x^2-5x-11$; Domain : $(-\infty,\infty)$ **b.** $-5x-3$; Domain : $(-\infty,\infty)$ **c.** $x^4-5x^3-11x^2+20x+28$; Domain : $(-\infty,\infty)$

    d. $\dfrac{x^2-5x-7}{x^2-4}$; Domain : $x\neq2,-2$ or $(-\infty,-2)\cup(-2,2)\cup(2,\infty)$ **e.** $2x^2-10x-14$; Domain : $(-\infty,\infty)$

    f. $3x^2-12$; Domain : $(-\infty,\infty)$ **g.** $5x^2-10x-26$; Domain : $(-\infty,\infty)$ **h.** $-x^2-10x-2$; Domain : $(-\infty,\infty)$

5. a. $8x-27$; Domain : $(-\infty,\infty)$ **b.** $6x-23$; Domain : $(-\infty,\infty)$ **c.** $7x^2-39x+50$; Domain : $(-\infty,\infty)$

    d. $\dfrac{7x-25}{x-2}$; Domain : $x\neq2$ or $(-\infty,2)\cup(2,\infty)$ **e.** $14x-50$; Domain : $(-\infty,\infty)$ **f.** $3x-6$; Domain : $(-\infty,\infty)$

    g. $17x-56$; Domain : $(-\infty,\infty)$ **h.** $11x-44$; Domain : $(-\infty,\infty)$

7. a. x^2-3 ; Domain : $(-\infty,\infty)$ **b.** x^2-2x-3 ; Domain : $(-\infty,\infty)$ **c.** x^3-x^2-3x ; Domain : $(-\infty,\infty)$

    d. $\dfrac{x^2-x-3}{x}$; Domain : $x\neq0$ **e.** $2x^2-2x-6$; Domain : $(-\infty,\infty)$ **f.** $3x$; Domain : $(-\infty,\infty)$

    g. $2x^2+x-6$; Domain : $(-\infty,\infty)$ **h.** $2x^2-5x-6$; Domain : $(-\infty,\infty)$

9. a. $-x^2-3$; Domain : $(-\infty,\infty)$ **b.** x^2-5 ; Domain : $(-\infty,\infty)$ **c.** $4x^2-4$; Domain : $(-\infty,\infty)$

    d. $\dfrac{-4}{1-x^2}$; Domain : $(-\infty,-1)\cup(-1,1)\cup(1,\infty)$ **e.** -8 ; Domain : $(-\infty,\infty)$

    f. $3-3x^2$; Domain : $(-\infty,\infty)$ **g.** $-3x^2-5$; Domain : $(-\infty,\infty)$ **h.** $3x^2-11$; Domain : $(-\infty,\infty)$

11. a. $\sqrt{x-2}+x$; Domain : $[2,\infty)$ **b.** $\sqrt{x-2}-x$; Domain : $[2,\infty)$ **c.** $x\sqrt{x-2}$; Domain : $[2,\infty)$

    d. $\dfrac{\sqrt{x-2}}{x}$; Domain : $[2,\infty)$ **e.** $2\sqrt{x-2}$; Domain : $[2,\infty)$ **f.** $3x$; Domain : $(-\infty,\infty)$

    g. $2\sqrt{x-2}+3x$; Domain : $[2,\infty)$ **h.** $2\sqrt{x-2}-3x$; Domain : $[2,\infty)$

13. a. $\sqrt{x} + \sqrt{9-x^2}$; Domain : $[0, 3]$ **b.** $\sqrt{x} - \sqrt{9-x^2}$; Domain : $[0, 3]$ **c.** $\sqrt{9x - x^3}$; Domain : $(-\infty, -3] \cup [0, 3]$

d. $\sqrt{\dfrac{x}{9-x^2}}$; Domain : $(-\infty, -3) \cup [0, 3)$ **e.** $2\sqrt{x}$; Domain : $[0, \infty)$

f. $3\sqrt{9-x^2}$; Domain : $[-3, 3]$ **g.** $2\sqrt{x} + 3\sqrt{9-x^2}$; Domain : $[0, 3]$ **h.** $2\sqrt{x} - 3\sqrt{9-x^2}$; Domain : $[0, 3]$

15. a. 4 **b.** 5 **17. a.** -5 **b.** 38 **19. a.** $117x + 160$ **b.** $117x - 68$

21. a. $-4x + 15$ **b.** $-4x + 5$ **23. a.** $x^2 + 8x + 10$ **b.** $x^2 + 2x - 2$ **25. a.** $\sqrt{2x - 2}$ **b.** $2\sqrt{x+5} - 7$

27. a. $\dfrac{3}{2x+7}$ **b.** $\dfrac{5x+16}{x+2}$ **29. a.** $5|x-1| - 2$ **b.** $|5x - 3|$ **31. a.** $\big||x-1| + 1\big|$ **b.** $\big||x+1| - 1\big|$

33. a. $\sqrt[4]{9-x}$ **b.** $\sqrt{9 - \sqrt{x}}$ **35. a.** $\sqrt{5 + \sqrt{x}}$ **b.** $\sqrt[4]{5 + x}$ **37. a.** $\dfrac{1 + 4x^2}{x^2}$; Domain : $(-\infty, 0) \cup (0, \infty)$

b. $\dfrac{1}{x^2 + 4}$; Domain : $(-\infty, \infty)$ **39. a.** $\big|1 - 5|3x - 2|\big|$; Domain : $(-\infty, \infty)$ **b.** $\big|3|1 - 5x| - 2\big|$; Domain : $(-\infty, \infty)$

41. a. 5 **b.** $-\dfrac{1}{7}$ **43. a.** $\dfrac{1}{6}$ **b.** $\dfrac{64}{9}$ **45. a.** 8 **b.** 5

47. a. 4 **b.** 0 **49. a.** 1 **b.** .75

CHAPTER REVIEW 2.8

1. $A \cup B = \{1, 2, x, l, p, 5, t\}$
$A \cap B = \{1, x\}$
$A \mid B = \{2, l, p\}$
$B \mid A = \{5, t\}$

3. $A \cup B = \{x \mid x \text{ is a prime number}\}$
$A \cap B = \{x \mid x \text{ is an odd prime number}\}$
$A \mid B = \{2\}$
$B \mid A = \phi$

5. $A \cup B = $ Set of real numbers
$A \cap B = \phi$
$A \mid B = $ Set of rational numbers
$B \mid A = $ Set of irrational numbers

7. $150x$ **9.** $2.1x$ **11.** $x^2 + 4$ **13.** $x + 12$ **15.** $-7x - 27$

17. $h(x) = \begin{cases} 3x - 2 & \text{if } x \geq \dfrac{2}{3} \\ 2 - 3x & \text{if } x < \dfrac{2}{3} \end{cases}$ **19.** $(3x + 7)^{1/3}$ **21.** $|9x - 2|$ **23.** $|x|(5x + 6)^{1/2}$ **25.** $x^{\frac{2}{3}}(8 + 4x)^{\frac{1}{3}}$

27. a. 12 **b.** 12 **c.** 0 **29. a.** -7 **b.** $2a^2 + 7a - 4$ **c.** $4xh + 2h^2 + 3h$ **31. a.** -3 **b.** $7a + 18$ **c.** $7h$

33. a. 5 **b.** $\sqrt{-9a - 2}$ **c.** $\sqrt{7 - 9x - 9h} - \sqrt{7 - 9x}$ **35.** undefined ; $-\dfrac{9}{5}$; $-\dfrac{7}{8}$ **37.** $\dfrac{8}{15}$; indeterminate; $\dfrac{8}{9}$

39. 2 ; $\dfrac{19}{11}$; $\dfrac{5}{4}$ **41. a.** 21 **b.** $h(4 + h)$ **43. a.** 21 **b.** $h(4 + h)$ **45. a.** 7 **b.** $4 + h$

47. a. 1 **b.** 8 **c.** $-1 - 2h - h^2$ **49. a.** 2 **b.** 3 **c.** $3 + 2h + h^2$

51. Domain : $(-\infty, \infty)$ **53.** Domain : $(-\infty, \infty)$ **55.** Domain : $\left(-\infty, \dfrac{5}{3}\right) \cup \left(\dfrac{5}{3}, \infty\right)$ **57.** Domain : $[-15, \infty)$

Range : $[-9, \infty)$ Range : $[-5, \infty)$ Range : $\left(-\infty, \dfrac{1}{3}\right) \cup \left(\dfrac{1}{3}, \infty\right)$ Range : $[0, \infty)$

59. yes **61.** No **63.** 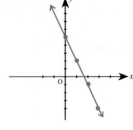 **65.**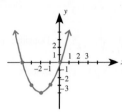

67. 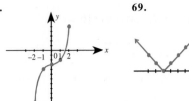 **69.**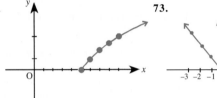

71. 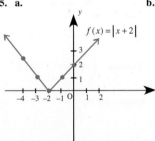 **73.** **75.** linear function **77.** cubic function

79. **a.** 1 **b.** -2 **c.** Increasing : $(-\infty, 1) \cup (1, \infty)$ $(-\infty, \infty)$

d. Domain : $(-\infty, 1) \cup (1, \infty)$ or all real except 1.

e. Range : $(-\infty, 1.5) \cup (1.5 \ \infty)$

81. **a.** 1 **b.** -1 **c.** Increasing : on $(-1, \infty)$.

d. Domain : $[-1, \infty)$ **e.** Range : $[0, \infty)$

83. $\dfrac{17}{32}$ **85.** No **87. a.** $5\sqrt{5}$ **b.** $\left(1, \dfrac{-19}{2}\right)$ **c.** $\dfrac{-1}{2}$ **89. a.** $\left|x^3 + 5x\right|$ **b.** $\left(x, \dfrac{-5x + x^3}{2}\right)$

c. undefined **91. a.** $\sqrt{x} - x^2$ **b.** $\left(x, \dfrac{\sqrt{x} + x^2}{2}\right)$ **93.** $-2a - h$ **95. a.** $x^3 - 6x + 5$ **b.** $x^3 - 3$ **c.** $-3x^4 + 4x^3 + 9x^2 - 15x + 4$

d. $\dfrac{x^3 - 3x + 1}{-3x + 4}$ **e.** $-27x^3 + 108x^2 - 135x + 53$ **f.** $-3x^3 + 9x + 1$ **g.** $3x^3 - 9x + 3$ **h.** $15x - 20$

97. a. $\sqrt{x+3} + x^2$ **b.** $\sqrt{x+3} - x^2$ **c.** $\sqrt{x+3} \cdot x^2$ **d.** $\dfrac{\sqrt{x+3}}{x^2}$ **e.** $\left(x^2 + 3\right)^{1/2}$ **f.** $x + 3$ **g.** $3\sqrt{x+3}$ **h.** $-5x^2$

99. a. $\dfrac{7}{6}$ **b.** 9 **101. a.** $\sqrt{7}$ **b.** 2 **103. a.** -1 **b.** 2

CHAPTER TEST 2.9

1. **a.** $S(x) = 6x^2$ **b.** $C(x) = 100x + 1000$

3. **a.** $2, \sqrt{4-h}$ **b.** $2, 2 - h - h^2$ **c.** $0, h$ **d.** $0, \dfrac{4h + h^2}{5 + h}$ **e.** undefined, $\dfrac{3 + h}{2h + h^2}$ **f.** $4, (2 + h)^2$

5. **a.** **b.** **c.** **d.**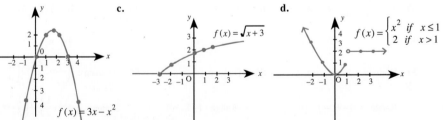

7. Estimated area $= 3.75$ **9.** $2x + h$ **11. a.** $\sqrt{x^2 - 9}$; Domain : $(-\infty, -3] \cup [3, \infty)$ **b.** $x - 9$; Domain : $[3, \infty)$

Chapter 3

SECTION 3.1

1. $x = -13$

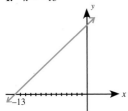

3. $x = \dfrac{-5}{11}$

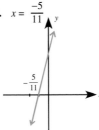

5. $x = \dfrac{29}{6}$

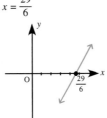

7. $x = \dfrac{14}{9}$

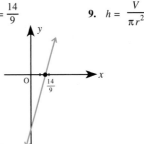

9. $h = \dfrac{V}{\pi r^2}$

11. $h = \dfrac{3V}{\pi r^2}$

13. $x = \dfrac{2y + 7}{3}$

15. $y = \dfrac{5(x - 3)}{7}$

17. $x = \dfrac{a + b}{a - b}, a \neq 5$

19. $x = 2$ or $x = 3$

21. $x = -1$ or $x = 4$

23. $x = \dfrac{-2}{15}$ or $x = 1$

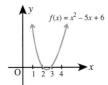

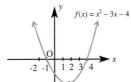

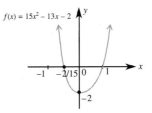

25. $x = \dfrac{3}{2}$ or $x = -1$

27. $x = \dfrac{2}{3}$

29. $x = -3$

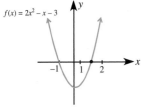

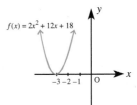

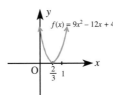

31. $x = \dfrac{\sqrt{17} - 1}{2}, \dfrac{-\left(\sqrt{17} + 1\right)}{2}$

33. $x = \dfrac{\sqrt{33} - 5}{4}, \dfrac{-\left(\sqrt{33} + 5\right)}{4}$

35. $\dfrac{5 \pm i\sqrt{15}}{2}$

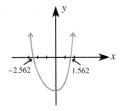

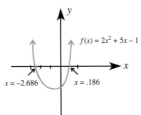

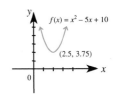

37. $x = \dfrac{-1 \pm i\sqrt{15}}{4}$

39. $(x + 0.414)(x - 2.414)$

41. $(2x - 3.562)(x + 0.281)$

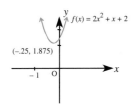

43. $x = 4, 1, -1$

45. $x = -1, 6$

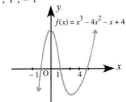

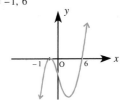

47. $x = 2,\ -1,\ 2$

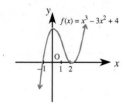

49. no real solutions

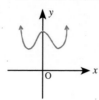

51. $x = -2,\quad x = \dfrac{7 \pm \sqrt{57}}{2}$

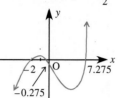

53. $x = 1,\quad x = 1 \pm \sqrt{3}$

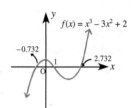

55. $x = 1,\quad x = -2,\quad x = -3,\quad x = 7$

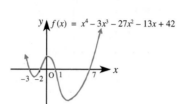

57. $x = -4,\quad x = -1,\quad x = 2,\ x = 3$

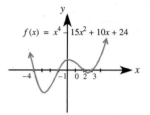

59.

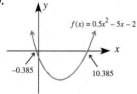

61.

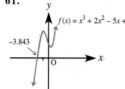

63.

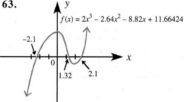

65. 4 units must be sold **67.** 20 feet , 30 feet **69.** 1.9 inches **71.** $x = 5$ or $x = 21$ **73.** $x^2 - 9x + 20 = 0$

75. $x^2 - 3x - 10 = 0$ **77.** $x^2 + 8x = 0$ **79.** $x^2 - 2x + 1 = 0$ **81.** $x^3 - 6x^2 + 3x + 10 = 0$

83. $x^4 + 2x^3 - 15x^2 = 0$ **85.** $x^4 - 13x^3 + 62x^2 - 128x + 96 = 0$ **87.** $x^3 - 2x^2 - 19x = 0$

89. $x^4 - 4x^3 + 20x - 25 = 0$ **91.** $x^5 - 15x^4 + 115x^3 - 495x^2 + 1080x - 918 = 0$

SECTION 3.2

1. $x = 12$

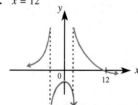

3. no solution

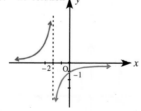

5. $x = 3$ and $x = \dfrac{-7}{2}$

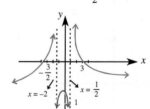

7. $x = 5.732$ and $x = 2.268$

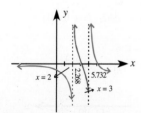

9. $x = 3.646$ and $x = -1.646$

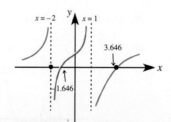

11. $x = -4$ and $x = 4$

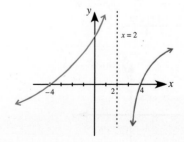

13. $x = 0$ and $x = 3$

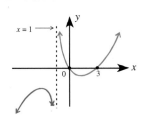

15. $x = 2$ and $x = -1$

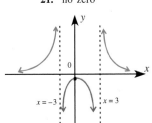

17. $x = -1$

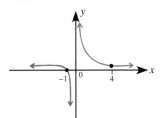

19. no zero

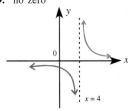

21. no zero

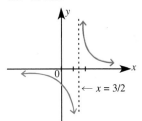

23. no zero

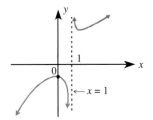

25. $x = 0$

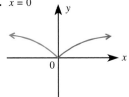

27. no real zeros

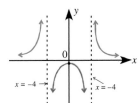

29. no real zeros

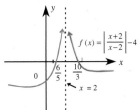

31. $83\frac{1}{3}$ % of the waste

SECTION 3.3

1. 2 and $\dfrac{-1}{4}$

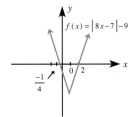

3. no solution

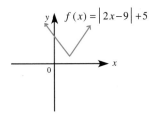

5. $\dfrac{10}{3}$ and $\dfrac{6}{5}$

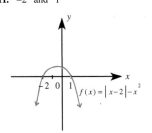

7. $\dfrac{-1}{5}$ and 5

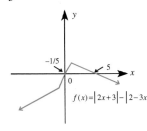

9. $-2 + 2\sqrt{3}$ and $-2 - 2\sqrt{3}$

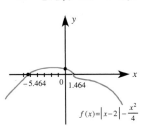

11. -2 and 1

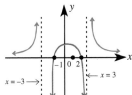

13. -1 and 2 **15.** 1 and $\dfrac{7}{3}$ **17.** No zero   **19.** No zero   **21.** -3, and 3 **23.** $\sqrt{2}$, and $-\sqrt{2}$.

25. $f(x) = \begin{cases} x - 5 & \text{if } x \geq 5 \\ 5 - x & \text{if } x < 5 \end{cases}$

27. $f(x) = \begin{cases} 2x - 3 & \text{if } x \geq 3/2 \\ 3 - 2x & \text{if } x < 3/2 \end{cases}$

29. $f(x) = \begin{cases} \dfrac{x}{3} - \dfrac{4}{5} & \text{if } x \geq \dfrac{12}{5} \\ \dfrac{4}{5} - \dfrac{x}{3} & \text{if } x < \dfrac{12}{5} \end{cases}$

31. $f(x) = \begin{cases} x-6 & \text{if } x \ge 4 \\ 2-x & \text{if } x < 4 \end{cases}$

33. $f(x) = \begin{cases} 2x-14 & \text{if } x \ge 9/2 \\ 4-2x & \text{if } x < 9/2 \end{cases}$

35. $f(x) = \begin{cases} x^2-9 & \text{if } x \ge 2 \text{ or } x \le -2 \\ -x^2-1 & \text{if } -2 < x < 2 \end{cases}$

SECTION 3.4

1. $x = 2$

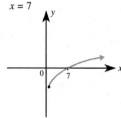

3. $x = 28$ and $x = -26$

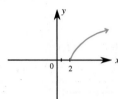

5. $x = 62$ and $x = -66$

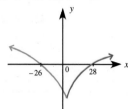

7. $x = 3$

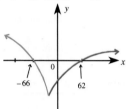

9. $x = 7$

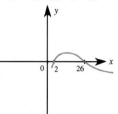

11. $x = 2$ and $x = 26$

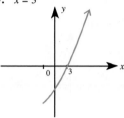

13. $x = 19$

15. $x = 24$

17. $x = 2$

19. $x = 3$

21. $x = \dfrac{7}{4}$

23. $x = 2$

25. $x = -1$ and $x = 6$ **27.** $x = -2$ and $x = 3$ **29.** $x = \dfrac{5+\sqrt{17}}{2}$

31. $x = 7$

33. $x = \dfrac{197}{4}$

35. $x = \dfrac{141}{4}$

37. $x = 2$

39. $x = 3$ **41.** 25 items

SECTION 3.5

1. $[-5, \infty)$ **3.** $(-\infty, -3]$ **5.** $(-\infty, -5)$ **7.** $\left(-\dfrac{7}{19}, \infty\right)$ **9.** $(2, 3)$ **11.** $\left[\dfrac{13}{4}, 4\right]$

13. $\left[\dfrac{32}{9}, \dfrac{14}{3}\right]$ **15.** $\left[-\dfrac{1}{4}, 0\right]$ **17.** $\left(-\infty, \dfrac{9}{7}\right]$ **19.** $\left(-\infty, -\dfrac{11}{3}\right)$ **21.** $\left[\dfrac{1}{17}, \infty\right)$

23. $(-\infty, -2] \cup [2, \infty)$

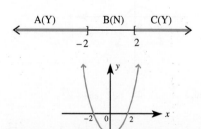

25. $(-3, 3)$

27. $[-1, 2]$

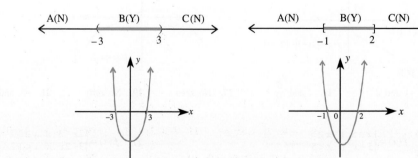

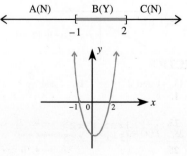

29. $(-\infty, -3) \cup (4, \infty)$

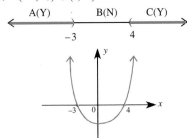

31. $(-\infty, -6] \cup [4, \infty)$

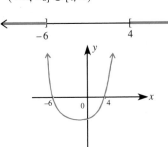

33. $[-3, 3]$

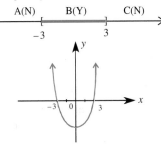

35. $(-\infty, -1] \cup [0, 1]$

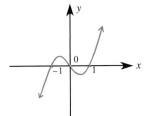

37. $(-2, 1) \cup (3, \infty)$

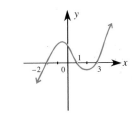

39. $\left(-\infty, -1-\sqrt{2}\right) \cup \left(-1+\sqrt{2}, \infty\right)$

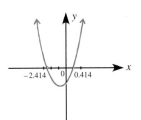

41. $(-\infty, -4.121) \cup (0.121, \infty)$

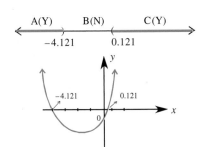

43. $(-\infty, -1] \cup [2, 3]$

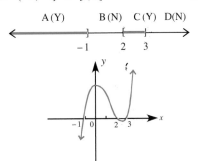

45. $[-3.15, -1.20] \cup [1.33, \infty)$

47. $(-0.49, 1.42)$ **49.** $(5, 20)$ **51.** For sales between 0.75 and 1.76   **53.** $(0, 1.9]$ **55.** $\{x : x \text{ is a whole number} \le 49\}$

57. $(-\infty, -5) \cup (3, \infty)$ **59.** $[-4, 6)$ **61.** $(-\infty, -2) \cup \left[-\frac{1}{2}, \infty\right)$ **63.** $\left(\frac{9}{7}, 3\right]$ **65.** $(1, 2) \cup (4, \infty)$

67. $(-\infty, -2) \cup (0, 4)$ **69.** $(-3, 1)$ **71.** $(2, 3) \cup (4, 7)$ **73.** $(-\infty, -1) \cup (1, \infty)$ **75.** $(-2.414, -2) \cup (0, .414)$

77. $(-\infty, -1.439) \cup (.339, 2) \cup (4.1, \infty)$ **79.** $(-\infty, -2.680) \cup (.607, 1) \cup (3.07, \infty)$ **81.** $(1, 5)$ **83.** $(-6, 2)$

85. $[-1, 3]$ **87.** $(4, 10)$ **89.** $(-\infty, -2) \cup (8, \infty)$ **91.** $(-\infty, 0] \cup [1, \infty)$ **93.** $\left(\frac{-7}{3}, 3\right]$

95. $\left(-\infty, \frac{-2}{3}\right] \cup [2, \infty)$ **97.** $[-3, 3]$ **99.** $[-1, 0] \cup [1, 2]$ **101.** $(L - 0.02, L + 0.02)$ **103.** $|x + 4| < \delta + 5$

SECTION 3.6

1. $x \ne 3$ **3.** $x \ne 3, x \ne -2$ **5.** $x \ne 0, x \ne 1$ **7.** $\left[\frac{4}{3}, \infty\right)$ **9.** $\left(-\infty, \frac{2}{7}\right]$ **11.** $(-\infty, -2] \cup [2, \infty)$

13. $(-\infty, 0] \cup [2, \infty)$ **15.** $(-\infty, -2] \cup [5, \infty)$ **17.** $[-3, 3]$ **19.** $x \ne 4$ **21.** $(-\infty, 2)$ **23.** $(-\infty, \infty)$

25. $(-\infty, \infty)$ **27.** $(-\infty, 0) \cup (3, 5) \cup (5, \infty)$ **29.** $(-\infty, 2) \cup (2, \infty)$

Section 3.7

1. $\frac{1}{2}, \sqrt{2}, -\sqrt{2}$ 3. $\frac{3}{5}, -2-\sqrt{3}, -2+\sqrt{3}$ 5. $-1, 1+i\sqrt{2}, 1-i\sqrt{2}$ 7. $\sqrt{3}, -\sqrt{3}, 2, -3$ 9. $\frac{1}{2}, \frac{2}{3}, i, -i$ 11. 1.89

13. 2.66 15. -2.11 17. $-.73, 2.73$ 19. $-2.04, 2.04$ 21. 5 23. $-5, \frac{5}{2}$ 25. $x^3 - 6x^2 + 11x - 6 = 0$

27. $8x^3 - 4x^2 - 2x + 1 = 0$ 29. $x^4 + 2x^3 - 9x^2 - 10x + 20 = 0$ 31. $256x^4 - 1568x^2 + 1681 = 0$ 33. $x^4 - 2x^3 + 3x^2 - 2x + 2 = 0$

35. $225x^3 + 180x^2 - 359x + 362 = 0$ 37. $x^3 - 5x^2 + 9x - 9 = 0$ 39. $x^4 + 2x^2 + 49 = 0$ 41. $x^5 - x^4 - 10x^3 + 10x^2 + x - 1 = 0$

43. No positive root, either two negative roots or two complex roots.   45. One negative root and either two positive roots or two complex roots.   47. One positive root and either two negative roots or two complex roots.   49. One positive root, one negative root, and two complex roots.   51. Either two negative roots and two positive roots, or two positive roots and two complex roots, or two negative roots and two complex roots, or no real root and four complex roots.   53. Roots lie between −3 and −2, and 0 and 1

55. One positive root lying between 1 and 3 , and two complex roots.   57. Two complex roots, real root lies between 0 and −1.

59. Two complex roots ; one root lies between −3 and −2, and the other real root lies between 2 and 3.   61. $\frac{1}{4}, i, -i$ 63. $\frac{1}{2}, 2, -\frac{3}{2}$

65. $\frac{3}{2}, -1+\sqrt{3}, -1-\sqrt{3}$ 67. $-2, \frac{1+\sqrt{2}}{2}, \frac{1-\sqrt{2}}{2}$ 69. $-\frac{1}{3}, \frac{5}{2}, \frac{5}{2}$ 71. $-3, 2, i\sqrt{5}, -i\sqrt{5}$ 73. $-\frac{3}{2}, \frac{2}{3}, 1-\sqrt{5}, 1+\sqrt{5}$

75. $-\frac{1}{3}, \frac{5}{2}, 1-i\sqrt{2}, 1+i\sqrt{2}$ 77. $-1, -1, 2$ 79. $-3, 1+i, 1-i$ 81. $1, -3, -\frac{3}{2}$ 83. $1, -1, -2, -3$ 85. $1, 2, 3, -3$

Chapter Review 3.9

1. $\frac{5x-9}{3}$ 3. $\frac{2A-bh}{h}$ 5. $-\frac{4}{5}$ and 2 7. $\frac{3+\sqrt{65}}{4}$ and $\frac{3-\sqrt{65}}{4}$ 9. $1, -2$, and $\frac{3}{2}$ 11. $-1, 1-\sqrt{2}$, and $1+\sqrt{2}$

13. $1, 2, -1+\sqrt{7}$,and $-1-\sqrt{7}$ 15. a. 4 sec. b. 1.342 seconds on the way up and 4.658 seconds on the way down   c. $(0.58, 5.42)$ sec.

17. x-values between 0 in. and 14.1 in.   19. -5 and -9 21. $\frac{1}{3}$ and -15 23. $\frac{7}{2}$ and $-\frac{3}{2}$ 25. $-\frac{69}{11}$

27. 1 and $-\frac{17}{7}$ 29. $6, -6$ 31. -20 and $-\frac{2}{5}$ 33. $f(x) = \begin{cases} 3x+11 & \text{if } x \geq -\frac{11}{2} \\ -x-11 & \text{if } x < -\frac{11}{2} \end{cases}$ 35. $f(x) = \begin{cases} -x+16 & \text{if } x < -\frac{7}{2} \\ -5x+2 & \text{if } -\frac{7}{2} \leq x < 3 \\ x-16 & \text{if } x \geq 3 \end{cases}$

37. $g(x) = \begin{cases} 5x-19 & \text{if } x \geq \frac{12}{5} \\ -5x+5 & \text{if } x \leq \frac{12}{5} \end{cases}$ 39. $g(x) = \begin{cases} -x-31 & \text{if } x \geq -20 \\ x+9 & \text{if } x < -20 \end{cases}$ 41. -3 43. 9 45. 3 and 7 47. 23 and -31

49. 14 51. $\left(-\frac{1}{10}, \infty\right)$ 53. $(-\infty, -5) \cup (10, \infty)$ 55. $(-3.646, 1.646)$ 57. $\left(-7, \frac{5}{3}\right)$ 59. $(-\infty, -12] \cup (-7, \infty)$ 61. $\left(-4, \frac{3}{2}\right)$

63. $\left(-\infty, -\frac{5}{3}\right) \cup (3, \infty)$ 65. $[-1.162, -.828]$ 67. $(-\infty, -5] \cup [7, \infty)$ 69. $x \neq -8, x \neq 0, x \neq 10$ 71. $(-\infty, \infty)$

73. $\frac{4}{3}, 2-i\sqrt{3}$, and $2+i\sqrt{3}$ 75. $-1.5, -.9$, and $.9$ 77. $.2$ and 2.8 79. $-\frac{1}{5}, -1$ 81. $x^4 - 8x^3 + 21x^2 - 14x - 10 = 0$

83. One negative root and either two positive roots or two complex roots.   85. Either two negative and two complex roots or four complex roots.   87. One positive, one negative, and two complex roots.   89. $\frac{1}{3}, 2-\sqrt{3}$, and $2+\sqrt{3}$ 91. $\frac{1}{2}, 1+\sqrt{2}$, and $1-\sqrt{2}$

Chapter Test 3.10

1. $-5, -1$, and $3/2$ 3. $\left[\frac{-11}{5}, 5\right]$ 5. $(-\infty, -2] \cup [5, \infty)$ 7. $1 \pm \sqrt{5}$ 9. a. $(-\infty, -7] \cup [7, \infty)$ b. $x \neq -1, x \neq 0, x \neq 1$

11. Three positive roots or one positive and two complex roots

Chapter 4

Section 4.1

1. $y = 3x + 5$ **3.** $y = -3x + 1$ **5.** $y = \dfrac{-10}{3}x + \dfrac{1}{3}$ **7.** $y = -2x + 5$ **9.** $y = \dfrac{2}{3}x + 5$

11. $y = -\dfrac{5}{2}x + 2$ **13.** $y = 2x + 9$ **15.** $y = \dfrac{3}{2}x - \dfrac{17}{2}$ **17.** $y = -\dfrac{1}{5}x - 1$ **19.** $y = 2x - 6$

21. $x = 1$ **23.** $y = -5$ **25.** $y = \dfrac{2}{5}x - 2$ **27.** $y = -\dfrac{2}{3}x + 1/3$ **29.** $y = \dfrac{3}{2}x$

31. $f(x) = -2x + 1$ **33.** $f(x) = 3x - 5$ **35.** $f(x) = 1.5x + 7$ **37.** $v(x) = -3{,}500x + 50{,}000$ **39.** $c(x) = 8x + 2{,}500$; \$8 per item

Section 4.2

1. 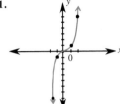   **3.** 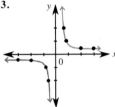   **5.** 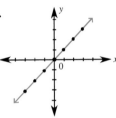   **7.**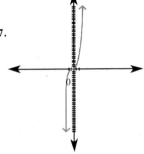

9. 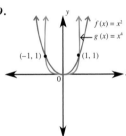   **11.** 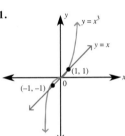   **13. a.** Yes   **b.** No   **15.** $(x + 5)^2 - 25$

17. $(x - 8)^2 - 64$ **19.** $\left(x + \dfrac{1}{2}\right)^2 - \dfrac{1}{4}$

21. $\left(z - \dfrac{1}{4}\right)^2 - \dfrac{1}{16}$ **23.** $\left(y - \dfrac{5}{4}\right)^2 - \dfrac{25}{16}$

25. $\left(y - \dfrac{9}{2}\right)^2 - \dfrac{81}{4}$ **27.** $2(x - 2)^2 - 8$

29. $2\left(z - \dfrac{7}{4}\right)^2 - \dfrac{49}{8}$ **31.** $3\left(t + \dfrac{5}{3}\right)^2 - \dfrac{25}{3}$ **33.** $\dfrac{1}{4}(y - 6)^2 - 9$

35.    **37.** 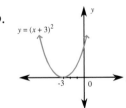   **39.** 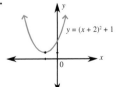   **41.**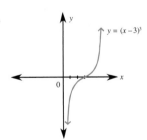

43. 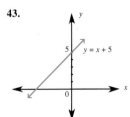   **45.** 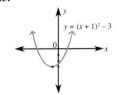   **47.** 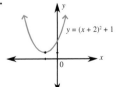   **49.**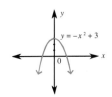

51.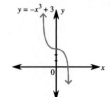

53.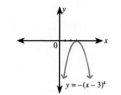

55.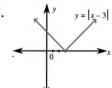

57.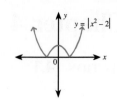

59.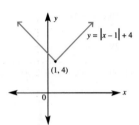

61.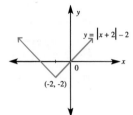

63.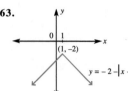

65.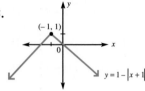

67.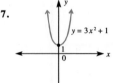

69.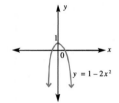

71.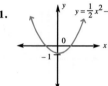

73.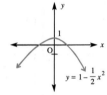

75.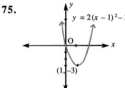

77.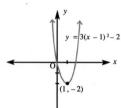

79.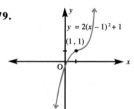

81.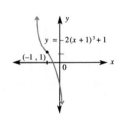

83.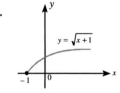

85.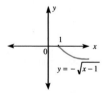

87.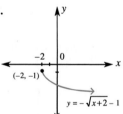

89.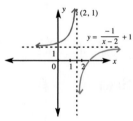

91.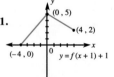

93. $\pi x^2 - \pi$

95. $x^3 - 8$

97. $x^3 - 2x^2 + 3x - 2$

99. $\dfrac{-7x + 21}{x + 2}$

101. $\sqrt{x+5} - 3$

103. Odd

105. Odd

107. Odd

109. Even

111. Odd

113. Even

115. Even

Section 4.3

1. (b) and (c)

3. (a) and (b)

5. (a) and (b)

7. (a) and (c)

9. (1, 5)

11. (−1, 3)

13. (2, 0)

15. (1 , 2)

17. (−2 , −1)

19. (3 , 1)

21. (−5 , −1)

23. $\left(\dfrac{1}{2}, 1\right)$

25. $\left(-\dfrac{3}{2}, -\dfrac{1}{2}\right)$

27. (−2, −3)

29. (−3 , −10)

31. $\left(\dfrac{-3}{2}, \dfrac{-5}{4}\right)$

33. $\left(\dfrac{5}{2}, \dfrac{-5}{4}\right)$

35. (0 , −8)

37. (1 , −2)

39. $\left(-\dfrac{3}{4}, \dfrac{-1}{8}\right)$

41. (1, 2)

43.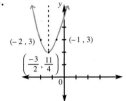

45.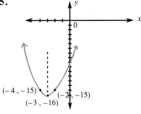

47.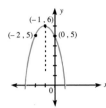

49.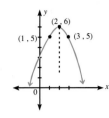

51.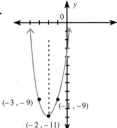

53.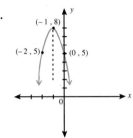

55.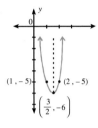

57.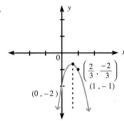

59.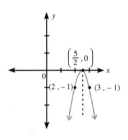

61.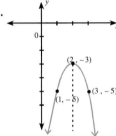

63. 300 ft , 90,000 ft^2 **65.** 1600 units **67.** 4 in

69. a. 256 ft   **b.** 4 sec   **c.** after 8 sec

SECTION 4.4

1. $10x - x^2$

3. $25x - \dfrac{1}{2}x^3$

5. $P(x) = x + \dfrac{100,000}{x}$

7. $x(24 - 2x)(16 - 2x)$

9. $A(x) = \dfrac{x(x+65)}{x-1}$

11. $A(x) = \dfrac{x^2}{4\pi} + \dfrac{\sqrt{3}}{36}(16-x)^2$

13. $D(x) = \sqrt{x^4 + x^2 - 2x + 1}$

15. $t(x) = \dfrac{x}{5} + \dfrac{\sqrt{9 + (4-x)^2}}{2}$

17. $A(x) = 4x\sqrt{16 - x^2}$

19. $C(x) = \left(1.25x^2 + \dfrac{18}{x}\right)$dollars

21. $V(x) = 10\pi x^2 - \dfrac{5\pi}{3}x^3$

23. $A(x) = (50 - x)(500 + 15x)$ **25.** 24 trees

SECTION 4.5

1.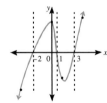

3.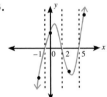

5.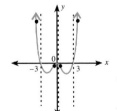

7.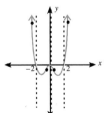

9.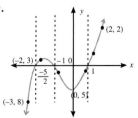

11.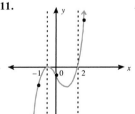

13.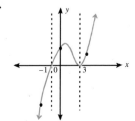

15.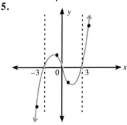

17.

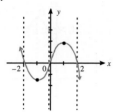

19.

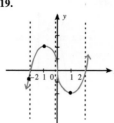

21. $5(1350)^6$

23. $-8(1120)^4$

25.

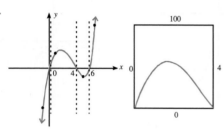

27. $5x^4$

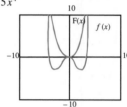

29. $-3x^3$

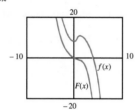

31. $3x^3$

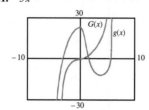

33. $2x^3$

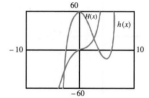

35. $3x^3$

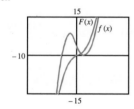

37. $5x^3$

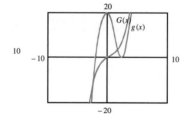

39. $3x^3$

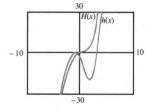

SECTION 4.6

1. $VA: x = \dfrac{-2}{3}$; $HA: y = 0$ **3.** $VA: x = \dfrac{3}{5}$; $HA: y = 0$ **5.** $VA: x = -5$; $HA: y = 7$ **7.** $VA: x = \dfrac{3}{2}$; $HA: y = 1$

9. $VA: x = 2$ and $x = -1$; $HA: y = 3$ **11.** No VA ; $HA: y = 5$ **13.** $VA: x = 4, x = -1$; $HA: y = 0$

15. $VA: x = \dfrac{1}{2}$ and $x = 3$; $HA: y = 0$ **17.** $VA: x = 2$; No HA   **19.** $VA: x = 2$; $HA: y = 1$

21.

23.

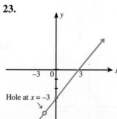

25.

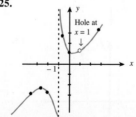

27.

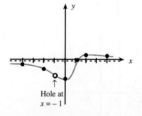

29.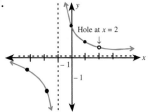

31.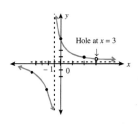

33.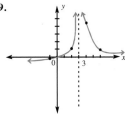

35.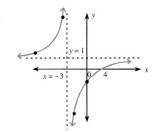

37.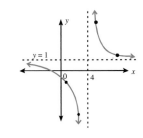

39.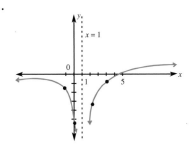

41.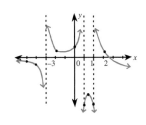

43.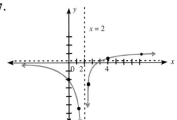

45.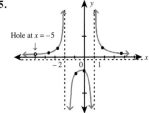

CHAPTER REVIEW 4.8

1. $y = \dfrac{-5}{4}(x + 1)$

3. $y = \dfrac{2}{5}x + \dfrac{23}{5}$

5. $y = 2x - 7$

7. $y = -3$

9. $2x + 3y = 6$

11. $y = -\dfrac{1}{2}x + 2$

13. $y = .35x + 2.3$

15. $\left(x - \dfrac{5}{2}\right)^2 - \dfrac{25}{4}$

17. $(y - 6)^2 - 36$ **19.** $2\left(t - \dfrac{7}{4}\right)^2 - \dfrac{49}{8}$

21. $3\left(z - \dfrac{5}{6}\right)^2 - \dfrac{25}{12}$

23. $(3, -4)$

25. $\left(\dfrac{5}{4}, \dfrac{-17}{8}\right)$

27. $(4, -16)$

29. $(3, 10)$

31. $(1, 2)$

33. $(1, 5)$

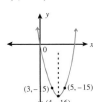

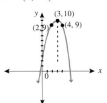

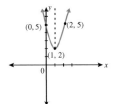

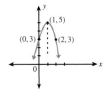

35.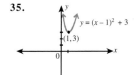

37.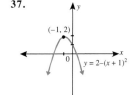

39.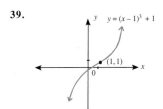

41.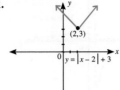

$y = |x - 2| + 3$ with vertex $(2,3)$

43.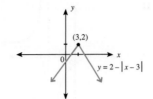

$y = 2 - |x - 3|$ with vertex $(3,2)$

45.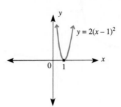

$y = 2(x - 1)^2$

47.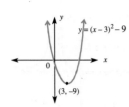

$y = (x - 3)^2 - 9$ with vertex $(3, -9)$

49.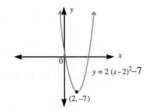

$y = 2(x - 2)^2 - 7$ with vertex $(2, -7)$

51.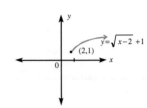

$y = \sqrt{x - 2} + 1$ with point $(2,1)$

53. odd function

55. even function

57. VA : $x = 3$, $x = 2$; HA : $y = 0$

59. VA : $x = 1$, $x = -1$; VA : $y = 5$

61. VA : $x = 0$, $x = 1$; no HA

63.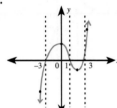

65.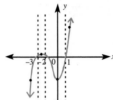

67.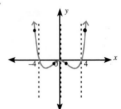

69.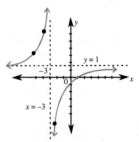

71.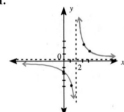

73.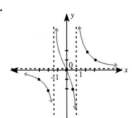

75.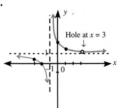

77.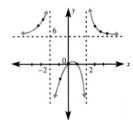

79.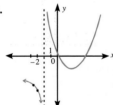

81. a. 3.125 sec

b. 161.25 ft

83. $C(x) = 6\pi x^2 + \dfrac{2000}{x}$

85. $D = \dfrac{8x}{5}$

CHAPTER TEST 4.9

1. $y = \dfrac{5}{3}x + 12$

3. a.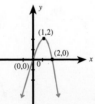

5. $C(x) = 30\pi x^2 + \dfrac{13.3}{x}$

b.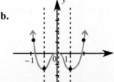

c.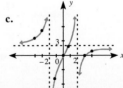

7.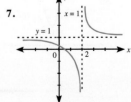

Chapter 5

SECTION 5.1

1. Yes   **3.** No   **5.** No   **7.** Yes   **9.** Yes   **11.** No   **13.** Yes   **15.** Yes   **17.** No   **19.** No

25. $\dfrac{x+11}{7}$; Domain : $(-\infty, \infty)$; Range : $(-\infty, \infty)$ **27.** $\dfrac{5-x}{8}$; Domain : $(-\infty, \infty)$; Range : $(-\infty, \infty)$

29. $\sqrt[3]{1-x}$; Domain : $(-\infty, \infty)$; Range : $(-\infty, \infty)$ **31.** $\sqrt[3]{x-2}$; Domain : $(-\infty, \infty)$; Range : $(-\infty, \infty)$

33. $x^2 + 1$; Domain : $[0, \infty)$; Range : $[1, \infty)$ **35.** $x^3 + 1$; Domain : $(-\infty, \infty)$; Range : $(-\infty, \infty)$

37. $\dfrac{3x-1}{x-2}$; Domain : $\{x \in R : x \neq 2\}$; Range : $\{y \in R : y \neq 3\}$ **39.** $\dfrac{2x}{x-1}$; Domain : $\{x \in R : x \neq 1\}$; Range : $\{y \in R : y \neq 2\}$

41. $\sqrt{x-1}$; Domain : $[1, \infty)$; Range : $[0, \infty)$

47.

x	5	2	3	1	0	7
$f^{-1}(x)$	-1	0	1	2	3	4

49.

x	0.6	0.5	1	0.75	0.7	0.68
$f^{-1}(x)$	-1	0	1	2	4	9

43.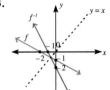

45.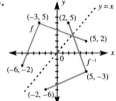

SECTION 5.2

1.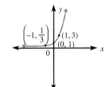

3.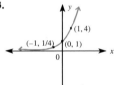

5.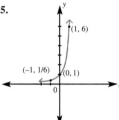

7.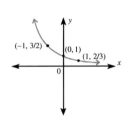

9.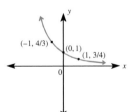

11.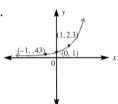

13.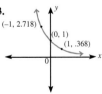

15.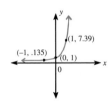

17.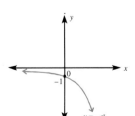

19.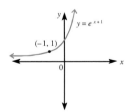

21.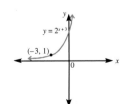

23.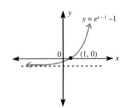

25. 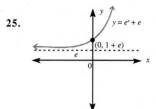 **27.**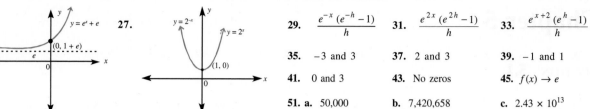

29. $\dfrac{e^{-x}(e^{-h}-1)}{h}$ **31.** $\dfrac{e^{2x}(e^{2h}-1)}{h}$ **33.** $\dfrac{e^{x+2}(e^{h}-1)}{h}$

35. -3 and 3 **37.** 2 and 3 **39.** -1 and 1

41. 0 and 3 **43.** No zeros **45.** $f(x) \to e$

51. a. $50,000$ **b.** $7,420,658$ **c.** 2.43×10^{13}

53. $f(x) \to \infty$ **55.** $94.47°$ **57. a.** $e^x(e^{4x}-1)$ **b.** $\left(x, \dfrac{e^x + e^{5x}}{2}\right)$

Section 5.3

1. $\log_2 8 = 3$ **3.** $\log_3 \dfrac{1}{9} = -2$ **5.** $\log_{10} 1 = -1$ **7.** $\log_5 8 = x$ **9.** $\log_r s = x$ **11.** $\log_e y = x$ or $\ln y = x$

13. $\log_e 1 = 0$ or $\ln 1 = 0$ **15.** $\log_3 \sqrt{3} = \dfrac{1}{2}$ **17.** $3^3 = 27$ **19.** $10^2 = 100$ **21.** $e^2 = e^2$ **23.** $4^3 = 64$

25. $a^c = b$ **27.** 1 **29.** 1 **31.** 1 **33.** 0 **35.** 4 **37.** -2

39. Does not exist **41.** 0 **43.** $\dfrac{3}{2}$ **45.** -3 **47.** $\dfrac{3}{2}$ **49.** $\dfrac{3}{2}$ **51.** $\ln x - 5$

53. $\dfrac{\log x - 3}{2}$ **55.** $\dfrac{\log(x+5)+4}{3}$ **57.** $(-8, \infty)$ **59.** $\left(\dfrac{1}{2}, \infty\right)$ **61.** $(-\infty, 1) \cup (1, \infty)$ **63.** $(-\infty, 0) \cup (0, \infty)$

65. $(-\infty, -4) \cup (4, \infty)$ **67.** $(-\infty, -4) \cup (-1, \infty)$ **69.** $(-2, \infty)$ **71.** Zero: $x = -1$; VA: $x = -\dfrac{5}{4}$ **73.** Zeros: $\pm\sqrt{10}$; VA: $x = 3, x = -3$

75. Zero: $\dfrac{2}{3}$; VA: $x = \dfrac{1}{3}$ **77.** No zero; No VA **79.** Zero: -1; VA $= x = -5$ **81.** Zeros: $-1\pm\sqrt{10}$; VA: $x = 2, x = -4$

83. 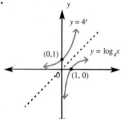 **85.** 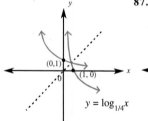 **87.** 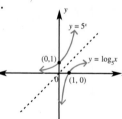 **89.**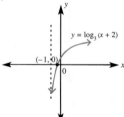

91. 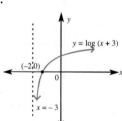 **93.** 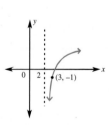 **95.** 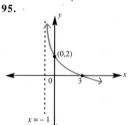 **97.**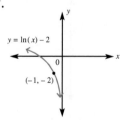

99. 4.6 **101.** 37.077 **103.** 4.11 years old **105. a.** $e^x - \ln x$ **b.** $\left(x, \dfrac{e^x + \ln x}{2}\right)$

Section 5.4

1. $3a + b$ **3.** $2 - a$ **5.** $2 + b - 2a$ **7.** $1 + a + b$ **9.** $2(a+b)$ **11.** $b - 1$ **13.** $2 + 2\log_3 x$

15. $1 + 3\log_5 y$ **17.** $3 + 2\ln x$ **19.** $3 + \log_3 x - 2\log_3 y$ **21.** $2 + 2\log_2 x - \log_2 y$ **23.** $1 + \dfrac{1}{2}\ln x - \ln y$

25. $2 + \dfrac{1}{2}\ln x - \dfrac{1}{3}\ln y$ **27.** $\dfrac{1}{2}\left[\ln(2x+1) - \ln(3x+7)\right]$ **29.** $\dfrac{1}{2}\ln(5x+9) - \dfrac{1}{3}\ln(2x-5)$

31. $2 \log_2(x + 2) + 3 \log_2 y - \frac{1}{2} \log_2 (x + 3)$ **33.** $\ln (x + 5) + \frac{1}{2} \ln (x + 2) - 2\ln x - \ln (x + 3)$

35. $3 \ln (x - 1) + 2 \ln (x + 2) - 2\ln (x + 5) - \frac{1}{2} \ln (x + 7)$ **37.** $\log 30$ **39.** $\log \frac{20}{3}$ **41.** $\log_2 5x^2$ **43.** $\log_3 11x^4$

45. $\log (x + 1)^2 (x + 2)^3$ **47.** $\log \dfrac{x^2 y}{25 (x + 7)^3}$ **49.** $\ln \dfrac{x^3 \sqrt{x + 2}}{(x + 1)^2}$ **51.** $\ln \dfrac{x \sqrt{x - 1}}{\sqrt[3]{x + 7} \, (2x + 5)^5}$ **53.** $\log_2 4x^3$

55. $\ln \dfrac{e \, x^3}{y^2}$ **57.** $\dfrac{\ln x}{\ln 5}$ **59.** $\dfrac{\ln (x + 1)}{\ln 3}$ **61.** $\dfrac{\ln \left(x^2 + 9\right)}{\ln 2}$ **63.** $\dfrac{\ln (5x + 9)}{\ln 10}$ **65.** $\dfrac{\ln (3x - 7)}{\ln a}$

67. 1.771   **69.** 1.465   **71.** 7   **73.** 5   **75.** 10   **77.** $\dfrac{7}{3}$

79. 9   **81.** 8   **83.** $9e$ **85.** $a^2 \cdot b^3$ **87.** $\log_2 (a + 1)$ **89.** $-\log_3 (b - 1)$

91. If the intensity is cubed, the loudness will triple.   **93.** It increases by $\log 2 \approx .301$ **95.** $\dfrac{A}{P}$ is squared

97. $\log_2 \left(\dfrac{x + h}{x - h} \right)^{\frac{1}{2h}}$ **99.** $\ln \left(\dfrac{x + h}{x - h} \right)^{\frac{1}{2h}}$

SECTION 5.5

1. $\dfrac{7}{3}$ **3.** $\dfrac{9}{7}$ **5.** 3.8074   **7.** 2.232   **9.** 3.7825   **11.** ± 1.9766 **13.** 5.5076

15. -1.5821 **17.** .966   **19.** -31.9811 **21.** -2.0433 **23.** .08473   **25.** 2.322   **27.** $\dfrac{8}{3}$

29. 3   **31.** $\dfrac{19}{5}$ **33.** $\dfrac{11}{2}$ **35.** 9   **37.** $1 \pm \sqrt{2}$ **39.** $\dfrac{-3 \pm \sqrt{13}}{2}$ **41.** 5

43. 4   **45.** 9   **47.** ± 3 **49.** 4   **51.** 2 and 64   **53.** $\dfrac{25}{8}$ **55.** 4

57. 3.16×10^{-7} **59.** 6,000 micrometers   **61.** 9.163

SECTION 5.6

1. 281 bacteria   **3.** 1,560 ticks   **5.** 5 billion   **7.** 6 hr 20 min   **9.** about 63%   **11.** 7.79 years

13. a. 11.18 mg   **b.** 269.7 days   **15.** 10,033 years   **17.** \$12,806   **19. a.** \$15,938.48   **b.** \$16141.43

   c. \$16160.11   **d.** \$16160.74   **21.** 13.2 years   **23.** 17.33 years   **25.** \$3.22 million

CHAPTER REVIEW 5.8

1. No   **3.** Yes   **5.** Yes   **7.** No   **9.** No

11. $\dfrac{x + 2}{9}$; Domain : $(-\infty, \infty)$; Range : $(-\infty, \infty)$ **13.** $x^2 + 2$; Domain : $[\,0, \infty)$; Range : $[2, \infty)$

15. $\dfrac{3x - 9}{x - 5}$; Domain : $\{x \in \mathbb{R} : x \neq 5\}$; Range : $\{\, y \in \mathbb{R} ; y \neq 3\}$ **17.** $\sqrt{x + 1}$; Domain : $[-1, \infty)$; Range : $[0, \infty)$

19. 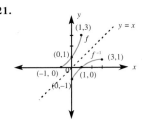   **21.** 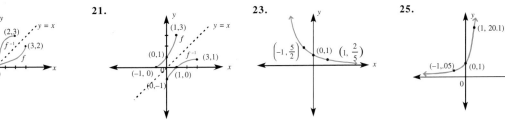   **23.** 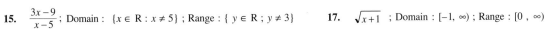   **25.**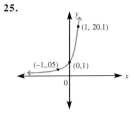

27.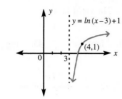

29.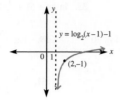

31. $(-\infty, \infty)$　**33.** $(1, \infty)$　**35.** $(-\infty, -5) \cup (5, \infty)$

37. $(2, \infty)$　**39.** $(-\infty, -1) \cup (4, \infty)$

41. 3 and -1　**43.** 0 and 4　**45.** $\dfrac{1}{3}$

47. $\dfrac{3}{4}$　**49.** $\dfrac{11}{9}$　**51.** 2.146

53. .784　**55.** $-.55$　**57.** 3　**59.** 1　**61.** 6 and 12　**63.** 2　**65.** 1 and 100

67. 4　**69.** $2 + 2 \log x + 3 \log y - 4 \log (x + 2)$　**71.** $3 + 2 \ln (x + 1) + 5 \ln (x - 2) - \dfrac{1}{2} \ln (2x + 1)$

73. $\log_2 4x (x + 3)$　**75.** $\ln \left[\dfrac{(x+1)^2}{\sqrt{x+2}\,(x-1)^3} \right]$　**77.** $\dfrac{2}{3}$　**79.** 4　**81.** $4e$

83. $\dfrac{\ln 5}{\ln 7}$　**85.** $\dfrac{\ln x}{\ln a}$　**87.** 1859.5 years　**89.** \$32,969.77

Chapter Test 5.9

1. $\dfrac{x+2}{x+7}$; Domain : $\{x \in \mathrm{R} : x \neq -7\}$; Range : $\{y \in \mathrm{R} : y \neq 1\}$　**3. a.** $(-\infty, \infty)$　**b.** $(-\infty, -1) \cup (5, \infty)$

5. $2 + 2 \ln (x + 3) + \dfrac{1}{2} \ln (x + 9) - 3 \ln (x - 2)$　**7. a.** $\dfrac{3}{2}$　**b.** 2　**c.** $8e^2$

9. a. 1,115 fruit flies **b.** 12 days　**11.** \$3,523.56

Chapter 6

Section 6.1

1. $m(t) = k t^2$　**3.** $p(q) = k \sqrt{q}$　**5.** $d(t) = \dfrac{k}{t}$　**7.** $I(m) = \dfrac{k}{m^2}$　**9.** $m(n, p) = k\, n\, p$　**11.** $s(d, r) = \dfrac{kd}{r^2}$

13. $F(M_1, M_2, r) = \dfrac{k\, M_1\, M_2}{r^2}$　**15.** $m(y) = k \sqrt{y}$　**17.** $m(x) = \dfrac{k}{x^2}$　**19.** $\rho(x, y) = k\, x\, y$　**21.** $m(x) = kx; \ k = 10$

23. $Z(t) = \dfrac{k}{t^2}$; $k = 20$　**25.** $F(x) = kx$; $k = \dfrac{45}{7}$　**27.** $V(x, y) = \dfrac{k\, x}{\sqrt{y}}$, $k = 75$　**29.** Direct　**31.** Joint　**33.** Inverse

35. None of these　**37.** Inverse　**39.** Inverse　**41.** Direct　**43.** 4.8 in　**45.** $\dfrac{600}{7}$ in^3　**47.** 2.5 lb

49. 256 feet　**51.** $\dfrac{2}{\sqrt{3}}$ sec　**53.** .071 ohm　**55.** 900 pounds　**57.** 1012.5 pounds

Section 6.2

1. $(x - 2)^2 + (y + 1)^2 = 25$　**3.** $(x + 3)^2 + (y - 2)^2 = 4$　**5.** $(x + 1)^2 + (y + 7)^2 = 1$　**7.** $(x + 2)^2 + y^2 = 16$　**9.** $(x - 1)^2 + (y - 2)^2 = 25$

11. $(x - 5)^2 + (y + 7)^2 = 25$　**13.** $(x - 4)^2 + (y + 1)^2 = 17$　**15.** $(x + 2)^2 + (y - 3)^2 = 10$　**17.** $(1, 3), \sqrt{5}$

19. $(-2, 5), 3$　**21.** $(-1, 0), \sqrt{3}$　**23.** $(0, 2), 4$　**25.** $(0, 0), 1$　**27.** $(-1, 0), 2$

29. $(0, 3), 4$　**31.** $(2, -3), 4$　**33.** $\left(-\dfrac{1}{2}, 1\right), \dfrac{3}{2}$　**35.** $(1, -2), 4$　**37.** $\left(-1, \dfrac{-3}{2}\right), \dfrac{\sqrt{129}}{6}$

39.
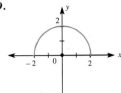

41.
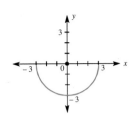

43.
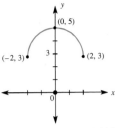

45.
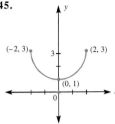

47. $y = -\dfrac{1}{2}x + \dfrac{5}{2}$ **49.** No. BC = 1.66 ft , CD = 1.08 ft, DE = 1.021 ft, and EF = 1.002 ft.

Section 6.3

1. $x^2 = 20y$ **3.** $x^2 = -12y$ **5.** $y^2 = 32x$ **7.** $y^2 = 12x$ **9.** $y^2 = 18x$ **11.** $x^2 = -y$

13. $F(0, 2)$; $V(0,0)$; Directix : $y = -2$ **15.** $F(0, 3)$; $V(0,0)$; Directix : $y = -3$ **17.** $F(4, 0)$; $V(0,0)$; Directix : $x = -4$

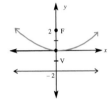  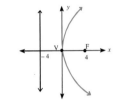

19. $F\left(-\dfrac{5}{2},0\right)$; $V(0,0)$; Directix : $x = \dfrac{5}{2}$ **21.** $F\left(0,-\dfrac{9}{2}\right)$; $V(0,0)$; Directix : $y = \dfrac{9}{2}$ **23.** $F(-1, 0)$; $V(0,0)$; Directix : $x = 1$

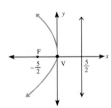 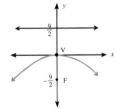 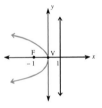

25. $F(1, 1)$; $V(0,1)$; Directix : $x = -1$ **27.** $F(-2, 2)$; $V(-2,0)$; Directix : $y = -2$ **29.** $F(1, 5)$; $V(1, 2)$; Directix : $y = -1$

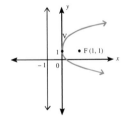 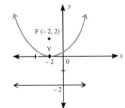 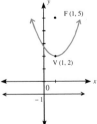

31. $F(2, -3)$; $V(2,1)$; Directix : $y = 5$ **33.** $F\left(\dfrac{7}{4},-1\right)$; $V(2,-1)$; Directix : $x = \dfrac{9}{4}$ **35.** $F\left(1,\dfrac{3}{2}\right)$; $V(1, 2)$; Directix : $y = \dfrac{5}{2}$

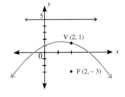 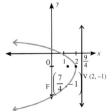 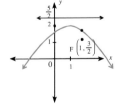

37. F(−3, 4); V(−4, 4); Directix : $x = -5$ **39.** F$\left(-2,-\frac{7}{2}\right)$; V(−2,−3); Directix : $y = -\frac{5}{2}$ **41.** F$\left(2,-\frac{7}{8}\right)$; V(2, −1); Directix : $y = -\frac{9}{8}$

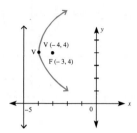

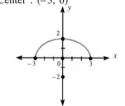

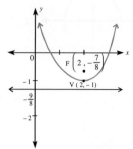

43. $x^2 = 12{,}100\ y$ **45.** 82.64 ft **47.** $\frac{9}{8}$ in from C **49.** 27 in from C

SECTION 6.4

1. $\frac{x^2}{25} + \frac{y^2}{9} = 1$ **3.** $\frac{x^2}{25} + \frac{y^2}{16} = 1$ **5.** $\frac{x^2}{5} + \frac{y^2}{9} = 1$ **7.** $\frac{x^2}{15} + \frac{y^2}{16} = 1$ **9.** $\frac{x^2}{16} + \frac{y^2}{25} = 1$ **11.** $\frac{x^2}{25} + \frac{y^2}{29} = 1$ **13.** $(x - 3)^2 + (y - 2)^2 = 16$

15. Foci : $\left(0,\pm 2\sqrt{3}\right)$
Vertices : (± 2, 0) and (0, ± 4)
Center : (0, 0)

17. Foci : (0, ± 4)
Vertices : (± 3, 0) and (0, ± 5)
Center : (0, 0)

19. Foci : $\left(\pm 4\sqrt{2},0\right)$
Vertices : (± 6, 0) and (0, ± 2)
Center : (0, 0)

21. Foci : $\left(\pm 2\sqrt{2},0\right)$
Vertices : (± 3, 0) and (0, ± 1)
Center : (0, 0)

23. Foci : $\left(1\pm 2\sqrt{2},0\right)$
Vertices : (−2, 0) , (4, 0), and (1, 1) , (1 −1)
Center : (1, 0)

25. Foci : $\left(0,1\pm\sqrt{5}\right)$
Vertices : (± 2, 1) ,and (0, 4) , (0, −2)
Center : (0, 1)

27. Foci : $\left(1,-2\pm\sqrt{5}\right)$
Vertices : (−1, −2) , (3, −2) , and (1, 1), (1, −5)
Center : (1, −2)

29. Foci : $\left(-1\pm\sqrt{5},2\right)$
Vertices : (−4, 2) , (2,2), and (−1, 4), (−1, 0)
Center : (−1, 2)

31. Foci : (1, −1) and (5, −1)
Vertices : $\left(3\pm 2\sqrt{2},-1\right)$, and (3,1),(3,−3)
Center : (3, −1)

33. Foci : $\left(2\pm\sqrt{6},-1\right)$
Vertices : (−1, −1) , (5, −1), and $\left(2,-1\pm\sqrt{3}\right)$
Center : (2, −1)

35. Foci : $\left(-3\pm 2\sqrt{5},0\right)$
Vertices : (−8, 0) , (2,0) , and $\left(-3,\pm\sqrt{5}\right)$
Center : (−3, 0)

37. Foci : $\left(5\pm\sqrt{2},-1\right)$
Vertices : (3, −1),(7, −1), and $\left(5,-1\pm\sqrt{2}\right)$
Center : (5, −1)

39. Foci : $\left(2,-6\pm\sqrt{2}\right)$
Vertices : $\left(2\pm\sqrt{3},-6\right)$ and $\left(2,-6\pm\sqrt{5}\right)$
Center : (2, −6)

41.

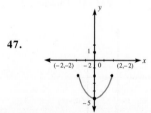

43.

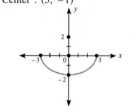

45.

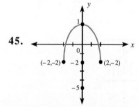

47.

49. $y = 18\sqrt{1 - \dfrac{x^2}{900}}$

51. 15.6 ft **53.** $\dfrac{x^2}{4{,}096} + \dfrac{y^2}{1{,}596} = 1$

55. (−9.6, 0) and (9.6, 0)

Section 6.5

1. $\dfrac{x^2}{9} - \dfrac{y^2}{16} = 1$ **3.** $-\dfrac{x^2}{9} + \dfrac{y^2}{16} = 1$ **5.** $\dfrac{x^2}{4} - \dfrac{y^2}{16} = 1$ **7.** $-\dfrac{x^2}{1} + \dfrac{y^2}{4} = 1$ **9.** $\dfrac{-36x^2}{64} + \dfrac{y^2}{64} = 1$ **11.** $4x^2 - 15y^2 = 196$ **13.** $4x^2 - y^2 = 11$

15. Foci : $\left(\pm\sqrt{11}, 0\right)$

Vertices : $(\pm 3, 0)$

Center : $(0, 0)$

Asymptotes : $y = \pm\dfrac{\sqrt{2}}{3}x$

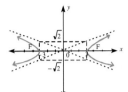

17. Foci : $\left(\pm\sqrt{34}, 0\right)$

Vertices : $(\pm 5, 0)$

Center : $(0, 0)$

Asymptotes : $y = \pm\dfrac{3}{5}x$

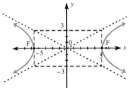

19. Foci : $\left(0, \pm\sqrt{13}\right)$

Vertices : $(0, \pm 3)$

Center : $(0, 0)$

Asymptotes : $y = \pm\dfrac{3}{2}x$

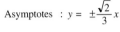

21. Foci : $\left(0, \pm\sqrt{41}\right)$

Vertices : $(0, \pm 5)$

Center : $(0, 0)$

Asymptotes : $y = \pm\dfrac{5}{4}x$

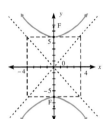

23. Foci : $\left(\pm\sqrt{41}, 0\right)$

Vertices : $(\pm 5, 0)$

Center : $(0, 0)$

Asymptotes : $y = \pm\dfrac{4}{5}x$

25. Foci : $\left(0, \pm\sqrt{5}\right)$

Vertices : $(0, \pm 1)$

Center : $(0, 0)$

Asymptotes : $y = \pm\dfrac{1}{2}x$

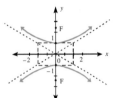

27. Foci : $\left(1 \pm\sqrt{13}, 2\right)$

Vertices : $(4, 2)$ and $(-2, 2)$

Center : $(1, 2)$

Asymptotes : $y = -2 \pm\dfrac{2}{3}(x-1)$

29. Foci : $\left(\pm\sqrt{13}, -1\right)$

Vertices : $(\pm 2, -1)$

Center : $(0, -1)$

Asymptotes : $y = -1 \pm\dfrac{3}{2}x$

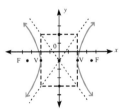

31. Foci : $\left(-2 \pm\sqrt{41}, 1\right)$

Vertices : $(3, 1)$ and $(-7, 1)$

Center : $(-2, 1)$

Asymptotes : $y = 1 \pm\dfrac{4}{5}(x+2)$

33. Foci : $\left(0, 1 \pm\sqrt{34}\right)$

Vertices : $(0, 6)$ and $(0, -4)$

Center : $(0, 1)$

Asymptotes : $y = 1 \pm\dfrac{5}{3}x$

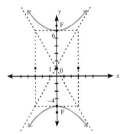

35. Foci : $\left(1, -2 \pm 2\sqrt{5}\right)$

Vertices : $(1, 0)$ and $(1, -4)$

Center : $(1, -2)$

Asymptotes : $y = -2 \pm\dfrac{1}{2}(x-1)$

37. Foci : $\left(3, 4 \pm 2\sqrt{2}\right)$

Vertices : $(3, 6)$ and $(3, 2)$

Center : $(3, 4)$

Asymptotes : $y = 4 \pm (x - 3)$

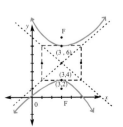

39. Foci : $\left(4 \pm \sqrt{2}, -4\right)$

Vertices : $(3, -4)$ and $(5, -4)$

Center : $(4, -4)$

Asymptotes : $y = -4 \pm (x - 4)$

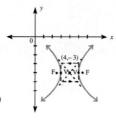

41. Foci : $\left(-1, -1 \pm \sqrt{13}\right)$

Vertices : $(-1, 1)$ and $(-1, -3)$

Center : $(-1, -1)$

Asymptotes : $y = -1 \pm \dfrac{2}{3}(x+1)$

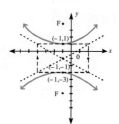

43. Foci : $\left(-2 \pm \sqrt{11}, 2\right)$

Vertices : $(1, 2)$ and $(-5, 2)$

Center : $(-2, 2)$

Asymptotes : $y = 2 \pm \dfrac{\sqrt{2}}{3}(x+2)$

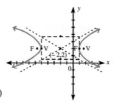

45. Foci : $\left(-2, 3 \pm \sqrt{13}\right)$

Vertices : $(-2, 5)$ and $(-2, 1)$

Center : $(-2, 3)$

Asymptotes : $y = 3 \pm \dfrac{2}{3}(x+2)$

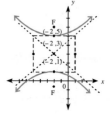

47. Foci : $(6, 2)$, and $(-4, 2)$

Vertices : $(-2, 2)$ and $(4, 2)$

Center : $(1, 2)$

Asymptotes : $y = 2 \pm \dfrac{4}{3}(x-1)$

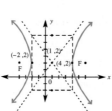

49. $-\dfrac{x^2}{900} + \dfrac{y^2}{1600} = 1$ **51.** Parabola   **53.** Circle

55. Ellipse   **57.** Hyperbola   **59.** Hyperbola

61. Parabola   **63.** Circle

CHAPTER REVIEW 6.7

1. $F(x) = kx$; $k = 20$ **3.** $G(r) = \dfrac{k}{r^2}$; $k = 60$ **5.** $A(x, y) = kxy$; $k = 5$ **7.** $\rho(x) = kx^2$; $k = \dfrac{1}{2}$ **9.** inverse   **11.** None of these

13. direct   **15.** inverse   **17.** $(x + 1)^2 + (y + 2)^2 = 1$ **19.** $(x - 2)^2 + (y + 3)^2 = 25$

21. $(x - 3)^2 + (y - 4)^2 = 10$ **23.** $(1, -2)$, 3 **25.** $\left(\dfrac{3}{2}, -1\right)$, 2 **27.**

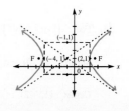

29. $y^2 = -8x$ **31.** Focus : $\left(\dfrac{3}{2}, -1\right)$

                Vertex : $(2, -1)$

33. Focus : $\left(-1, \dfrac{7}{4}\right)$

      Vertex : $(-1, 2)$

35. $x^2 = 1{,}125 y$ Directix : $x = \dfrac{5}{2}$

33. Directix : $y = \dfrac{9}{4}$

37. $y = 20\sqrt{1 - \dfrac{x^2}{1{,}600}}$

39. Foci : $\left(1 \pm \sqrt{5}, -1\right)$

Vertices : $(1, 1)$, $(1, -3)$ and $(-2, -1)$, $(4, -1)$

Center : $(1, -1)$

41. Foci : $(-2, 2)$ and $(0, 2)$

Vertices : $\left(-1 \pm \sqrt{3}, 2\right)$ and $\left(-1, 2 \pm \sqrt{2}\right)$

Center : $(-1, 2)$

43.

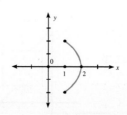

45. Foci : $\left(-1 \pm \sqrt{13}, 1\right)$

Vertices : $(-4, 1)$, and $(2, 1)$

Center : $(-1, 1)$

Asymptotes : $y = 1 \pm \dfrac{2}{3}(x + 1)$

47. Foci : $\left(1, -2 \pm \sqrt{13}\right)$

Vertices : $(1, 1)$ and $(1, -5)$

Center : $(1, -2)$

Asymptotes : $y = -2 \pm \dfrac{3}{2} (x - 1)$

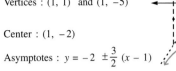

49. Hyperbola   **51.** Parabola

Chapter Test 6.8

1. $A(x) = 4x^2$

3. a.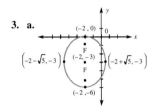

b.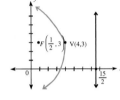

c.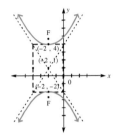

d.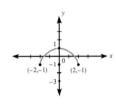

Chapter 7

Section 7.1

1. $(1, -1)$ **3.** $(2, -5)$ **5.** $(10, 8)$ **7.** $(1, -3)$ **9.** $(2, -9)$ **11.** $\left(\dfrac{74}{14+5\pi}, \dfrac{70-12\pi}{14+5\pi}\right)$ **13.** $(1, -1, 1)$

15. no solution **17.** Tapes : 4 and CDs : 8   **19.** $\$11.30/$ hr   **21.** $-\dfrac{1}{2}x^2 + \dfrac{53}{10}x + 4$ **23.** $\left(\dfrac{9}{2}, \dfrac{11}{2}\right)$

Section 7.2

1. $(0, 0)$ and $(1, 1)$ **3.** $(0, 0)$ and $(1, 1)$ **5.** $(1, 2)$ and $(-1, 2)$ **7.** $(0, -6)$ and $(3, 0)$ **9.** $\left(-\dfrac{2}{3}, -2\right)$ and $(1, 3)$

11. $\left(\dfrac{5+\sqrt{13}}{2}, \dfrac{1+\sqrt{13}}{2}\right)$ and $\left(\dfrac{5-\sqrt{13}}{2}, \dfrac{1-\sqrt{13}}{2}\right)$ **13.** $(6, 2)$ **15.** no solution

Section 7.3

1. $y = x^2 + 2$

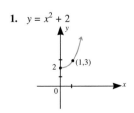

3. $y = \dfrac{1}{x}$

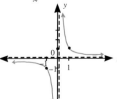

5. $y = x + 2$

7. $y = \pm x^{3/2}$

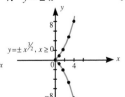

9. $x = t$, $y = t^2 - 3t$

SECTION 7.4

1. $\begin{bmatrix} 5 & -7 & | & -1 \\ 2 & 1 & | & 2 \end{bmatrix}$

3. $\begin{bmatrix} 0 & 1 & -2 & | & 9 \\ 1 & 2 & 0 & | & 5 \\ -1 & 0 & 3 & | & 7 \end{bmatrix}$

5. $\begin{bmatrix} 2 & -3 & 1 & -1 & 7 & | & 1 \\ 1 & 2 & 0 & 0 & 0 & | & 5 \\ 0 & 0 & 2 & 2 & 0 & | & 4 \\ 1 & -1 & 0 & 3 & 1 & | & 8 \end{bmatrix}$

7. $\begin{array}{r} -y + 2z = 7 \\ x\ \ \ +3z = 2 \\ -5x - y + 8z = 1 \end{array}$

9. $(-1, 1)$

11. $(2, -5)$

13. $\left(\frac{7}{2} y + 10, y \right)$

15. $(-1, 1, 0)$

17. $\left(\frac{47}{29}, \frac{-42}{29}, \frac{49}{29} \right)$

19. $(-1, 2, -1)$

21. no solution

23. An infinite number of solutions, all of the form $(2z + 25, -z - 6, z)$

25. An infinite number of solutions, all of the form $(-2z + 1, 3z, z)$

27. $(0, 0, 0)$

29. An infinite number of solutions, $\left(-\frac{4}{7} z, -\frac{5}{14} z, z \right)$

31. $A : 5 ; C : 2 ; E : 4$

SECTION 7.5

1. 2×2

3. 2×3

5. 1×1

7. No

9. Yes

11. $x = -1$, $y = 5$, $z = -7$ and $t = 9$

13. $\begin{bmatrix} 12 & -1 & 2 \\ 7 & 11 & -8 \end{bmatrix}$

15. $\begin{bmatrix} 1 & -11 & 11 \\ 14 & 11 & -2 \end{bmatrix}$

17. $\begin{bmatrix} 5 & 17 & -9 \\ 14 & 39 & -34 \end{bmatrix}$

19. $\begin{bmatrix} -9 & -23 & 23 \\ 28 & 20 & -1 \end{bmatrix}$

21. $\begin{bmatrix} 31 & 25 & -25 \\ -28 & -16 & -5 \end{bmatrix}$

23. $\begin{bmatrix} 2 & -4 & 6 \\ 14 & 18 & -10 \end{bmatrix}$

25. An infinite number of solutions of the form $(-y - 4, \ y)$.

27.

		< $20,000	> $20,000
		Salary	
Sex	Female	120	72
	Male	280	150

SECTION 7.6

1. No

3. Yes, 2×2

5. Yes, 2×5

7. Yes, 5×5

9. -5

11. $[7 \quad 25]$

13. $[10 \quad -2 \quad 14]$

15. $\begin{bmatrix} -1 & 6 \\ 14 & -11 \end{bmatrix}$

17. $\begin{bmatrix} -8 & 3 \\ 13 & 21 \\ -12 & 10 \end{bmatrix}$

19. $\begin{bmatrix} -1 & -1 & 9 \\ 3 & -4 & 15 \end{bmatrix}$

21. $\begin{bmatrix} 1 & 0 & -2 \\ -1 & 5 & 0 \\ 0 & 1 & -3 \end{bmatrix} = D$

23. $\begin{bmatrix} -8 & 12 & 19 \\ -1 & 7 & -32 \\ -19 & 29 & 42 \end{bmatrix}$

25. $\begin{bmatrix} -17 & 27 & 31 \\ 0 & 4 & -25 \end{bmatrix}$

27.

	Grower		
	#1	#2	#3
Cost	[227	148	133]

SECTION 7.7

1. Yes

3. Yes

5. No

7. No

9. $\begin{bmatrix} -2 & -1 \\ 5 & 3 \end{bmatrix}$

11. $\begin{bmatrix} 1 & -3 \\ -\frac{3}{2} & 5 \end{bmatrix}$

13. $\begin{bmatrix} 2 & -1 \\ -5 & 3 \end{bmatrix}$

15. $\begin{bmatrix} \frac{3}{2} & -1 \\ -\frac{5}{2} & 2 \end{bmatrix}$

17. $\begin{bmatrix} -1 & 3 & -1 \\ 1 & -1 & 0 \\ 0 & -1 & 1 \end{bmatrix}$

19. $\begin{bmatrix} -\frac{1}{2} & 1 & \frac{1}{2} \\ \frac{1}{2} & -2 & -\frac{3}{2} \\ \frac{1}{2} & 1 & \frac{1}{2} \end{bmatrix}$

21. $\begin{bmatrix} -\frac{1}{4} & 1 & \frac{1}{2} \\ -\frac{1}{4} & 2 & -\frac{1}{2} \\ \frac{1}{4} & -1 & \frac{1}{2} \end{bmatrix}$

23. $\begin{bmatrix} -\frac{7}{15} & \frac{8}{15} & \frac{3}{5} & \frac{1}{3} \\ \frac{2}{3} & -\frac{1}{3} & 0 & \frac{-1}{3} \\ \frac{4}{15} & \frac{11}{15} & \frac{1}{5} & \frac{1}{3} \\ -\frac{8}{15} & \frac{7}{15} & \frac{2}{5} & \frac{2}{3} \end{bmatrix}$

SECTION 7.8

1. 17

3. 0

5. 9

7. -37

9. 19

11. -10

13. 40

15. 50

17. 6

19. $(-2, 1)$

21. $(5, -1)$

23. $(-2, 1, -1)$

25. $(2, -1, 1)$

27. $(0, -2, 1)$

29. 3 units^2

CHAPTER REVIEW 7.10

1. $(2, -1)$ **3.** $(1, -2)$ **5.** Soyabeans : 400 and Corn : 600   **7.** $(3, -1, 2)$

9. An infinite number of solutions of the form $(2 - z, -z, z)$ **11.** $(4, 3)$ **13.** No solution

15. An infinite number of solutions, all of the form $\left(-7z + \dfrac{3}{2}, 2z - \dfrac{1}{2}, z\right)$ **17.** \$1,600 in the 5% account and \$2,400 in the 6% account

19. $\begin{bmatrix} 26 & -11 & 12 \\ 17 & -8 & 10 \\ 49 & -22 & 26 \end{bmatrix}$ **21. a.**

		Fabric	**Material** Stuffing	Trim
Location	I	5100	13,000	6,900
	II	4100	10,200	5,600

b.

		Cost
Location	I	19,700
	II	15,840

23. No solution   **25.** $(3,5)$ and $(1, -1)$ **27.** $S(x) = .4x^2 - .8x + .7$

CHAPTER TEST 7.11

1. $(2, -1)$ **3.** $(1, -1, 2)$ **5.** $f(x) = 2x^2 - x + 4$ **7.** $\begin{bmatrix} 6 & 22 \\ 25 & 27 \end{bmatrix}$ **9.** $\dfrac{x^2}{25} + \dfrac{y^2}{9} = 1$

Chapter 8

SECTION 8.1

1. 14, 17, 20, and 23   **3.** 28, 33, 38, and 43   **5.** 81, 243, 729, and 2,187   **7.** 9   **9.** 0   **11.** $-\dfrac{1}{512}$

13. 58   **15.** -20 **17.** $f(n) = \left(\dfrac{1}{4}\right)^{n-1}$ **19.** $f(n) = 3n + 2$, $n \geq 1$ **21.** $f(n) = (-1)^{n-1} \cdot 2$

SECTION 8.2

1. 2, 1, 0, -1, and -2 **3.** 0, 4, 8, 12, and 16   **5.** 3, $\dfrac{11}{2}$, 8, $\dfrac{21}{2}$, and 13   **7.** 7, 9, and 11   **9.** $-3, -\dfrac{5}{2}$, and -2 **11.** $2n - 3$

13. $3n - 6$ **15.** $-\dfrac{3}{2}n + \dfrac{33}{2}$ **17.** 1   **19.** $\dfrac{89}{4}$ **21.** $\dfrac{25}{6}, \dfrac{16}{3}, \dfrac{13}{2}, \dfrac{23}{3}$, and $\dfrac{53}{6}$ **23.** 18   **25.** 17   **27.** 16

29.   **31.**   **33.**

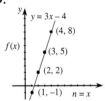   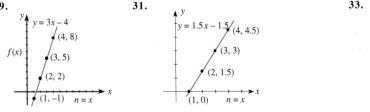   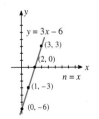

SECTION 8.3

1. 1, -2, 4, -8, and 16   **3.** $-2, -6, -18, -54$, and -162 **5.** 5, 20, 80, 320, and 1,280   **7.** $-6, 18, -54, 162$, and -486

9. 2^{n-1} **11.** $4(3)^{n-1}$ **13.** $\dfrac{1}{2^{n-3}}$ **15.** 6   **17.** 6   **19.** 1, $\dfrac{1}{3}$, and $\dfrac{1}{9}$ **21.** 8   **23.** 10

25.
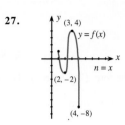

27.

SECTION 8.4

1. $2 + 4 + 6 + 8 + 10 + 12 + 14 + 16 + 18 + 20$ **3.** $1 - 2 - 5 - 8 - 11 - 14$ **5.** $2 + 5 + 10 + 17 + 26 + 37 + 50$

7. $3 + 6 + 12 + 24 + 48 + 96 + 192 + 384$ **9.** $45 - 135 + 405 - 1215 + 3645 - 10935 + 32805$ **11.** $0 + 3 - 8 + 15 - 24$

13. $\displaystyle\sum_{n=1}^{35} (3n - 1)$ **15.** $\displaystyle 5\sum_{n=1}^{20} (-1)^n$ **17.** $\displaystyle 3\sum_{n=1}^{6} \frac{1}{3^{n-1}}$ **19.** yes   **21.** No   **23.** No   **25.** 10,100

27. 8,125   **29.** $-17,300$ **31.** 1,092   **33.** 198   **35.** $\dfrac{3n}{2}(n - 3)$ **37.** $\dfrac{n}{2}(3n + 1)$ **39.** $\dfrac{n}{2}(3n + 7)$

SECTION 8.5

1. No   **3.** Yes   **5.** Yes   **7.** $\dfrac{3}{2}\left[1 - \left(\dfrac{1}{3}\right)^{15}\right]$ **9.** $3\left(2^{15} - 1\right)$ **11.** $\dfrac{8}{3}\left[1 - \left(\dfrac{1}{4}\right)^n\right]$

13. $\dfrac{1}{2}\left[1 - (-3)^n\right]$ **15.** $1 - \dfrac{1}{4^n}$ **17.** 3   **19.** Does not exist   **21.** $\dfrac{3}{4}$

SECTION 8.6

1. $a^4 + 8a^3 + 24a^2 + 32a + 16$ **3.** $p^5 - 5p^4q + 10p^3q^2 - 10p^2q^3 + 5pq^4 - q^5$ **5.** $\dfrac{1}{256}x^4 + \dfrac{1}{8}x^3y + \dfrac{3}{2}x^2y^2 + 8xy^3 + 16y^4$

7. $a^5b^5 - 10\ a^4b^4c + 40\ a^3b^3c^2 - 80\ a^2b^2c^3 + 80\ a\,b\,c^4 - 32\ c^5$ **9.** $1{,}024\,x^{10} + 15{,}360\ x^9y + 103{,}680\ x^8y^2 + 414{,}720\ x^7y^3$

11. $128\,x^7 - \dfrac{448}{3}\,x^6y + \dfrac{224}{3}\,x^5y^2 - \dfrac{560}{27}\,x^4y^3$ **13.** $20{,}412\,x^6y^2$ **15.** $28{,}160\,x^4$ **17.** $8{,}064\ a^{10}b^{15}$ **19.** 160   **21.** 1,215

CHAPTER REVIEW 8.8

1. None   **3.** None   **5.** None   **7.** $4n + 1$ **9.** 4^n **11.** $(-1)^{n-1}2^n$ **13.** 3, 11, 14, 27, and 35

15. $3, \dfrac{3}{2}, \dfrac{3}{4}, \dfrac{3}{8}$, and $\dfrac{3}{16}$ **17.** $6, -3, \dfrac{3}{2}, -\dfrac{3}{4}$, and $\dfrac{3}{8}$ **19.** 9   **21.** $3, \dfrac{9}{2}, 6, \dfrac{15}{2}, 39, \dfrac{21}{2}, 12$

23. $\dfrac{2}{3} + \dfrac{3}{5} + \dfrac{4}{7} + \dfrac{5}{9}$ **25.** $\dfrac{2^2}{3} + \dfrac{2^3}{3^2} + \dfrac{2^4}{3^3} + \ldots$ **27.** Arithmetic, $3n - 2$ **29.** Arithmetic, $\dfrac{1}{2}(n + 1)$

31. Geometric, $\left(\dfrac{(-1)^{n-1}}{2^{n-3}}\right)$ **33.** $n\,(2n + 1)$ **35.** $3(2^n - 1)$ **37.** $\dfrac{8}{3}\left[1 - \left(-\dfrac{1}{2}\right)^n\right]$ **39.** $\dfrac{3n}{2}(-n + 1)$

41. 6   **43.** 1.25   **45. a.** $81x^4 + 216x^3 + 216x^2y^2 + 96xy^3 + 16y^4$ **b.** $81x^4 + 216x^3 + 216x^2y^2 + 96xy^3 + 16y^4$

CHAPTER TEST 8.9

1. a. $11 - 6n$ **b.** $4\left(\dfrac{1}{10}\right)^{n-1}$ **3.** 3   **5.** $25\,ft$ **7.** $243 - 810a + 1{,}080a^2 - 720a^3 + 240a^4 - 32a^5$

INDEX

INDEX